CROSSROADS

Land and Life in Southwest Asia

SOUTHWEST ASIA
CONIC PROJECTION
SCALE OF MILES
0 50 100 200 300 400
SCALE OF KILOMETRES
0 100 200 300 400
Capitals of Countries
Other Capitals
International Boundaries
Railroads
Copyright by C. S. HAMMOND & CO., N.Y.
Longitude
East of
Greenwich
55°
60°
65°
70°
75°
40°
35°
30°
25°
20°
15°
CASPIAN SEA
U. S. S. R.
Kyzyl-Kum Desert
Kara-Kum Desert
CHINA
Sinkiang
Pamir
Hindu Kush
JAMMU AND KASHMIR
AFGHANISTAN
IRAN
PAKISTAN
BALUCHISTAN
SIND
INDIA
Thar or Indian Desert
Dasht-i-Kavir
Dasht-i-Lut
Registan
SEISTAN
Makran
GULF OF OMAN
ARABIAN SEA
TRUCIAL COAST
SULTANATE OF MASQAT
QATAR
BAHREIN
Rub' al Khali
Rann of Kutch
Gulf of Kutch
G. of Masira
Sauqira Bay
Qamr Bay
KURIA MURIA IS. (Aden)
DIU (Port. India)
Nukus
Tashauz
Urgench
Khiva
Tashkent
Namangan
Andizhan
Kokand
Fergana
Leninabad
Bukhara
Samarkand
Stalinabad
Chardzhou
Krasnovodsk
Kizyl-Arvat
Ashkhabad
Mary
Termez
Faizabad
Mazar-i-Sharif
Meshed
Tehran
Babol
Sari
Samnan
Sabzawar
Nishapur
Herat
Kabul
Peshawar
Rawalpindi
Srinagar
Jammu
Sialkot
Amritsar
Lahore
Kashan
Isfahan
Yezd
Kerman
Shiraz
Kazerun
Borazjun
Bandar Abbas
Lingeh
Ghazni
Kandahar
Quetta
Dera Ismail Khan
Dera Ghazi Khan
Multan
Bahawalpur
Bikaner
Jodhpur
Sukkur
Shikarpur
Larkana
Hyderabad
Karachi
Gwadar
Zahidan (Duzdab)
Zabul (Nasratabad)
Chagai
Masqat
Matrah
Sharja
Dubai
Abu Dhabi
Doha
Ahmadabad
Rajkot
Bhavnagar
Jamnagar
Porbandar
Junagadh
Veraval
Salala

CROSSROADS

Land and Life in Southwest Asia

GEORGE B. CRESSEY
Maxwell Professor of Geography
Syracuse University

J. B. LIPPINCOTT COMPANY · Chicago · New York · Philadelphia

THE LIPPINCOTT GEOGRAPHY SERIES

CLARENCE F. JONES, *Editor*

Library of Congress Catalog Card Number: 60-11518

Designed, Printed, and Bound at the Lakeside Press, R. R. Donnelley & Sons, Company

Chicago, Illinois, and Crawfordsville, Indiana

Title page photo of Lebanon, Courtesy of Iraq Petroleum Company

The Theme

THIS BOOK HAS BEEN WRITTEN around three principal ideas—the crossroads character of Southwest Asia, the role of water in its economy, and the way in which man is changing the landscape.

A major asset of the area is its centrality, and the chief justification for any use of the term *Middle* East lies in Southwest Asia's strategic position between Europe, Africa, and the bulk of Asia. Since the beginnings of history, its people have served as middlemen at the crossroads of civilization.

Most of Southwest Asia is dry, and if the area did not have high mountains to capture passing moisture and hold it in the form of snow, most of the area would be a desert. Man's survival has depended on his ingenuity in managing water.

During the hundred centuries of known history, there have been many changes in land use and livelihood. With the introduction of modern techniques, and thanks to royalties from oil, dramatic transformations are now under way. The world must reassess the significance of Southwest Asia. To further this understanding, geography provides inventory and evaluation.

Acknowledgements

A VOLUME SUCH AS THIS would not have been possible without the assistance of many people. I am indebted to scores of friends for hospitality and guidance in the field, to scholars in every country, to missionaries, to corporations, to government agencies both national and American, and to many strangers who have helped to pull my car out of rivers or deep mud. A number of specific acknowledgements are listed in the various chapters. To Marion and Nainai I owe a special debt: for encouragement, for help in many ways, and for willingness to make adjustments when necessary.

Each writer stands on the shoulders of those who have preceded him so that hundreds of ideas here presented originated with someone else. Students in several research seminars have helped to sharpen my understanding.

The illustrations have been selected with some care and represent an essential part of the CROSSROADS story. I am indebted to all who have contributed photographs. Most of the maps are original compilations and have been drafted by my research assistant, Theodore M. Oberlander, to whom I am happy to record my appreciation. Place names are spelled as in *Webster's Geographical Dictionary*.

During the preparation of this volume I held a Fulbright research appointment in Iraq and a Smith-Mundt professorship in Lebanon. Research grants have come from the United States Educational Foundation in Iraq, the American University in Beirut, the American Philosophical Society, and Syracuse University. The contribution of the latter in the form of released time, secretarial and drafting services, and research grants is most gratefully acknowledged. If such aid had not been available and if all expenses in preparing this volume were included in the sale price, the cost would be increased several fold.

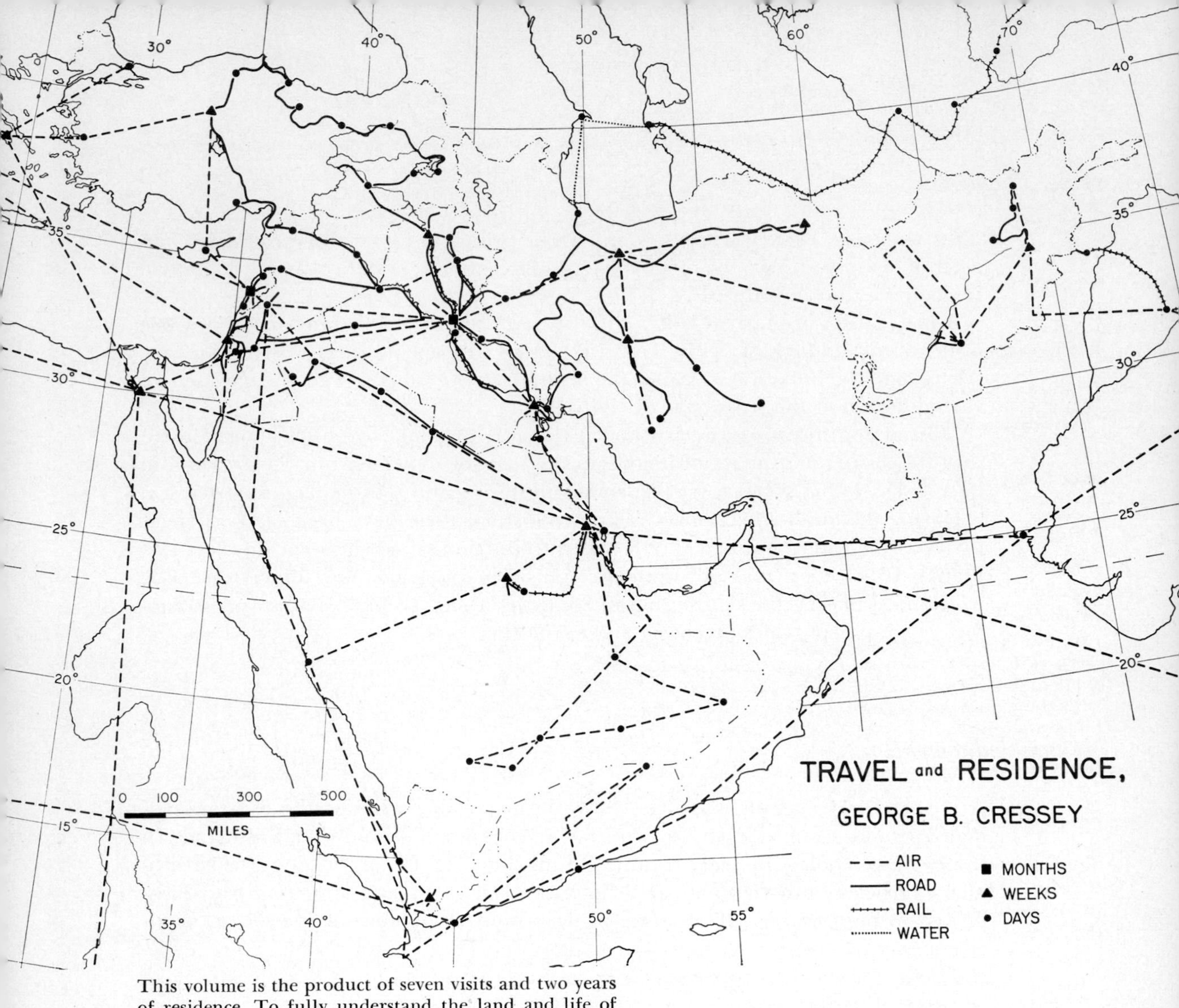

This volume is the product of seven visits and two years of residence. To fully understand the land and life of Southwest Asia would require a lifetime in each area.

Conversion Tables

1 hectare	= 2.47 acres	1 acre	= 0.405 hectare
100 hectares	= 1 square kilometer	640 acres	= 1 square mile
1 square kilometer	= 0.386 square miles	1 square mile	= 2.59 square kilometers
1 kilogram	= 2.2 pounds	1 pound	= 0.454 kilogram
1° centigrade	= 9/5° Fahrenheit	1° Fahrenheit	= 5/9° centigrade
1 meter	= 3.28 feet	1 foot	= 0.305 meter
1 kilometer	= 0.621 mile	1 mile	= 1.61 kilometers

1 jerib (Iran)	= 2.47 acres
1 dunum (Palestine)	= 0.222 acre
1 dunum (Turkey)	= 0.618 acre
1 meshara (Iraq)	= 0.618 acre
1 feddan (Egypt)	= 1.04 acres

Contents

PAGE

The Theme v
Acknowledgements v
Conversion Tables vi

PART ONE—THE OVER-ALL APPROACH

Chapter 1—Place

The first question in geography is "where." Places have personality as well as location.

Brown, White, Green, and Black 3
Three Cultures 10
Flight to the East 13
Flight to the South 18
Geostrategy 23
The Political Pattern 26
References 29

Chapter 2—People

The most interesting question in geography is "who." People are of prime importance in any evaluation of area. Who lives where and why?

Population Patterns 33
Geographical History 41
The Races of Swasia 44
Mesopotamian Empires: Babylon and Assyria . 48
Persian Empires: The Achaemenid Period . . 54
Arab Empires: The Ommiad and Abbasside . 56
Turkish Empires: The Ottoman 59
Three Travelers 62
References 66

Chapter 3—Land

Man lives very close to the earth; this calls for an understanding of land forms and underlying geology. How much of what is where?

Geology and Structure 69
Land Forms 76
Igneous Activity 79
Earthquakes 81
Sand Dunes 83

PAGE

Chapter 4—Climate

Climate provides an all-enveloping environment; to understand its components is to measure some of the potentials for livelihood.

The Mediterranean Regime 93
Pressures and Air Mass Movements 97
Local Winds 98
Temperature 102
Precipitation 104
Water Requirements 107
Climatic Regions 111
References 116

Chapter 5—Rivers

Water holds one of the keys to life in Southwest Asia. Rivers provide the avenues for its transport from the humid highlands to the dry lowlands.

Rivers in the Desert 119
The Zayandeh Rud and the Isfahan Oasis . 124
Wadi Hanifah: A Sample from Arabia . . . 127
The Jordan River and the Dead Sea . . . 130
The Menderes River in Turkey 134
The Helmand River of Afghanistan . . . 136
The Shatt-al-Arab, the River of the Arabs . 140
Qanats and Karez 149
References 155

Chapter 6—Land Use

Man's welfare depends on his skill in converting soil, water, and sunshine into food. Many social and political problems have grown out of man-land relations.

Arable Land 157
Tenancy 160
Food Crops 162
Technical Crops 169
Livestock 171
Forests 174
References 175

PAGE

Chapter 7—Mineral Resources

Minerals provide the basis for modern industrialization, but Southwest Asia appears to be poorly supplied, except for oil.

Mineral Wealth 177
Sources of Power 181
The Metals 183
Nonmetallic Resources 188
References 191

Chapter 8—Oil

Two thirds of the world's petroleum lies beneath the surface of Southwest Asia; its spectacular development is a modern economic miracle.

Retrospect and Prospect 193
A Preface from Geology 201
Reserves and Production 203
Pipelines and Refineries 206
Country Descriptions 209
References 221

Chapter 9—International Contacts

All through history, Southwest Asia has been a transit zone between Europe, Africa, and Asia. Here is a crossroads area of world-wide importance.

Land of the Six Seas 223
New Avenues by Air 227
International Trade 228
Recent History 232
Political Problems 235
American Policy in Swasia 242

PART TWO—THE REGIONAL ANALYSIS

Chapter 10—Turkey

Turkey is the home of one of the three major cultures which characterize Southwest Asia. Out of the old Ottoman Empire arose Swasia's first republic.

Istanbul and Ankara,
Old Turkey and the New 247
History, Then and Now 253
Six Profiles 256
Agriculture and the Food Supply 267
Raw Materials for Industry 272
Patterns of People and Land 281
Turkey's Prospects 285
References 288

PAGE

Chapter 11—Arabia

Arabia was the cradle of the Arab and Islamic cultures. Although much of the area is desert, it holds a fascinating story of land and people.

Arabian Journeys 293
Desert Agriculture 309
The Bedouin 318
Cities in the Desert 321
Highland Oases 328
The Political Framework 332
References 340

Chapter 12—Egypt

Herodotus once wrote that Egypt was the gift of the Nile, and it remains so now. Today, Egypt owns the Suez canal and bids for leadership in the Arab world.

Egypt and the Arab World 349
The Nile: Water in the Desert 354
People and Livelihood 361
The Suez Canal: Egypt's Second River . . . 363
References 368

Chapter 13—Iraq

Ancient Mesopotamia has become Iraq. Its future depends on the wise management of the Tigris and Euphrates, now made possible through royalties from oil.

Changing Landscapes 371
Land and Soil 382
Agriculture 390
Baghdad and Other Cities 397
Highways, West and East 402
References 404

Chapter 14—The Levant

The lands east of the Mediterranean, known as The Levant, have long been a contest area between Arabia, Egypt, Turkey, and Iran. Here lie the grasslands which form the Fertile Crescent.

Sea Coast, Mountains, Valleys, and Desert . 409
Mediterranean Climate 416
The Tides of History 424
Syria: Water and Food 432
Syria: Countryside and City 438
Syria: Problems and Prospects 445
Lebanon: Progressive Mountain Land . . . 447
Lebanon: Gateway to the East 453
Jordan: Present and Past 455
Jordan: Land and Minerals 459
References 465

PAGE

Chapter 15—Israel

Tiny Israel is a dynamic country, developing with dramatic speed. Since the environment has only limited potentials, Israel's economic viability is still to be established.

Historical Preface 473
Agriculture, Old and New 479
Population Patterns 487
Economic Viability 491
References 496

Chapter 16—Iran

Persian culture is one of Swasia's richest. The Iranian landscape is characterized by snow-covered mountains, arid plains, irrigated oases, and oil fields.

Past and Present 501
Water for Crops 504
Land Use 509
Resources for Industry 512
Geographic Regions 515
Iranian Cities 529
Problems and Prospects 536
References 540

Chapter 17—Afghanistan

Afghanistan is the ancient Aryana, the land of the Aryans. Today it holds a complex of races living around the towering Hindu Kush Mountains.

Four Roads 545
The Afghan Landscape 556
Time and People 560
Seven Regions 566
Livelihood and the Future 578
References 581

Glossary 583

Index 587

Maps

PAGE

Preface

Travel and Residence vi

Chapter 1—Place

Brown, White, Green, and Black 8
Major Swasian Culture Areas 12
Airways 24
Political Divisions, Cities 27

Chapter 2—People

Rural Sedentary Population 37
Nomadic Areas 38
Urban Population 40
The Fertile Crescent 42
Assyrian Empire 49
Persian Empire 55
Arab Empires 57
Ottoman Empire 58
Alexander's Empire 63

Chapter 3—Land

Geology 72
Geomorphic Units 73
Landforms 75

Chapter 4—Climate

Precipitation 105
Potential Evapotranspiration 108
Koeppen Climatic Regions 112

Chapter 5—Rivers

Hydrography 121
The Zayandeh Rud Basin 124
Landforms near Isfahan 125
Wadi Hanifah Basin 127
The Jordan Basin 131
The Buyuk Menderes Basin 134
The Helmand Basin 138
The Shatt-al-Arab Basin 140
Qanuts Near Tehran 153

Chapter 6—Land Use

Cultivated Land 159
Natural Vegetation 174

Chapter 7—Mineral Resources

Major Mineral Deposits 179

PAGE

Chapter 8—Oil

Oil Fields and Pipelines 199

Chapter 10—Turkey

Turkey 250
Topographic Profiles 256
Tectonic Regions and Mineral Deposits . . 275
Geographic Regions and Rural Population . 282

Chapter 11—Arabia

The Arabian Peninsula 294
Agriculture 309
Faults in the Red Sea Area 331

Chapter 12—Egypt

The Nile 355
The Nile Delta and the Suez Canal 365

Chapter 13—Iraq

Iraq 373
Abbasside Irrigation System 376
Central Iraq 384
Southern Iraq 385
Land Use 391
Baghdad—Population and Dikes 399

Chapter 14—The Levant

The Levant States 410
Rainfall Matches Elevation 423
Arab Refugees 431
Irrigation in Syria 437
Damascus and the Ghuta 441

Chapter 15—Israel

Land Classification. 480
Palestine Settlements in 1875 and 1952 . . 489

Chapter 16—Iran

Iran 506

Chapter 17—Afghanistan

Afghanistan 546
Land Use 579

Tables

PAGE

Chapter 1—Place

Area and Population 28

Chapter 2—People

Kurdish Population 47
Historical Development of Southwest Asia . 50–51

Chapter 3—Land

Land Form Regions 78

Chapter 4—Climate

Highest Recorded Temperatures 103
Monthly Duration of Climatic Types . . . 105
Water Balance for Izmir, Turkey 109
Water Balance for Isfahan, Iran 109
Climatic Tables 113, 114, 115

Chapter 5—Rivers

Precipitation in the Shatt-al-Arab Basin . . 145
Discharge Data for the Euphrates 147
Discharge Data for the Tigris 147
Discharge Data for the Karun 147
Discharge Data for the Shatt-al-Arab . . . 147
Flood Frequencies at Samarra 148
Shatt-al-Arab Water Budget 149

Chapter 6—Land Use

Land Use 161
Agricultural Production 165
Forest Land 175

Chapter 7—Mineral Resources

Coal Production 182
Gold Production 185
Iron Ore Production 186
Lead and Zinc Production 186
Chromium Production 187
Other Metallic Production 187
Salt Production 189
Other Nonmetallic Products 189

Chapter 8—Oil

Major Oil Fields and Concession Ownership. 196
Production by Companies 200
Oil Royalties 200
World Oil Reserves and Production 203
Total Crude Oil Production 205
Refinery Capacity 209

PAGE

Chapter 9—International Contacts

Coast Line Relations 224
Commercial Airports 228
Middle East Exports 228
International Trade 231

Chapter 10—Turkey

Turkish Data 249
Turkish Cities 253
Land Utilization in Turkey. 268
Turkish Crops 271
Turkish Power Production 276
Turkish Nonmetallic Mineral Production. . 276
Turkish Metal Production 276
Large Turkish Dams 277
Turkish Iron Production. 279

Chapter 11—Arabia

Saudi Arabian Population 317
The Arabian Peninsula 332

Chapter 12—Egypt

Egypt Data 350
Three Arab States 353
Nile Water Budget 357
Maritime Distances 368

Chapter 13—Iraq

Iraq Data 371
Land Use in Iraq 393
The Cities of Iraq 397
The Growth of Baghdad 400

Chapter 14—The Levant

Syria Data 432
Damascus Rainfall 433
Potential Syrian Irrigation 435
National Income in Swasia 448
The Population of Lebanon 448
Lebanon Data 450
Jordan Data 458
Jordan Agriculture 463
Dead Sea Salts 464

PAGE

Chapter 15—Israel

Israel Data 474
Palestine Population 479
Israel Agriculture 485
Israel Production 496
Israel Foreign Trade 496

Chapter 16—Iran

Iran Data 501
Agricultural Water Supply in Iran 504
Land Use in Iran 510
Iranian Crops 511
Oil Production in Southwest Iran 514
Mineral Production in Iran 514
Zagros River Basins 524
Iranian Cities 532
Iranian Plan Organization 538

Chapter 17—Afghanistan

Afghanistan Data 546
Cities of Afghanistan 547
The People of Afghanistan 565
Helmand Basin Irrigation 575
Vertical Crop Limits 578
Afghan Mineral and Industrial Production . 580

Climatic Charts

PAGE

Abadan 518
Adana 262
Aden 327
Aleppo 420
Amman 421
Ankara 270
Baghdad 401
Bahrein 321
Basra 401
Beirut 419
Damascus 419
Deir-ez-Zor 420
Eilat 492
Erzurum 271

PAGE

Haifa 492
Isfahan 518
Izmir 270
Jerusalem 421
Jidda 320
Kabul 559
Kandahar 559
Kermanshah 516
Meshed 517
Mosul 400
Riyadh 321
Samsun 262
Seistan 519
Tehran 517

CROSSROADS

Land and Life in Southwest Asia

CHAPTER 1

Place

Brown, White, Green, and Black
Three Cultures
Flight to the East
Flight to the South
Geostrategy
The Political Pattern
References

BROWN, WHITE, GREEN, AND BLACK

FOUR COLORS characterize the landscapes of Southwest Asia. If one might fly high enough to see all of the area in a broad panorama, man and most of his works would unfortunately disappear, but these four colors should stand out.

More than a million square miles of this corner of Asia are dry, for the most part barren desert. These arid lands appear brown for much of the year, taking on a greenish cast only after the scanty rains. Brown is thus the prevailing color of Southwest Asia.

Another million square miles are mountainous. Since they are high enough to extract some moisture from the passing winds and since this precipitation comes in winter as snow, the second distinctive landscape color is white. The extent of the snow cover varies with the season; in the spring it extends far down the mountain slopes, by fall it retreats to the highest elevations. Snow is typically a mountain phenomenon; only in the northern parts of Southwest Asia does snow fall on the lowlands. White is the second meaningful color.

Green, the third color, represents the cultivated fields, irrigated in many places since there are only limited areas where rainfall alone is sufficient. While agriculture forms an important basis for livelihood, the total crop area measures only 125,000 square miles, or 5 per cent of the whole. Like the fluctuating extent of the snow cover, the area of green varies with the season. Not all of the agricultural area is green each year, for fallowing is common. Cultivated land is limited to the vicinity of mountain-born rivers and to areas of dry farming.

The final color suggests the magic of petroleum, spectacular in its new economic significance but actually developed in no more

(Opposite) Through this triumphal arch at Palmyra have passed generals and merchants from half the ancient world. Palmyra lies on the edge of the Fertile Crescent, crossroads of Southwest Asia. (Courtesy Iraq Petroleum Co.)

Brown landscapes characterize a great part of Southwest Asia. In some places there are shifting sand dunes; elsewhere there is a dry steppe; vegetation is everywhere sparse. This scene is from central Saudi Arabia near Kharj. (Courtesy Standard Oil Co. of New Jersey.)

than a few thousand square miles. The oil industry is dramatic and has involved billions of dollars, but the black of the scattered oil fields is microscopic in area, scarcely recognizable from the air. In all, oil fields cover less than 0.1 per cent of the whole area. Some countries appear to be largely without oil, but the known fields are spread across an area 1,700 miles long.

Brown deserts, white snow-covered mountains, green fields, black oil; these colors characterize Southwest Asia. Of the four, white is by far the most valuable. Oil production is spectacular, but it will some day end; the future of the area as a whole lies in the wise management of its limited water.

These colors are closely interwoven. Every country except Lebanon contains deserts or areas of semiaridity with less than eight inches of rainfall. Deserts are not monotonously uniform; it is only that their pattern in some places is cut in larger pieces than in humid lands. The same type of land form and of scanty vegetation may continue for a hundred miles with little change. One scarcely realizes how large the world really is until he drives day after day across the empty desert.

In places the desert is covered with shifting sands, either in loose sheets or in great dunes; some are reddish, others tan or light yellow. Elsewhere the ground is blanketed by a veneer of pebbles which forms a desert pavement, thus preventing the wind from shifting the underlying sand. This desert ar-

Mountains occupy a million square miles and are snow-covered and white for a part of the year. These snow fields serve as a reservoir for the storage of winter moisture into the dry summer. This grove of the famous cedars lies on the slopes of the Lebanon range. (Courtesy Iraq Petroleum Co.)

mor may consist of chert or of whatever resistant rock is present or nearby. Across wide areas, rock lies at the surface: igneous or sedimentary, folded or horizontal, as the case may be. Elsewhere, the broad beds of seemingly aimless wadis characterize many areas. Here and there are the mud flats of interior basins, in places with a transitory playa lake or a crust of salt.

Many shades of color may be found in the desert, from the bright red of certain sandstones, through the browns and yellows of the dunes, the many buff shades of sedimentary rock, and the reddish black of volcanic formations, to the glistening white of salt flats. Traces of green appear after the light winter rains, but when averaged together, the characteristic landscape color is brown.

Hills and mountains surround many of these deserts. Only the small states of the Persian Gulf lack highlands, and mountains are everywhere within sight or just beyond the horizon, except in central Arabia. In six countries they reach heights of 10,000 feet. For the most part, the mountains of Southwest Asia are geologically young and therefore rugged. Slopes are steep, the rivers torrential, and erosion rapid. Many mountain areas are as uninhabited as the desert; travel in them is certainly more difficult than in the deserts.

Mountain landscapes have colors as varied as the deserts, but most of them are on the dark side. There is more green than in the desert, but almost nowhere is there a solid

Green fields dot the dry lands wherever there is water. Some cultivation depends on wells, springs, or canals; elsewhere modest rainfall permits dry farming. The total agricultural area in Southwest Asia measures only 125,000 square miles. This oasis is in eastern Saudi Arabia. (Courtesy Arabian American Oil Co.)

cover of vegetation. The few forests are of dark coniferous trees; scrub and scattered brush is more common. Grasses become green in the spring, but are brown for most of the year. Neither rock nor vegetation supplies the most meaningful color.

While almost all of Southwest Asia is dry, most mountains receive snow. In the higher elevations this snow cap lasts well into the summer, and it is the melting snow which enables mountain-fed streams to flow the year around; without this storage of moisture there could be no summer irrigation in the lowlands. White is thus the most significant color in our panorama.

If analogies are helpful, one may think of Southwest Asia in terms of the southwestern United States. Both have comparable winter rainfall and vegetation; both have similar associations of young mountains and interior basins. The Sierra Nevadas thus resemble the Taurus of Turkey and the Zagros of Iran, while the deserts of the Great Basin are analogous to those of Syria and Iran. Arabian conditions, hotter than most of the United States, find some similarity in the Sonoran Desert of Mexico. In like measure, the snow-fed lower Colorado River resembles the life-bringing Tigris and Euphrates.

Brown, white, green, and black are not the usual colors from which to make a rainbow, but out of them is emerging a spectrum of progress and promise. Cities in every country are in the midst of dramatic modernization, new roads and airports have revolutionized accessibility, and in the field of agriculture large scale irrigation projects

Oil installations introduce a black element into the otherwise brown, white, or green landscapes. Although petroleum production is revolutionizing the economy of several countries, the total area underlain by producing oil fields covers only a few thousand square miles. Here is the terminal at Ras Tanura along the shallow Persian Gulf. (Courtesy Standard Oil Co. of New Jersey.)

are beginning to alter the barren landscape.

Four colors are not enough to characterize Southwest Asia. They present the background of assets and limitations against which man must operate, but it is man rather than nature who holds the future. This book is a study of problems and prospects. Any forecast must consider the greatest of all assets: human ingenuity. During the ten millenia of recorded history, man has used the land in many ways. Dramatic transformations are under way and the landscape is in the midst of change.

This volume deals with Southwestern Asia, a term which may conveniently be contracted to Swasia.[1] This takes in the area between Turkey, Iran, and Afghanistan and south to Saudi Arabia, inclusive. Within this triangle lie Syria, Lebanon, Jordan, and Israel (sometimes collectively termed the Levant); Iraq; and the smaller states of the Arabian Peninsula. Egypt lies to one side (outside of Southwest Asia) but is considered briefly in a separate chapter.

This large area forms a geographic *realm,* a term used for one of the major coherent divisions of a continent. Within each realm are several large areas known as *provinces,* while these in turn are divided into geographic *regions*. Each category of classification has an increasing unity in physical and cultural features, according to its scale.

Southwest Asia is often known as the Near

[1] George B. Cressey: "Swasia," *Professional Geographer,* IX (1957), 11–12.

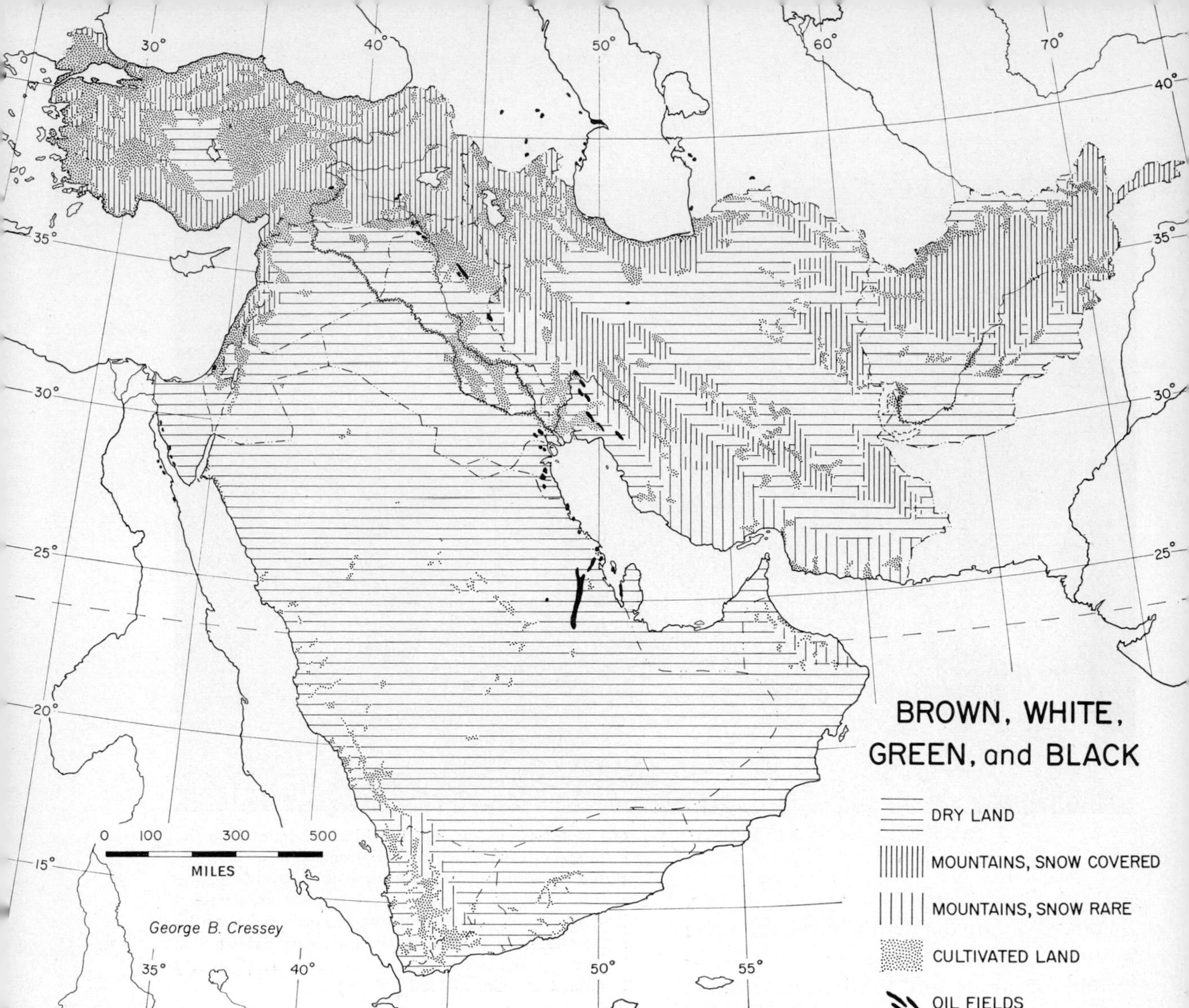

One function of geography is to identify "How much of what is where." This map presents the interrelated pattern of dry lands, snow-crowned mountains, cultivated areas, and oil fields. It is important to recognize that at this scale, only generalized patterns can be shown.

East, or as the Middle East.[1] These terms imply something as to its external relations for they are inventions of Europeans. To Britain or France, Asia was "East"; the Orient. At the extreme end of the continent lay the Far East, namely China, Japan, and the area beyond Singapore. Closer at hand, along the Mediterranean, was the Near East. This latter expression has always been vague. To some, it began at the gates of Bucharest and so included the Balkans and Greece. In certain cases it included Egypt and extended to the frontier of India, thus taking in Iran and Afghanistan; with other writers it stopped with Mesopotamia. At times, the Near East was coextensive with the old Ottoman Empire, hence the inclusion of the Balkans. India lay between the Near and the Far East and was thus termed the Middle East.

[1] G. Etzel Pearcy: "The Middle East, an Indefinable Region," *U.S. Dept. of State Bulletin,* March 23, 1959, Publication 6806.

The people of Turkey have contributed one of Southwest Asia's distinctive cultures; old but new. These Turkish skiers are enjoying the snowy slopes of Mount Olympus, near Bursa. (Courtesy Turkish Press, Broadcasting, and Tourist Department, Ankara.)

The terminology became further confused during World War II when the British designated the theatre of their operations in North Africa as the Middle East Command. The present usage of the term Middle East is highly uncertain; it is sometimes taken to include everything from Atlantic North Africa to East Pakistan, and south to Ethiopia and The Sudan, thus covering an area which measures 6,250 miles from west to east, and 2,900 miles from north to south. This seems geographically indefensible. More commonly, the term Middle East is roughly coextensive with Swasia, plus or minus Afghanistan and Egypt. The terms Near East and Middle East are not used in this volume since both reflect foreign conceit and do not recognize the intrinsic right of a realm to stand by itself.

The United States Department of State uses the term Near East for its regional division which includes Greece, Crete, Cyprus, Turkey, The Sudan, United Arab Republic (Egypt and Syria), Lebanon, Israel, Jordan, Saudi Arabia, Yemen, Kuwait, Bahrein, Qatar, Trucial Oman, Muscat and Oman, Aden and the Aden Protectorate, Iraq, and Iran. When the Department of State uses the phrase Middle East with reference to a general area it may also include Afghanistan, West Pakistan, Ethiopia, and sometimes Libya. The National Geographic Society described the Near East in 1952 as including all of the Near East as defined by the Department of State except Greece, Crete, and Su-

Arab High School students at Kut are representative of modern Iraq; proud of their heritage but anxious to become oriented to the modern world. (Courtesy Iraq Petroleum Co.)

dan. The wartime British Middle East Supply Center took in twenty-seven political entities, including all of those named plus Cyrenaica, Malta, Tripolitania, British Somaliland, Eritrea, ex-Italian Somaliland, and French Somaliland. An official British map of 1958 limited the Middle East to Southwest Asia, minus Afghanistan, plus Egypt and Libya.

If the term Middle East is to be used at all, its justification is to be found in the centrality which it implies, for the area is strategically located at the crossroads between Europe, Africa, and the bulk of Asia.

THREE CULTURES

THREE MAJOR CULTURES characterize Swasia. These cultures are distinct in ethnography, roughly equal in numbers, and similar in their common adherence to Islam. The oldest in continuity is Persian, the largest in extent is Arab, the most modernized is Turkish. These are not all, for few parts of the earth exhibit a more diverse cultural history; repeated waves of outsiders have swept through the mountains and across the plains. Kurds, Jews, and Armenians are but samples of the many ethnic minorities. The new State of Israel is one of the most dynamic areas in Southwest Asia and represents a fourth culture area.

Persian culture is one of the area's oldest; now in the midst of rapid change as education transforms Iran. These girls are in a teachers' training class near Tehran. (Courtesy Near East Foundation.)

This is a very human realm, even if partly empty. Deserts and oases are merely the setting for man's development. If it is easier to generalize about climate or land forms, they should not obscure the prime importance of man and his activities, and of their distribution.

Turkish, Arab, and Persian culture each makes its distinctive impress on the landscape. The slender Ottoman-style minarets are found only in Turkey; Bedouin tents go with the Arabian desert; and the blue tiled domes of the Iranian mosques spell old Persian influence. These factors of regional difference reflect cultural orientation. Persia and Afghanistan have many characteristics derived from inner Asia. Arab lands look in part to northern Africa. Turkey would like to feel that it is a portion of Europe.

While geography commonly deals with the visible landscape, it is interested in all those factors which give personality to place. The Turkish Revolution of the early twentieth century thus sets that country apart. So likewise does the surge of nationalism in the various Arab lands. Persian thought is less changed, but even in Iran there are pregnant ideas of land reform and political development.

All the world is the heir of the cultures which arose in Southwest Asia. Christianity

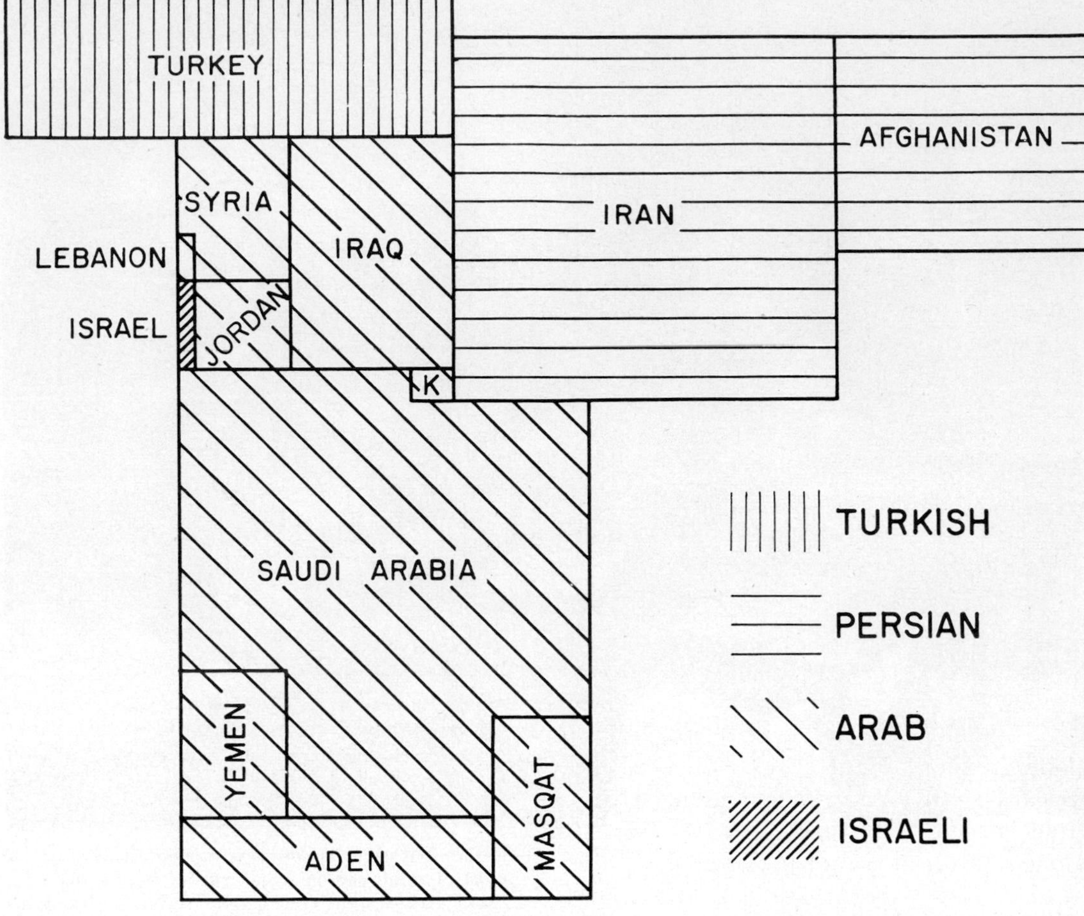

MAJOR SWASIAN CULTURE AREAS

The Turkish, Persian, Arab, and Israeli cultures are shown in proportional size in this diagrammatic chart. Many minority peoples must be added to make the picture complete.

and Islam have a common base in Judaism; Jerusalem is a pilgrimage center for three religions. European civilization looks back to Greece and Rome, but they in turn trace many items to Egypt and Mesopotamia. Even India and China had important early contacts with Swasia, as with Arab traders who voyaged to Canton, or with Buddhism which passed across Afghanistan. If the West fails adequately to weigh Southwest Asia, it is the cultural loss not of the countries of Southwest Asia, but of the peoples of the Western world.

One should not expect uniformity in an area of 2.4 million square miles, but there is an over-all consistency in the human response, and a unity in the basic geography. In every country nomads roam the waterless plains or move up and down the mountain

The Beirut Airport is the principal gateway for the dozens of airlines which serve Southwest Asia. Direct services lead to every continent. The annual number of airline passengers is equal to the total of those who transit Suez. (Courtesy Middle East Airlines.)

slopes in quest of grass. Farmers depend on irrigation water brought by seasonal rivers from distant snow peaks. Cities flourish along caravan routes old and new, or next to magic oil fields. The plains of Arabia are larger than those of Iran, but both have common problems of life amidst aridity. Highland agriculture in Turkey has its parallels in Afghanistan. Many water problems are international and need to be considered on a regional basis; Iraq requires the Euphrates but its flow comes from Turkey, and en route Syria has its claims on the water. The Helmand begins in Afghanistan but is also used for irrigation in Iran. Egypt lives on the Nile, but the Nile is equally vital for the Sudan, up river. Nomads pay little attention to political boundaries.

These are lands of vivid cultural contrasts. The traveler is continually surprised at the bewildering differences between great wealth and bitter poverty, between sophisticated education and ignorance. Magnificent ruins stand alongside mud huts, Cadillacs are paralleled by donkey trains. Swasia has suddenly changed from camels to planes. Thoroughly modern cities form cultural oases in the midst of nomadic pastures; but one steps across the outermost irrigation ditch and passes abruptly from green crops to lifeless desert.

FLIGHT TO THE EAST

Two AERIAL TRANSECTS may provide an appropriate preview of the geographic landscape. The first would be a flight from Beirut on the Mediterranean eastward to Damascus, Baghdad, Tehran, Kabul, and the Khyber Pass leading to Pakistan. The second is a trip southward from the Black Sea to Aden by way of Turkey, Iraq, Kuwait, Saudi Arabia, and Yemen. No combination of airlines serves this second route, but the first is flown regularly. If the flight eastward is taken in summer, that southward might be visualized in winter.

As one enters the airport terminal in Beirut, he should pause a moment to notice the long line of counters serving the airlines which stop here. Overhead are the insignia of more than three dozen companies. A third of the airlines are the great intercontinental carriers whose giant planes pause at Beirut on their way around the world, another third are primarily European companies which also serve this area, still others are local lines since every country feels it necessary to have an airline to fly its national flag.

All international air terminals are interesting, but Beirut rates high in the colorful array of its transit passengers and in the destinations involved. The major airlines find it profitable to use the newest long-range planes; in contrast, some of the local lines operate with equipment long since obsolete elsewhere. In the control tower are a battery of teletype machines and radio telephones which provide traffic control and weather information from London to Colombo.

Beirut is by no means the busiest of the world's airports, for some of its airlines have only a few flights a day, but there are not more than a handful of terminals anywhere which rate higher in the number of companies represented or in the many destinations served. Thousands of passengers fly in or out of Beirut every day, probably more than those who transit the Suez Canal. Direct services without change of plane link

Mountains, deserts, and oases characterize the east-west cross section from Beirut to Kabul. These sample scenes are from Lebanon, Iraq, and Iran.

Beirut with Tokyo, San Francisco, Sydney, Cape Town, and Buenos Aires, as well as New York and London.

The Beirut airport occupies a coastal terrace between the mountains and the sea, so narrow that the two runways can only be at a small angle to each other. On one side is the unbelievably blue Mediterranean, on the other rise the Lebanese mountains, dotted with fruit and olive groves which surround ancient villages. As the plane takes off, the traveler will need to observe quickly, for the landscape changes almost at once. Directly north of both runways is the promontory occupied by the city of Beirut. Here is one of the few partly sheltered bays along the eastern Mediterranean, and the harbor has helped to make Beirut the chief commercial and cultural gateway to the lands of Southwest Asia.

The flight over the mountains to Damascus takes but half an hour. In this time one passes from the crowded coastal fringe, across two mountain ranges and a central down-faulted valley, to the edge of the Syrian Desert. Even in midsummer, snow crowns the highest peaks. While Beirut in July is uncomfortably warm and humid, these mountains provide a cool resort area for thousands of tourists from the torrid plains of Iraq and Egypt.

Many of the Lebanese slopes are bare and soilless, a result of deforestation and overgrazing, but groves of the famous cedars and scattered orchards are reminders that forests once covered the mountains. Each bit of good land is in use, whether it be a ribbon of flood plain, a rounded summit, or a three-foot terrace along the contour. So far as na-

Rugged peaks and dry plains alternate in these glimpses of Iran and Afghanistan (Courtesy USOM Lebanon, Aramco, Iranian Oil Participants, James A. Cudney.)

ture permits, this is a prosperous landscape. Lebanon is a small country, but commerce and agriculture have given it the highest standard of living of any Arab state.

Syria is different. As the plane circles over Damascus, one sees an oasis of green amid a desert of brown. The city owes its life to a river which breaks through the mountain wall and provides water for an intricate network of irrigation ditches on its broad alluvial fan. In contrast to the narrow streets of Beirut, Damascus has more room, at least in the newer areas. Whereas the former city faces west to the sea, Damascus looks east to the desert. Both are capitals and cities of over half a million. The summer weather in Beirut is very hot, but Damascus is even more uncomfortable though dry. The sun blazes down from a cloudless sky, and the traveler welcomes any shade.

Between Damascus and Baghdad lie 500 miles of desert—flat, empty, desolate, and apparently lifeless. Here and there a few black tents mark a Bedouin encampment, but the nomads and their camels are scarcely visible from the air. Even after the light winter rains, the landscape has only a slight greenish cast; in summer one is not aware that there is ever any vegetation. Yet, amid this aridity, the land forms everywhere betray the work of running water. Short showers and effective run-off may be years apart, but the network of wadis and shallow basins give evidence of sculpture and deposition by water. Sand dunes are present but uncommon. If the aerial traveler is observant, he may see one or two examples of dry farming, but these are clearly marginal.

Just before reaching Baghdad the observer sees the startling magic of water in the desert. One looks down on the muddy ribbon of the Euphrates and, a moment farther on, the Tigris. These twin rivers bring water from melting snows in Turkey and make Mesopotamia one of the world's major oases. Green and brown meet along knife edge boundaries as canals, old and new, distribute this imported water.

Although this is summer and the desert appears to be quivering from heat waves, the traveler is not prepared for the fiery furnace which greets him when the door of the plane is opened at Baghdad. The temperature is probably well above 110°F., perhaps almost 120°F., and the sun is merciless. It affords little comfort to point out that the humidity is low. This fact, however, is of practical advantage for in many homes and offices air is blown through a damp screen so that it is cooled by evaporation. One wonders how people can live in such heat, and how ancient empires could have flourished.

Eastward from Baghdad lies Tehran, another 500 miles away. A few minutes after take off, the landscape changes from the imperceptible flatness of the Iraq alluvial plain to the stark and rugged Zagros ranges of Iran. Great folds betray the origin of the mountains, and much of the area is "on edge." Scarcely a tree is to be seen, nor are people much in evidence. One automobile road winds laboriously beneath our aerial course, but elsewhere travel is a matter of mountain trails.

The higher peaks of the Zagros receive some winter snow, now largely gone, but the mountains of Lebanon have already robbed the westerly winds of their moisture before they reached Iran. A few open valleys have a bit of cultivation, with water supplied from small canals or wells, but 90 per cent of the country seems almost as desolate as Syria and Iraq.

The topography of the Zagros leads to a major difference between nomadic life in the mountains of Iran and the Syrian deserts to the west. In both areas existence becomes a quest for grass. In the mountains there is "vertical nomadism," or transhumance, where the cattle and sheep are taken to the higher and greener pastures during the summer, Swiss style, and then moved down slope as the mountains become too cold in winter. Or it may be that tribes migrate from one side of the range to the other. In the plains, nomadism is "horizontal" for there is no topographic alternative.

Tehran, fortunately, is not quite so hot as Baghdad for it has an elevation of 4,000 feet. The city lies on a broad alluvial slope to the south of the high Elburz Mountains, snow covered the year around. Small aqueducts or *jubes* flow down the sides of many streets. Irrigated gardens make both Tehran and Damascus stand out from the air, for the rainfall is too low for the countryside to remain green without irrigation, certainly in the dry summer.

Even though we have been flying eastward for five hours, we are not halfway across Southwest Asia. This is a big realm, both similar to and unlike the United States. Lebanon and Syria are replicas of California; the rest is more like an expanded Arizona and Utah. One thing is clear from our aerial reconaissance; most of Swasia is barren and brown, and were it not for the mountains with their snows there could be but little life.

Iran occupies a great highland basin almost surrounded by mountains. Many of these ranges are more than two miles in height; to the northeast of Tehran is the volcanic cone of Demavend, rising to 18,934 feet, the highest peak in all Swasia west of the Hindu Kush. The interior of the country is so dry that only in a few places do streams ever reach the ocean; instead they end in salt lakes or mud playas. This is the measure of an extreme continental climate; the lowland precipitation is probably under five inches.

To the east of Tehran our aerial route again crosses a desert even more foreboding than that in Syria since for many miles there is no possibility of nomadic life. Here is a succession of desolate lands: the Desert of Salt, the Desert of Lut, the Desert of Death. For a thousand miles there is no airport or city worthy of a name. Maps show many place names, but most of these are merely desert watering holes or ruins. One does not appreciate how large the world is, even in the age of flight, until one crosses such deserts for hours at a time. If one's plane must make a forced landing, it is hopeless to "walk out."

Imperceptibly, one passes from Iran to Afghanistan. Both countries are similar in their combination of dry plains and snow-capped mountains. Life in each is confined to ribbon oases along some stream fed by rain or snow which falls in the mountains. In Afghanistan, however, the towering Hindu Kush Mountains occupy the center of the country and the lowlands lie to the north and south. Near the border of the two countries, we enter the basin of the Helmand River, second only to the Tigris and Euphrates in its potential for irrigation. Here we may look down on the magic of modern engineering with great dams, modern canals, and the reclamation of hundreds of square miles of desert.

Next comes the ancient city of Kandahar, with its new international airport. An hour later we reach Kabul, the capital city of Afghanistan, which lies in a fertile basin at the southern edge of the snow crowned Hindu Kush. Since Kabul has an elevation of around 6,000 feet, the weather is delightful even in midsummer. Still another hour on eastward and we may fly over the Khyber Pass to the plains of the Indus in Pakistan. Here summer monsoon rain replaces the winter rain of the Mediterranean regime, and this change marks the appropriate limit of Swasia as a geographic realm.

Afghanistan may seem remote from the Western world, but in the bazaars of Kabul one may buy his favorite American breakfast cereal. Here too is the most modern street lighting. As one walks down the main streets, it is well to recall that they were paved as a gift from the Soviet Union.

Our route from Lebanon across Afghanistan has covered 2,200 miles. The author has flown it between dawn and dusk of a single day. Or the trip can be made by car in two weeks, again the experience of the writer. This is a land of great distances. One reads in the Old Testament of the orders given by Darius for the rebuilding of the Temple in Jerusalem. Darius was then at Persepolis in Iran; today it requires seven days of hard driving to travel from Iran to Jordan; at that time it must have taken many weeks.

From the plane, one sees only the broad relations of the terrain; by auto the traveler comes closer to reality, but, if one is to know the people and their problems, he must travel as they travel, eat as they eat, sleep where they sleep, and feel as they feel. Books are poor substitutes for out-of-door geography.

FLIGHT TO THE SOUTH

A FLIGHT ACROSS Swasia from north to south repeats many of the features which we have just seen, with differences in temperature due to latitude. Only an irregular combination of air services will give us a north-south transect, so that our trip must be in part imaginary. For variety this aerial journey will be taken in winter.

The northernmost parts of Swasia border the Black and Caspian seas. Both are coastal areas with a narrow plain backed by high mountains; both shores are areas of abundant rainfall and almost subtropical conditions; neither coast is representative of more than a small district.

Our trip begins near the eastern end of the

These scenes along a line from the Black Sea to the Arabian Sea are from the Taurus Mountains, Agar Gouf near Baghdad, and the junction of the Tigris and Euphrates rivers.

Black Sea in Turkey, at the seaport of Trabzon. Here there is an airport whose situation resembles that of Beirut, for level land is limited and the mountains rise inland abruptly to elevations of two miles. Since no scheduled plane services lead southward, we will start inland by car. Our immediate destination is Erzurum in the valley of the upper Euphrates. To reach it the road crosses three high passes. Deep snow covers the mountains in winter and even sometimes falls along the coast at Trabzon. We will be fortunate if our road is not blocked by snow. The mountains have splendid forests, although the more accessible areas have been deforested. One can imagine that when the snow melts in the valleys it will uncover prosperous agricultural fields. Erzurum, at 5,000 feet above sea level, is bitterly cold; here we change from car to a plane and it will not be surprising if bad weather delays the take off. No commercial services lead to Iraq, so we must charter a plane.

As with Iran, Turkey is encircled by snow mountains. To the north these are the North Anatolian Mountains, to the south lie the Taurus Mountains. In eastern Turkey, along the line of our route, the two systems merge so that the interior plateau of Anatolia largely disappears. This was once the home of Armenians, but they have disappeared and Turkey is sensitive to any present day geographical use of the term.

From Erzurum we fly south to Mosul, just inside the border of Iraq, 250 miles distant. Much of the landscape en route is dazzlingly white, for rugged mountains rise to heights of three miles and the snow cover is exten-

Much of the Arabian Peninsula is a land of sand dunes and nomads in contrast to the terraced agriculture of the Yemen highlands. (Courtesy Turkish Information Office, Iraq Petroleum Co., Aramco, and Bruce Conde.)

sive. These ranges contain the source of both the Tigris and Euphrates, most of whose summer flow comes from melting snow. Amid the mountains are several enclosed basins, such as that of Lake Van with its bordering volcanos.

While the topographic pattern of Turkey resembles that of Iran, the former is farther north and hence cooler, and the precipitation is somewhat greater. Some plains in Turkey receive enough moisture so that they can be cultivated without irrigation, and our route takes us over several good farming areas. Both countries have vertical nomadism, but the people and flocks which spread across the mountain pastures of Turkey in the summer are now out of sight in sheltered lowlands.

Shortly after entering Iraq, the mountains end, and we fly over the rolling plains of Mesopotamia. Snow seldom covers the ground; instead we see the bare surface of the steppe. This is the so-called Fertile Crescent, a discontinuous area of marginal farm land which surrounds the Syrian Desert in an arc which extends from Kirkuk in Iraq westward to Homs in Syria, with projections at both ends which link the Persian Gulf and the Nile. Winter is the rainy season, and once the weather becomes a little warmer, the land will suddenly become green with crops of wheat and barley.

If we might make a detour westward to the Mediterranean, thus to the right of our line of flight, we would discover one reason for the moderate rainfall which creates the Fertile Crescent. This cultivated area lies opposite a gap in the mountains, known as the Syrian Saddle, which forms an avenue for rain-bearing winds from the Mediterranean. Whereas the mountains of Lebanon block moisture and create the Syrian Desert in their lee, the low-level Syrian Saddle permits rain to reach the interior.

Much history has taken place in these grasslands of ancient Assyria, and from the air one may see the outline of ruins such as Nineveh or Nimrud which mark vanished cities. It was this grassland which provided migration routes from Mesopotamia to the Mediterranean, as followed by Abraham.

While flying over Mosul, one might have looked far to the right and seen a few brilliant lights, but their significance would not have been realized until we passed Kirkuk and discovered that these fires marked oil fields. Kirkuk is one of the great petroleum fields of the world. Along with the oil occur large amounts of gas, too high in hydrogen sulphide for any present use. This is flared off with huge fires which light up the desert sky for miles around. On our earlier flight from Beirut to the Khyber, we may not have been aware of oil, unless we spotted the trace of desert pipe lines from Kirkuk to the Mediterranean. So important are these pipe lines that they have been called Iraq's third river.

As we approach the head of the Tigris and Euphrates Delta, between Mosul and Baghdad, we see the first of the elaborate irrigation systems which make Iraq liveable. Modern diversion dams on both rivers lead water into large canals, and these in turn divide and redivide until the total canal network amounts to many thousands of miles.

Irrigation seems attractive, but it creates problems. From the air it is obvious that large areas have become water-logged through the application of too much water. It is not enough to bring water to the fields, the surplus must then be removed by drainage ditches. Furthermore, when the water table is brought too close to the surface, capillary action lifts moisture; and, when this evaporates, its chemical load is left behind. Alongside areas drowned by careless irrigation are others which glisten as though covered by a heavy frost; this is salt. No less than 22 million tons of salt and other soluable chemicals accumulate in the irrigated lands of Iraq each year. Small wonder that large areas have been abandoned as farmland.

The Persian Gulf area appears to hold two-thirds of the world's petroleum reserves, and the development of oil has profoundly influenced domestic economy and international geopolitics. This well is at Qatif in Saudi Arabia. (G.B.C.)

Mesopotamia has a rich history, but, unlike the Nile where stone was available nearby, the empires of the Tigris and Euphrates had mud civilizations since the only building material was sun dried brick. The traveler must not expect to find in Babylon or Ur the architectural glories of ancient Egypt.

When our plane comes down at Baghdad on this southward flight during the winter, we find weather which is quite different from that which we found in summer. Unlike Turkey, central Iraq has only a mild winter so that a top coat will be enough. Frost is rare, and, since the annual precipitation measures only five inches, there is not much chance that bad weather will prevent our plane from landing. The landscape is still barren, but in a few months the irrigated fields will come to life.

From Baghdad we fly south to the busy seaport of Basra near the head of the Persian Gulf, 600 miles from Mosul. Even though the Persian Gulf is "around the corner" from Suez, a dozen fair-sized steamers are usually tied up along its docks. Downstream, large tankers load oil from the fields of southern Iraq.

Beyond Basra, we enter areas with truly fabulous petroleum reserves. The sheikdom of Kuwait, smaller than New Jersey, produces about 2 million barrels a day. Southwestern Iran is not far behind, and farther on is Saudi Arabia which is as rich as Kuwait. Oil in the desert is no less miraculous than water in the desert. Every day oil brings millions of dollars in royalties to the lands around the Persian Gulf. Kuwait has no river, and fresh water is not even available in wells, so that it was formerly necessary to bring in water by boat. To supply its inhabitants, great evaporation plants now produce millions of gallons of distilled water a day.

Three airports around the head of the Persian Gulf compete for international traffic: Basra in Iraq, Kuwait, and the refinery center of Abadan in Iran. None has yet attracted much traffic. Farther south are rival airports at Dhahran in Saudi Arabia and at Bahrein.

Beyond Kuwait, our destination is Aden at the southern tip of Arabia, 1,200 miles to the south. Only two things break the monotony of the long flight across the desert wilderness, the spectacular city of Riyadh and the highlands of Yemen. Hour after hour the desert unfolds beneath us; red sand gives place to yellow sand, sometimes in a sea of dunes; bare gravel changes to black lava; aimless wadis alternate with chaotic badlands; ancient mountains are nearly buried by their own rubble. So desolate and impenetrable are these wastes that they are the only parts of Swasia never captured by an outside conqueror. The population is indeed scanty, but here is the fountain home of the desert Arab.

In the heart of this desolation lies Riyadh, the magic capital of Saudi Arabia, where royalties from oil are transferring a local market town into a modern city. Even during our winter visit Riyadh is warm; dust whirls sweep across the ground and in the summer the heat must be very trying. Small wonder that the new palace has a 5 million dollar air-conditioning plant.

Riyadh lies in Arabia Deserta; far to the south lies Arabia Felix, the "happy land" of Yemen, where greater altitude gives lower temperatures and more rain. Yemen is a highland oasis, with elevations of one and two miles above the encircling desert. This means fifteen to thirty inches of rain in place of two to four inches in the surrounding lowlands. Here is prosperous agriculture with elaborately terraced mountain sides. Nearly half the people of the Arabian peninsula occupy these southern highlands; many of them are the purest examples of the so-called Mediterranean race. Here presumably once lived the Queen of Sheba.

Farther south we come to the edge of Arabia and the British colony of Aden near the entrance to the Red Sea. There may be places with a worse climate than Aden, but there are not many. Someone has described the nearby Red Sea as being like "Hell, with the sun blazing down on it." If it were not for the demands of shipping, air traffic, and military strategy, Aden would find little reason for its being. To these should be added the great new oil refinery. The rainfall amounts to only three inches a year.

We have been aloft, from the Black Sea to the tip of Arabia, for over 2,000 miles, a distance almost equal to our east-west transect. Whereas many major airlines operate west to east between the Mediterranean and Pakistan, north to south air travel is limited to unconnected local services. Even with a chartered plane, the trip would require a full day. It may thus be appropriate to add that, once we are in Aden, half a dozen airlines are available to take us on our way in other directions.

It would indeed take an adventurer to attempt the trip by land. Some Turkish highways are good, but not those in the east. Not a single road crosses the border between Turkey and Iraq. Only desert trails lead to Kuwait. Across Arabia one may drive almost at will where there are rolling plains, but elsewhere vast sand dunes, trackless lava fields, and rough escarpments stop all wheeled vehicles. Yemen has a few roads, but what roads! The author has traveled along much of the route and advises the casual tourist to stay at home.

On the flight eastward from Beirut to the Khyber Pass, the summer skies are nearly cloudless. Convection currents produce a little turbulence in the afternoon, but the relative humidity is so low that condensation occurs only at very high elevations. Dust storms and haze are more of a handicap to navigation than clouds.

In our winter flight we may have observed that polar air masses sometimes push south to the Persian Gulf, with frontal conditions that bring rain, thunder, and poor visibility. The advance of these cool air masses is often associated with the passage of the cyclonic storms which parade eastward from the Mediterranean. Planes are seldom grounded, but flying conditions are poor.

GEOSTRATEGY[1]

WHY DOES Southwest Asia deserve attention? This is not a rich land either in agriculture or commerce. Except for fabulous reserves of oil, the area is poor in mineral wealth. Although larger than Western Europe, and two-thirds the size of the United States, much of it is unproductive desert with a scanty population. No one pretends that here lies a vast potential market, as perhaps in India. Nor is this an area which is apt to produce great volumes of merchandise for export. Something else must characterize Southwest Asia, for it has been the goal of world conquerors since the days of Alexander the Great. Part of the answer lies in its strategic location; here is one of the world's great crossroads.

Bordering and projecting into this tricontinental realm are six seas and three gulfs: the Caspian, Black, Aegean, Mediterranean, Red, and Arabian seas; and the Aden, Oman, and Persian gulfs. A map of Swasia might thus carry the title "Land of the Six Seas." Elsewhere, the limits include two straits: the Bosporus and Dardanelles; an isthmus: Suez; and lie near five mountain chains: the Little Caucasus, Kopet Dagh, Hindu Kush, Sulaiman, and Kirthar ranges. Much of the realm is bordered by a series of land bridges and straits between the penetrating seas.

If there were no political considerations, the geographic limits of the realm might follow the shoreline and the crests of these mountains. On the other hand, the cultural realities of countries as significant as the Soviet Union and Pakistan cannot be overlooked, and their political frontiers are the boundaries here used. There is no need to quibble over whether Asia extends to the Suez Canal or stops at the edge of Egypt, or whether Turkey in Europe is a part of Asia, or whether Baluchistan belongs in the same geographic region as Afghanistan; for convenience, political boundaries are followed. While Egypt lies in Africa rather than in Asia, it is considered in Chapter 12.

One cannot appreciate the commanding importance of Southwest Asia without visualizing global relations. The world's greatest intercontinental highway crosses the North Atlantic by ship and by air. In second place is the route from Western Europe to Asia via the Mediterranean. By sea, this avenue includes Gibraltar and Suez, or in some cases the Bosporus; otherwise one must sail around Africa. The Suez Canal may not be absolutely essential, but any interruption in its availability creates widespread difficulties.

The great circle air route from London to New Delhi passes far to the north of the Mediterranean, but flights across Soviet territory involve political problems. To go farther south, say over central Africa, requires detours whose extra mileage is only apparent on a globe. Flights from London or Paris bound for India and beyond find it desirable to come down at some intermediate city. Cairo or Istanbul are possible airports, but Beirut has a more important hinterland.

[1] For a definition and discussion of geostrategy, see George B. Cressey: *Asia's Lands and Peoples*. New York: McGraw Hill, rev. ed. (1951), 8, 27–32.

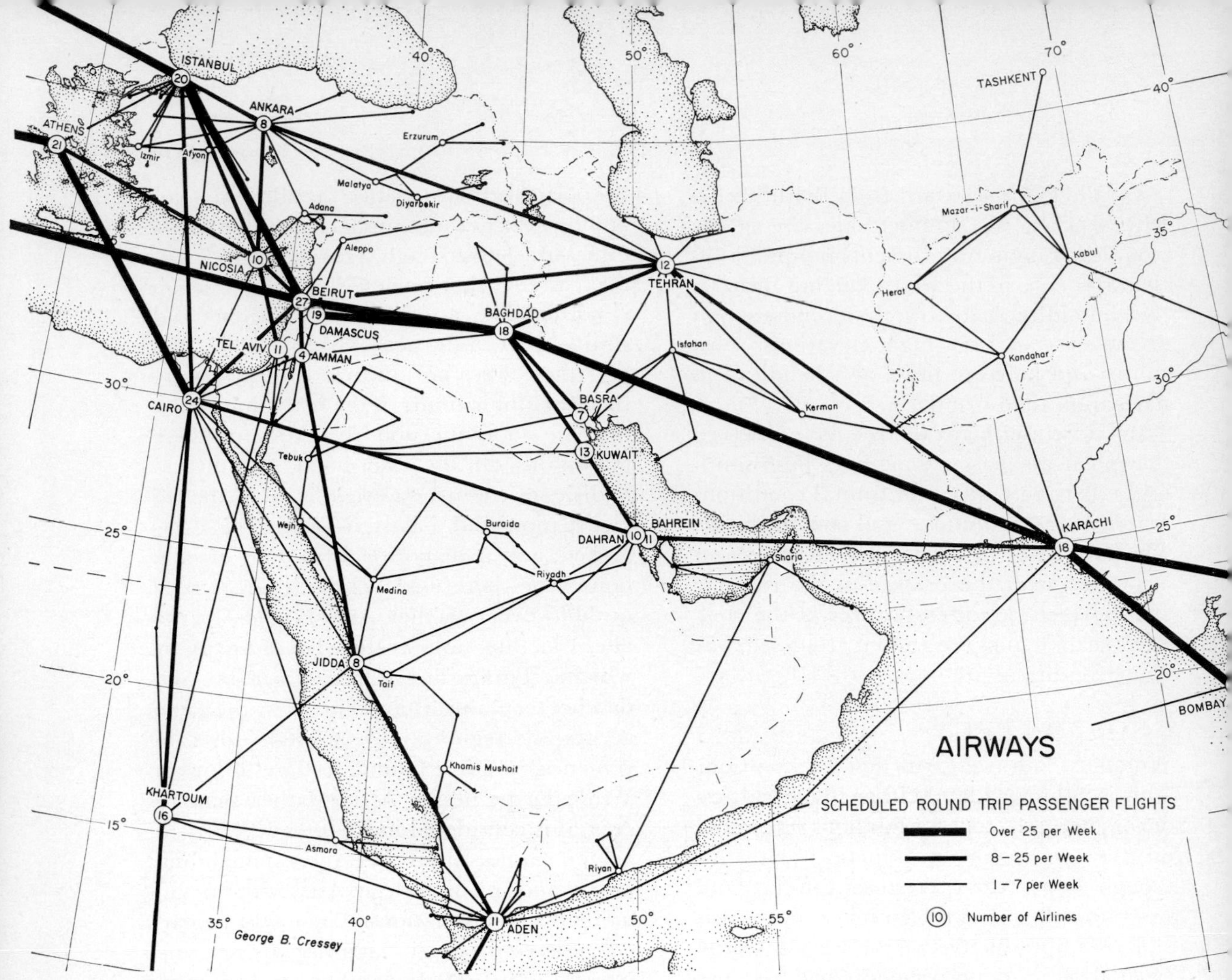

Strategic airways cross Swasia to link Europe with Eastern Asia. Beirut, Cairo, and Istanbul are ports of call for many round-the-world services. Local lines serve scores of airports. Data for 1959. (Compiled by Henry George.)

Some route across Swasia is a necessity for modern air travel. If prohibited air space should be created between the Mediterranean Sea and the Persian Gulf, the results to world trade would be as serious as a closing of the Suez Canal and the Red Sea.

Although Southwest Asia occupies a commanding position along world sea and air highways, its interior is relatively difficult of access. Rugged mountains encircle it on all sides. Continuous chains cross Afghanistan and Iran near the Soviet frontier and also along the south and east next to Pakistan. Turkey has ranges in the north and south, and access from the Aegean Sea is not easy. The eastern Mediterranean is bordered by highlands in Syria, Lebanon, and Israel. The Arabian Peninsula has a succession of mountains along the shores of the Red and Arabian seas.

This nearly continuous rampart is breeched only by the Persian Gulf and a few passes. The Khyber and nearby Bolan gateways have been avenues to Pakistan since man began to migrate. The Cilician Gates have long provided the major access to southern Turkey. A gap in the mountains of the eastern Mediterranean known as the Syrian Saddle serves as a lowland route from the coastal plain to upper Mesopotamia.

Kuwait has the world's largest oil loading terminal; offshore submarine pipes supplement the deepwater piers. Most of Europe depends on oil from the Persian Gulf. (Courtesy Kuwait Oil Co.)

In addition to being encircled by mountains, deserts further isolate Southwest Asia from its neighbors. This is true across the Isthmus of Sinai or the sandy deserts of southern Afghanistan. Other arid lands in neighboring countries add to this isolation and contribute to the identity of Swasia as a distinct geographic realm.

Overland travel from Europe to India is not yet important, although the railroad network is expanding and roads are rapidly being improved. Any traffic by land must pass through corridors even more restricted than the aerial gateways previously described.

Turkey, Iran, and Arabia occupy three corners of a triangle. Between these large centers of power, both present and past, are a series of smaller unstable states whose number and names have shifted with the centuries. Just as each of the three large areas has been a target for the other two, and for outside powers as well, so the central area has repeatedly fallen prey to pressures from Turkey, Iran, Arabia, or foreign invaders as under Alexander or Allenby. At the moment, these smaller countries are independent and include Iraq, Syria, Lebanon, Jordan, and Israel, plus the sheikdoms of the Persian Gulf. Political stability is still to be assured.

No area is an island aloof; no country can ever again withdraw inside a Great Wall. Whatever the appropriateness of the term *Middle* East, this corner of Asia does hold a middle position between three continents and six seas. Its external geopolitical and geoeconomic relations are thus as vital as its domestic problems.

Many outside countries have interests in

present day Swasia. Most of Europe depends on the Persian Gulf for its oil. To Britain, this area commands the sea and air routes to the Commonwealth in Asia. Suez was once a part of the lifeline of its Empire. For the Soviet Union, here is the only uncushioned part of its long frontier, an area where it can bring effective pressure on the West. Russia has long had dreams of an outlet to the Mediterranean or of a warm water port on the Persian Gulf. Across this area, Germany once planned a Berlin-to-Baghdad Railway. Since the days of the Crusades, France has assumed an interest in the Christian minorities along the eastern Mediterranean. Italian activities in the Red Sea go back for many decades. To Egypt, Swasia is the fountain of its religion and an area of possible political consolidation. Pakistan and India lie to the east, perhaps without major concern in Southwest Asia at the moment but with basic long range interests. Farther away, the United States is interested in global strategy and in oil. All of these relations have their roots in geography. Small wonder that most of Southwest Asia has not fully been its own master for more than half of the past 2,000 years.

The political problem of the present century centers around the disappearance of Turkish power following the collapse of the Ottoman Empire, the ending of British and French Mandates and special concessions, the inability of local governments to achieve full strength, and the contest between nearby Russia and distant America to fill the void. Some of these are considered in Chapter 9, International Contacts.

THE POLITICAL PATTERN

THE STATES of Swasia range from large sovereign nations, such as Saudi Arabia and Iran, several times the size of Texas, to tiny sheikdoms along the Persian Gulf whose poorly defined borders include only a spot of desert. All of these add up to 2.4 million square miles, about the size of Western Europe and somewhat smaller than the continental United States.

Three large countries form a rough triangle, Turkey in the northwest, Iran in the east, and Saudi Arabia to the south. Between them is a group of smaller states: Iraq, Jordan, the Syrian province of the United Arab Republic, Lebanon, Israel, two Neutral Zones, and the Persian Gulf sheikdoms of Kuwait, Bahrein, Qatar, and the Trucial Coast, each quasi-independent but under the protection of Great Britain. To the east is Afghanistan. In the far south are Masqat, Yemen, Aden, and the Aden Protectorates.

This has long been an area of shifting frontiers, and many boundaries are still in dispute. Prior to World War I, the Ottoman Empire spread from Turkey to the southern corners of Arabia. Saudi Arabia and the Arab states are new creations. British control is now limited to Aden and a nominal external control over the Aden Protectorate and the Persian Gulf states, but she once held mandates over Iraq, Jordan, and Palestine. France was formerly the mandate power in Syria and Lebanon.

In population, Turkey and Iran lead with over 20 million each; Afghanistan is a good third. Several other nations are in the multimillion class, while the Trucial States have only a few thousand each. The total population of Swasia is around 85 million, roughly half the figure for the United States. This volume is not primarily concerned with Egypt, but that country adds 25 million more.

The table on page 28 includes official data on area and population. Many of the figures are only estimates, since accurate maps and proper census figures are lacking. Some boundaries have never been surveyed, so that the areas for the Arabian Peninsula depend on where the boundary is drawn. The population totals for Afghanistan, Saudi Arabia, and Yemen are in some doubt.

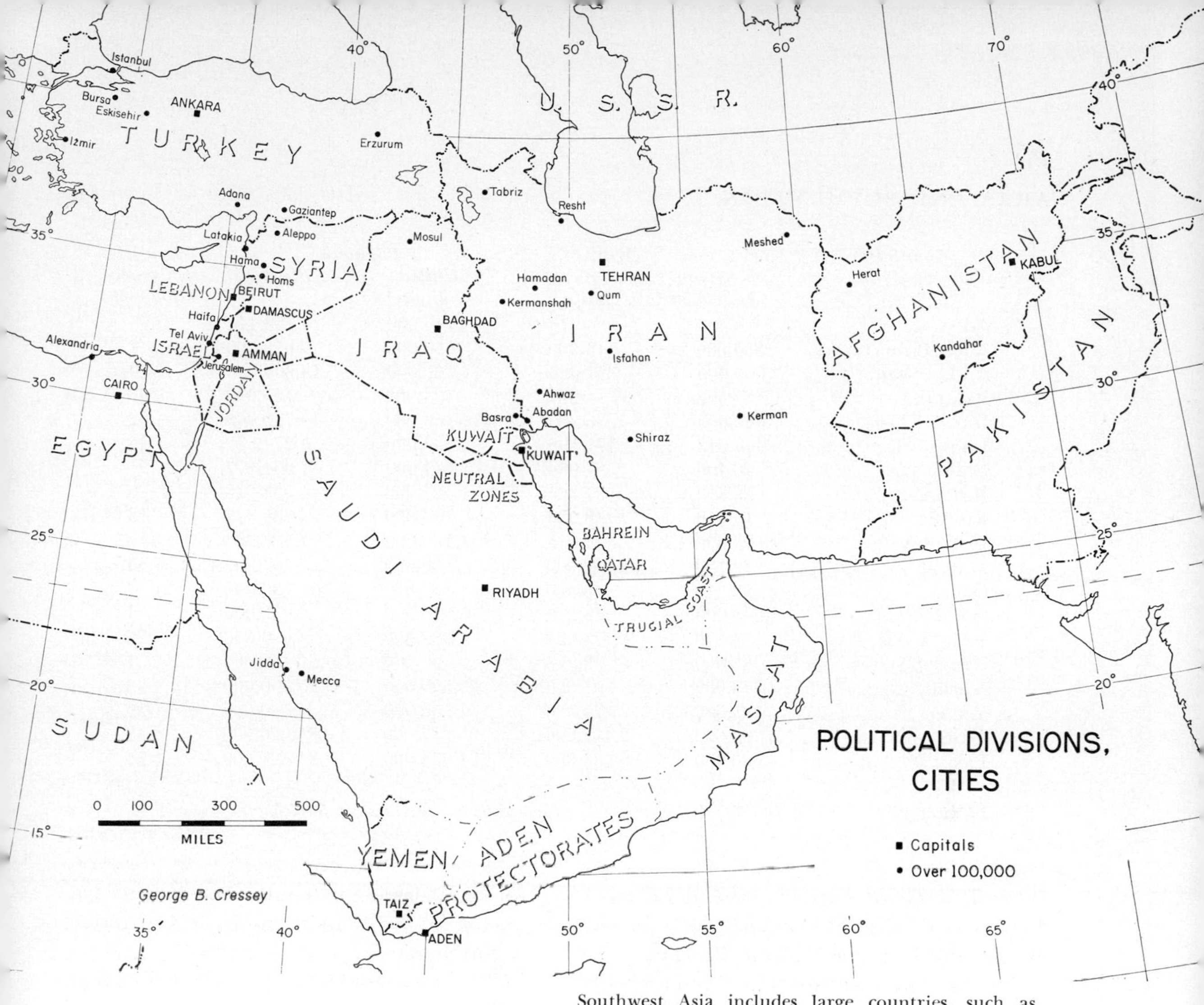

Southwest Asia includes large countries, such as Saudi Arabia and Iran, twice as big as Texas, as well as tiny sheikdoms the size of a county. The area as a whole is larger than the United States east of the Rocky Mountains.

Every major country of Swasia has experienced revolution during the twentieth century, in several cases more than once. The oldest republic, Turkey, was created in 1920; others are midcentury in origin. Even monarchies such as Iran have witnessed a change of dynasties. The following paragraphs highlight these situations.

Aden has been a British possession since 1839, originally administered from Bombay but since 1937 a colony with an increasing measure of local autonomy. Adjoining it are a number of petty states grouped into the Eastern and Western Protectorates.

Afghanistan includes the ancient Aryana, a multiracial country inhabited by Pushtus, Persians, and many others. Afghanistan was formerly an emirate but became a constitutional monarchy in 1926. The legislative power is vested in the king, an appointed senate, and an elected national assembly. The country lacks free access to the sea and is bounded by neighbors who have not always been friendly: the Soviet Union, Pakistan, and Iran.

Bahrein, Kuwait, Qatar, and the Trucial States are independent sheikdoms whose foreign relations and defense are under the di-

AREA AND POPULATION

Country	Area		Population		Density
	Square kilometers [1]	Square miles [2]	United Nations [1]	Britannica [2]	per square kilometer [1]
Aden	207	75	140,000	138,441	676
Aden Protectorate	290,080	112,000	650,000	650,000	2
Afghanistan	650,000	251,000	13,000,000	13,000,000	20
Bahrein	598	231	124,000	125,000	207
Iran	1,630,000	636,293	19,253,000	19,723,000	12
Iraq	444,442	171,599	6,538,000	6,274,579	15
Israel	20,700	7,984	1,937,000	1,964,677	94
Jordan	96,610	37,301	1,527,000	1,538,028	16
Kuwait	15,540	8,000	208,000	206,177	13
Lebanon	10,400	4,015	1,525,000	1,525,000	147
Masqat	212,380	82,000	550,000	550,000	3
Qatar	22,014	8,500	37,000	30,000	2
Saudi Arabia	1,600,000	618,000	6,036,000	6,036,000	4
Syria (UAR)	184,479	71,227	4,082,000	4,080,000	22
Trucial States	83,600	32,278	80,000	80,000	1
Turkey	776,980	301,380	25,500,000	25,500,000	33
Yemen	195,000	75,290	4,500,000	4,500,000	23
Southwest Asia	6,233,030	2,417,206	85,687,000	85,920,902	12
Egypt (U.A.R.)	1,000,000	386,000	24,026,000	24,020,000	24

[1] *United Nations Statistical Yearbook, 1958.* [2] *Encyclopaedia Britannica Book of the Year, 1959.*

rection of Great Britain. Several of these Persian Gulf areas were at one time a part of Persia, and Iran lays claim to Kuwait.

Iran became a constitutional monarchy in 1907 and is ruled by a shah, a national assembly or *Majles,* and a senate. The former Qajar Dynasty ended in 1925. The name of Iran was officially adopted in 1935, replacing the term Persia. In 1955, Iran joined with Iraq, Great Britain, and Pakistan in the Baghdad Pact. The country is divided into ten administrative provinces or *ustan,* and in turn into seventy-six counties.

Iraq, the ancient Mesopotamia, started its modern history in 1919 as a British mandate under the League of Nations. When this was terminated, Iraq became a constitutional monarchy, and in 1958 a revolution established a republic. There are fourteen provinces or *liwa,* plus three districts.

Israel is a republic formed in 1948. The Zionist state occupies the major part of the former Palestine mandate. The country is a democracy, with an assembly or *Knesset.*

Jordan was created as a British mandate in 1922 following World War I; it was then known as Trans-Jordan but the name was changed in 1946 when Jordan became a constitutional monarchy. Following the termination of Britain's mandate in Palestine, Jordan took over territory on the west bank of the river.

Lebanon is a republic with a constitution which came into effect in 1926, although the French mandate did not terminate until 1944. Because of the delicate religious balance between Christians and Moslems, the electoral law allocates deputies on a communal basis, and there are provisions whereby the president is always a Christian Maronite, the premier a Sunni Moslem, and the speaker of the chamber a Shia Moslem. Attempts to undermine the pro-Western character of the government led to a request for aid under the Eisenhower Doctrine in 1958, with the landing of American troops.

Masqat, sometimes spelled Muscat, is an independent monarchy in which the Sultan has absolute authority; the present royal line dates from 1741 so that Masqat has the oldest continuous government in Southwest Asia. The area includes the interior highland known as Oman, ruled by an Imam, so that the country is occasionally known as Masqat and Oman.

Saudi Arabia became a sovereign monarchy in 1927, following the conquest of most of the peninsula by Abdul Aziz, but the name of Saudi Arabia dates only from 1932. The King rules with the advice of an appointed consultative assembly. The royal flag, green with crossed swords, carries the Koranic text, "There is no God but Allah and Mohammed is his prophet." The religious law of Islam is the common law of the land.

Syria achieved its independence as a republic in 1941, following a period of French mandate control after World War I. In 1958 it merged with Egypt to form a province of the United Arab Republic. Greater Syria was once coextensive with the lands of the eastern Mediterranean, covering the area known as the Levant. There are nine administrative districts or *mohafazets*.

Turkey has been a republic since 1923, when the Treaty of Lausanne defined the boundaries of postwar Turkey. Prior to that time it had been the base for the Ottoman Empire, whose Sultan also served as the Caliph of Islam. The present area corresponds to what is traditionally known as Asia Minor, plus a small section in Europe. The country is divided into provinces or *vilayets*, once known as *sanjak*.

Yemen is an absolute monarchy, ruled by an Imam. The territory was once a part of the ancient kingdom of Sheba. Yemen is federated with the United Arab Republic but retains its own sovereignty.

REFERENCES

The preparation of this volume began with the organization of a bibliography of 3,000 references, half of them in languages other than English. The lists at the end of each chapter include only the more accessible and recent items. Outstanding sources are starred (*).

General Geography

Blanchard, Raoul: "Asie Occidentale," in GEOGRAPHIE UNIVERSELLE, VIII. Paris: Armand Colin (1929).

Bowman, Isaiah: "The Mohammedan World," *Geog. Rev.*, XIV (1924), 62–74.

* Birot, Pierre, and Dresch, Jean: LA MEDITERRANEE ET LE MOYEN ORIENT. Paris: Presses Universitaires de France (1953, 1956).

Cressey, George B.: ASIA'S LANDS AND PEOPLES. New York: McGraw Hill, rev. ed. (1951).

Dubertret, L., and Weulersse, J.: MANUEL DE GEOGRAPHIE, SYRIE, LIBAN, ET PROCHE ORIENT. Beirut: Imprimerie Catholique (1940).

* Fisher, W. B.: "Unity and Diversity in the Middle East," *Geog. Rev.*, XXXVII (1947), 414–435.

* Fisher, W. B.: THE MIDDLE EAST. London: Methuen; New York: Dutton (1956). [The best geography text]

Gibert, A., and Fevret, A.: "Notes sur la Geographie du Proche Orient," *Rev. de Geog. de Lyon*, XXIV (1949), 151–163, 279–288.

Hogarth, D. G.: THE NEARER EAST. New York: Appleton (1902).

Newbigin, Marion I.: MEDITERRANEAN LANDS. New York: Appleton-Century-Crofts (1924).

Oxford Regional Economic Atlas: THE MIDDLE EAST AND NORTH AFRICA. New York: Oxford Univ. Press (1960).

Place

* Randall, John, and others: "Southwest Asia," in Ginsburg, Norton, Ed., THE PATTERN OF ASIA. Englewood Cliffs, N. J.: Prentice-Hall (1958).

Semple, Ellen Churchill: THE GEOGRAPHY OF THE MEDITERRANEAN REGION. New York: Holt (1931).

Travel and Description

Douglas, William O.: WEST OF THE INDUS. New York: Doubleday (1958).

* Huxley, Julian: FROM AN ANTIQUE LAND. New York: Crown (1954). [Excellent travel observations]

Sitwell, Sacheverell: ARABESQUE AND HONEYCOMB. London: Hale (1957).

The Arab World

Ahmad, Nafis: MOSLEM CONTRIBUTION TO GEOGRAPHY. Lahore: Ashrans (1947).

* Antonius, George: THE ARAB AWAKENING. Beirut: Khayat's College Book Cooperative (1948).

Atiyah, Edward: THE ARABS. Baltimore: Penguin (1955).

Edmonds, C. J.: KURDS, TURKS, AND ARABS. London: Oxford Univ. Press (1957).

Harrison, Paul W.: THE ARAB AT HOME. New York: Crowell (1924).

Hourani, A. H.: MINORITIES IN THE ARAB WORLD. London: Oxford Univ. Press (1947).

Huzayyin, S. A.: ARABIA AND THE FAR EAST. Cairo: Royal Egyptian Geog. Soc. (1942).

Izzeddin, Nejla: THE ARAB WORLD. Chicago: Regnery (1953).

* Moscati, Sabatino: ANCIENT SEMITIC CIVILIZATIONS. London: Elek (1957).

Smith, C. G.: "Arab Nationalism: A Study in Political Geography," *Geog.,* XLIII (1958), 229–242.

Thomas, Bertram: THE ARABS. New York: Doubleday, Doran & Co. (1937).

VanEss, John: MEET THE ARAB. New York: John Day (1943).

Background Literature

* Anon: THE MIDDLE EAST (annual). London: Europa (1957). [General survey and directory, country by country]

Anshan, Ruth, and others: MID EAST—WORLD CENTER. New York: Harpers (1956).

Bonne, Alfred: THE ECONOMIC DEVELOPMENT OF THE MIDDLE EAST. London: Kegan Paul (1945).

Bonne, Alfred: STATE AND ECONOMICS IN THE MIDDLE EAST. London: Kegan Paul, Trench, Trubner (1948).

Bonne, Alfred: "Land and Population in the Middle East," *Middle East Jour.,* V (1951), 39–56.

* Bullard, Reader, Ed.: THE MIDDLE EAST: A POLITICAL AND ECONOMIC SURVEY. London: Oxford Univ. Press, 3rd. ed. (1958). [Excellent analysis, country by country, issued by Royal Institute of International Affairs]

Campbell, John C.: DEFENSE OF THE MIDDLE EAST. New York: Council on Foreign Relations and Harpers (1958). [Symposium]

East, W. G., and Spate, O. H. K., Eds.; THE CHANGING MAP OF ASIA. New York: Dutton, 2nd. ed. (1953).

* Ellis, Harry B.: HERITAGE OF THE DESERT. New York: Ronald (1956).

ENCYCLOPEDIA OF ISLAM. Leyden and London (1913).

Fisher, Sydney N.: SOCIAL FORCES IN THE MIDDLE EAST. Ithaca: Cornell Univ. Press (1955). [Symposium]

Fisher, W. B.: "South West Asia" in East, W. G., and Moodie, A. E., Eds.: THE CHANGING WORLD. Yonkers-on-Hudson: World (1956).

Frey, Ulrich, and others: "Vorder and Sudasien," in KLUTE HANDBUCH DER GEOGRAPHISCHEN WISSENSCHAFT. Potsdam: Akademische Verlagsgesellschaft Athenaion (1937).

Gelhorn, Eleanor Cowles: MCKAY'S GUIDE TO THE FAR EAST AND THE MIDDLE EAST. New York: D. McKay (1959).

Great Britain Board of Trade: OVERSEAS ECONOMIC SURVEYS. London: H. M. Stationery Office. [Series of country reports, frequently revised]

Hachette: LES GUIDES BLEUS, MOYEN-ORIENT: LIBAN, SYRIE, JORDANIE, IRAK, IRAN. Paris: Hachette (1956).

Hall, Harvey P., Ed.: MIDDLE EAST RESOURCES. Washington: Middle East Inst. (1954).

Hoskins, Halford L.: THE MIDDLE EAST: PROBLEM AREA IN WORLD POLITICS. New York: Macmillan (1954). [Symposium]

Ireland, Philip W., Ed.: THE NEAR EAST: PROBLEMS AND PROSPECTS. Chicago: Univ. of Chicago Press (1942).

Jackh, Ernst: BACKGROUND OF THE MIDDLE EAST. Ithaca: Cornell (1952).

Lenczowski, Ed.: THE MIDDLE EAST IN WORLD AFFAIRS. Ithaca: Cornell Univ. Press (1956).

Lengyil, Emil: WORLD WITHOUT END: THE MIDDLE EAST. New York: John Day (1953).

* Richardson, F. L. W. Jr., and Batal, James: "The Near East," in Linton, Ralph, Ed., MOST OF THE WORLD. New York: Columbia Univ. Press (1949), 461–547.

Speiser, E. A.: THE UNITED STATES AND THE NEAR EAST. Cambridge: Harvard Univ. Press (1950).

Thayer, Philip W., and others: TENSION IN THE MIDDLE EAST. Baltimore: Johns Hopkins Press (1958).

Toynbee, Arnold J.: THE ISLAMIC WORLD. London: Oxford Univ. Press (1927).

U. S. Bureau of Foreign and Domestic Commerce: WORLD TRADE INFORMATION SERIES, ECONOMIC REPORTS. [Series of basic data studies on each country, frequently revised]

Regional Magazines

Asian Review. London.

* *Bulletin Societe de Geographie d'Egypt*. Cairo.

* *Iraq Petroleum*. London: The Iraq Petroleum Company.

* *Journal Royal Central Asian Society*. London.

Middle East Affairs. New York.

Middle East Business Digest. Beirut.

Middle East Journal. Washington.

Palestine Exploration Quarterly. Jerusalem (Now *Israel Exploration Quarterly*).

Bibliographies

American Friends of the Middle East: BOOK CATALOGUE AND FILM LIST. New York: Amer. Friends of the Middle East (1956).

Burke, Jean T.: AN ANNOTATED BIBLIOGRAPHY OF BOOKS AND PERIODICALS IN ENGLISH DEALING WITH HUMAN RELATIONS IN THE ARAB STATES OF THE MIDDLE EAST. Beirut: American Univ. of Beirut (1956).

Economics Research Institute: A SELECTED AND ANNOTATED BIBLIOGRAPHY OF ECONOMIC LITERATURE ON THE ARABIC SPEAKING COUNTRIES OF THE MIDDLE EAST, 1938–1952. Beirut: American Univ. of Beirut (1954).

Field, Henry: BIBLIOGRAPHY ON SOUTHWESTERN ASIA, Coral Gables, Fla: Miami Univ. Press (1953, 1955, 1956).

CHAPTER 2

People

Population Patterns
Geographical History
The Races of Swasia
Mesopotamian Empires: Babylon and Assyria
Persian Empires: The Achaemenid Period
Arab Empires: The Ommiad and Abbasside
Turkish Empires: The Ottoman
Three Travelers
References

POPULATION PATTERNS

No one knows how many people live in Southwestern Asia; the total is probably over 85 million, but, whatever the figure, it will be larger tomorrow. Census figures of fair reliability are available for Turkey and Iraq, but the data for countries such as Afghanistan and Saudi Arabia are highly uncertain. Does the latter have 4 million or 6 million? Are there really 13 million people in Afghanistan?

On the basis of official figures supplied by the various countries, the *Statistical Yearbook* of the United Nations puts the total population at upwards of 85 million; roughly 3 per cent of all mankind. The distribution of these people is uncertain, but it appears that over 10 million, probably 12 per cent, live in cities with populations over 25,000. About 55 million people are farmers, some 7.5 million are nomads, and an additional million are unsettled refugees. The remainder live in villages or small towns.

These millions of people represent the widest range in wealth and culture. Some are landless serfs, others are world citizens in the finest sense. Prosperity and poverty live side by side. Some contrasts are partly related to the environment, some are matters of social evolution, others are political by-products. Few places in the world have witnessed more history, or are experiencing such sweeping changes. It should not be surprising if there are occasions when rapid evolution erupts into violent revolution.

The cultural landscape of Swasia is full of vivid contrasts. Near the head of the Persian

(Opposite) Cuneiform inscriptions record the far-flung conquests of Mesopotamia. This remarkably lifelike handbag is at Nimrud, capital of Assyria. (Courtesy Iraq Petroleum Co.)

Gulf, swamps cover thousands of square miles. Here live a specialized people, the Marsh Arabs, whose income is derived from the rice, fish, and reeds of this submerged land. A few tens of miles to the east or west, where a superabundance of water gives way to extreme aridity, Bedouin Arabs roam the desert with their flocks in search of scanty pasture. South of the swamps is the modern port city of Basra, stocked with merchandise from across the Seven Seas; here other Arabs live a westernized urban existence, some in poverty, others in wealth.

Similar contrasts exist side by side within each country. In Iran, irrigation creates sharp boundaries between the green and the brown. Dwellers on the two sides of the outermost irrigation canal have quite different views of the world. Some of the most vivid differences are those related to oil; in such areas money is available in large amounts, so that within the company compound there is green grass, air conditioning, and a way of life utterly unlike that of the nearby indigenous population.

People of many ethnic groups live in Swasia. This is a Turkish peasant from Samsun. (Courtesy Turkish Information Office, New York.)

Not all of the differences in people make a visible impression on the landscape. The contrasts between Shia and Sunni Moslems are of geographic significance, as are the location of racial minorities such as Kurds or Armenians, yet they are not usually mapped. Some people have lived in their chosen environment for many generations; when they move to a new situation, profound social and economic changes follow. The well-established moral codes of the nomad do not automatically fit the life of a factory worker in a city. Sociological maps would thus reveal gradations in custom and mentality.

Many of these contrasts in people are too detailed to show up on maps of the area as a whole. This is one of the dangers in compressing the complexity, often multidimensional, of many square miles into a few square inches.

Geography asks many questions; the first is usually "where"; in second place comes "who." Since man is the most interesting element in most landscapes, maps of population distribution present basic information and raise fundamental questions. To understand their meaning is to know much about a country. It should be remembered that people do not form a continuity, as does temperature or soil; instead they have a discontinuous distribution. One may observe some of the physical features of the earth from a high-flying plane, but individuals are usually too dispersed to be seen as individuals. Maps are necessarily a simplification.

Here and there across Swasia are concentrations of people, often a reflection of good land, or of commerce and industry. In some cases these are oases of settlement, with knife-edge boundaries along the last irrigation ditch, abruptly separated from one another by emptiness. Elsewhere there is merely a transition from dense to sparse population. There are few if any places where one may drive for ten miles across continuous farmland without noting differences in population density. Unevenness in population is the rule.

Among all the many possible kinds of maps, those which show where people live are the most meaningful. At least three population maps are necessary for Swasia. The first locates rural sedentary people, for the most part farmers. The second attempts to show the distribution of nomads, but, since they do not stay put, no map can be more than suggestive. The third map portrays urban distributions. Still a fourth map is called for as long as the million refugees remain unsettled around the borders of Israel, since it would distort the true pattern to add them to the normal agricultural population (see page 431).

These paragraphs provide only an introduction to population problems; further aspects will be considered in the various country chapters to follow.

The most striking features on the map of rural sedentary population in Southwest Asia are the many uninhabited areas. Thousands of square miles are either without people or have such a sparse population that the density is negligible. In contrast, other sections appear congested. Everywhere man is irregularly distributed.

While this is perhaps the most important map in the book, the information on which it is based is very unsatisfactory. Even where acceptable census totals are available by countries, there may be little evidence as to detailed distribution. In other countries the population pattern merely reflects information as to areas of cultivation or the arrangement of land forms.

Large parts of Southwest Asia are empty.

This Arab boy lives in a Syrian village; he wears the head scarf known as a *kafiyah*. (Courtesy Iraq Petroleum Co.)

If one were to descend by parachute at a random location and start out on foot, it might be days before one would find a farmer or a nomad, or even any sign of their occupancy. Only in limited districts may one see cultivated fields. If a population map were prepared on a square mile grid, 90 per cent of the checkerboard would be essentially without people.

It is not enough to observe on the map that some rural areas appear dark while others are light; in terms of satisfactory livelihood it may well be that the most overpopulated areas are those with a scanty population per square mile, while the most hopeful areas for additional settlement lie in districts which already support a large population. What we need, but what no one has yet prepared, is a map showing the opti-

Kurdish people occupy the highland areas where Turkey, Iraq, and Iran meet. (Courtesy Iraq Petroleum Co.)

mum density, area by area. The ideal ratio of man to land varies with technology and standards of living.

The pattern of rural sedentary population reflects two situations. In regions where there is enough rain for normal cultivation or dry farming, and where land forms and soils permit, people are spread rather evenly. This is the case along the coasts of the Mediterranean, Black, and Caspian seas. In these situations, however, mountains lie close to the shore, and the coastal population forms only a fringe of settlement. Somewhat better topographic situations may be found in interior valleys, as in the Bekaa of Lebanon, the Orontes basin in Syria, and the valleys which drain toward the Aegean in western Turkey. Evenly dispersed settlement also occurs in the subhumid plains of Anatolia, the Fertile Crescent of Iraq and Syria, and in the uplands of Yemen.

Where rainfall is limited, permanent settlement depends on irrigation. There are thus areas of concentrated population in the Tigris and Euphrates valleys and in the many oases along the base of humid mountains such as the Zagros and Elburz. Such settlement patterns are apt to be linear, following rivers and canals rather than the more even distribution where man occupies all of the land; densities are also much greater.

Figures as to the density of population per square mile have little meaning when applied to entire countries. The ratio of man to land varies widely from place to place. The most densely-inhabited areas are the ribbon oases in Iraq and Iran where the population amounts to several hundred per square mile. Conditions along the Nile are even more congested. The coasts of the Caspian and Black seas are also crowded. Western Turkey, northwestern Iran, and the lands near the eastern Mediterranean and in highland Yemen, come next, with rural populations which range from twenty-five to a hundred people in each square mile. The latter figure is roughly the concentration in eastern rural North America. The bulk of Saudi Arabia, Kuwait, western Iraq, eastern Jordan, and eastern Syria have a rural density of less than two. The salt deserts of Iran and the Rub al Khali of Arabia are completely empty; such areas account for 10 per cent of the realm. Somewhat more than half of Swasia has from two to twenty-five people per square mile. This includes Afghanistan and eastern Iran, central Iraq, and the fringe of Arabia. These dry areas roughly correspond in density to parts of the American Great Basin.

In comparison with the United States where the density is about fifty per square mile, Swasia as a whole has an average of thirty. In terms of food producing agricultural land, the density rises to 300 people per square mile. This is the difference between the arithmetical and the physiological

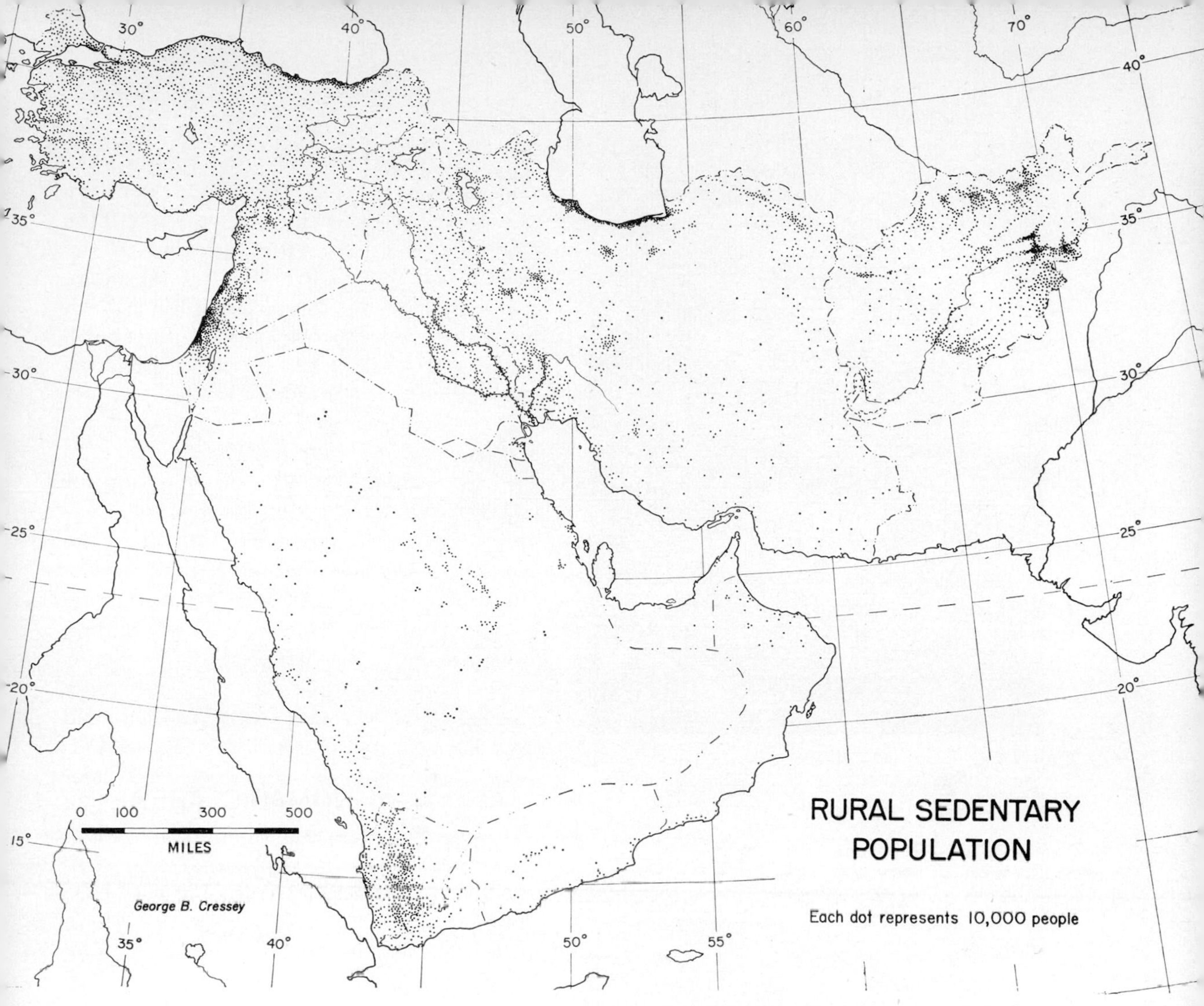

No map is more meaningful than that of where people live; it both states a fact and raises a question as to why some areas are crowded while others are empty. While this is a map of people, it serves also as a measure of agricultural potential.

density. Both figures of thirty and 300 are well below world averages.

To understand the reasons for these inequalities is to know the significance of the environment and of history. The pattern of population reflects the conditions of climate, soils, terrain, and vegetation as well as location and mineral resources.

Since nomads represent geography in motion, one can only map areas within which they migrate. In general, they occupy the semiarid lands intermediate between the absolute desert and areas of cultivation. Many square miles are involved, but the population supporting capacity is limited. Few deserts are entirely without people, but in the driest parts of Arabia and Iran, years may elapse between nomadic penetration. Bedouin tribes in the desert of northern Arabia and its extension into Syria regularly migrate hundreds of miles each season.

Some nomads spend part of each year as farmers or seek jobs in cities, as in Iraq where they have created slums on the fringe of Baghdad. Within recent decades, tens of thousands of nomads have given up their wandering life and have become agriculturalists, in places under government pres-

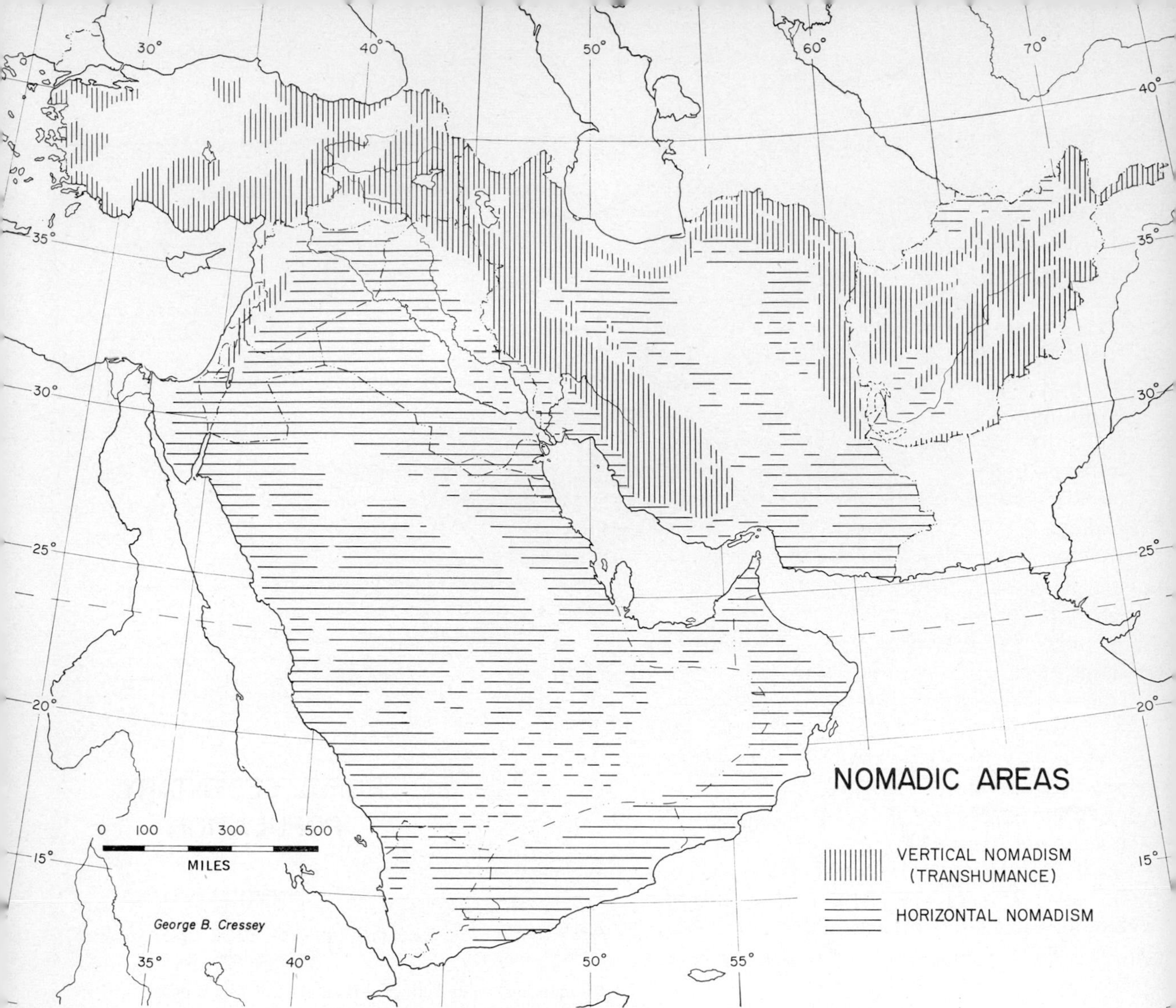

Nomadism represents man in motion, so that this map merely indicates the areas in which migratory pastoralism prevails. In mountain lands, people move up and down the slopes according to the seasonal distribution of grass; in the desert plains the migration is horizontal.

sure. Others might do so but for the hold of their tribal chiefs. It is clear that nomadism represents a declining type of land use.

Two types of nomadism prevail. One, which might be termed horizontal, exists in the deserts. Here, migrations reflect rainfall and pasture. The other, of a vertical character, describes tribes moving up and down mountain slopes seeking seasonal pasture. This type is known as transhumance and is prevalent in southeastern Turkey, western Iran, and Afghanistan. The nomads of Turkey are chiefly Kurds, while in Iran there are the Bakhtiari, Lurs, and Qashgai.

Ten million Swasians live in cities. The preparation of a map of cities presents fewer problems than that of rural people, although many uncertainties remain. While all of the larger urban areas have been identified, it is probable that there are additional centers of around 50,000 people not shown on the accompanying map.

The growth of these cities reflects many factors. Political conditions influence capital cities, such as Ankara and Riyadh. Religious centers provide a focus, as at Jerusalem and Mecca. Commerce is the basis for the seaports along the Mediterranean, so that Beirut serves half a dozen countries. Oases have developed around water, as at Isfahan or Meshed. Oil developments account for new centers around the Persian Gulf. Many settlements are essentially market towns, as those which serve the deserts of Arabia and Iran. Where cities are present amid mountains they obviously mark fertile valleys, as at Kermanshah and Hamadan.

City patterns vary from the rectangular street arrangement of new suburbs to the chaotic lanes of overgrown villages. Morphology reveals history. Many ancient cities were once surrounded by walls, but few of these remain. Traces of old fortifications and of a central fort or *gala* are widespread. Where the city walls have been torn down, circular boulevards take their place.

Almost every city is in the midst of dramatic growth, scarcely duplicated anywhere in a twentieth-century world characterized in all continents by urbanization. Cities are growing faster than nations. New functions have brought new suburbs. In many cities, the former center of town with its bazaar trade has been superceded by newly-located wide streets and European style shops.

A surprising number of cities are without rail connections, and many are not even on a navigable waterway or the sea. This is notably true in Iran where half a dozen cities with populations over 100,000 have no railway. Although Beirut, Damascus, and Jerusalem each have railroads, the lines are of little commercial importance.

Cities are strikingly localized, with a notable concentration near the eastern Mediterranean. Four cities exceed half a million in population: Istanbul, Beirut, Baghdad, and Tehran. Two dozen others have from 100,000 to 500,000 people. Centers with 50,000 to 100,000 are also some two dozen in number.

To develop a city with a population of over a million, it appears necessary to have a country with 20 million people, as is the case with Istanbul and Tehran, or Cairo. Cities of half a million, such as Baghdad and Beirut, require an economic hinterland of 5 million, either in their home country or in their tributary area.

The accompanying population maps represent patterns in transition. Each decade sees an increase in total numbers and marked shifts in distribution. Cities grow, usually with the larger outstripping the smaller. New agricultural developments, in irrigation or techniques, attract additional settlers. Large estates are divided into

Bakhtiari tribesmen migrate up and down the slopes of the Zagros Mountains in Iran. (Courtesy Iranian Oil Participants.)

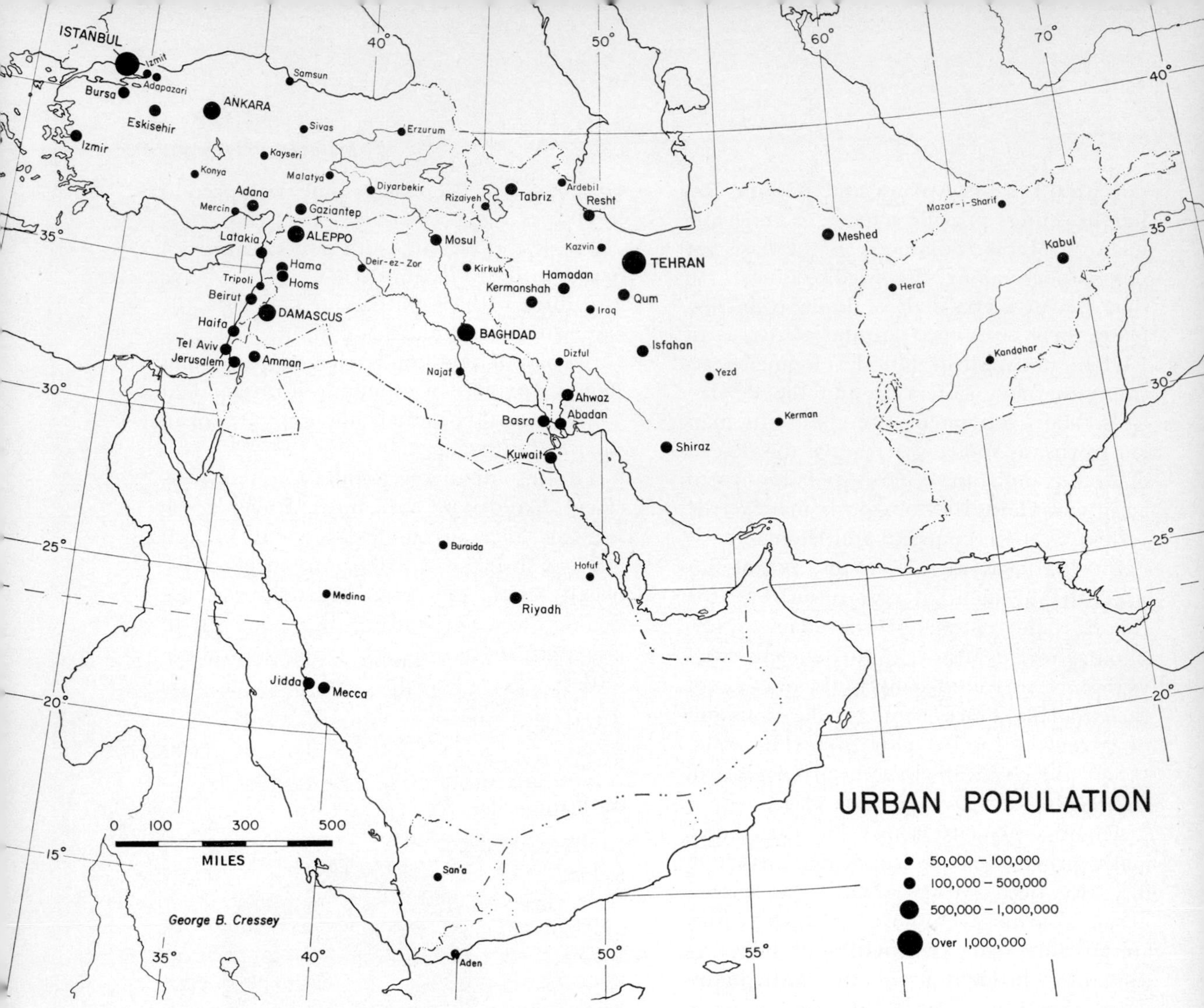

The development of most urban centers in Southwest Asia reflects commerce and political considerations rather than primary production or industry. Every city is growing rapidly, with remarkable expansion in the central business district and upper class residential areas.

smaller holdings. Settlement advances or retreats along desert frontiers with each fluctuation in rainfall.

Land takes on new values with changing technology. What we see in the twentieth century is merely one scene from a long moving picture. In terms of present values, it seems probable that the distribution of mountains and deserts and of coasts and rivers, will always be reflected in the maps of where men live.

There is little way of estimating the maximum capacity of Swasia to support more people and at higher standards. Geography can inventory and evaluate the available land but it is up to the agriculturalist to know how it can be used, or to the engineer to know how irrigation may be expanded. As the population grows, these adjustments become more pressing. More food will be needed, and it seems likely that this must come largely from the more intensive utilization of presently cultivated areas rather than from new marginal land.

The manifold environments of Swasia present varied challenges. Only in an old, old land such as this could people have learned how to live so successfully amid such varied and often harsh restrictions. This has been possible through long experimentation and specialized occupations.

One further aspect of Swasia's centrality may be found in the worldwide pattern of settlement. The global center of population lies north of the realm, 500 miles beyond the Aral Sea.[1] In other words, if all of mankind were to meet at a common point, each traveling by the shortest distance, they would congregate here.

GEOGRAPHICAL HISTORY

History has its roots in geography, for time does not exist without space. Swasia provides exacting landscapes, and for ancient man the environment was probably more of a confining factor than today. Early man lived most successfully where the original environment was favorable; the food supply was localized, travel of necessity tended to follow natural avenues, and states developed around coherent areas. As empires grew, new space relationships became necessary.

The history of Southwest Asia is set in a physical frame which has not materially changed for many millennia. Rivers have shifted their courses, harbors have become silted or opened, rainfall has fluctuated during decades or even centuries, mountain passes are more or less open with variations in snow cover, soils are depleted or elsewhere renewed by flood deposits, accumulations of salt or of silt cause irrigated lands to go out of cultivation, and wars may so devastate an area that it remains underpopulated for a century. Such changes are obvious, but they do not in themselves represent long-range dessication or major alterations in the natural landscape. The ruins of ancient cities, now amid desolate landscapes, all have remains of aqueducts, reservoirs, and special water-conserving facilities which show that aridity was a problem then as now. Environmental uniformity is more obvious than change.

Southwest Asia does not lend itself to either cultural or political unity. Mountain ranges bar passage, and interior basins lack contact with their neighbors. Nomads cannot carry much feed for their flocks, hence they must move along grassland avenues or step precariously from one oasis to another.

Iran lacks a logical political focus since the several fertile and inhabited regions are scattered around the circumference of the central deserts and are thus isolated one from the other. The various historic capitals of the country have been transitory for it has proven difficult to centralize the national administration. Since the provinces were diverse and a common focus was lacking, the material strength of the Persian empires depended on personal allegiance to a king. Loyalty was not to the idea of a nation, but to the person of the ruler.

Turkey is equally fractionalized, with topographic barriers which isolate the coasts from the several interior basins. The political problems of dry interior basins are different from those of the humid, seafaring coast. The ancient capital of Constantinople was off-center, and the present seat of government at Ankara is a compromise.

The problem of unity in ancient Syria and Palestine reflects the same situations in miniature; the Hebrews of the hills were traditionally in conflict with the Philistines along the coast. The interests of commercial Phoenicia were quite in contrast to the desert dwellers to the east. Only rarely was there a political entity. Present day Lebanon

[1] Centers of population for a single country usually mean that half the people live north or south, and east or west, of an established point. To roughly determine the population center for the world as a whole, a metal globe was opened and weights fastened in the interior near the center of population for each country and proportional to its numbers. The hemispheres were then reassembled and the globe allowed to roll until it came to rest. This point is north of the Aral Sea at 62° 45′ E. and 53° 52′ N.

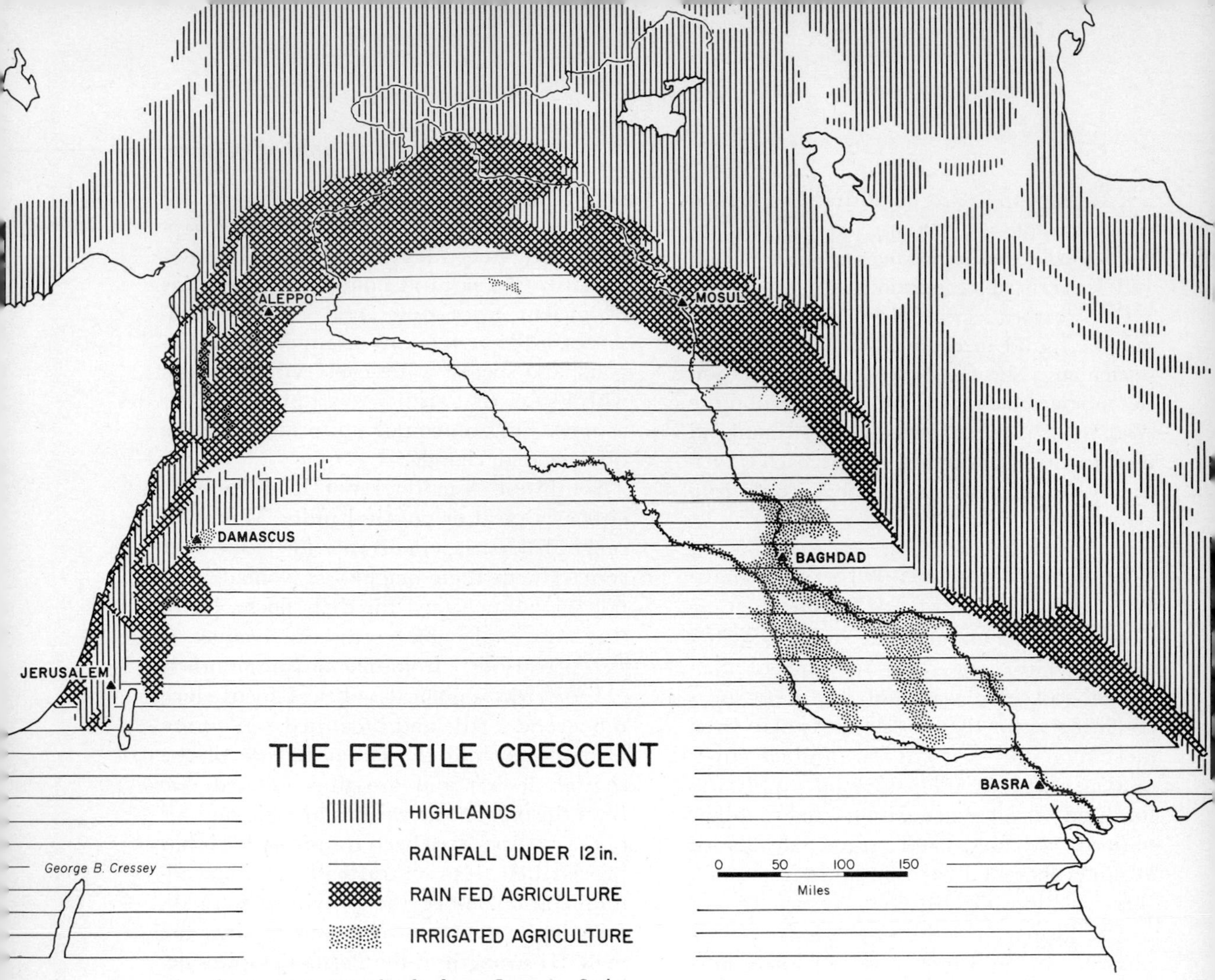

The short grass steppelands from Iraq to Syria, known as the Fertile Crescent, have long provided a corridor for commerce and migration from the Tigris-Euphrates Valley and the Persian Gulf to the Mediterranean Coast and Egypt.

reflects similar conflict between mountain and lowland people.

The topography of Arabia gives the possibility of easy travel, but here barriers of distance and aridity are scarcely less serious than land forms elsewhere. Coherence has to wait on easy communication.

The most favored area for movement and unity is along the Fertile Crescent, the arc of level and subhumid land between the mountains and the desert which links the head of Persian Gulf and the eastern Mediterranean. This more or less continuous grassland unites the valleys of the Tigris and Euphrates with the Levant coast by way of the north Syrian steppe. Contact was thus made possible between Mesopotamia and Egypt, and the Fertile Crescent became the world's first great international highway. The historian, James Brestead, has defined the area: [1]

> This fertile crescent is approximately a semicircle, with the open side toward the south, having the west end at the southeast corner of the Mediterranean, the center directly north of Arabia, and the east end at the north end of the

[1] James Henry Brestead: *Ancient Times, A History of The Early World.* Boston: Ginn, 101. Quoted by permission.

Persian Gulf. It lies like an army facing south, with one wing stretching along the eastern shore of the Mediterranean and the other reaching out to the Persian Gulf, while the center has its back against the northern mountains. The end of the western wing is Palestine; Assyria makes up a large part of the center; while the end of the eastern wing is Babylonia.

This great semicircle, for lack of a name, may be called the Fertile Crescent. There is no name, either geographical or political, which includes all of this great semicircle. Hence we are obliged to coin a term and call it the Fertile Crescent. It may also be likened to the shores of a desert-bay, upon which the mountains behind look down—a bay not of water but of sandy waste, some five hundred miles across, forming a northern extension of the Arabian desert and sweeping as far north as the latitude of the northeast corner of the Mediterranean. This desert-bay is a limestone plateau of some height—too high indeed to be watered by the Tigris and Euphrates, which have cut canyons obliquely across it. Nevertheless, after the meager winter rains, wide tracts of the northern desert-bay are clothed with scanty grass, and spring thus turns the region for a short time into grasslands. The history of Western Asia may be described as an age long struggle between the mountain peoples of the north and the desert wanderers of these grasslands—a struggle which is still going on—for the possession of the Fertile Crescent, the shores of the desert-bay.

Of the beginning of civilization we know very little. The earliest recorded events took place in established towns along the Crescent; such as at Jericho in Palestine, at Jarmo in northern Iraq, and around Ur in southern Iraq. None of these represent true beginnings. Each decade brings new archaeological discoveries and known history is pushed back farther and farther.

Long before these urban developments man had made the transition from nomadism to settled life; from food collecting to food producing. Harold Peake has suggested that this step took place somewhere near the center of the Crescent. The date is unknown but many millennia B.C. We know that these people used sickles, made by fitting sharp flints into curved bones. The teeth of such implements as have been found are polished by considerable use, suggesting that they were used to harvest grain. Stone mortars were used for grinding. The domestication of animals apparently came later.

From what we now know, it appears that Jericho in the lower Jordan valley may be the oldest town in the world. Carbon-14 dating near the base of excavations in the ancient mound takes us back to 6800 B.C. with suggestions that the village began ten thousand years ago. There was then a neolithic community which had not yet begun the manufacture of pottery. Even in early times, Jericho had a well-developed culture, and it is evident that we must revise our ideas as to the beginnings of civilization. As Kathleen Kenyon has written, "It has already been established that a date of *c.* 6000 B.C. was comparatively late in the history of neolithic Jericho."

Many of the known historic movements in Swasia reflect the struggles of nomadic tribes who were trying to displace sedentary populations already in possession of the more attractive areas. This is the ancient conflict between the desert and the sown area, between the brown waste and the green fields, between the dwellers in tents and in houses. Settled populations have been continuously modified by fresh nomadic blood. A parade of empires has risen and fallen but in the desert the life of the Bedouin has remained essentially unchanged. It is well to recognize that the nomad is not backward, but rather that his way of life is different. In terms of his restricted environment, his adjustments may be as equally advanced as those of the townsman.

We do not yet know what has caused desert people, so many times in history, to surge into the surrounding grasslands. Perhaps it was related to minor climatic cycles which led to a diminution of the always scanty pasture. Perhaps it was a great personality who could command leadership. Possibly it was a weakening in the strength of townsmen and farmers, thus tempting the nomad to make sustained raids.

In many cases, new empires set up by desert peoples reached an early peak and then gradually deteriorated as the vigor brought in from nomadic life was lost in the comforts of the court.

Many of the pages which follow will discuss the topographic corridors which have repeatedly been the avenues of history. Gateways such as the Khyber Pass or the Cilician Gates, grassland avenues like the Fertile Crescent, or shoestring oases as along the Tigris have been significant since man first moved. Waterways such as the Bosporus or the entrances to the Persian Gulf and the Red Sea still loom large in international politics.

This Persian peasant is smoking the water pipe known as a *hookah.* (Courtesy Iranian Oil Participants.)

THE RACES OF SWASIA

A GREAT ARRAY of people have moved across the plains of Swasia, some of them originating here, others advancing from the outside. Their ethnic and cultural relations are both vague and complex. Certainly there is nothing which can be called a pure "race"; the various ethnic groups are the result of long intermixing.

One great strain, which we call the Semitic peoples, came out of the Arabian deserts. Another group are the Indo-Europeans who came from the north and are here known as Persians. Still a third source has contributed the Turks, chiefly from central Asia. It may be convenient merely to speak of Arab, Persian, and Turkish cultures; but these are not all for there have been repeated contacts with inner Asia, with what is now Pakistan, with Egypt, and with Greece and Rome. The Crusaders were not temporary pilgrims since their kingdoms lasted more than two centuries. The fact that this volume necessarily has geographical limits should not imply any isolating gulf from neighboring areas.

The term Semite is properly used for a language rather than a sharply defined race. In general, Semitic peoples have occupied the area from the Mediterranean to the Tigris, and from the Taurus to Aden. Successive waves have appeared, apparently emerging from the deserts of Arabia. It has alternately been suggested that the common homeland lay in Mesopotamia, or within the Fertile Crescent, or even in Africa, but the best judgment points to the Arabian peninsula as the source area, perhaps even to Yemen. The peninsula was clearly the original home of the latest excursion, that of the Arabs. Since interior Arabia is the one part of Swasia which was never conquered by outside people, the Semites in their homeland represent the purest ethnic stock of the area.

Semitic people include the Akkadians who appeared during the fourth millennium, roughly about 3500 B.C.; along with them were the Assyrians and later the Chaldeans. Each of these groups ended up in the Tigris and Euphrates valleys. Their cultural unity with other Semitic people is shown by the striking similarities in language as revealed through a study of the cuneiform inscriptions. Amorites and Canonites, together with Phoenicians, emerged in the third millennium, say 2500 B.C., moving into Syria and the central part of the Crescent. The Hebrews appeared from 1500 to 1200 B.C. at the same time as the Aramaeans; the general destination of both groups was Syria and Palestine. About 500 B.C. the Nabataeans and other pre-Islamic Arabs occupied Sinai and Petra. The Moslem Arabs, as we know them today, date from A.D. 700; within a century they became masters of an empire which reached from the Atlantic to the gates of China, larger than the Roman Empire at its zenith.

Of all these Semitic people, only the Hebrews and Arabs are important today. Jews and Arabs are closely related, since Hebrew and Arabic are cognate Semitic languages. Both people are the result of many mixtures, especially the Jews who have non-Semitic Hittite and Hurrian blood.

The changing ideas which resulted from Jewish migrations may be seen in their evolving concept of Yawah or Jehovah. Originally the name was that of an Arab Bedouin deity, adopted by the Jews during the forty years of their wanderings in the Sinai peninsula. As the Jews settled down in Palestine they departed from the worship of Yawah, the god of flocks and herds in favor of Baal, the god of cultivation. Later, when

Hunting with falcons is a popular sport in Arabia. (Courtesy Arabian American Oil Co.)

the Judean Jews were transported to Babylon, they came into contact with Zoroastrian ideas. These pictured the world as the scene of a struggle between good and evil, between light and darkness, and between Ormazd (or Ahura Mazda) and Ahriman. The concept of God was thus modified, while the idea of Satan as a personification of evil owes something to the ideas of Ahriman.

From the Semites the world has its three great monotheistic religions: Judaism, Christianity, and Islam. It is important to recognize that, whereas Judaism looks to the Old Testament, Islam draws from both the Old and the New Testaments. Moslems recognize all the Jewish prophets; Mohammed is merely the latest messenger from God.

About the same time that the first wave of Semites appeared in Mesopotamia, a comparable group moved into the valley of the Nile where they mixed with earlier peoples to form the present Hamites, related to but distinct from the Semites. The Egyptians cannot be classed as Semites or proper Arabs, and only with the promulgation of a Constitution in 1956 has Egypt proclaimed itself an Arab state.

It is unfortunate that the European world knows less of its debt to Persian and Turkish cultures, for the West can no longer afford to remain uninformed about any part of the East.

The term Indo-European refers to a broad group of people who date back to the Stone Age. They are known to be akin from anthropologic and linguistic similarities, but are nevertheless diverse in detail. This family had its homeland in eastern Europe and Central Asia and were essentially a cattle-raising people who used horses rather than camels as did the Semites. The term Aryan is equally applicable and is found in the ancient and now resurrected name of Afghanistan, Aryana. Most people of Western Europe trace their ancestry back to Indo-European stock.

The earliest Indo-European representatives in Iran may have been the Hurrians and the Kassites, both of whom lived in the western Zagros and are best known for their conquest of Mesopotamia. Sometime during the first millenium B.C., a series of Aryan migrations moved south from central Asia. Three main streams brought the Medes into northwest Iran, the Persians to the east and south, and a Sanskrit group into India. These Indo-European migrants mixed with the earlier inhabitants, and were in turn later modified by Arab and Mongol invaders.

While the bulk of the present inhabitants of Iran and of Afghanistan are Aryan, the countries have neither racial nor linguistic unity. Persian-speaking Iranians comprise two-thirds of Iran's population. The remaining people are in tribal groups such as the Bakhtiari, Kurds, Turkmen, or Arabs. In Afghanistan, the 60 per cent of the population who are proper Afghans, or Pathans, speak Pushtu. Turkish-speaking people, also known as Tajik, comprise 30 per cent of the population. The variation of Turkish known as Uzbek is spoken by 5 per cent, while the Mongol group known as Hazara account for 3 per cent.

Present day Turkey is relatively homogeneous, with the Kurds as the only important minority group. Centuries of mixture have brought many blood strains, but most of these people were Ural-Altaic in language and a mixture of Caucasian and Mongol in blood. Relatives of the Turkish Turks may be found in the Asian peoples known as Uigurs, Uzbeks, Turkmen and Kirghiz.

The first great historic invasion was that of the Hittites in the second millenium B.C. Twentieth century Turkey finds pride in tracing back a racial unity which is said to have persisted for forty centuries and which purports to lead back to central Asian origins as "the original human language and culture." The evidence for such statements is unsubstantiated.

The Kurds are among the more interesting people of the mountains which continue from Iraq into Turkey and Iran. They are colorful in dress, friendly, but with a fierce sense of independence. Also they have preserved a distinct culture. The Kurds are probably Aryan in origin and may be the descendents of the ancient Medes. Most of them are Sunni Moslems, and they tend to hate the Arabs. Agitation for an independent Kurdish state was active during World War I when the Treaty of Sevres, August 10, 1920, recognized their rights to independence. There is no census of Kurdish populations but the total probably exceeds 3 million.

Some Kurds are purely nomadic, but most live in small villages. The houses usually stand in groups, each occupied by several related families. Since the village may lie on ground too steep and rocky to be cultivated, the houses are at different levels. The walls

This is the Kurdish village of Agra, set in the rocky landscape of northern Iraq not far from the borders of Turkey and Iran. (Courtesy Iraq Petroleum Co.)

are built of stone and mud, with basement rooms for storage while those above are for dwelling. A few houses have two stories with an outside ladder. The most valuable part of the house are the roof beams, which may have been used in still earlier houses. Cooking is done over a fire pit in the center of the room; there is no chimney so that the smoke finds its way out through cracks in the ceiling.

Carleton Coon has described the Kurdish fields [1]:

> The land outside the village looks as if it had been carved by a cosmic cubist, for although the main sweeps of the landscape are plainly diagonal, the actual surfaces are horizontal and vertical. Step after step, terrace after terrace, show the work of hundreds and thousands of patient men, generation after generation, whittling patchwork fields out of the mountain. These terraces describe a whole palette of subtly graded shades of green, from the rich bluish-

[1] Carleton S. Coon: *Caravan: The Story of the Middle East,* 299. New York: Holt (1958). Quoted by permission.

KURDISH POPULATION

Turkey	1,500,000
Iraq	800,000
Iran	600,000
Syria	250,000
Soviet Armenia	20,000
Total	3,170,000

green of onion patches near the bottom of the valley to the pastel of young wheat stalks high on the sides. At the very bottom a line of shiny blue divides the slopes: water. This bed will be dry during irrigation time. When the grist mill is grinding, the stream will seem to start in the middle of its course, where it churns out from under the paddlewheels.

Southwest Asia has provided the stage for diverse cultures, some of which developed into great international empires. In almost every case, the people who controlled the central area came from somewhere else. This is an area of migration; few areas on earth have been so much a crossroads. In his list of twenty-one historic civilizations, Toynbee has pointed out that seven arose here. Several others, such as the Egyptian, developed nearby. The following sections discuss those which had their base in Iraq, Iran, Arabia, and Turkey.

Similar historic reviews might have been provided for the lands of the eastern Mediterranean from Palestine to Syria, and for Afghanistan, but neither area was the homeland of a great political empire. Instead these were transitional areas; in the first case for Egypt, Mesopotamia, Arabia, and Turkey; and in the second between Persia, India, and central Asia. The historical sequence is shown in the accompanying chronological chart. The following sections make no attempt to describe the complete sequence of events but provide a glimpse as to the coreland and maximum extent of a few great dynasties.

MESOPOTAMIAN EMPIRES: BABYLON AND ASSYRIA

THE EARLIEST detailed knowledge of Mesopotamian civilization comes from southern Iraq where known history goes back to the fourth millennium B.C. In this area the Tigris and Euphrates spread across their delta to form vast swamps and lakes amidst an otherwise arid landscape. This is an environment entirely different from anything else in Swasia. Here arose the country of Sumer. It is of interest to note that the settled inhabitants then spoke with contempt of the surrounding nomadic people "who do not know houses and who do not cultivate wheat." Similar nomads still surround the area today, fifty centuries later.

The Sumerians had an irrigation system, knew how to cultivate barley, kept domestic animals, and had a copper-age culture. We know little as to where they came from, possibly from the highlands of Edom to the east; at least they did not speak a Semitic language. The most famous of their cities was Ur, improperly termed "Ur of the Chaldees" since the Chaldeans came much later. Later on, this was the home of Abraham before he migrated to Palestine. The first dynasty of Ur lasted from about 2500 to 2400 B.C.

Among Sumerian legends is that of a great flood, which is not surprising in such an environment. Mesopotamian floods have been recurrent since long before the arrival of man. Some are related to concentrated precipitation in the upper Tigris basin while others result from rapid snow-melt in the Turkish mountains. Natural levees border the rivers, and, when these are overtopped, wide areas may remain inundated for months. When heavy runoff coincides with southerly winds which raise water levels in the Persian Gulf, flooding may be especially severe.

Farther north, where the Tigris and Euphrates approach each other in central Iraq, was the land of the Akkadians, a Semitic speaking people. Led by their king, Sargon, who ruled from 2336 till 2281 B.C., they conquered the Sumerians and set up a united kingdom. At one time this stretched to the Mediterranean where there appear to have been contacts with Egypt. Later on came King Ur-nammu, 2118–2101 B.C.

While the Sumerians and Akkadians appear to us as living far back in history, it is

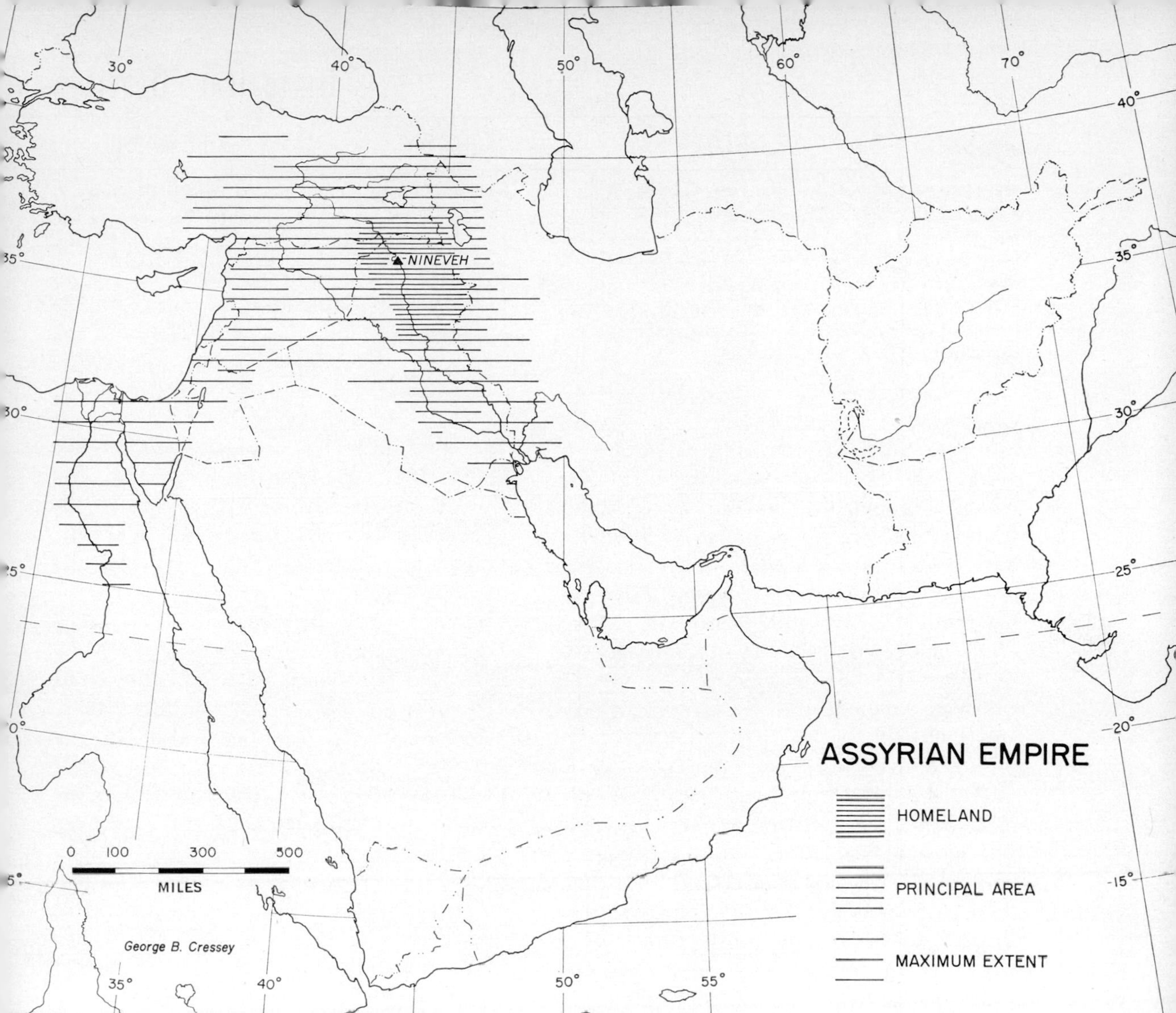

From its core area around Nineveh in the central Tigris Valley, the ancient Assyrian Empire spread across Mesopotamia and the Fertile Crescent, and at one time reached westward to Egypt. This map indicates the maximum limits around the seventh century B.C. (Compiled by Jack Fisher.)

well to realize that a large part of the evolution of civilization took place in still earlier times.

In general, the name Babylonia is used for the flat, delta lands of southern Mesopotamia, desert in climate but with easy irrigation, while Assyria refers to the somewhat more humid hills and rolling country to the north. Babylonia has only five inches of rainfall and is either a desert or a vast delta swamp. Assyria has almost three times as much rainfall and is a grassland with rich chestnut brown soils where crops may be grown without irrigation.

Successive kingdoms arose in each area, only to be interspersed with times of invasion and decay. While these political events were related to administrative and military situations, it may also be true that empires fell when the accumulation of silt in the irrigation canals and of salt in the cultivated fields became so excessive that there was not the money or management for correction.

Babylon had only a mud civilization, for

Historical Development

	ARABIA	TURKEY	LEVANT
	SAUDI ARABIA, 1932 Abdul-Aziz, 1926 OTTOMAN RULE, 1869-1918	REPUBLIC OF TURKEY, 1922- Kemal Atatürk, 1920-38 OTTOMAN EMPIRE, 1299-1922 SELJUK KINGDOM, 1040-1300	ISRAEL, 1948 BRITISH MANDATES: Jordan, 1920-46; Palestine, 1920-48 FRENCH MANDATES: Syria, 1920-44; Lebanon, 1920-44 OTTOMAN RULE, 1517-1918 CRUSADES, 1097-1291 Saladin, 1174-1193
1000 AD	ARAB EMPIRES UNDER CALIPHS (MECCA), 632-661 Mohammed, 570-632; Hegira, 622 NABATAEAN KINGDOM (PETRA), c. 200 BC-AD 105	BYZANTINE EMPIRE (CONSTANTINOPLE) 330-1453 Justinian, 527-565 ARAB INVASIONS, 632-1038 ROMAN RULE, 133 BC-AD 330	OMMIAD CALIPHATE (DAMASCUS) 661-750 PALMYRA, 42 BC-AD 292 Queen Zenobia Jesus Christ, 4 BC-AD 31
AD / BC	HIMYARITE KINGDOM, 525-115 SABAEAN KINGDOM (YEMEN), 650-115 Marib Dam collapse, 542 Queen of Sheba? MINAEAN KINGDOM (YEMEN), c. 950-c. 650	SELEUCID RULE, 312-189 MACEDONIAN EMPIRE Alexander the Great, 336-323 PERSIAN RULE, 546-334 LYDIANS, c. 670-546 PHRYGIAN EMPIRE, 1000-700	Pompey captured Jerusalem, 63 SELEUCID EMPIRE, 312-64 PERSIAN RULE, 539-332 JEWISH EXILE, 586-538 JUDEAN KINGDOM, 933-586 Hezekiah, 715-687 Solomon, 973-933 David, 1013-973
1000 BC		HITTITE EMPIRE, c. 1750-1200	HEBREWS IN PALESTINE, ARAMAEANS IN SYRIA Moses, c. 1200 PHILISTINE INVASIONS FROM SEA, 1200 Abraham, c. 1650-c. 1550
2000 BC			*Caucasian & Semitic cultures, 2500*
3000 BC	*Semitic culture, 3500*		JERICHO, 7000

# of Southwest Asia

MESOPOTAMIA	IRAN	AFGHANISTAN	
BRITISH MANDATE: Iraq, 1920-32	PAHLAVI DYNASTY, 1926 QAJAR DYNASTY (TEHRAN), 1794-1925 D'ARCY OIL CONCESSION, 1901	BARAKZAI DYNASTY, 1835- Dost Mohammed, 1835-1863 DURRANI DYNASTY, 1747-1835	
OTTOMAN RULE, 1534-1918	SAFAWID DYNASTY (ISFAHAN), 1500-1794 Shah Abbas I, 1586-1628	MOGUL PERIOD, 1526-1738 Baber, 1505-1530	
MONGOL RULE, 1258-1534 Hulugu captured Baghdad, 1258	MONGOL RULE Tamerlane, 1380-1393 Genghis Khan, 1219-1227 Hafiz, c. 1325-1388 Marco Polo, 1271 & 1295 Saadi, c. 1184-1291	AFGHAN PERIOD, 1000-1526 MONGOL RULE, 1220- GHAZNEVID EMPIRE, 997-1186 Mahmud, 997-	
			1000 AD
ABBASSIDE CALIPHATE (BAGHDAD), 750-c. 1100 Harun al Rashid, 786-809	Firdausi, 999		
ARAB INVASION, 636	ARAB INVASION, 641	ARAB INVASION, 647	
	SASSANIAN EMPIRE, c. 226-651 Shapur I, 241-272 NESTORIAN CHURCH FOUNDED, c. 489		
	PARTHIAN EMPIRE (CTESIPHON) 250 BC-AD 229		
			AD BC
	Arsaces VI, c. 171-138		
SELEUCID EMPIRE, 312-138			
PERSIAN RULE, 539-331	ACHAEMENID DYNASTY (PERSEPOLIS & SUSA) c. 700-331 Xerxes, 486-465 Darius I, 522-486 Cyrus II, 550-530	GRAECO-BUDDHIC PERIOD 329-	
CHALDEAN EMPIRE (BABYLON) 625-539 Nebuchadrezzar II, 605-562 Nabolpalassar, 626-605	MEDIA (ECBATANA=HAMADAN) c. 675-550 Zoroaster, c. 630		
ASSYRIAN EMPIRE (NINEVEH & NIMRUD) 2025-606 Ashurbanipal, 668-630 Tiglath-pileser III, 745-727	MANNEAN KINGDOM (HASANLU) 1000-800		
			1000 BC
Tiglath-pileser I, 1114-1076			
MITANNI KINGDOM *(Hurrians)* c. 1520-1350			
KASSITE CONQUEST, 1590-1167 HITTITE INVASION FROM NORTH, 1594			
FIRST BABYLONIAN DYNASTY, 1894-1594 Hammurabi, c. 1792-1750 AMORITES (MARI), 2000		VEDIC *(Aryan)* EMPIRE 2000-1500	
THIRD DYNASTY OF UR, c. 2118-2010			
			2000 BC
Ur-Nammu, 2118-2101			
AKKADIAN DYNASTY *(Semites)*, 2336-2156 Sargon I, 2336-2281			
	ELAMITES (SUSA), c. 2850-635		
FIRST DYNASTY OF UR, c. 2500-c. 2400			
			3000 BC
Sumerian culture, c. 3400			
JARMO, 4750	*Caspian culture, 5000*		

The great ziggurat at Ur rises above the dry plain of the Euphrates, a reminder of the ancient achievements of Babylonia. (Courtesy Iraq Petroleum Co.)

stone was absent and sun-dried bricks were the chief building material. The ruins of Ur and Babylon are thus mere heaps of mud, meaningful to the archaeologist but disappointing to the tourist. Assyria, in contrast, had limited access to stone so that its ancient palaces contain monumental statues.

The Babylonians were the first to divide a circle into 360 degrees, thus enabling the horizon to be plotted and maps to be designed by angular measurement. They regarded the earth as round, centered on Babylon, and surrounded by an ocean which they named the Briny Waters. Outside this ocean lay seven islands, possibly symbolizing the seven zones or climates into which their world was divided. These led to an outer circle of the Heavenly Ocean. Later, they adopted the four cardinal points.

The oldest known world map is on a Babylonian clay tablet dating from the fifth century B.C. On it the earth was pictured as a hemisphere which floated on the ocean. There were seven levels, divided into four sectors representing four neighboring countries. The earth was the counterpart or image of heaven, with the gods dwelling on top of a mountain, and the departed spirits living in an underworld which resembled the later Hebrew Sheol or the Greek Hades.

Some of the early geographical knowledge of the Babylonians dealt with canals, since their design and maintenance was a prime concern of government. These operations are described on thousands of clay tablets;

This rock relief at Nash-i-Rustam near Persepolis commemorates the capture of the Roman Emperor Valerian by the Achaemenian King Shapur I. (Courtesy Courtauld Institute of Art.)

other tablets deal with the enumeration of countries or of places with which trade was carried on.

The first Babylonian Dynasty lasted from 1894 to 1594 B.C. and included all of Assyria during the reign of Hammurabi, *c.* 1792 to 1750 B.C., well known for his codification of the law and for his skill as an administrator. So rich is our store of information of his time that we probably know more about Mesopotamia in 1700 B.C. than of Britain in A.D. 1400. Then came waves of invasion, with the Hittites from Turkey, the Kassites from Iran, and later the Hurrians from Syria who set up the Mitanni Kingdom, 1520 to 1350 B.C.

The Assyrian Empire, with its capital at Nineveh, continued from *c.* 2035 until 606 B.C. Among its kings were Tiglath-pileser, I, 1114–1076 B.C., and Ashurbanipal, 668–630 B.C. During the ninth century B.C., Assyria extended from near the Persian Gulf in an arc through Turkey and Syria to Palestine.

The Chaldeans then set up an empire at Babylon, marked by the reign of Nabolpolassar, 626 to 605 B.C., and Nebuchadnezzar II, 605 to 562 B.C.

While no Mesopotamian kingdom ever penetrated eastward into the mountains of Iran, repeated incursions from Iran spread west over the lowlands. This was notably true when the great Persian Dynasty, to be described in a later section, engulfed the area of the Tigris and Euphrates. Then followed the period of the Arab Caliphates and after that the Ottoman Turks.

Through all this history of the area now called Iraq, it is well to recognize the limited areas of good grazing land, of possible rain-fed agriculture, and of potential irrigation. To the dweller in the surrounding deserts and mountains, each of these more favored environments must have been magnetic. Iraqi history has developed in an area of sharply circumscribed possibilities.

PERSIAN EMPIRES: THE ACHAEMENID PERIOD

WHEREAS BOTH Babylon and Assyria are essentially flat and mountainless, Persia is ringed and crossed by rugged ranges. These mountains enclose numerous basins with interior drainage. Scarcely a river breaks through the Zagros or Elburz to reach the sea, and most of the canyons which penetrate the mountains are too rugged for easy travel. Unlike Mesopotamia with its unifying rivers, Persia is composed of isolated fractions.

Less is known of early Persia than of Iraq, but a series of empires succeeded one another, especially in the west and northeast. In the mountains and coastal lands near the Persian Gulf we have considerable information for the Elamite Kingdom which lasted from *c.* 2850 to 635 B.C. The capital was at Susa, now Shush, where French archaeological research has revealed a rich culture. Although in conflict with the Sumerians, Elam turned its back on the rest of Persia, and its history belongs to the Mesopotamian orbit. This was followed from 1847 to 1171 B.C. by the Kassite Empire, an Indo-European invasion which introduced the horse to Iran. Later on the Kassites spread into Babylonia for nearly a century.

The first great period of Persian history is that of the Achaemenid Empire, *c.* 700 to 331 B.C. In 550 B.C., Cyrus II, then king of Persis or Persia, conquered the Medes and established the first unified Iranian nation. Cyrus ruled from 550 to 530 B.C. He was followed by a succession of great kings such as Darius I, 522 to 486 B.C., and Xerxes, 486 to 465 B.C.

Under the Achaemenids, the Persian Empire spread from beyond the Hindu Kush in the east westward to the Mediterranean, making it a truly international nation. Through these contacts, many new influences were introduced into Persian life, at first from Mesopotamia and later from Greek and Arabian sources.

The Achaemenid Empire was divided into a series of provinces, each governed by a "satrap" and controlled by itinerant inspectors. Central authority was made more efficient by a system of military highways which linked the strategic centers. Only three routes of this once-extensive system are now known. One road led westward from Persepolis and Susa, the capitals, to Sardis in western Turkey. Another route extended east from Hamadan across northern Persia to Balkh and Samarkand. A third connected Seistan with Kabul via the Helmand Valley.

During this period the Persians made a notable contribution to ancient civilization through the development of the Zoroastrian faith. Zoroaster's dates are uncertain but somewhat precede Cyrus and Darius. Against a pagan polytheism, he established a universal system of ethical and metaphysical ideas, a religion in the modern sense. All good men are the helpers of the single Lord of Good, Ormazd, with whom trust and light are associated. His opposite was Ahriman, lord of evil and darkness. Man's duty is to choose the light, speak the truth, and combat evil; by his free choice he determines his fate. Zoroastrianism's monotheism is expressed in the phrase, "There is only one God, and no other is to be compared to Him. The Creator is invisible, just and worthy of adoration." The creed is summarized in the declaration, "Perform good actions, and refrain from evil ones." The association of Ormazd with light encouraged the extension of fire worship,

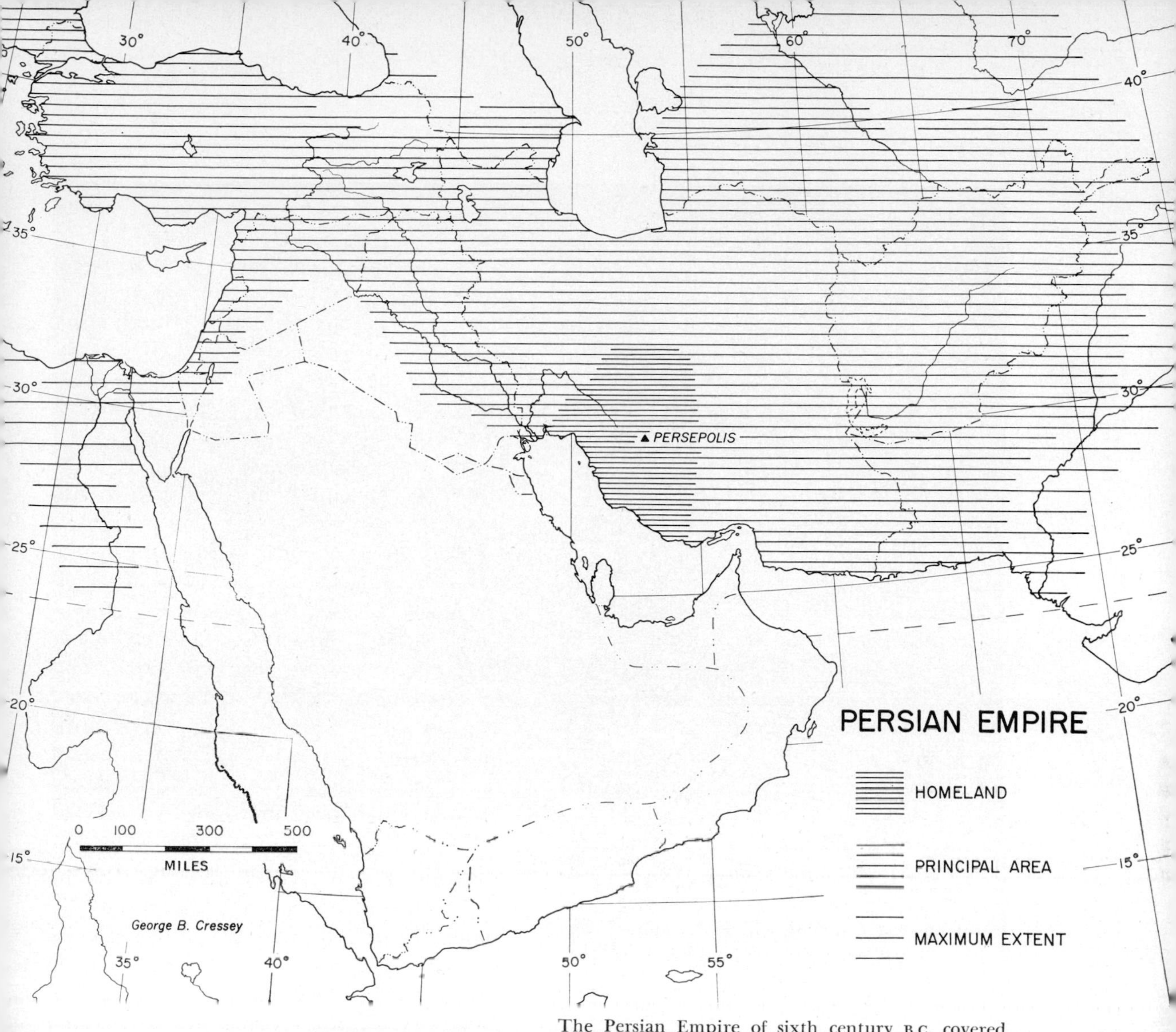

The Persian Empire of sixth century B.C. covered all of Southwest Asia, except for Arabia, and at its maximum extended into Soviet Middle Asia. The coreland centered around Persepolis in southwest Iran. (Compiled by Jack Fisher.)

and Iran still has temples where the eternal fire has remained unextinguished for centuries. The modern adherents are known as Parsees.

The ruins of the great palace at Persepolis, destroyed by Alexander in 325 B.C., remain as one of the most impressive monuments of antiquity. In Southwest Asia they rank with Palmyra and Petra. The plan of the buildings with their many columns was Persian, but the ornamentation was borrowed from Mesopotamia. Elaborate sculptures in bas-relief depict processions of people bringing tribute from afar. Whereas Iranian camels are today of the one-humped dromedary variety, those shown in Persepolis are all two-humped bactrian camels.

The Achaemenid Empire fell with the conquests of Alexander the Great, after whose death his generals established the Seleucid Dynasty. Later came the Parthian Empire 250 B.C.–229 A.D., the Sassanid Empire 226–651, and the Arab conquest in 641. Modern history centers around the Safawid Dynasty, 1500 to 1794, and the Qajar Dynasty, 1794 to 1925. All of these were pe-

The ancient city of Samarra, north of Baghdad, was the capital of the Abbasside Empire from 836 to 876 A.D.; only faint street patterns and the ruins of the great mosque with its circular minaret remain. The golden-domed Shiah mosque in the present city dates from the seventeenth century. (Courtesy Iraq Petroleum Co.)

riods of greatness, but they did not match the territorial extent of the Achaemenid.

ARAB EMPIRES: THE OMMIAD AND ABBASSIDE

THE SEMITIC peoples of Arabia have several times developed important kingdoms. In the far south these included the Sabaean and Himyaritic kingdoms of Yemen, while in the north was that of the Nabataeans at Petra.

Following the death of Mohammed in 632, the Arab empires under the Caliphs spread far beyond Arabia and came to rule millions of square miles, extending from Spain to India.

Mohammed had a daughter named Fatima but left no male children, so that the correct line of succession is a matter of dispute. The unification of the Arabian peninsula and its conversion to Islam was largely the work of Mohammed's father-in-law, Abu-Bekr. He thus became the first Caliph, or successor, 632–634.

The Shiites believe that the true sequence of the Caliphate was through Ali, actually the fourth Caliph but to be regarded as the first, and stress the theocratic concept of the state. The Imam or "he who leads in prayer," is thus both spiritual and temporal head.

On the other hand, Sunni or orthodox Moslems favor a different line of succession and stress certain traditions (sunna) of Mohammed as equal in authority to the Koran. Their idea of the state is more secular; they are today the most numerous group.

Two dynasties of the Caliphate Empire

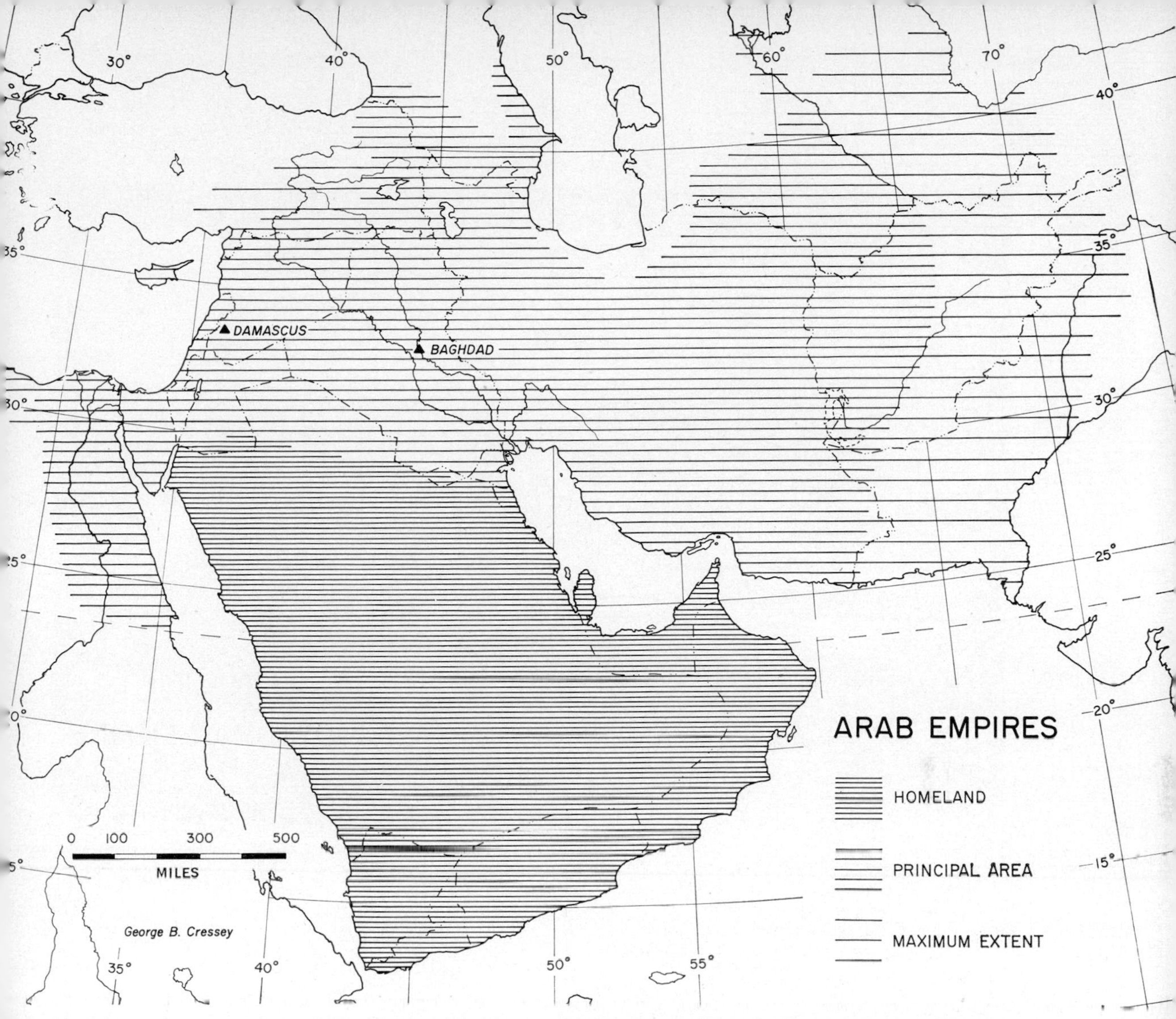

The Arab Empires under the Caliphs looked to Mecca and Medina for their spiritual base, but the Ommiad and Abbaside Caliphs ruled from Damascus and Baghdad. This was a development of the seventh and eighth centuries, A.D. (Compiled by Jack Fisher.)

may be distinguished. Under the Ommiad at Damascus the succession lasted from 661 until 750. Then follows the Abbasside dynasty in Baghdad from 750 until 1100. The Ommiads were Sunni Moslems, whereas the Abbassides were ardent Shiites. During the Ommiad period, the Dome of the Rock in Jerusalem was built (in 691). This mosque supposedly marks the spot where Abraham was about to sacrifice Isaac, where Christ ascended, and where Mohammed stopped on his way to heaven.

Two Abbasside rulers stand out: Mansur (754–775), who established the capital at Baghdad, and Harun al-Rashid (786–809). Since the authority of most Caliphs was primarily spiritual, many semi-independent kingdoms arose so that in their later stages both empires came to be composed of semi-autonomous units.

The original homeland of central Arabia did not lend itself to being the seat of a widespread empire, so that the centers of population and of power have always been peripheral. The oases of Damascus and Baghdad lay around the margins of greater

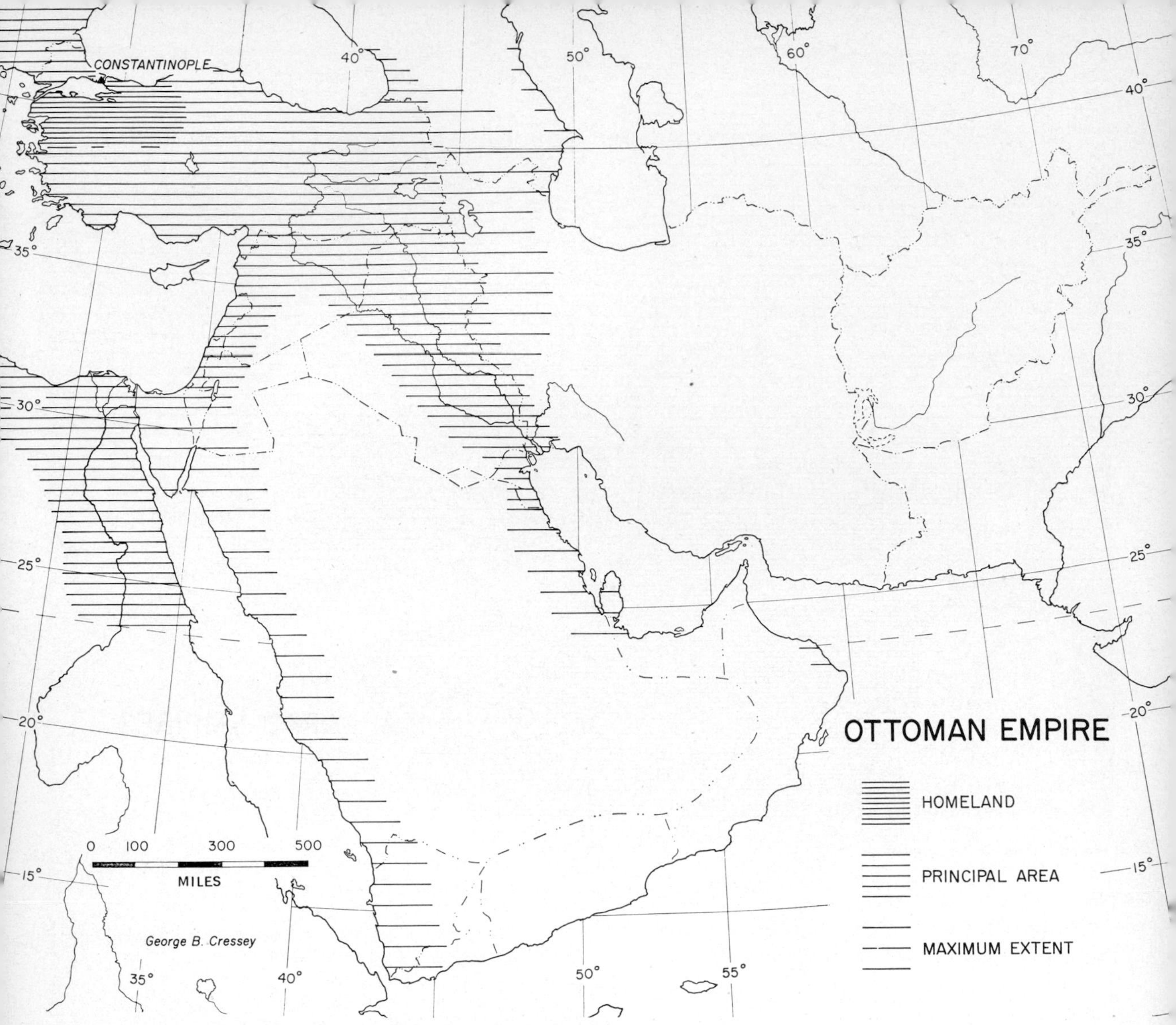

The sixteenth century Turkish Empire of the Ottomans expanded southward from a base around Constantinople to reach the Persian Gulf and Red Sea. The Turks also spread westward into Europe. (Compiled by Jack Fisher.)

Arabia and became the meeting point of the Bedouins and townsmen. To these capitals moved caravans from all the Eastern world.

When Mansur selected the site of Baghdad, he did so since, "Here is the Tigris to put us in touch with lands as far as China and bring us all the seas yield as well as the food products of Mesopotamia, Armenia and their environs. Then there is the Euphrates to carry for us all that Syria, al-Raqqah and adjacent lands have to offer." [1] Small wonder that this focus led to the legendary adventures so brilliantly commemorated by Scheherazade in "The Thousand and one Nights."

Under the Ommiads and Abbassides, Arabia became one of the world's great centers of culture and learning, perhaps with more creative scholarship than any other civilization from the seventh to the twelfth centuries. Arabic is still the language for 50 million people, while Islam commands the

[1] Quoted in Phillip Hitti: *History Of The Arabs.* London: Macmillan (1956), 292.

Istanbul contains many monuments to the glories of the old Turkey. The Sultan Ahmed Mosque appears to the right, while Saint Sofia lies to the left. The latter was built as a church, converted to a mosque, and is now a museum. (Courtesy Turkish Press, Broadcasting, and Tourist Dept., Ankara.)

allegiance of one eighth of mankind. The spread of the Arab empire was in part an economic phenomena, fostered by the desire of the desert nomad to find a better life in the bordering steppes and oases. It also had spiritual motives, for while Islam is a religion it is also a state and a culture; Arabism triumphed before Islam and spread first. Few people have ever assimilated into their culture, speech, religion, and physical types more aliens than have the Arabs.

In its heartland, the Arab world was characterized by the camel and the palm. Horses came with Indo-European cultures from east of the Caspian Sea, but the camel was better adapted to desert life. With a bag of dates and a goatskin of water, the nomad could travel far. The history which began with Bedouin raids and ended with an empire reveals latent qualities which are too easily overlooked in the twentieth century.

This was a period when geography flourished, in part because travel became extensive. Every faithful Moslem was supposed to make the pilgrimage to Mecca at least once during his life. Every mosque must face exactly toward Mecca, and the daily prayers must be said in that direction. Arab traders reached China by sea and by land and pushed south to Zanzibar.

TURKISH EMPIRES: THE OTTOMAN

THREE GREAT empires have had their base in Turkey; the Hittite, the Byzantine, and the Ottoman.

The earliest kingdom was that of the Hittites which flourished from 1750 to 1200 B.C. These were a pastoral people, apparently of Indo-European connections from north of the Black Sea, who first appeared in Cappadocia in north central Turkey where they absorbed an early agricultural people. The contacts of the Hittite Empire included both Babylonia and Egypt. Modern Turkish historians take pride in this early culture of Anatolia and regard it as ancestral to their own.

The Empire of Byzantium was the successor to Eastern Rome. The name comes from the ancient city which Constantine I rebuilt in 330 A.D. as Constantinople. The Empire lasted for eleven centuries, but with shifting boundaries. The eastern limits reached to the Euphrates and represented a balance against Persian pressure, while to the south the area included much of the Levant and at times even North Africa. To the west and north Byzantium spread well into Europe and Russia, so that it was an inter-continental kingdom. While Greek was the official language, oriental influences became increasingly strong.

The third empire was that of the Ottomans, 1299–1922. In the year 1227, a band of several thousand nomadic Turks was driven out of their homeland in the steppes of inner Asia by pressure from the Mongols. They migrated into Anatolia and received land near Ankara from the Sultan of the Seljuk Empire, another Turkish group. Both had become Moslem in their original Asiatic homeland and spoke Ural-Altaic languages. The new arrivals proved to be helpful and later obtained additional land to the west and south. In 1299, they achieved their independence under Othman.

This was a stormy period, with pressure from both Mongols and groups to the south, but the Turks gradually took over the western part of Anatolia and developed the Ottoman Empire. This resulted in the capture of Constantinople in 1453 and the fall of Byzantium. Before the end of the fifteenth century, they ruled much of what is now Turkey as well as an equally large area across The Straits in the Balkans.

The early period of Turkish history was confined to inner Anatolia since many of the coastal ports were held by European states. A major victory over Venice in 1499 was only one of a long series of naval conflicts for the control of the Aegean and of Cyprus.

Pressure from the east became strong in the days of Tamerlane (Timur), who even captured Ankara in 1402 and went on to Izmir. During the sixteenth century, trouble arose with Persia, in part over the conflict between Sunni Moslems in Turkey and the Shias who dominated Iran. The present Iranian frontier was defined in 1639.

The dominions of the Ottoman Sultans reached their farthest extent toward the end of the seventeenth century, especially under Suleiman the Magnificent, 1496–1566. The tri-continental empire then reached from Poland to Mesopotamia and south to Arabia and Egypt. In 1517, Sultan Selim I captured Mecca and the holy places of Islam and so made himself Caliph, the defender of the Moslem faith. The Caliphate remained in Turkey until 1923, when it was abolished.

The European portions of the Empire, along with Egypt, steadily slipped away during the 1860's. South of the Caucasus, the Russian frontier advanced in 1878 to include Batumi and Kars. In the same year, Britain secured control of Cyprus in return for a guarantee of assistance to Turkey should she be attacked by Russia.

The Ottoman Empire in Asia fared scarcely better, though it persisted longer. The opening of the Suez Canal in 1869 enabled Turkey to transport troops to the Red Sea and for a while re-establish control of Arabia and of Yemen, 1872–1912. The area of Hasa, along the Persian Gulf, was occupied from 1871 till 1913. Lebanon received a measure of autonomy in 1861, due to her Christian population.

The need of foreign capital for railroads and other improvements led to concessions which produced German, French, and British spheres of influence. Russia and Italy also attempted to secure similar zones. When World War I ended and Turkey was defeated, there was some hope that free Arab Asia might develop as a single unit. Instead, the area was broken up into separate mandates.

The Ottomans began as pastoral nomads, and it has been suggested that their administration reflected this type of social and military institution. Nomads have little attachment to the land which they traverse and no interest in industry or commerce. The Turks wanted peace and tribute; their subject people took the place of their former flocks of sheep and herds of cattle. The Ottomans ruled as absolute autocrats, largely through thousands of janissaries who were virtually slaves. There was no attempt to weld the empire into a unified culture or administration. At no time was this varied area ever effectively united, and local autonomy increased toward the periphery.

Although the Turks were ardent Moslems and clashed continually with their Christian neighbors, they permitted minority faiths and cultures to persist under the *millet* system of local autonomous political jurisdiction, each with its own language, culture, courts, and taxes. Adherents of the various Christian churches and Judaism were thus given *millet* status, a kind of ecclesiastical state within a Moslem superstate. Relics of this system still prevail in former Turkish areas. This is a reflection of Mohammed's advice "Let there be no compulsion in religion."

In modern times, citizens of European powers were also given special rights in the form of extraterritorial status and thus freed from the requirements of Turkish law. This was only one of the *capitulations* forced on the declining Ottoman Empire by the West. The first of these capitulations was granted to France whereby Francis I was given jurisdiction over his own subjects and, by inference, over all Christians, and also over the holy places within the Empire. This led later to France's demand for mandates over Syria and Lebanon because of their partial Christian population.

The task of governing the Ottoman Empire was complicated by the nature of the country. Mountains barred travel, and the various fertile areas were isolated and peripheral. Extensive districts were semiarid. Then, as now, communications posed a problem. The early Turkish nomads favored the areas of nomadism and transhumance in interior Anatolia, whereas the fixed inhabitants lived in the coastal plains.

Anatolia has an advantage in its central position at the crossroads of the ancient highways between Asia and Europe, but this bridge-like position also makes it a battleground for rival powers. A strong government can capitalize on this, but a weak government must over-extend itself. With a prosperous and homogeneous people, an ambitious government can concentrate on foreign expansion, but with diverse racial groups living at a low economic level, the Ottoman Sultans found themselves handicapped. Only a genius for government on the part of the great rulers kept the Empire going.

Constantinople, now Istanbul, was the capital of the Ottomans for six centuries, as it had been for the earlier Byzantines. Its hilly site along the Bosporus is one of the most beautiful in the world, while its commanding position along a key waterway makes it of great strategic value. Into its bazaars flowed commerce from Russia and also from China and the Indies, especially in the days before the sea routes around Africa became available. Small wonder that the early Caliphs termed themselves "Lords of the Upper and Lower Seas."

THREE TRAVELERS: ALEXANDER, MARCO POLO, AND IBN BATUTA

MANY TRAVELERS have left accounts of their wanderings, and there is even geographic lore in the stories of Sinbad the Sailor. The following paragraphs refer to three of these: Alexander the Great, 336–323 B.C.; Marco Polo, 1254–1324; and Ibn Batuta, 1304–1378. Marco Polo may be better known to the Western world than Ibn Batuta, but the latter's contribution to early geography is equally significant as far as Arab geography is concerned, although unknown to Europe for several centuries following his death.

Alexander the Great

Few people in antiquity traveled so widely as Alexander the Great. For centuries his records supplied Europe with much of its knowledge of Asia. Geographers and map makers accompanied him on most of his journeys, and he made important contributions to hydrography, ethnography, and botany.

Alexander succeeded to the throne in 336 B.C. at the age of twenty, and in 334 B.C. crossed the Dardanelles in preparation for his invasion of Persia. His travels first took him along the Aegean, then controlled by the Persian fleet, and later to central Anatolia.

Before Alexander was able to have his first encounter with Darius III, it was necessary to cross the Taurus Mountains by way of the Cilician Gates, in order to reach the coast north of Iskenderon. Alexander chose this narrow coastal plain as the site for the Battle of Issus (333 B.C.) so that Darius would not have room to maneuver. Although Alexander won the battle and later captured Darius' war chest in Damascus, the Persian king and many of his troops escaped.

Alexander then turned south via the classic route of conquerors along the Mediterranean, past the ancient cities of Byblos, Sidon, and Tyre and reached Egypt in 332 B.C., where he laid out the city of Alexandria, the first of at least sixteen cities of the same name which he founded. Here, as elsewhere, Greek settlers were made the basis of city development.

In 331 B.C., Alexander returned to Asia and crossed the upper Euphrates and again defeated the Persians in a great battle of Gaugamela on the plains near Erbil, then called Arbela. The plain of battle was selected by Darius because of the ease with which he might maneuver his chariots, but the battle was won when Alexander made an outflanking attack through rougher ground to the south. This victory is acclaimed as one of the fifteen decisive battles of history.

Then followed a southward advance across Mesopotamia to Babylon and Susa, and eastward through the difficult Persian Gates of the Zagros Mountains to reach Darius' capital at Persepolis. The coin and bullion captured here and at Susa had a value of some 200 million dollars. This victory made Alexander ruler of western Asia. Since Darius III was still alive, Alexander pursued him north to Ecbatana, the modern Hamadan, and thence into northern Iran where Darius III was killed by one of his own satraps.

It was now necessary to occupy the empire which he had captured. Alexander thus travelled east to Meshed and Herat, south to the Seistan Basin, and up the Helmand Valley to Kabul. From central Afghanistan he made an excursion across the Hindu Kush into Bactria and Turkestan in 328 B.C. and then turned east, in part via the Khyber Pass, to the Indus River which he followed to its mouth. This venture into India was disappointing, for Alexander thought that he was entering the last peninsula on earth,

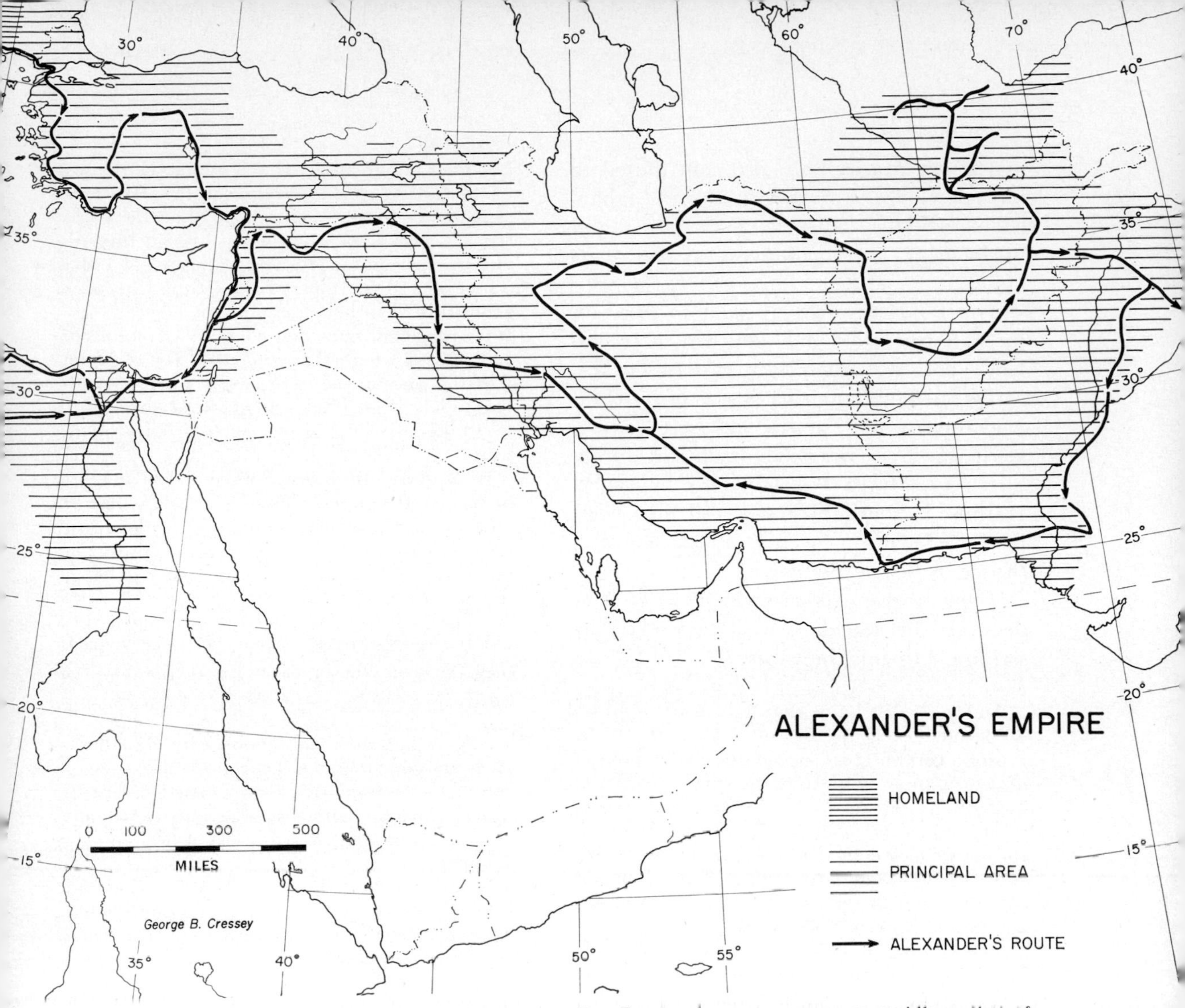

Few Empires have ever grown so rapidly as that of Alexander the Great in the fourth century B.C. when it extended from the Nile to the Indus. (Compiled by Jack Fisher.)

just beyond which lay the Ocean of the East.

Alexander's return trip westward across southern Persia was difficult for the Makran coast was dry and inhospitable, and there was no Persian royal highway to follow, as elsewhere. While Alexander marched overland, his fleet explored the coast and developed the first sea route from India to the Persian Gulf. He reached Susa in 324 B.C. and died of fever the following year at the age of thirty-two.

Alexander is properly known as "the Great" because for the first time he linked Europe and Asia and vastly enlarged the Mediterranean world's understanding of the lands to the east. His stature as an administrator is matched by his contributions to geography.

Marco Polo

The second of our travelers is Marco Polo, who returned to Venice at the end of the thirteenth century. This was at a time when Mongol conquests and the conflict between the Crusaders and Arabs had isolated Europe from familiarity with the interior of Asia. While best known for his descriptions of Cathay, Marco Polo also contributed to our knowledge of Turkey, Iran, and Afghanistan. He left Venice with his father and uncle in 1271, returning twenty-four years later.

The Polos traveled by boat to Acre on the Palestine coast and went first to Jerusalem. Their route then led to eastern Turkey, across northern Iraq, the deserts of Iran and Afghanistan, the Pamirs, and on to China, a trip of three and a half years. On the return trip, Marco Polo traveled by sea to Hormuz in southern Persia and then overland to Trabzon on the Black Sea and thence by boat to Venice.

The exuberant style in which Marco Polo described his travels is well known. In describing Armenia, he wrote: [1]

And you must know that it is in this country of Hermenia that the Ark of Noah exists on the top of a certain great mountain, on the summit of which snow is so constant that no one can ascend; for the snow never melts, and is constantly added to by new falls. Below, however, the snow does melt, and runs down producing such rich and abundant herbage that in summer cattle are sent to pasture from a long way round about, and it never fails them.

The country is bounded on the south by a kingdom called Mosul, the people of which are Jacobite and Nestorian Christians, of whom I shall have more to tell you presently. On the north it is bounded by the Land of the Georgians, of whom also I shall speak. On the confines from Georgiania there is a fountain from which oil springs in great abundance, insomuch that a hundred shiploads might be taken from it at one time. This oil is not good to use with food, but 'tis good to burn and is also used to anoint camels that have the mange. People come from vast distances to fetch it, for in all the countries round about they have no other oil.

Harun al Rashid and the days of the "Arabian Nights" had long since ended when Marco reached Baghdad, but some of the glamour remained. Marco Polo wrote:

Baghdad is a great city which used to be the seat of the Calif of all the Saracens in the world, just as Rome is the seat of the Pope of all the Christians. A very great river flows through the city, and by this you can descend to the Sea of India. There is a great traffic of merchants with their goods this way; they descend some eighteen days from Baghdad, and then come to a certain city called Kisi, where they enter the Sea of India. There is also on the river, as you go from Baghdad to Kisi, a great city called Basra, surrounded by woods, in which grow the best dates in the world.

In Baghdad they weave many different kinds of silk stuffs and gold brocades, such as *nasich*, and *nac*, and *cramoisy*, and many other beautiful tissues richly wrought with figures of beasts and birds. It is the noblest and greatest city in all those regions.

During his travels across the "very great country" of Persia, he visited the city of Yezd:

. . . It is a good and noble city, and has a great amount of trade. They weave there quantities of a certain silk tissue known as *Yasdi*, which merchants carry into many quarters to dispose of. The people are worshippers of Mahommet.

When you leave the city to travel further, you ride for seven days over great plains, finding harbour to receive you at three places only. There are many fine woods, producing dates, upon the way, such as one can easily ride through; and in them there is great sport to be had in hunting and hawking, there being partridges and quails and abundance of other game, so that the merchants who pass that way have plenty of diversion. There are also wild asses, handsome creatures. At the end of those seven marches over the plain you come to a fine kingdom which is called Kerman.

When Marco Polo reached Kerman, he wrote:

In this kingdom are produced the stones called turquoises in great abundance; they are found in the mountains, where they are extracted from the rocks. There are also plenty of veins of steel and *ondanique*. The people are very skilful in making harness of war; their saddles, bridles, spurs, swords, bows, quivers, and arms of every kind are very well made indeed, according to the fashion of those parts. The ladies of the coun-

[1] All quotations are from the *Book Of Ser Marco Polo* as translated by Henry Yule. London: John Murray (1871).

try and their daughters also produce exquisite needlework in the embroidery of silk stuffs in different colours, with figures of beasts and birds, trees and flowers, and a variety of other patterns. They work hangings for the use of noblemen so deftly that they are marvels to see, as well as cushions, pillows, quilts, and all sorts of things.

In the mountains of Kerman are found the best falcons in the world. They are inferior in size to the peregrine, red on the breast, under the neck, and between the thighs; their flight is so swift that no bird can escape them.

On quitting the city you ride on for seven days, always finding towns, villages, and handsome dwelling-houses, so that it is very pleasant travelling; and there is excellent sport also to be had by the way in hunting and hawking. When you have ridden those seven days over a plain country, you come to a great mountain; and when you have got to the top of the pass, you find a great descend which occupies some two days to go down. All along you find a variety and abundance of fruits; and in former days there were plenty of inhabited places on the roads, but now there are none; and you meet with only a few people looking after their cattle at pasture. From the city of Kerman to this descent the cold in winter is so great that you can scarcely abide it, even with a great quantity of clothing.

As Marco Polo crossed Afghanistan, he described the uplifted peneplains of Badakhshan as follows:

Those mountains are so lofty that 'tis a hard day's work from morning till evening, to get to the top of them. On getting up, you find an extensive plain, with great abundance of grass and trees, and copious springs of pure water running down through rocks and ravines. In those brooks are found trout and many other fish of dainty kinds; and the air in those regions is so pure, and residence there so healthful, that when the men who dwell below in the towns, and in the valleys and plains, find themselves attacked by any kind of fever or other ailment that may hap, they lose no time in going to the hills; and after abiding there two or three days, they quite recover their health through the excellence of that air.

Ibn Batuta

Ibn Batuta was born in Tangier, fifty years after Marco Polo, and during his lifetime visited every Moslem land, plus cities such as Constantinople and Peking. These journeys totaled 75,000 miles, a record probably not surpassed until the age of steam. While he was primarily a theologian, he was at the same time an observant human geographer.

At the age of twenty-one, Ibn Batuta started on a pilgrimage to Mecca. "I set out alone, finding no companion to cheer the way with friendly intercourse, and no party of travellers with whom to associate myself." Later on he wrote, "I made it a habit on my journey never, so far as possible, to cover a second time any road I had once travelled." His route was invariably circuitous, as when he traveled from Basra to Baghdad by way of Persia.

His first trip took him to Cairo, Damascus, Mecca, Basra, Isfahan, and Baghdad. On his next journey he traveled through the Red Sea to Aden, along the African coast, around Arabia to Oman and Hormuz and then back across Arabia to Mecca. The third trip included Syria, Turkey, Russia as far north as 54°, Afghanistan and India. On the fourth expedition he spent several years in India and went on to Ceylon, Java, and China, returning through Sumatra, Persia, Iraq, and Syria. A fifth journey included Spain, Africa, and Egypt, ending at Tangier in 1355.

On his first visit to Asia, he reported that[1] "No one is allowed to pass into Syria (Palestine) without a passport from Egypt, nor into Egypt without a passport from Syria . . . as a measure of precaution against spies from Iraq." When he came to the ancient seaport of Tyre, where Alexander had been able to capture the offshore island only by constructing a causeway, Ibn Batuta wrote as follows:

It is this city of Tyre which has become proverbial for impregnability, because the sea sur-

[1] All quotations are from *Ibn Batuta, Travels In Asia and Africa,* translated by H. A. R. Gibb. London: Routledge and Kegan Paul.

rounds it on three sides and it has two gates, one on the landward side and one to the sea. That on the landward side is protected by four outer walls each with breastworks, while the sea gate stands between two great towers. There is no more marvellous or more remarkable piece of masonry in the world than this, for the sea surrounds it on three sides and on the fourth there is a wall under which the ships pass and come to anchor. In former times an iron chain was stretched between the two towers to form a barrier, so that there was no way in or out until it was lowered.

Ibn Batuta made at least four pilgrimages to Mecca. On the first, when he started south from Damascus, he described the trip as follows:

The caravan stopped for four days outside Karak, where preparations were made for entering the desert. Thence we journeyed to Maan, which is the last town in Syria. . . . From Tabuk the caravan travels with great speed night and day, for fear of the desert. Halfway through is the valley of al-Ukhaydir, which might well be the valley of Hell. One year the pilgrims suffered terribly here from the samoon-wind; the water supplies dried up and the price of a single drink rose to a thousand dinars, but both buyer and seller perished.

Ibn Batuta waxes enthusiastic over Tabriz, Isfahan, and Shiraz. Of the latter he writes:

Thence we travelled across a stretch of open country inhabited by Turks, and reached Shiraz, a densely populated town, well built and admirably planned. Each trade has its own bazaar. Its inhabitants are handsome and clean in their dress. In the whole East there is no city that approaches Damascus in beauty of bazaars, orchards and rivers, and in the handsome figures of its inhabitants, but Shiraz. It is on a plain surrounded by orchards on all sides and intersected by rivers, one of which is the river known as Rukn Abad, whose water is sweet, very cold in summer and warm in winter. The people of Shiraz are pious and upright, especially the women, who have a strange custom. Every Monday, Thursday, and Friday they meet in the principal mosque to listen to the preacher, one or two thousand of them, carrying fans with which they fan themselves on account of the great heat. I have never seen in any land so great an assembly of women.

As Ibn Batuta passed along the southern coast of Arabia, he described the famous trade in incense, and the dependence on fish as food for man and beast:

We left Dhufar for Oman in a small ship belonging to a man from Masira. On the second day of our journey we disembarked at the roadstead of Hasik, which is inhabited by Arab fishermen. Here they have a great quantity of frankincense trees. They have thin leaves out of which drips, when they are slashed, sap like milk. This turns into a gum, which is the frankincense. The people living in this port are dependent on fishing for their food and the fish they catch is the *lukham,* which is like a dogfish. They slice these fish up, dry them in the sun and use them for food, and built their houses with the fish bones, using camel skins for roofs.

As the traveler crossed Afghanistan, he described the snow-capped Khawak Pass, 13,000 feet high, north of Kabul:

Another reason for our halt was fear of the snow, for on the road there is a mountain called Hindukush, which means "Slayer of Indians," because the slave boys and girls who are brought from India die there in large numbers as a result of the extreme cold and the quantity of snow. The passage extends for a whole day's march. We stayed until the warm weather had definitely set in, and crossed this mountain by a continuous march from before dawn to sunset. We kept spreading felt cloths in front of the camels for them to tread on so that they should not sink in the snow.

REFERENCES

Albright, W. F.: FROM STONE AGE TO CHRISTIANITY. Baltimore: Johns Hopkins Press (1940). [Archaeology]

Baker, J. N. L.: HISTORY OF GEOGRAPHICAL DISCOVERY AND EXPLORATION. rev. ed., London: Harrup (1937).

Beazley, C. Raymond: THE DAWN OF MODERN GEOGRAPHY. 3 vols. London: (1897–1906).

Beckingham, C. F.: ATLAS OF THE ARAB WORLD AND THE MIDDLE EAST (1960).

Brokelmann, Carl: HISTORY OF THE ISLAMIC PEOPLE. London: Routledge (1936).

Bunbury, E. H.: A HISTORY OF ANCIENT GEOGRAPHY. 2 vols., London: Murray (1879).

* Coon, Carleton S.: CARAVAN: THE STORY OF THE MIDDLE EAST. New York: Holt (1958). [General anthropology]

Coon, Carleton S.: THE SEVEN CAVES. New York: Knopf (1957).

Fisher, Sidney N.: THE MIDDLE EAST, A HISTORY. rev. ed., New York: Knopf (1957).

Frankfort, Henri: THE BIRTH OF CIVILIZATION IN THE NEAR EAST. Bloomington: Indiana Univ. Press (1954).

Hitti, Philip: HISTORY OF THE ARABS. London: Macmillan (1956).

Ibn Battuta: IBN BATUTA TRAVELS IN ASIA AND AFRICA 1325–1354. Translated by H. A. R. Gibb, London: Routledge and Kegan Paul (1957).

Kirk, George E.: A SHORT HISTORY OF THE MIDDLE EAST. New York: Praeger (1955).

Marco Polo: BOOK OF SER MARCO POLO. Translated by Henry Yule, London: John Murray. (1871).

Moscati, S.: THE FACE OF THE ANCIENT ORIENT. London: Routledge, Keegan Paul (1959).

Rondot, Pierre: "The Minorities in the Arab Orient Today," MIDDLE EASTERN AFFAIRS, X (1959), 214–228.

* Roolvink, R. F.: HISTORICAL ATLAS OF THE MUSLIM PEOPLE. Cambridge: Harvard (1957).

Shepherd, William R.: HISTORICAL ATLAS. Pikesville, Maryland: The Colonial Offset Co., Inc. (1956).

Smith, C. G.: "Arab Nationalism: A study in Political Geography," *Geography,* XLIII (1958), 229–242.

Sykes, Percy: A HISTORY OF EXPLORATION. rev. ed. New York: Macmillan (1936).

CHAPTER 3

Land

Geology and Structure
Land Forms
Igneous Activity
Earthquakes
Sand Dunes

GEOLOGY AND STRUCTURE

THE GEOLOGY of Southwest Asia falls into two major categories. In the south and west there is an area of rolling plains and hills, developed on a basement of Archeozoic crystalline rocks. These ancient igneous and metamorphic formations form a resistant and stable block. They are exposed in western Arabia; farther east and north these crystallines continue underground as far as the Persian Gulf and the Euphrates. Above them is a veneer of horizontal and largely undisturbed sedimentary formations, which become increasingly thick as they extend eastward and northward so that the basement floor comes to be several miles below sea level.

So massive is this section of the earth's crust that no important folding has occurred since the Cambrian period. This ancient area is thus known as a shield. Because of its resistance to horizontal compression, the few earth movements have been dominantly vertical such as uplift, subsidence, and faulting. Broad warping and doming have occurred locally, as in the Arabian oil fields; elsewhere the sediments lie horizontally.

This stable area is part of a much larger shield or massif which extends from Africa to India and is known as Gondwanaland; at an early period in earth history it may have formed an ancient continent. Its unity should not be obscured by the later faulting which created the Red Sea. The first major element in Swasian topography is thus given the structural title of the Gondwana Stable Block.

The second major geological unit is the Tethys Foldland, to the north and west of Gondwanaland. This was once a zone of deposition, but is now an extensive mountain area. During much of the time from the early Paleozoic well into the Cenozoic Era, a long narrow sea known as Tethys spread across this part of Asia. This ancient Mediterranean occupied a geosyncline, a great trough which slowly subsided as layer after

(Opposite) Sand dunes and desert wastes cover vast areas of Southwest Asia. This camel caravan is bound for Abqaiq in eastern Arabia. (Courtesy Standard Oil Co. of New Jersey.)

Great masses of marine sediments have been folded and uplifted to form the mountains of northern Iraq. This scene is near Amadiya. (Courtesy Iraq Petroleum Co.)

layer of sediments accumulated. Successively there were advances and retreats of the sea, subsidence with the deposition of thousands of feet of sediments, uplift with partial erosion, and repeated folding and thrusting. Some of these sediments were derived from Gondwanaland to the south, then an upland undergoing erosion; other contributions came from a similar ancient land mass to the northeast known as Angaraland. The Tethys Sea at times spread far beyond the area of the present Foldland so that the sediments which cover eastern Arabia and Iraq represent marginal overlaps.

Where this sea once lay, and out of the formations there accumulated, have now arisen great mountain chains, folded in Appalachian style. This mobile zone extends from the Alps to the Himalayas and beyond and is an area of close folding and strong thrusting, largely directed from the north, between the stable blocks of Gondwana and Angara. These Tethys structures account for the oil fields of western Iran and northern Iraq. Here and there are small, relatively resistant areas which have escaped deformation; some of these now form plateaus or interior basins.

The boundary between the Gondwana Stable Block and the Tethys Foldland is placed at the westernmost limit of close folding. The tectonic features which controlled the visible structures are deep-seated and largely unknown. The crystalline basement near the boundary lies at a depth of several miles and is thus beyond all but geophysical

Careless cultivation and overgrazing have stripped many hillsides in the Levant to the bare rock. These limestone ledges are in Lebanon. (Courtesy **U. S. Operations** Mission, Beirut.)

soundings. We can only say that folding appears to extend this far and that there is presumably an underlying structural reason.

The boundary follows the base of the Taurus and Zagros mountains across southern Turkey and eastern Iraq. It might be logical to include the Sinjar and Jebel Hamrin anticlines as outliers, but such a limit would take in a broad zone of horizontal sediments and level land similar to the plains farther south.

In place of a two-fold division into Gondwanaland and Tethys, W. B. Fisher has suggested a third intermediate area which he calls the Median Zone.[1] This belt includes the Persian Gulf, Mesopotamia, and the Levant in a sort of structural crescent. It is true that both folding and crystallines are largely absent, but the lack of deformation suggests the presence of a deep-seated resistant mass so that this zone is here classed with the Gondwana Stable Block. That part of Fisher's Median Zone beneath the Persian Gulf and along the Tigris-Euphrates Delta is now receiving heavy sedimentation and is a sort of modern geosyncline; the rest of the zone is undergoing erosion.

The stratigraphic sequence throughout Swasia is extensive. Sedimentary rocks cover all of the Persian Gulf and Mesopotamian areas, the bulk of Arabia, half of Turkey, three quarters of Iran, and large but unknown areas in Afghanistan. Paleozoic for-

[1] W. B. Fisher: *The Middle East*. New York: Dutton (1950), 12–18.

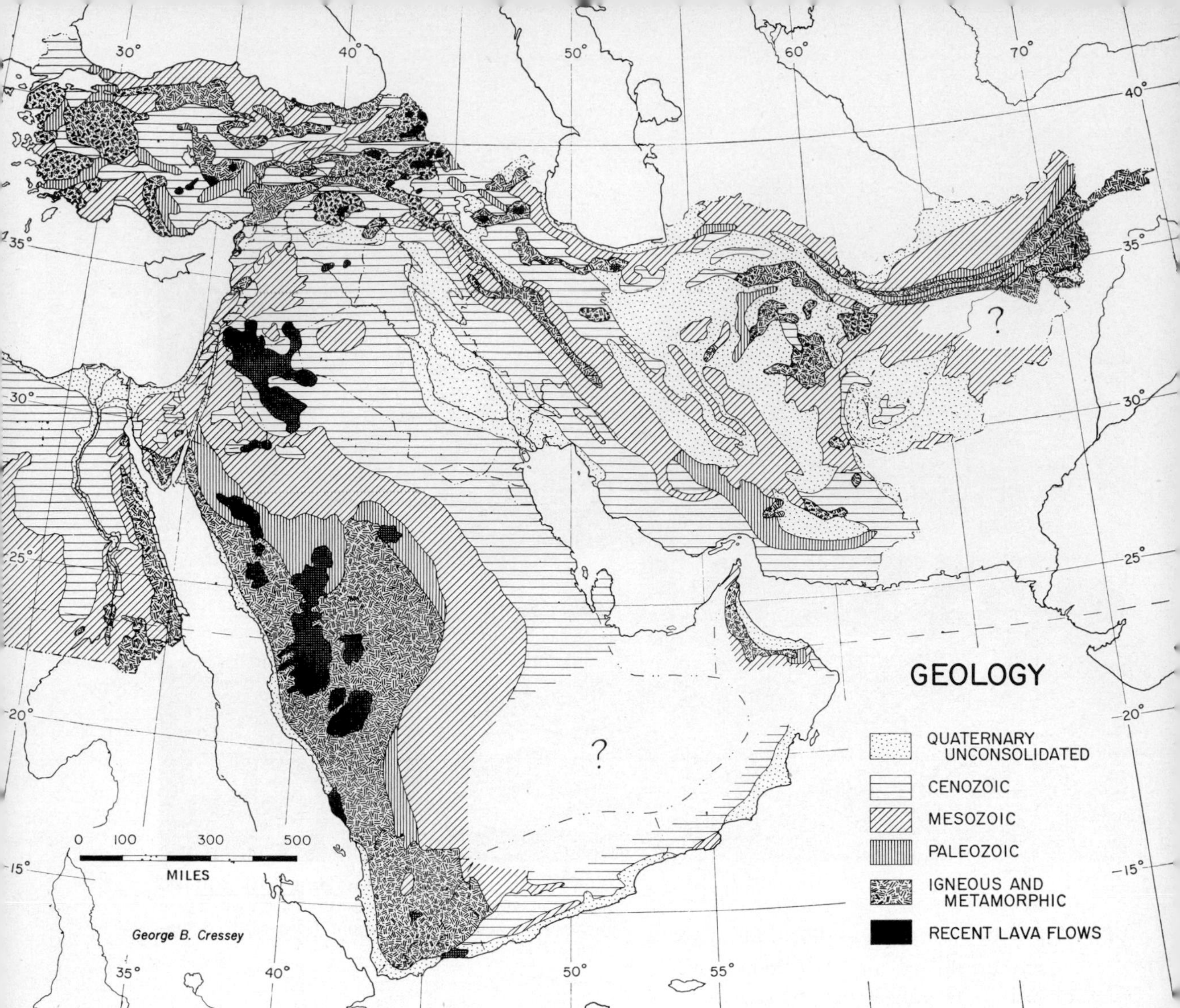

Geology supplies the foundation on which land forms and culture are superimposed. Ancient crystalline rocks and modern lava flows occupy the west and north, with progressively younger and weaker sediments toward the Persian Gulf. While this is a map of historical geology, it also reveals something as to lithology and land form. (Based in large part on data from the Arabian American Oil Co.)

mations are poorly represented on the surface, with scattered occurrences in Turkey and Afghanistan, and to a lesser extent in Iran and central Arabia. Elsewhere, Paleozoic rocks are buried beneath later formations. The Mesozoic era provides a wide display of Triassic and Cretaceous formations, thousands of feet thick and well developed in all of the folded mountains. Cenozoic beds, usually thin, are widespread in Syria, Iraq, Arabia, and Iran.

Mountain building occurred in the late Jurassic and toward the end of the Mesozoic, with further folding in the Eocene, Miocene, and Pliocene. Some of the later stages were accompanied by deep-seated faulting which brought lava to the surface and developed extensive lava flows, as near Damascus.

As a result of this geologic evolution, a festoon of mountains crosses Europe and Asia in a double chain. One of these, that on the north, forms part of the "alpide" oro-

The landscape of Swasia is the product of both depositional and erosional agents, operating in a wide variety of situations. (Prepared by Theodore M. Oberlander.)

genic system; this includes the northern Alps, the Carpathians, and the northern Balkan mountains. Within Turkey and parallel to the Black Sea, the alpide system is known as the Pontus or North Anatolian Mountains. In Iran they continue south of the Caspian as the Elburz, which apparently merge into the Kopet Dagh Range of northeastern Iran near the Soviet border. Eastward in Afghanistan they become the Paropamisus, Koh-i-Baba, and Hindu Kush mountains. The alpide system extends almost across Asia and is represented farther east in the Kunlun and Astin Tagh ranges of northern Tibet and the Chin Ling (Tsinling) of eastern China.

The twin range of the alpides, farther south, is known as the "dinaride" system. In Europe this is made up of the southern Alps and the folds of Yugoslavia, Albania, and southern Greece. Within Turkey the dinaride chain continues as the Taurus and Anti-Taurus mountains. These structures are present through Iran as the Zagros Range, a great folded chain which extends to the southern end of the Persian Gulf. Here the structures turn eastward toward Pakistan and are known as the Makran Mountains; they then continue northeast across Baluchistan and eventually join the Himalaya. Their continuation reaches the Pacific.

The Pontus and Taurus ranges on the two sides of Turkey are quite unlike in structure. Whereas the latter is built of folded sediments and has a quite irregular trend, the Pontus axial lines are straighter and the mountains contain extensive volcanic and igneous areas. Iranian structures are simpler, for both the Elburz and Zagros are composed of relatively straight folds. Afghanistan has two converging structures, the east-to-west Hindu Kush, and the northeast-to-southwest Sulaiman which swings across Baluchistan to form the Iranian Makran.

In two places the separate alpide and dinaride mountain festoon meet to form highlands, complex in structure and topography. One of these is at the Turkish-Iranian border and is known as the Armenian Highland; the other lies where Afghanistan and China join in the Pamir Highland, the "roof of the world." Elevations in each area reach three miles, and the linear character of the nearby ranges is replaced by complicated structures and topography.

The intervening space between the alpide and dinaride mountain ranges is occupied by rigid and essentially unfolded masses, though not so resistant as the Arabian Shield. The first of these, in interior Turkey, is known as the Anatolian Plateau. The second, in central Iran, is the Persian Plateau which continues into the Seistan Basin of Afghanistan. Interior Iran is difficult to organize structurally, but two local highlands stand out. Roughly parallel to the Zagros are a series of open folds which form a linear range known as the Median Mountains. In eastern Iran there is a broad upland with an approximate north-south trend and folded structures which somewhat separates the Persian Plateau from Afghanistan. Neither of these ranges is comparable to the great Elburz or Zagros systems.

To the south of this sequence of folded mountains the pattern is quite different, although in places there is also a double series. Parallel to the eastern Mediterranean and continuing along the Red Sea, that is from the Turkish border to Aden, there is a line of mountains, largely fault block in character.

In Syria these are twin ranges, the Alma Dag or Amanus and the Kurd Dag and its southern continuation in the Jebel Zawiyeh separated by a syncline which forms the Ghab lowland, drained by the Orontes River. In Lebanon the syncline changes to a graben which accounts for the Bekaa lowland, occupied by the Litani River. On either side are the high Lebanon and Anti

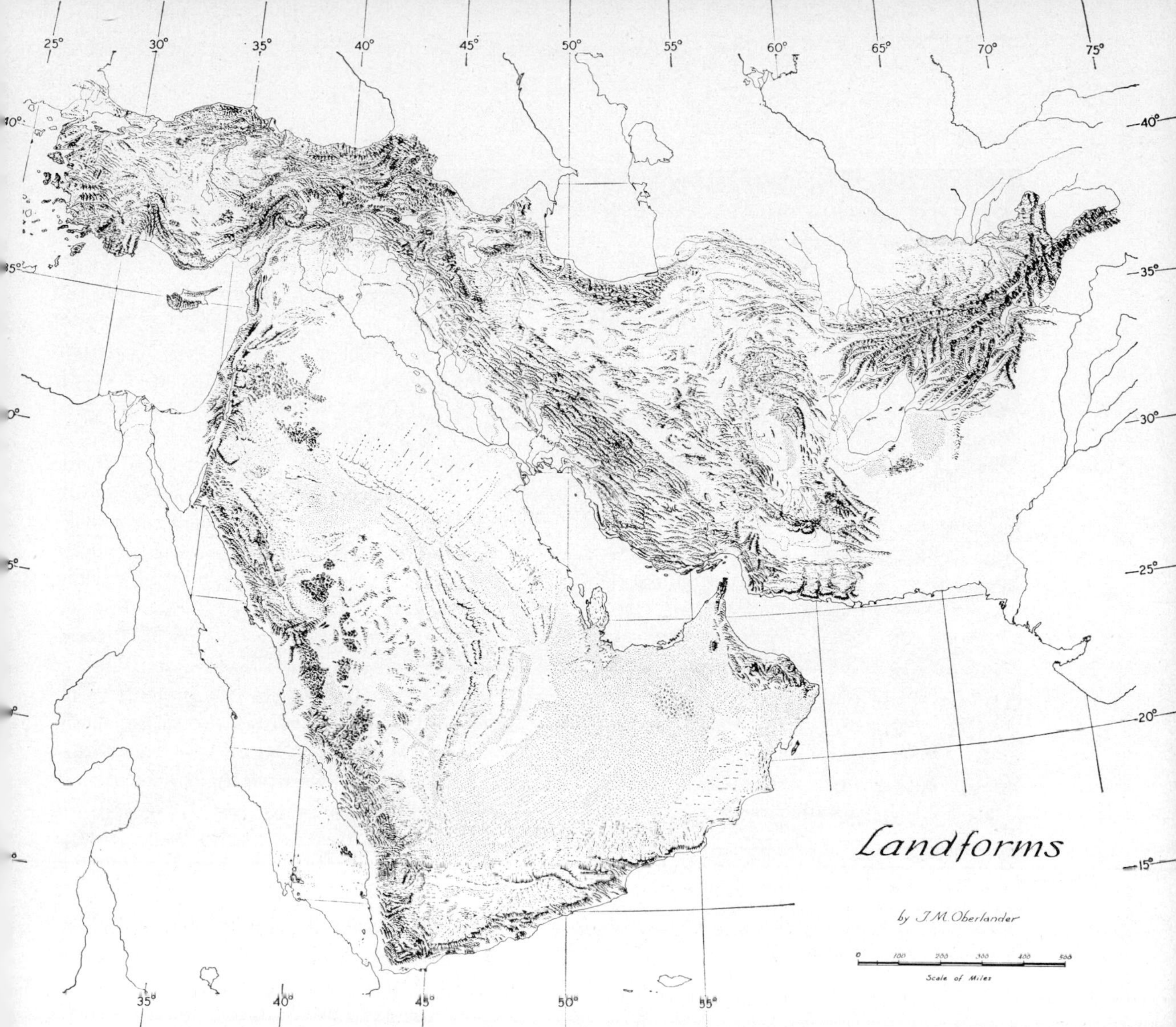

The topographic pattern of Southwest Asia is a result of the geologic structure and the agencies which have carved the underlying rocks. (Compiled by Theodore M. Oberlander.)

Lebanon Mountains. The fault structure continues in Palestine where the graben is occupied by the Jordan River, the Dead Sea, and the Wadi Araba. To the west and east lie the hills of Judea and the Moab uplands.

Fault escarpments continue southward through Arabia parallel to the Red Sea, with the sea itself occupying the enlarged graben. The line of one-sided mountains produced by the faulting extends through the Hejaz and the Asir, reaching its culmination in the two-mile-high Yemen Mountains.

The western and southern limits of Arabia are defined by faults. Near the entrance to the Dead Sea the roughly north-south pattern is replaced at 90 degrees by east-west fault lines. Escarpments of lower elevation thus continue past Aden and the Hadhramaut.

Concentric with the crystalline limits in central Arabia is a series of crescentic ridges developed on the outcrop of hard sedimentary formations where they dip away from

Deep dissection characterizes many of Swasia's mountains; few of them have a forest cover, so runoff and erosion are rapid. This scene is near Aden. (Courtesy British Overseas Airline Co.)

the old land mass. These escarpments or cuestas form the Tuwaiq Mountains and are erosional rather than structural.

The Oman Mountains occupy southeastern Arabia and are Iranian in their folding.

LAND FORMS

RUGGED MOUNTAINS and broad plains characterize the landscape of Southwest Asia, respectively white or brown for part of the year. In Turkey, Iran, and Afghanistan the mountains dominate; in Syria, Iraq, and Arabia it is the plains which are important. In total extent these two types of terrain are roughly equal. This suggests that half of Swasia has slopes too steep for normal agriculture, even if climate were suitable.

Land forms also have their bearing on the construction of roads. Even where the overall surface is of low relief, local features such as sand dunes, badlands, and broad wadis interfere with normal utilization. It cannot be emphasized too often that the conventional relief map which shows elevations by bands of successive colors can be very misleading when one attempts to infer land *form* or local relief from average elevation.

Almost all of Swasia is surrounded by mountains; only along the Persian Gulf is the 500-foot contour more than ten miles from the shore. The chief exceptions are in northern Afghanistan along the Soviet frontier, across the Sinai Peninsula toward Egypt, and along the Makran Coast next to Pakistan. Southern Iraq and eastern Arabia offer the only frontiers where one can penetrate

Rapid runoff leads to overloaded rivers which develop valley flats and alluvial fans, as along the lower Arghandab near Kandahar in Afghanistan. (Courtesy Morrison-Knudsen-Afghanistan.)

Swasia very far without crossing mountains.

Many of the mountains are geologically young and thus are subject to vigorous erosion. Occasional earthquakes are reminders that uplift is still under way. Slopes tend to be steep, and, where they are unprotected by vegetation, runoff is rapid. In places, the forces of uplift seem to be running ahead of the powers of gradation; elsewhere featureless plains reflect long continued erosion or deposition.

River problems are considered in some detail in the following chapter. Since rainfall is low, except on some windward slopes, the drainage network has a coarse pattern. Many streams are intermittent, in fact due to the seasonal rainfall there would be little runoff in summer if it were not for the storage of mountain moisture in the form of snow.

Bordering most mountains are broad alluvial fans where some of the eroded material has paused on its downward way. In many areas the mountain pattern provides no outlet for drainage to the surrounding seas so that sediments accumulate in interior basins; even on outer slopes the rainfall may be so limited that rivers wither and drop their load long before reaching the sea, as around the Arabian Peninsula where not a single stream flows the year around. Only the Tigris, Euphrates, and Karun have important deltas.

The Arabian Peninsula, with its northward extension in Syria and Iraq, is the largest of the lowlands; around three sides are highlands which contribute debris. For the most part, this is a rolling plain, the product of long-continued erosion. Here and there are residual hills, broad wadis, deflation hollows, or sand dunes. Erosion predominates, but there are occasional depositional basins. The horizon is typically flat in all directions, and one may travel for many hundreds of miles without encountering local relief of more than a few hundred feet.

The desert aspects of these plains are discussed in Chapter 4 on climate.

Turkey, Iran, and Afghanistan repeat the pattern of mountains and plains on a somewhat smaller scale, each with plains up to a hundred miles in extent. Here and there are transient lakes, shallow bodies of water which last for a few days after the rare rains, then become an expanse of mud for a few weeks, and finally revert to a dry salt-encrusted flat for months and years. Depositional surfaces are more widespread than in Arabia.

A traverse across Southwest Asia thus shows a succession of steep-sided ranges and broad lowlands. No matter how broad the desert, or how rugged the mountain, the traveler eventually changes from one landscape to the other.

Geography usually deals with areas too large to be seen in a single view. One may stand on the hills west of Damascus and see all of the city at a glance and thus give meaning to the map. Or one may fly along the Tigris River and watch its changing pattern, but the entire drainage basin is never in sight at one time. Even if one could be high enough over Lebanon to cover the entire country in a single photograph, the details of fields and people would disappear. This limitation challenges our imagination and makes it necessary to keep a sense of dimension and proportion. Maps are a necessity, but are valid only as we use them wisely.

In the adjoining classification of the land forms of Swasia, the major category refers

LAND FORM REGIONS

I. Gondwana Stable Block
- A. Hadhramaut–Dhufar Uplands
- B. Yemen–Asir Highlands
- C. Hejaz–Midian Uplands
  1. Hejaz Scarp
  2. Hejaz Hills
  3. Midian Coastal Hills
- D. Levant Uplands
  1. Sinai Uplands
  2. Palestine Hills
  3. Lebanon Mountains
  4. Syrian Hills
- E. Arabian–Syrian Lowlands
  1. Rub al Khali Dunes
  2. Nejd Scarps and Dunes
  3. Hasa Plains
  4. Syria–Iraq Plains
  5. Sinjar–Hamrin Hills
- F. Babylonian Lowland

II. Tethys Foldlands
- A. Anatolian Highlands
  1. Aegean Hills
  2. Pontus Mountains
  3. Taurus Mountains
  4. Anatolian Basins
- B. Armenian Highlands
- C. Persian Highlands
  1. Elburz Mountains
  2. Zagros Mountains
  3. Makran Mountains
  4. Median Mountains
  5. East Persian Mountains
  6. Inner Persian Basins
- D. Oman Highlands
- E. Afghan Highlands
  1. Hindu Kush–Paropamisus Mountains
  2. Helmand–Registan Basins

III. Angara Stable Block
- A. Turanian Lowlands
  1. Oxus (Amu Darya) Plain

Hot springs near Denizli in Turkey have developed Yellowstone-style terraces of tufa as a reflection of deep-seated igneous activity. (Courtesy Turkish Information Office, New York.)

to structural history. The second subdivision is based on over-all elevation. The term lowland is used for areas below 2,000 feet, highlands refer to elevations above a mile, while uplands represent intermediate elevations. In third rank, regions are defined in terms of land forms, such as mountains, escarpments, plains, or basins.

IGNEOUS ACTIVITY

LAVA FLOWS cover several hundred thousand square miles. They extend southward from the shores of the Black Sea and are parallel with the Red Sea to Aden, with only local interruptions, and from the Aegean eastward into Afghanistan. Southwest Asia has few volcanoes which are currently active, but there are many which have erupted within historic times. Elsewhere, volcanism dates back into the Mesozoic Era and beyond. Several great symmetrical peaks such as Ararat and Demavend reach more than three miles in height. Hot springs occur in Yemen and western Arabia.

For the most part, the recent lava areas represent broad flows without volcanic peaks. In some places the lava fields are relatively smooth, but more commonly they have a rough surface. Elsewhere there are fresh ash and lava cones, up to a thousand feet in height, encircled by lava flows which radiate for a mile or more. Such areas of cones, craters, and lava fields are known to the Arabs as *harra*.

In over-all distribution, these volcanic areas roughly form a horseshoe around the margins of Swasia. Lava flows are entirely

Volcanic peaks, such as Mount Agri, dominate eastern Turkey. Rising air currents produce stationary cumulus clouds. (Courtesy Turkish Press, Broadcasting, and Tourist Dept., Ankara.)

absent in eastern Saudi Arabia, most of Iraq, and the southwestern third of Iran.

Something of the same pattern prevails for ancient igneous and metamorphic formations. Such rocks cover extensive areas in western Arabia and in Turkey. In Iran, there are linear developments along the Zagros and Elburz mountains, and in Afghanistan in the Hindu Kush.

Turkey leads in the current extent of volcanism and also in the number of large volcanic cones. Most of these lie in interior and eastern Anatolia rather than in the mountain ranges to the north or south. The largest and most famous Turkish volcano is Mt. Ararat, 16,946 feet in height, which lies near the borders shared with Iran and the Soviet Union. The peak is surrounded by a wide expanse of lava, and on its slope is the parasitic cone of Little Ararat, 12,878 feet high. The symmetrical cone of Suphan on the shore of Lake Van reaches 14,547 feet, and Erciyas rises to an elevation of 12,840 feet. Many others exceed 10,000 feet. Somewhat lower, but once much larger, is Nemrut, 9,900 feet high, which is topped by a superb explosion crater, with a lake nearly five miles in diameter. Its last eruption occurred in the fifteenth century.

Turkey has had its full share of igneous activity, for altered volcanic rocks are among the most ancient formations known. During the Triassic Period there were widespread submarine volcanic flows. From the Cretaceous into the Eocene period, vigorous outbursts continued, creating piles of acidic lavas and ash which reached a thickness of 4,500 feet. Activity was renewed in the Miocene with intermittent eruptions to the present. In eastern Turkey some of these lava sheets form tablelands; elsewhere the flows have been dissected. The basin of Lake Van is formed by a lava flow which dams an old valley.

In Iran, the highest volcanic peak is Mt. Demavend in the north, within sight from Tehran. Demavend rises symmetrically above the Elburz range to a height of 18,934 feet and carries snow throughout the year. This is the highest peak in all of Eurasia west of the Hindu Kush. At least four other Iranian volcanoes exceed 10,000 feet: Savalan, 15,784 feet, and Sahand, 12,172 feet, in the northwest; and Bazman, 11,447 feet, and Taftan, 13,262 feet, in the extreme southeast. Only the last shows much activity. Iranian volcanism is best developed in the extreme northwest next to Turkey and in the southeast toward Baluchistan.

Syria and Jordan exhibit quite different igneous activity. Instead of great peaks there are broad lava domes, in places topped by ash cones rising a few hundred feet. Immense fields of scoriaceous basalt, broken into irregular blocks, make cross-country travel all but impossible. South of Damascus lies the broad dome of Jebel Druze, but although it reaches an elevation of 5,900 feet there are few noticeable peaks. This particular area covers 3,000 square miles, and the lava accumulation is as much as 4,000 feet thick; some parts show fresh lava, but there has been little activity within historic times.

Western Arabia has extensive lava flows. They extend parallel to the Red Sea and underlie most of Yemen where about 2,000 feet of trap rock was poured out during the Eocene Period. Proceeding southward the Arabian lavas are progressively older than those in Syria. In Yemen most areas of igneous rock are thus old enough to have become deeply dissected. Along the Gulf of Aden, however, there are several recent volcanic districts with fresh craters. One such crater is occupied by the city of Aden.

EARTHQUAKES

On a world map of earthquake zones, the mountain areas of Swasia stand out prominently. The seismic intensity appears to be not less than that of California and Japan. This is an area where deep-seated stresses and strains continue to operate. Stability has not been achieved, so that, when pressures exceed the elastic limit of the rocks, rupture occurs.

Major faults cross Turkey and Iran; others extend south through the Levant and along the Red Sea. Associated with each of the systems are local fault patterns. The remarkably straight course of several rivers is due to the fact that they follow fault lines. Where these valleys provide natural avenues of travel, as in western Turkey, they often account for the site of cities so that the loss of life during quakes has been serious. Seismic activity is not confined to the mountains for important shocks are also recorded from unfolded areas.

The earliest known earthquake in Turkey occurred in A.D. 33 near the eastern end of the Sea of Marmara. Up to the end of the nineteenth century, nearly 200 destructive shocks were recorded in that country. The incomplete character of the early records is suggested by the fact that several dozen severe quakes have occurred during the present century.

Turkey has three earthquake zones of the first category. In each of these, disastrous shocks have occurred repeatedly since antiquity, with severe damage to nearby settlements. There are also four areas of secondary character where shocks are frequent but rarely serious. No part of Turkey is entirely free from earthquakes.

Great fault scarps border the Dead Sea, a reflection of its graben origin. This view shows the potash works near Sodom. (Courtesy Israel Office of Information, New York.)

First category seismic zones include the following areas:

1. North Anatolia is more or less a ribbon of tectonic depressions, grabens, faults, and overthrusts. This zone extends from the Marmara Basin nearly 1,000 miles east to the Araks Valley on the Iranian border. Two major cities at either end of the fault give it the name of the Izmit–Erzurum line. In importance, it may be compared to the San Andreas fault in California. Most of the great earthquakes of the twentieth century have occurred here, as at Erzincan in 1939.

2. The Aegean–Marmara Zone in western Anatolia has a network of faults and grabens resulting from the subsidence of the Aegean Sea at the end of the Pliocene. Some of these structures extend eastward well into Anatolia, as along the hundred mile graben of the Menderes River. Although Izmir experienced a major quake in 1939, this zone has been relatively inactive since the second half of the nineteenth century when it was the dominant Turkish earthquake area.

3. The Syrian graben structure extends into the southernmost part of Turkey near Iskenderon and continues to the northeast past Maras. Its extension is to be found around the tectonic depression of Lake Van. No major quakes have occurred here for more than a century.

Secondary zones are present in inner Anatolia around Afyon Karahisar, Kayseri, and

Kirsehir; and also near the Mediterranean in the Adana–Ceyhan region.

The Erzincan shock of 1939 was the strongest ever measured in Turkey. Unfortunately it occurred at night during a winter blizzard when the temperature stood at 2° F. The initial motion was the most violent so that there was no opportunity for people to escape from their homes. Erzincan was reduced to ruins and 6,600 buildings were entirely destroyed; most of them had been built of stone cemented with mud. The devastated area covered 15,000 square miles and resulted in the loss of 23,148 lives. The first shock involved movement along a fault near Erzincan. This movement released stresses in the surrounding fractured zone so that a month later movement suddenly took place along most of the known faults within a radius of 100 miles, and several new faults appeared. Erzincan has recorded twenty-six severe shocks since the year 1011. Nearby Erzurum has been destroyed thirteen times, while Kars and other cities along the fault have repeatedly been devastated.

The record in Iran is almost as destructive. The most serious shocks have occurred around Tabriz in the Armenian Highlands, where 40,000 people lost their lives in 1042; and in the Elburz Mountains north of Tehran. Major earthquakes have also taken place in the south, as at Kerman, Shiraz, Lar, and Qishm Island.

The eastern shore of the Mediterranean is paralleled by major fault systems which form the Jordan Valley and its northward extension into Syria. This has been the focus of repeated movement. Many of the ancient temples and other monuments of antiquity in this area, Roman and others, have been partially destroyed by earthquakes, and where their columns are still standing one may find instances where individual stones have been offset a few inches.

Arabian earthquake zones border the Red Sea and turn eastward along the southern coast. The great rift which separates Asia from Africa originated during the Eocene period, with faulting continuing into the Pliocene. Both upward and downward movements have taken place during historic time along the coasts of Yemen and the Hadhramaut. Arab historians record numerous earthquakes, most of them moderate in intensity. One occurred in Aden in 1387, another near Mocha in 1394, still others in Yemen during the ninteenth century.

SAND DUNES

Sand dunes cover some 30 per cent of Arabia, 5 per cent or more of Iran and Afghanistan, 2 or 3 per cent of Iraq, Jordan, Syria, and Israel, and small areas in Turkey. In total, they represent half a million square miles.

It might be interesting to speculate on the volume of sand involved, but there are few data as to the thickness. The bulk of the sand is in the Rub al Khali of southern Arabia, the empty quarter which covers 229,000 square miles inclusive of the Jafura. As an approximation, the average thickness of active dune sand here may be 100 feet. If so, the volume of sand in this great waste would exceed 4,000 cubic miles.

Outside Arabia, other areas of high dunes occur in the Lut Desert of southern Iran and the Registan of southern Afghanistan. Elsewhere, a veneer of shifting sand covers wide areas. The total volume is quite unknown, but is clearly to be measured in thousands of cubic miles.

Where did this sand come from? The grains, of course, are largely of quartz, and as such their origin goes back exclusively to crystals in granite or in quartz veins. Between such an origin and their present distribution lies a long history. Some of the dunes are marginal to present or former shore lines, either of the sea or of transitory inland lakes. Other dunes are related to withering rivers, commonly in the lee of the river's flood plains or around their terminal basins. Some sand areas have resulted from the disintegration of weak sandstone formations.

Desert processes produce several types of surfaces unique to arid lands. Where wind action is strong, it exports everything moveable, leaving a bare surface veneered by residual gravels which form a desert pavement or armor. If this surface is flat, one may drive over these small stones at will, provided that his car is equipped with balloon tires. Areas in Swasia which are carpeted by such pebbles are probably as extensive as the dune sections.

The finest particles, of silt or clay size, are readily lifted high into the air by turbulence and removed entirely outside their source area. Dust storms during the dry season are common in areas where rivers have deposited fine sediments, as in Iraq. Where these silts accumulate they form deposits of loess. Such accumulations develop where the dust is trapped by steppe grasses; loess is thus to be expected in the grasslands of the Fertile Crescent and on humid mountain flanks as in Iran. Few areas of thick loess have been described in Swasia, but it is widespread next door in Soviet Middle Asia.

Due to the selective and sorting action of the wind, sand is separated from the residual lag gravels and the far-traveling silt and is swept into fluid forms known as dunes. When sand is moved by running water, it obviously travels downhill and accumulates at the lowest elevation; with wind transport it may migrate up-slope and be widely distributed irrespective of the topography.

Little is known about the great sand areas of Iran and Afghanistan, but they include dunes several hundred feet in height. In several cases these border the great salt flats, known as *kavir,* which occupy the center of enclosed basins. In Iran, the sand area of the Rig-i-Jinn measures ten by fifty miles; other dune areas to the north and east are almost as large. The barren sands of the Lut Desert cover an area of thirty by a hundred miles. The dune areas of southern Afghanistan are even larger, for the Registan Desert includes a sand cover of 14,000 square miles. Several of these areas are essentially uninhabited and have rarely been visited by outsiders.

At least 325,000 square miles of Saudi Arabia are covered by active sand dunes, largely devoid of all but the most scanty vegetation. In the north lies the Great Nafud, 300 miles from east to west and half that distance from north to south, a total of 26,500 square miles. Southeast from the Great Nafud are several streamers of sand of which the easternmost arc is known as the Dahna; this continues southward in a narrow 700-mile arc to join the Rub al Khali. To the west of it lie several roughly parallel Nafuds, each a long sand ribbon about ten miles wide and up to 150 miles long. Numerous other sand deserts occur in central Arabia; among them is the Nafud ad Dahy, southwest of Riyadh, which is almost as large as the Great Nafud. Isolated dune areas also occur on the borders of Yemen and Oman.

The sand dunes of central Arabia lie in the area known as the Nejd. Some of their sand is derived from wadis which bring material from escarpments to the west; some comes from the weathering of local sandstones. Dune types here include the familiar migrating crescentic or barchan dune, usually merged; numerous irregular forms; and particularly a unique dome-shaped dune. Presumably as a result of varying wind direction of like intensity, these dome-shaped dunes are circular or somewhat elliptical. In size the domes average half a mile across, with heights to 400 feet. The broad upper surface of these relatively stable domes is covered by small mobile sharp-crested "S" shaped or sigmoidal dunes. In places scattered vegetation partially stabilizes the sand.

Shifting sands cover half a million square miles of Southwest Asia. This dune complex with its scattered vegetation is a part of the Great Nafud near Hail in Saudi Arabia. Bedouin tents occupy bare ground in the upper right; rocky mountains line the horizon. (Courtesy Arabian American Oil Co.)

Around the dunes are broad deflation hollows. Similar isolated elliptical or block dunes, 300 feet high, are present in the southernmost Rub al Khali.

Here as elsewhere, dune migration consists of rolling the sand up the gentle windward slope, 5° to 15°, to the crest where it drops down the steep lee face on a gravity or slip slope of 32°. Since the rate of migration is inversely related to the mass of the dune, large dunes move more slowly than smaller forms.

Measurements of two active dunes near Dhahran show an annual movement of twenty feet for a dune forty feet high, as compared with a migration of a hundred feet for a twelve-foot dune. Such speeds are uncommon, and large dunes in areas of opposing winds may move very little.

The Rub al Khali

The Rub al Khali is by far the largest sand area in Arabia.[1] It extends in an east-west direction from the Oman to the Tuwaiq mountains and from the Persian Gulf south to the Hadhramaut Plateau. To the southwest is the isolated but comparable Ramlat Sabatain. Few of the conventional sources seem adequate to account for the vast masses

[1] I am indebted to the Arabian American Oil Company and to Petroleum Concessions, Ltd., for the rare opportunity of making three trips into the Rub al Khali—G. B. C.

of sand. Merely to say that this sand has been here for a long geologic time does not provide the answer. Some of it may have moved inland from the floor of the Persian Gulf during the Pleistocene Period when much of the Gulf was dry. Some may have migrated long distances from sandstone outcrops in the northwest. More likely, the Rub al Khali sands have been derived from transitory streams which over the millennia have flowed out of the encircling highlands of Yemen, the Hadhramaut, and Oman.

Only in a few places in the Rub al Khali is there any indication as to the work of running water. Valleys, alluvial fans, and playas are largely absent, although after the more concentrated rainfalls surface water may appear briefly. Such rain as falls disappears by evaporation so that there is no runoff to the sea. Wind and ground water are the chief agents which shape the surface. Traces of old shore lines border a few salt flats but are uncommon. Since there is little movement of detritus to the sea, this is a terminal area.

Dune forms are obviously the product of the wind, but continuous meteorological observations are lacking for the interior of Arabia. The dominant wind direction appears to be from northern quadrants, chiefly the shamal which here blows strongest in December and January and again in May and June. Northerly winds are occasionally interrupted by those with southerly or easterly components. In the northern areas of Arabia the winds usually blow from the northwest, in alignment with the Trans-Arabian Pipeline. At Dhahran, near the Persian Gulf, the prevailing direction is N.20°W; the same is true in Qatar and Oman. Farther south the winter winds apparently come directly from the north and then still farther south shift to northeast. Monsoon winds from the Indian Ocean, with southerly components, sometimes influence the extreme south.

Annual wind conditions within the Rub al Khali can only be surmised, and the unusual dune patterns do not lend themselves to the conventional analysis. Daily winds, perhaps thermal in origin, characterize some areas as in the southwest. It is best to avoid the use of dune terms such as longitudinal or transverse which imply a sure knowledge of wind directions and to replace them by linear and crescentic. Exploration parties of the Arabian-American Oil Company report that strong winds are uncommon but do occur. On April 11, 1957, there were sixty mile an hour winds from the west, with an inch of rain. In 1956 the eastern Rub al Khali experienced seventy-five mile per hour winds.

Four types of sand terrain are present in the Rub al Khali; two of them are unique.

1. Rolling sand surfaces, more or less stabilized, are known to the Arabs as *zibarr*. In some ways this sheet sand resembles a low ground moraine with its unorganized swells and depressions. Distinct dune units are uncommon, slopes are gentle and slip slopes rare, and there may be broad flat areas of sheet sand. The relief is measured in a few tens of feet. Zibarr dunes usually represent residual sand, preserved in senile dune forms that have no slip slopes. Areas of such sand cover many square miles, but the volume of sand is small. Much of the Jafura south of Dhahran falls in this category. Where clumps of vegetation are present they may lead to the accumulation of sand hummocks or dunelets. Both the vegetation and this type of surface are known by the term *dikaka*.

2. The term dune complex or sand sea may be applied to a complex area of mobile sand, generally with a relief of several tens of feet or even a hundred feet. Dune movement is obvious, and there may be numerous steep lee slopes facing in various directions, but there is no clear over-all pattern. Areas such as this are sometimes spoken of as "con-

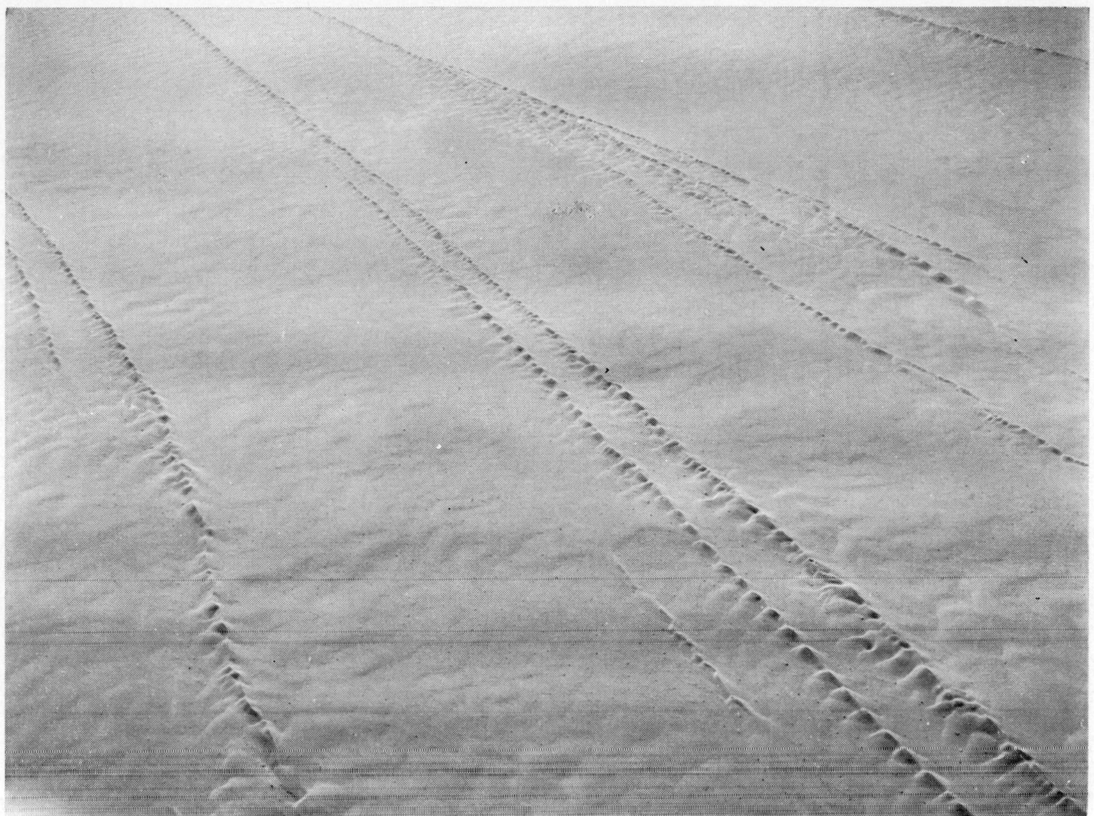

Linear dune ridges, known as *uruq,* extend for tens of miles across the Rub al Khali in Arabia. In most cases, the *uruq* is complex and measures several hundred yards wide rather than a single line as shown above. (Courtesy Arabian American Oil Co.)

fused," but such a term merely reflects the mental state of the observer. There is usually a system if one has the patience to search for it. Multi-directional winds are commonly involved. True isolated barchan dunes are rare since there are few areas with uni-directional winds and just the right amount of sand. Both partly developed barchan crescents and amphitheaters are mixed with irregular ridges. In some cases, there is a linear alignment at right angles to the wind. Parts of the central Rub al Khali fall into this category, as do the Great Nafud and Dahna. Such sandy wastes are known as *erg* in the Sahara.

3. Linear or *uruq* dunes are among the more unique features of the Rub al Khali. These are parallel and sharp-crested ridges, compound but remarkably regular, which occupy the western half of the desert. Comparable forms in North Africa are known as *seif* dunes.

As seen from the air the uruq resemble giant ripples. Individual dunes may extend for miles, with instances of 100 miles in an unbroken line. More than 250 of these linear dunes exceed twenty-five miles in length. Each uruq has a width from several hundred yards up to two miles, and a height of 100 to 200 feet. Between them are long lowland avenues, known as *shuqqan.* These linear depressions may be as wide as the uruq and are often so flat floored and firm that they form natural landing fields for light planes.

The uruq ridge usually appears from the air as light brown or tan, in contrast to the more reddish and coarser sand of the intervening lowlands. When examined on the ground, most uruq are composed of several separate dune ridges. The cross section from shuqqan to shuqqan is asymmetrical, with a gradual rise across an increasing complex of sinuous ridges and lee slopes, each one a few tens of feet in height, until from the last crest the dune drops in an abrupt slip slope to the next lowland.

The crest line of the dune may be a scalloped ridge, often an alternating series of "S" shaped or sigmoidal dunes resembling elongated and merged barchans, end to end and facing in alternating directions. This implies two-directional transverse winds at right angles to the uruq line, whereas true barchans represent uni-directional winds.

Individual sigmoidal dunes may be a mile or more in length, with a width of several hundred yards and a height of 100 feet. The cross section is triangular, with slopes of 10° to 32°. Sigmoidal dunes thus have alternate slip faces to the northwest and southeast. It is the succession and overlap of these individual sigmoids which give the uruq its continuity. Every strong wind changes the local contour of the dunes, but there is little indication of net movement for the uruq as a whole.

Many uruq ridges have several crescentic hooks or feathers at their northeastern ends; elsewhere the alignment is essentially unbroken. These spurs extend diagonally into the shuqqan, always on the eastern side of the uruq. Some of these are curved into crescentic hooks. Wherever these hooks develop into clearly developed barchans, one horn is in line with the uruq. In a few cases the spurs form cross dunes, at right angles to the uruq and extending to the next line, thus making a trellis pattern.

In places, the lowland shuqqan is covered with zibarr sheet sand or with a low dune complex. Elsewhere it is veneered with coarse grit or one-half inch pebbles. In a few places there is silt or marl with fresh water shells, or a salt-crusted surface which forms a foundation floor. Whereas travel across the loose sand of the uruq is trying, the shuqqan provides natural avenues. Evidence concerning the permanence of the shuqqan is found in the presence of large numbers of artifacts (such as near 46°E., 19°N.) within a few hundred yards of active dunes. These spear points and scrapers have apparently remained undisturbed for several thousand years.

Within the uruq zones there are occasional depressions, up to fifty feet in depth, which slightly resemble craters or even glacial kettle holes. These generally have at least one slip face but steep slopes may border the hollow on all sides. This suggests that an advancing barchan may have partly surrounded other dune forms. Wind scour may also be a minor factor, for the floor of the crater may expose a sand-free marl or gravel surface. Similar clean surfaces are commonly present within the horns of active crescentic dunes.

The origin of uruq dunes requires much more study. The linear alignment is from northeast to southwest, but there is no agreement as to how this is related to the dominant wind direction. Since most steep slopes face the southeast, the effective winds might be thought to be transverse, at right angles to the crest line, especially from the northwest. On the other hand, there is some indication that each uruq ridge represents the much elongated right limb of a barchan. This would suggest a longitudinal wind.

4. The eastern Rub al Khali is dominated by some of the most amazing dunes on earth. These are the sand mountains or pyramid dunes, sometimes termed star dunes because several ridges radiate from the crest.

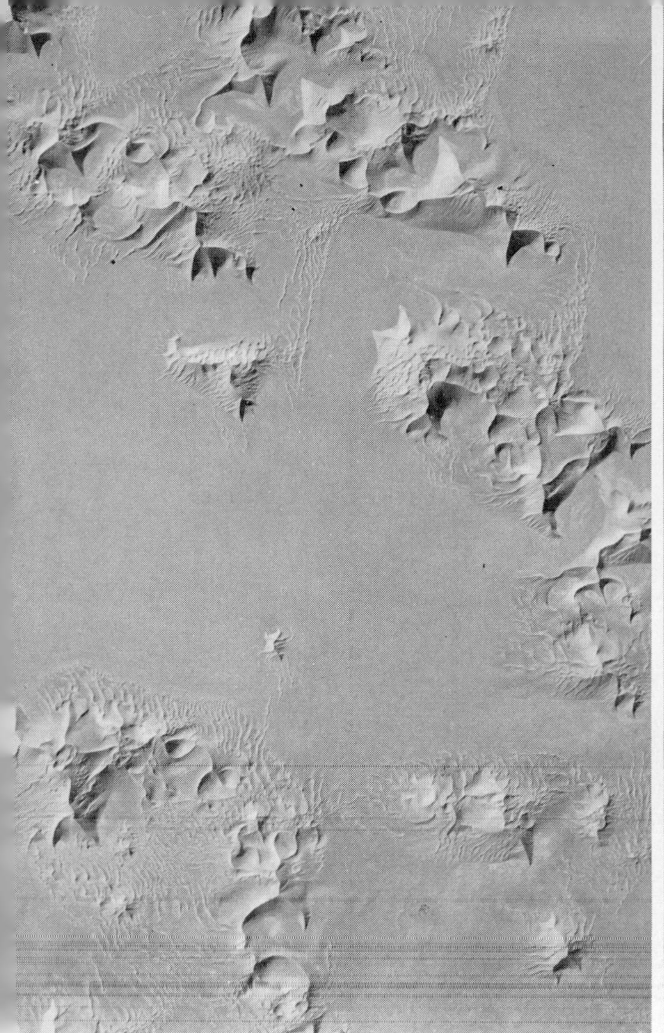
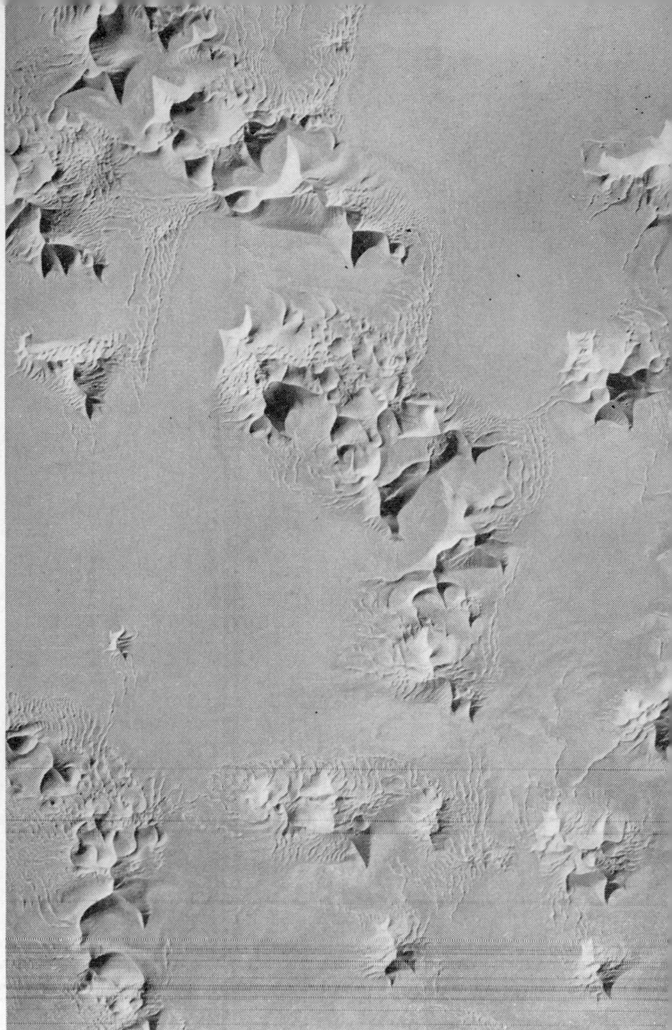

The eastern Rub al Khali has some of the most remarkable sand mountains on earth. Most of the giant dunes here shown exceed 500 feet in height. The photographs are mounted as a pair so that they may be examined with a stereoscope. (Courtesy Arabian American Oil Co.)

Comparable dunes are reported in the Dahna and the Nafud. They number in the thousands, and heights of 600 and 700 feet are common, with even higher elevations reported.

The most remarkable feature of these isolated peaks is that many are steep on all sides, even with steep slopes from top to bottom for each direction of the compass. In places these are slip slopes at 32°, elsewhere slopes reach 24°. Where there is a slight difference in slope, the somewhat gentler windward side is toward the northwest. Some sand mountains form simple pyramids or isolated "Matterhorns," others are more complex and may merge. If any alignment or regional pattern is to be detected, it is from northwest to southeast, forming a ridge.

Almost everywhere the sand mountains rest on a smooth basement floor. This is a *sabkha* or salt flat, whose origin calls for further study. Rainfall in the Rub al Khali averages but two or three inches a year. Where this falls on the dunes, it quickly sinks below the surface and is protected from evaporation. The moisture eventually joins the ground water around the base of the dunes. In the effective absence of subsurface drainage, the water table may be within a

This view of sand mountains in the Rub al Khali was taken from the crest of one of the dunes shown on the opposite page. The trailer camp of an oil party appears on the *sabkha* flat. (G. B. C.)

few feet of the surface. As capillary action lifts moisture to the surface, it evaporates and leaves behind its chemical load of salt and gypsum. Around the base of a dune, where more water is available, the surface is cemented with rock-like hardness and the cementing process may have caused it to be broken into polygonal blocks, three to five feet across and a foot or two in thickness. Toward the center of the sabkha, with less moisture, there may be only a cardboard-thin crust.

Sand mountains have a diameter of half a mile and are spaced from this distance to two miles apart. In places the area of sand to sabkha has a ratio of one to one, elsewhere the figure is one to four or five. From the air, the dunes have a rich, warm, red color in contrast to the sabkha which varies from a whitish collar around the dunes to a light gray elsewhere, depending on the accumulation of salt.

The size and stability of these sand mountains presents unsolved problems. Aerial photographs taken two decades apart show no perceptible change. Certainly their bulk is so large that even if the winds were unidirectional, movement would be slow, and it is clear that the effective winds do come from various directions.

On most sides sand mountains join the sabkha flat abruptly at the base of the lee slope. Most of the sabkha is swept clean of sand, but aerial observation shows numerous cases where sand trails stream off to leeward from the giant dunes. In places this is merely a sheet, a few inches in thickness; elsewhere there is a parade of tiny barchans a few feet in height. Most of this migrating sand moves along the surface by saltation, but some is carried in suspension by strong winds. Such a sand stream may continue along the surface until it joins the next mountain, or it may be dissipated once it leaves the sheltering lee of its parent sand mountain. Due to shifts in effective winds, these sand streams do not always point in the same direction.

As already indicated, the northwest faces appear to be the chief sides where accumulation takes place. This is also the principal side for the development of ripple marks. Here, too, is the chief place where scanty vegetation may be present. Not only does the occurrence of ripple marks indicate upward sand movement, but in numerous instances there are a series of small, superimposed dunes, ten to thirty feet high, which mount pick-a-back on the windward side of the pyramid. Since these are small, they move more rapidly than the larger dune and gradually climb to the summit where they lose their identity as their sand plunges down the lee slope.

Apparently, then, sand mountains grow by the accretion of material which is moved across the sabkha flat by northwest winds. This sand migrates up the windward face of the dune until it is incorporated in the main mass. In most areas, the sand mountains have a relatively uniform height. This apparently represents a growth limit, possibly related to stronger winds. When this height is reached, the dune loses sand during gale winds and an equilibrium is reached.

Obviously, winds blow from several directions so that dune movement is reversed. The net result appears to be remarkable stability. If the migration were considerable, the salt crust which now appears as a collar around each dune would come to be uniformly developed across the entire sabkha. The fact that this is generally not the case suggests that the big dunes do not change their position.

Just as occasional depressions are present within the uruq dunes, so some sand mountains have giant craters which extend down 200 feet to the white sabkha floor. These craters probably represent hollows formed by the advancing slip faces of dune ridges. Since they may have steep sides in all directions and clean floors, some wind scour may also operate.

CHAPTER 4

Climate

The Mediterranean Regime
Pressures and Air Mass Movements
Local Winds
Temperature
Precipitation
Water Requirements
Climatic Regions
References

THE MEDITERRANEAN REGIME

SOUTHWEST ASIA has a modified Mediterranean type climate, with increasing continentality and aridity eastward. The delightful conditions which prevail around the Mediterranean Sea with mild rainy winters, hot dry summers, and beautiful blue skies for much of the year are similar to climates of southern California, central Chile, the tip of South Africa, and southern Australia.

The climate of Southwest Asia results from the realm's intermediate position with respect to global wind circulation and its location in the continent. To the north is the zone of irregular westerlies with its variable pressures and parade of cyclonic storms. Throughout the year most of Swasia is an area of high pressures, decreasing southward, with steady northerly winds, elsewhere known as the trade wind belt. Northward lies the great land mass of Eurasia while southward are tropical seas and India. These relations are modified by local topography and water bodies.

If the rest of Eurasia could be ignored and conditions were idealized, summers would then be characterized by northerly winds blowing toward a low pressure belt north of the Equator. Since the air is moving equatorward and is progressively being warmed, and since it is derived from dry descending air out of a subtropical high pressure area near latitude 30°N., no rain is to be expected.

In winter, with the sun in the southern hemisphere, most of the realm would still have northerly winds, but it would occasionally be invaded by the irregular westerly circulation of middle latitudes. This would bring variable weather and occasional rain

(Opposite) Snow-covered mountains are present in every country outside the Arabian Peninsula. These ski slopes are at Ab-Ali near Tehran. (Ewing Galloway.)

Mediterranean type forests cover many windward slopes, or would do so if man permitted. The road to Jerusalem leads through the Judean Hills where precipitation averages 20 inches. (Courtesy Israel Government Tourist Office, New York.)

associated with the conflict between polar and tropical air masses and the resulting cyclonic storms.

While the normal situation for these latitudes points to hot, dry, uniform summers and cool, wet, variable winters, it is obvious that Swasia is not a detached continent and that its actual climate departs from the ideal. Summer drought is therefore associated with descending air which blows out of Eurasia toward low-pressure centers in Arabia and India. Winter rain is brought by a southward shift in the paths of weak cyclonic storms which pass over the northern part of the area in this season, thus bringing variable weather.

In its basic climatic characteristics, Southwest Asia fits into the Mediterranean pattern. No uniformity is to be expected, however, for the 2.5 million square miles of the realm are spread across thirty degrees of latitude, and cover a vertical range of nearly four miles. Some windward slopes receive 100 inches of rain, while some deserts are essentially rainless. With increasing distance from the sea comes increasing seasonal contrast in temperature. Seasonal aridity dominates almost everywhere.

There are numerous parallels between Southwestern Asia and the Southwestern United States. The Gulf of California has similarities to the Red Sea, though the latter

NOTE: I am indebted to my colleague, Prof. Douglas B. Carter, for assistance with this chapter.

Sparse bunch grass or steppe vegetation characterizes most of the areas which receive from 10 to 20 inches of rain. This is a view of the central plain in Lebanon known as the Bekaa. (Courtesy U. S. Operations Mission, Beirut.)

extends farther south and is warmer. The climate of southern California resembles that of Lebanon and Israel, with northern California having some similarities with the Turkish coasts. Arizona and New Mexico are not unlike interior Syria and northern Arabia; both are separated from a moist coast by a mountain screen. North America has nothing as hot and dry as central Arabia, but the Great Basin resembles somewhat the Iranian basins. The deep penetration of the Mediterranean Sea and the greater land mass of Eurasia obviously introduce large differences.

In a broad sense, the rainfall regime of Swasia forms a transitional zone between the year around moisture of Europe and the summer rain of the Indian monsoon. Two mountain systems mark the divides. In the north, the Pontus and Elburz ranges separate a humid north slope with both summer and winter rain from a dry interior with dominantly winter precipitation. In the south, the discontinuous line of the Yemen, Oman, and Makran mountains mark the northern penetration of the summer monsoon, here never more than feebly developed.

The problem of climatic variation has received much attention, but without conclusive evidence. In geological terms change is obvious, for the balance between inflow and evaporation in the Jordan Valley was once such that the Dead Sea overflowed to the Mediterranean. The ruins of ancient cities amid currently dry lands suggest times of greater moisture, but these settlements were

Climatic changes are suggested by the widespread occurrence of ruins in the midst of presently uninhabited areas, as at Subeita in the Negeb of southern Israel. In most instances, however, ancient aqueducts and cisterns suggest that water was a problem then as now. (Courtesy Israel Government Tourist Office, New York.)

all provided with aqueducts and cisterns which indicate that there were problems of aridity then as now. Biblical references to "lands flowing with milk and honey" may be in relation to still drier areas elsewhere.

After an evaluation of the evidence, Fisher concludes: [1]

During Neolithic times, a period of desiccation accompanied the final retreat of the ice-cap in Eurasia, but by the opening of the historic era this increase in aridity, had come to an end. Environmental changes which have supervened during the last five or six thousand years can be traced to one or more of the following causes: (a) lowering of the bed of the streams as the result of normal erosion, this has also lowered the water table in the soil itself and left many irrigation canal intakes above the new water level; (b) soil erosion due to wasteful agricultural methods, or to destruction of existing types of vegetation; and (c) misrule, war, and invasion.

In a detailed study of late glacial and post glacial climates, Butzer writes as follows: [2]

Reviewing the climate of the historical period, it is clear that there has been no long-term desiccation since "Roman times," rather we may divide the associated climatic phase into two subphases. . . . the first period c.850 B.C.–A.D. 700 was generally characterized by lake levels equal to or lower than those of the present, by numerous records of warm summers and severe droughts and very few references to cold winters

[1] W. B. Fisher: *The Middle East*. New York: Dutton (1950), 56. Quoted by permission.

[2] Karl W. Butzer: "Late Glacial and Postglacial Climatic Variation in the Near East," *Erdkunde*, XI (1957), 21–34.

or wet years; . . . . the subsequent phase, except for two intervals in the twelfth and twentieth centuries, was characterized by lake levels well above those of the present, by many cold winters, and other indications of a greater rainfall or lower evaporation. . . . Within this latter period we can identify distinct but temporary maxima of humidity from A.D. 700–1000, during the late thirteenth, the early fifteenth, the first half of the seventeenth and the beginning of the nineteenth centuries.

PRESSURES AND AIR MASS MOVEMENTS

THE GENERAL PATTERN of atmospheric pressure across most of Southwest Asia is remarkably simple. In both winter and summer the isobars extend roughly east-west, with a gradient to the south and southeast throughout the year. The details are not so simple.

In summer, sea level pressures across northern Turkey average 1011 millibars, decreasing to 1007 in the southeast. Syrian pressures decline from 1007 to 1002, again toward the southeast. Across Iran, the isobars which represent millimeters of pressure reduced to sea level decrease from 1008 near the Caspian Sea to 995 in the far southeast. Iraq has pressures which decline from 1008 to 1003. Afghan isobar gradients slope from 1003 to about 995. Less is known of Arabian conditions, but the isobar lines tend to extend more nearly north and south, with pressures decreasing from 1004 near the Red Sea to less than 1000 along the Persian Gulf.

All of this reflects a weak gradient from the variable high pressure over Europe toward the steady low over the Persian Gulf and India. Winds thus tend to be northerly, with local variations between northwest and northeast.

Winter isobars are more irregular. In Turkey there is a local Black Sea low of 1018 millibars, but in general pressures decline southward from a maximum of 1020 in the extreme east, to 1017 along the Mediterranean. A low-pressure cell of 1016 millibars centers over Cyprus and southern Palestine; beyond this there is high pressure in North Africa. Syria likewise shows a gradient to the southwest, from 1019 to 1016 millibars. Iran and Afghanistan have more nearly east-west isobars, with pressures of 1023 millibars in the north decreasing to 1016 in southern Iran. Central Iraq is crossed by the 1017 millibar isobar, extending from northwest to southeast.

Arabian data are fragmentary but show a southerly gradient. Local high pressure areas develop over the Sahara and Arabia in winter, with an intervening trough over the Red Sea. This trough is sometimes displaced northward to join the strong Mediterranean low over Cyprus; when it moves eastward into southern Iraq, it brings an inflow of warm air into Mesopotamia from the Persian Gulf. As summer approaches, the Mediterranean low moves east to the Persian Gulf and beyond and becomes more intense.

Whereas summer pressures are relatively uniform, winter conditions are merely a statistical average resulting from the eastward parade of depressions and compressions. Nevertheless, the over-all pressure gradient in winter is strongly from the north and northeast, with winds blowing outward from the Siberian high toward the belt of low pressure which lies south of the equator.

Topography modifies these wind directions. Many mountain ranges exceed two miles in elevation so that local circulation may depart from the normal by ninety degrees.

While Turkey as a whole may average 1019 millibars in January and 1009 in July, and Iran has a similar range of 1021 to 1003, or Syria 1017 and 1005, this shift from winter high pressure to summer low pressure does not involve reversing winds, but is merely part of the continent-wide pattern.

Since there is no important shift in wind direction between summer and winter and since the temperature change from season to season is relatively rapid, spring and fall are only brief transitional periods. For the most part, Swasia has only two seasons, summer and winter.

In southernmost Arabia and Iran, the tendency for northerly winds is sometimes interrupted by the edge of the monsoon circulation over the Arabian Sea which brings winds with a southerly component. These winds may also be related to local low pressure areas in the interior of each country.

Calms are frequent in the basins of Turkey and Iran. Still other modifications are described in a later section on local winds.

Upper air movements are strongly from the west or northwest at all seasons. Our understanding of high level jet streams and their influence on surface weather is still incomplete. It appears that at times during winter, mid-latitude jet streams shift southward, and there is some suggestion that this shift is related to surface storm tracks. The development of high altitude aviation will call for a greatly increased study of the upper atmosphere and may in turn throw light on surface forecasts.

During winter months, five types of air masses enter Swasia. One brings dry continental polar air (cP) from Europe via Turkey. Comparable air arrives from a source area within the Soviet Union as an outburst from the Asiatic high pressure area. The third type supplies maritime polar air (mP) from the North Atlantic, modified by the loss of rain as it moves across Europe but adding moisture from the Mediterranean; this Atlantic air sometimes penetrates to Pakistan. Finally, tropical air masses occasionally arrive from the south, either dry continental tropical air (cT) coming from Africa, or moist maritime tropical air (mT) from the direction of the Red Sea or the Persian Gulf.

Associated with these air mass movements are migrating depressions or low pressure areas with cold fronts. Such conditions develop about every two weeks in winter. These cyclonic storms generally move eastward from the Mediterranean, in cases as far as India and even China. The path of these storm tracks across Southwest Asia varies widely; most of them pass south of Turkey and continue across Syria and Iran. Some paths lie near the Black Sea, others touch Arabia.

It has already been suggested that this variable weather is related to high level jet stream changes. There is also the possibility that it is related to pulsations in the size and position of the great Siberian high pressure area. As this enlarges and presses south and west, storm paths in southern Asia should be shifted toward the Equator.

LOCAL WINDS

Several local and seasonal winds deserve attention. The following paragraphs deal with the shamal, sirocco, foehn, dust storms, and others.

The *shamal* is a remarkably constant wind which blows down the Mesopotamian corridor from the north and northwest during four or five summer months, chiefly from June to September. In origin, this may be continental polar air, warmed during its passage across the Soviet Union and by subsidence. At this summer season there are no migrating depressions to interrupt the pressure gradient, so that the shamal blows steadily, often nine days out of ten. While strong during the day time, it usually lulls to a breeze at night. The term shamal comes from the Arabic word for "north," but it is commonly used only for summer winds.

The shamal brings extremely dry air, allowing intense penetration of the sun's heat to the surface of the land. The combination of solar insolation plus subsidence causes high temperatures which frequently rise to 120°F. Fortunately the breeze produces some cooling effect. Occasionally the shamal arrives late; June can then be the most uncomfortable month in the year, with

Water is in short supply in most parts of Swasia, as in the Khuzistan area of Iran. Many devices are used to bring it to the fields; here is a weighted pole arrangement known as a *shadoof*. (Courtesy Development and Resources Corp., New York.)

temperatures rising to 120°F. for several days, with little accompanying wind. At night radiation brings relief, for the thermometer may drop to the upper 70's, and most people sleep on the flat roofs. Dust storms and thin haze are frequent. Mirages may be associated with the over-heating of surface layers of the air.

Because of the intense heat and brilliant sun, people remain indoors during mid-day. Many older homes in Iraq have a basement living room or *sirdab*, sometimes well underground, which is used during the summer; shafts lead to wind vents on the roof which are turned away from the shamal in order to create a circulation. Evaporative coolers are widely used; these are simple arrangements allowing air to move through a moist screen, blown either by an electric fan or depending on the wind. So low is the humidity that large amounts of moisture are evaporated, thus yielding cool air. Such devices are impractical around the Persian Gulf where the humidity is too high.

While the shamal proper is limited to interior Syria, Jordan, Iraq, and western Iran, comparable hot dry winds are found elsewhere. The Seistan Basin of southeastern Iran and the Helmand Valley of southern Afghanistan are noted for the "Wind of 120 days," known in Persia as the *bad-i-sad-o-bist*. This blows steadily from the north and northwest from June to September, and is a gale of hot parched air, often filled with dust and salt. Velocities may reach seventy miles per hour, but the daily average is fifteen miles per hour. Northwest Iran has a similar wind known as the *bakharz,* meaning "where the wind blows."

Etesian winds have long been recognized along the shores of the Aegean. These also are steady northwest winds, which are appreciated in Turkey since they mitigate the summer heat and occasionally bring rain. They blow regularly and strongly from April to September. The word etesian, meaning annual, is of Greek origin; in Turkish the winds are called *meltimi*.

The *sirocco* is a dry, dusty desert wind which blows from the south and southeast. It thus involves a mass of continental tropical air. The sirocco is especially frequent in the early and late summer: April until early June, and September into November. In many places it may bring the highest temperatures of the year, even as early as March or as late as October.

As low-pressure areas move eastward across Syria, they draw in large volumes of heated air from Arabia. This continental tropical air is very dry and usually dusty. The first indication of the approach of a sirocco is a fall in barometric pressure and humidity, and the appearance of a dust haze. Daytime temperatures soon become excessively hot and oppressive. As the wind increases in velocity, occasionally reaching gale force, violent dust storms develop. The combination of high temperature and low humidity leads to excessive evapotranspiration, so that growing crops may be damaged by dessication.

While sirocco winds commonly last only a day at the beginning and end of their seasons, they may blow for three or four days when well developed. In some cases, the sirocco is more pronounced during the daytime; the wind begins shortly after sunrise, reaches a maximum in the early afternoon and ceases toward evening. This reflects instability in the continental tropical air mass, especially under the influence of diurnal heating. Velocities of over fifty miles per hour have been recorded, with relative humidities under 30 per cent. Temperatures usually exceed 100°F. except along the coasts. As the depression passes on, cool winds from the northwest suddenly replace the sirocco, causing temperatures to drop as much as 30°F. in two hours, with an increase in humidity from 30 to 80 per cent.

While the sirocco is a hot weather phenomenon, occasional dry and dusty east winds occur during the winter. These bring bitterly cold weather and are known as "cold siroccos."

The sirocco is well developed over Israel, Jordan, Lebanon, Syria, and Iraq. In Iran, the warm southeasterly wind in front of a depression is known as the *simoon,* or poison wind. In Egypt it is called a *khamsin,* Syria and Lebanon describe it as the *shlour,* in Iraq the term *sharqi* is used. Along the Persian Gulf, the sirocco is called *kaus,* and is sometimes followed by strong southwesterly gales called *swahili*.

Foehn winds develop when air crosses mountains and then moves downslope and warms through compression. Such conditions develop in the upper Tigris and Euphrates valleys, especially along the southern Taurus Mountains of Turkey. In summer months, this adiabatic warming may produce a temperature increase of 10°F. and a considerable decrease in relative humidity. Along the Black Sea Coast, winter winds which descend a mile or two from the Pontus Mountains and the Armenian Plateau may experience a temperature rise of 40°F. Similarly warm winds occur along the southern slopes of the Zagros and Makran ranges in Iran when air spills outward from the

Where wells are used, water may be raised by animals which walk down an inclined plane whose length measures the depth of the well. These donkeys are at Kharj in central Saudi Arabia. (Courtesy Standard Oil Co. of New Jersey.)

plateau. Where foehn winds follow valleys, the velocities may be high; this is especially true when they are attracted by low pressure areas in nearby deserts.

Along the coast of southern Iran in winter, there are sometimes northeast winds known as *nashi* which appear to represent an outflow of cold air from the plateau. As they descend there is some foehn warming effect. These nashi winds resemble the bora. Short-lived gales along the coasts of Syria and nearby Turkey, called *raghiehs,* are caused by outbursts of air from behind the Taurus Mountains. The winds rise suddenly and may last for two or three days. While there is presumably a warming effect, they are known chiefly for their hazard to shipping.

Dust storms are associated with strong, gusty winds and broad land surfaces covered with loose material such as river silts. Rarely can the wind move gravel, which remains as a desert pavement. Only with high velocities and considerable turbulence are sand particles lifted more than a few tens of feet or carried far; sand dunes advance by surface action. Silt, however, is easily picked up by light winds and may be carried to a height of many thousand feet and to distances in hundreds of miles.

True sand storms are rare, but all areas except the more humid portions of Swasia occasionally experience dust storms. These may range from a thin haze, which has traveled hundreds of miles from its source area, to solid black clouds where visibility is reduced to ten feet. While flying, it is not uncommon to see a sharp upper limit to a dust zone, perhaps at 5,000 feet, which extends to the horizon like a cloud bank. Such dust may persist for days. Airports, as at Baghdad, are occasionally closed for a few hours by dust storms.

A dust storm is usually defined as one in which the dust-laden wind reaches a force of four on the Beaufort scale, in other words, thirteen to eighteen miles per hour, with visibility less than 1,000 yards. Gustiness and turbulence are aids in keeping dust in suspension. The blackest storms often occur with the sharp rise in velocity which accompanies the front of a moving depression. Places in Iraq and Iran usually experience from four to twelve bad dust storms a year, and almost every month has days in which the visibility is less than a mile. Dust storms may occur at any season, but are less frequent after rainy periods while the ground is wet. Most summer dust storms come from the northwest, and appear to be associated with small variations in the pressure gradient, especially during the shamal.

The following account from an unknown writer describes a storm in southeastern Iran:

> At mid-day, the horizon became yellow, and a huge tawny cloud rolled towards us. The wind blew freshly but not hard and at the same time the whole sky became overcast. In a short time the squall had passed, leaving scattered sand-eddies careening over the ground. An hour later the phenomenon was repeated with greater force and denser clouds of sand, while thunder reverberated in the distance. An hour later more thunder occurred and a yellow bank of sand-cloud advanced rapidly from the west, greatly decreasing visibility. Soon afterwards the strong southeasterly wind returned, bringing with it more swirls of yellow dust.

TEMPERATURE

Since the over-all relief of swasia exceeds 25,000 feet, and the north to south extent is 2,060 miles, wide ranges in temperatures are to be expected.

The normal rise in temperature with decreasing altitude is 3.3°F. per 1,000 feet. Jerusalem lies at an elevation of 2,500 feet, while the Dead Sea is 1,286 feet below sea level; this implies a difference of 12.5°F. Jerusalem occasionally has snow, but it never falls on the Dead Sea. To the north lies Mt. Hermon, 9,232 feet, so that its average temperature should be 30.4°F. lower than corresponding positions at sea level; snow persists well into the summer.

Temperatures also increase equatorward. The annual average at Istanbul is 57°F. while 2,000 miles south at Aden the figure is 85°F. This is a change of some 1.4°F. per hundred miles, or 1°F. per degree of latitude.

Differences in the seasonal range of temperature are related to the moderating influence of the sea as compared with wide fluctuations which are found with continentality. Beirut, on the Mediterranean, has January and July averages of 57°F. and 80°F. respectively, whereas 900 miles due east at Tehran, which has an elevation of 4,000 feet, corresponding figures are 36°F. and 86°F.

Much of Southwest Asia has summer temperatures which are hot to very uncomfortable, reflecting the intensity of solar heating through the dry desert air. Only the mountains and some sea coasts are comfortable. At many stations, August is the warmest month, so that September may be hotter than June. Coastal Beirut reaches a mean daily maximum of 89°F. in August, whereas interior Damascus fifty miles east, has an average of 97°F. in August and also four months above 91°F. Baghdad, 450 miles farther inland, continuously has a mean daily maximum of 105°F. or over from June through September; May and October average 97°F. and 93°F. respectively. Similar interior influences are shown in Turkey. Istanbul has a mean daily maximum of 82°F. in both July and August, as compared with 86°F. for the same months in upland Ankara.

Temperatures of 100°F. or over may be

HIGHEST RECORDED TEMPERATURES[1]

Station	*°F.*	*Month*	*Months over 100° F. mean.*
Afghanistan			
Kabul	104°	August	2
Kandahar	111°	June	6
Arabian Peninsula			
Aden	106°	June	3
Jidda	117°	June	9
Kuwait	119°	June	8
Muscat	116°	June	8
Riyadh	113°	June and July	8
Iran			
Abadan	123°	August	7
Bushire	115°	August	8
Isfahan	108°	August	4
Seistan	119°	June	8
Tehran	109°	July and August	4
Iraq			
Baghdad	121°	July	7
Basra	123°	July	7
Mosul	124°	July	7
Levant			
Aleppo	117°	June	5
Amman	109°	June	6
Beirut	107°	May	3
Damascus	113°	August	5
Haifa	109°	June	6
Turkey			
Adana	109°	June, Aug. and Sept.	6
Ankara	100°	July and August	2
Izmir	108°	July	5
Sivas	98°	July	0
Urfa	115°	July	5

[1] Air Ministry, Meteorological Office, London: *Tables of Temperature, Relative Humidity and Precipitation for the World.* Part V, Asia (1958).

experienced almost anywhere in Swasia below a mile in elevation. Maximum data for the various countries are shown in the accompanying table. The highest recorded temperatures in Swasia appear to be in the plains of Khuzistan in southwestern Iran, where the thermometer has reached 129°F. in June. This may be compared with the world maximum of 136°F. recorded at Azizia in North Africa on September 13, 1922.

Mirage occurs when high ground temperatures warm the calm air near a flat surface so that its density differs from air immediately above. This distorts the line of sight and falsifies visual distances. As a result, distant scenes appear above the horizon, or there is a refraction which shows nonexistent objects. The appearance of lakes in the desert is due to the apparent lowering of the sky below the horizon.

Winters can be cold anywhere north of Arabia, abnormally so for the latitude, due to the steady invasion of polar air. The months of December, January, and February have about the same temperatures, especially in the west. March is sometimes as cold as February, but southerly sirocco winds may bring even during March the highest temperature of the year. Freezing temperatures occasionally occur at Beirut and Basra, both at sea level. Zero, Fahrenheit, is experienced in much of interior Iran and interior Turkey. Snow patches on the higher mountains persist through the summer, and the Elburz range has small glaciers.

The lowest recorded temperatures include —35°F. during February at Sivas in central Turkey; Tabriz, —18°F.; and —11°F. at Meshed in Iran during January.

Wide seasonal temperature range, as a measure of continentality, reaches its maximum for this realm in the interior of Turkey and Iran. An eastward sequence of Turkish and Iranian stations shows a difference between the average of the warmest and coldest months as follows: Izmir, 34°F.; Ankara, 41°F.; Erzurum, 51°F.; and Tabriz, 64°F.

PRECIPITATION

MOST OF SWASIA is inherently a transition zone, intermediate between the humid lands of midlatitudes and the rainy tropics well to the south. For half of the year much of the area is a desert; during the other half it ranges from wet to semiarid.

The pressures and wind patterns of Southwest Asia are such that, even if all mountain barriers and bordering seas were removed, the landscape would be characteristically brown. Arabia, Syria, and Iraq would still average five inches of rain or less, while Turkey and northern Iran might receive fifteen inches. Both the amount and the duration of the rain diminish southward. Much of the moisture is of Atlantic origin, although the six surrounding seas make local contributions.

The actual pattern of precipitation is far from uniform. Great ranges stand in the path of the winds, and as the air rises over these barriers, it is cooled and forced to yield its moisture. Few highland weather records are available; but at the base of the Pontus Mountains in northeastern Turkey, the Black Sea port of Rize registers an average of 105 inches, and the mountains are presumably much wetter.

At the other extreme in moisture are dry areas in the lee of mountains, or locations where the circulation is such that rain is rarely to be expected. Large areas in southern Arabia and southeastern Iran seldom experience rain. Years may pass with scarcely a drop, and one might conclude that they are truly rainless; then a sudden shower demonstrates that precipitation may occur. To say that a station's average is one or two inches a year, only means that there may be ten to twenty inches brought by the few sporadic storms in the course of a decade. Even this average is so uncertain that it may require a century or two to establish a fair record.

The bulk of the area has Mediterranean type winter rain or snow and summer drought. The chief exceptions are the extreme north and the far south. The northern parts of Turkey and Iran reach the middle latitudes, an area with migrating depressions which occasionally bring summer rain. Most Black and Caspian sea stations have at least one inch every month throughout the year. Southernmost Arabia borders on the monsoon area, although it is too far off to yield more than a minimum of rain. The highlands of Yemen thus have a summer peak.

The increasing aridity eastward from the Mediterranean is shown by the computations of Combier.[1] On the basis of the formula of Emberger, he finds the following monthly distributions by type.

Three mechanisms account for the pre-

[1] Charles Combier: "Apercu sur Les Climates de la Syria et du Lebon," Beirut (1954), pamphlet.

MONTHLY DURATION OF CLIMATIC TYPES

	Desert	*Arid*	*Dry*	*Subhumid*	*Humid*
Beirut	0	5	2	2	3
Damascus	5	3	1	2	1
Baghdad	6	2	3	1	0

cipitation: orographic, frontal, or convectional displacement; these are related to topography, to cyclonic storms, or to sharp thermal movements.

The most obvious explanation for the distribution of rainfall lies in the mountain systems. Each of the great ranges, the Pontus, Taurus, Lebanon, Elburz, and Zagros, receive heavy precipitation on their windward sides. This usually exceeds thirty-five inches; at many stations the total is over eighty inches.

All of lowland Swasia is dry; only windward slopes receive as much as 20 inches. Large areas average less than 5 inches a year, some of them no more than half this amount, whereas precipitation reaches 100 inches on the mountains facing the Black and Caspian seas. (Based on Douglas B. Carter; except the Arabian Peninsula: Edgar Rosenan, Laboratory of Climatology.)

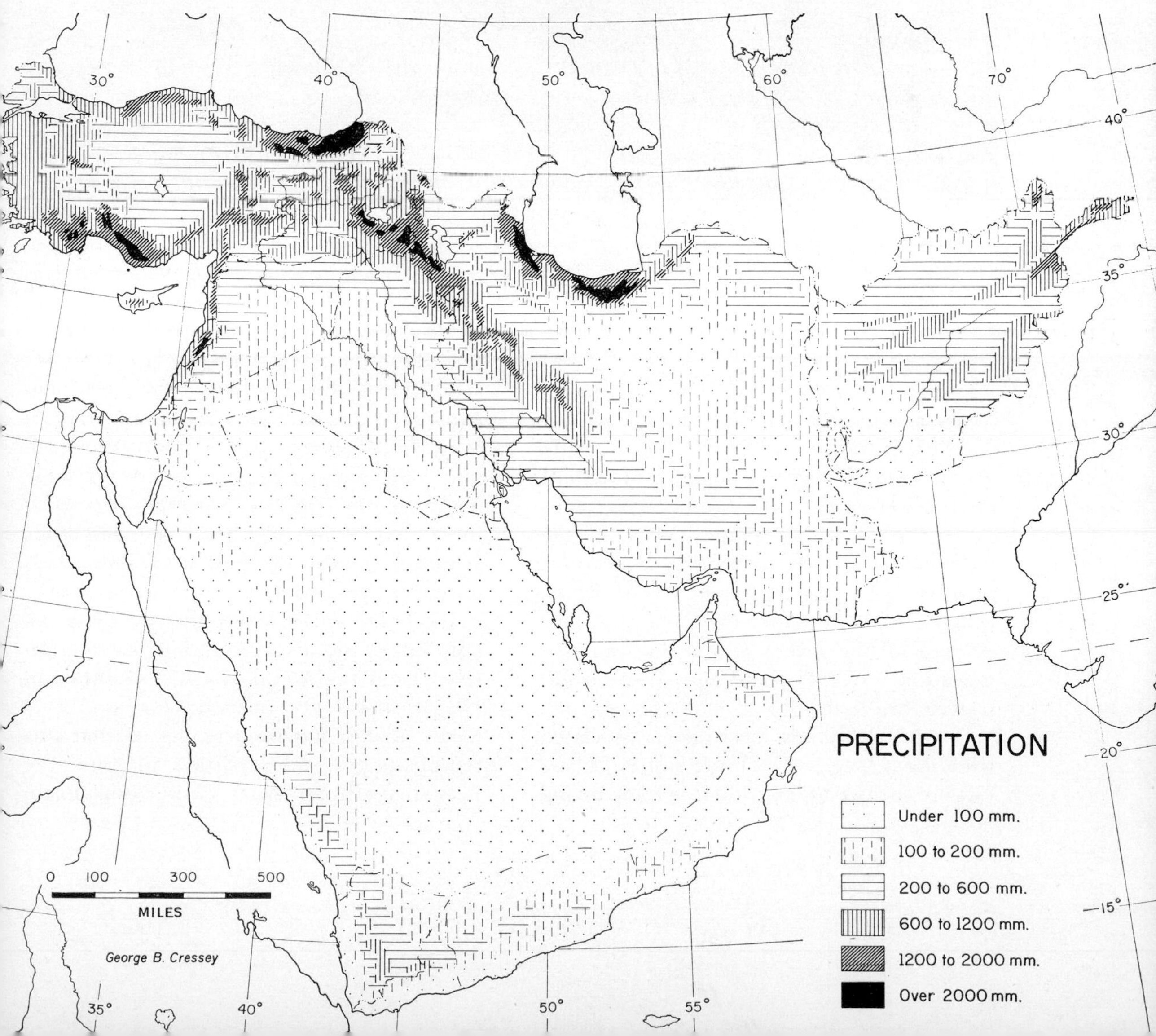

Heavy snow covers most higher mountains and persists well into the summer months to feed the lowland rivers. Here is Mount Olympus in Turkey. (Courtesy Turkish Press, Broadcasting, and Tourist Dept., Ankara.)

Snow surveys are unavailable, but upper slopes accumulate ten to twenty feet and more, and snow remains well into the summer or even throughout the year. Mountain roads are frequently blocked by snow. This carry-over of winter precipitation in the form of a snow reservoir is a priceless natural asset since it enables many rivers, which would otherwise be dry in summer, to flow throughout the year. Without this source of irrigation water, lowland agriculture could scarcely be carried on.

Over the lowlands, most rain is associated with the passage of cyclonic storms. These low pressure areas, with their accompanying fronts, parade eastward from the Mediterranean several times a month during the winter. Cyclonic storms do not always yield rain, but where there is a strong inflow of humid air in the southeast quadrant and an accompanying indraft of cool air to undercut it from the northwest, frontal action may produce showers. Such precipitation is commonly gentle and may continue for two or three days. Where a pronounced cold front advances rapidly, rainfall may amount to several inches in a day.

While the source of this moisture presumably lies in the distant Atlantic, some is derived from the Mediterranean. Rainfall in Iraq is usually associated with southerly winds, and it has been suggested that this represents tropical maritime air from the Persian Gulf. Northern Turkey and northern Iran may also derive some moisture from the adjoining Black and Caspian seas. The various seas which border Swasia have a limited capacity to yield much moisture. If the evaporation amounts to one-fifth of an inch per day, and if it takes half a day for air to cross the Red Sea or bodies of similar size, not much precipitation can result. Clearly, a long period is required for an air mass to pick up much maritime moisture.

The maximum precipitation to be expected from frontal action is unknown, but it might be considerable. For instance, a well developed depression which remains stationary for several days over Iraq and eastern Syria, with a front extending roughly from north to south, may draw large masses of moist air from the south over the valleys of the Tigris and Euphrates. This air would converge into a funnel, marked on the left by the front and to the right by the confining Zagros Mountains. Such conditions could well yield several inches of rain a day for several days, thus causing concentrated runoff and exceptionally high flood levels. If well developed and recurrent within a week, Baghdad might be seriously inundated.

The third cause of rain is buoyant lifting, where convectional action locally raises a column of air high enough to cause saturation, condensation, and precipitation. In humid lands, this is usually a summer phenomenon, but in Southwest Asia the air is then so dry that the condensation level may be too high.

Many stations report periods of concentrated rainfall, even an inch an hour or three or four inches in a day. In some cases, these involve thunderstorms and hail.

Variability in rainfall from year to year, even in moderately rainy climates, may show an extreme ratio of 50 per cent between the total in wet and dry years; in dry lands the ratio increases. Precipitation records for Jerusalem show an average of 22 inches; seven years in sequence give totals of 40, 26, 17, 14, 44, 14, and 24 inches. As many as fourteen successive years have been below the average, with a sequence of eight years above the average. At Bushire, on the Persian Gulf, a six-year sequence brought 14, 13, 2, 15, 24, and 8 inches.

In an area of variable and little understood rainfall, one cannot safely predict without a long period of observation. Biel has suggested that eighty years of records are required for Iraq in order to achieve the same measure of reliability as given by thirty years of records in humid lands. Even this is not really enough, since new extremes are continually being established. Once in a century, or once in a thousand years, there are exceptional rains. The only certainty is that the known rainfall data are an inadequate guide; the ultimate maximum or minimum may differ widely from past experience, even by 100 per cent.

While the humidity is characteristically low, the rainy shores of the Caspian Sea and the desert margins of the Persian and Oman gulfs both experience relative humidities of 80 to 90 per cent. Along the damp Caspian Sea coast, malaria was so prevalent in the rice areas that it led to the expression among the hill people of "Go to Gilan and die." High, sticky humidities also prevail near the Mediterranean and Black seas. The combination of temperatures around 120°F. and humidities of 70 per cent make the shores of the Red Sea and Persian Gulf among the most uncomfortable places in the world. When the air is stagnant and there is negligible evaporation from one's lungs, body temperatures may rise to 108°F. and heat stroke may occur.

WATER REQUIREMENTS

WHILE PRECIPITATION MAPS express the total intake of moisture from the atmosphere, they do not reflect the amount needed to support vegetation or to balance evaporation. The amount of moisture required in a given area,

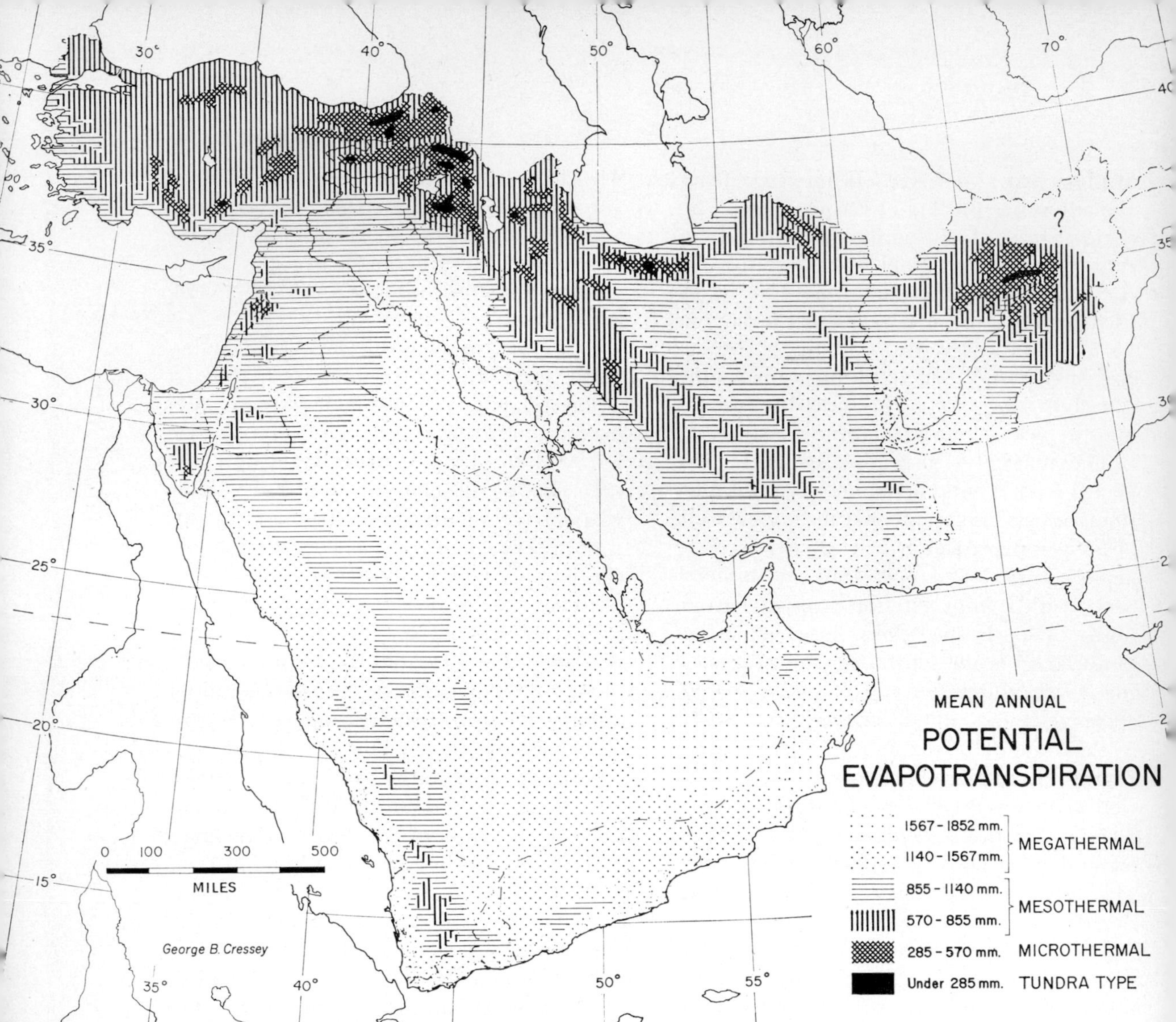

Evapotranspiration is a measure of water in the ground or plants in terms of the energy available for its conversion into atmospheric moisture. The over-all aridity of Southwest Asia is obvious. Parts of highland Turkey, Iran, and Afghanistan receive almost enough precipitation to balance potential evaporation, but in the southern corner of Arabia the evapotranspiration capacity reaches 75 inches. Even the cultivated areas of Iraq have figures of 35 inches. (Douglas B. Carter, Laboratory of Climatology.)

in other words the thirstiness of the air, depends on the heat available for evaporation and transpiration; this has been termed by Thornthwaite the potential evapotranspiration. Where this varies from the precipitation, there is a water surplus or a water deficit. While these items cannot readily be measured directly everywhere, they may be mapped by formulae which include factors such as elevation and latitude.

The soil acts as a bank, receiving deposits from rain or snow and allowing withdrawals through evaporation. Evaporation is largely a matter of available energy, for some 80 per cent of solar energy will be devoted to the evaporation process if moisture is present, either from ground water or from vegetation.

Examples from Turkey and Iran, month by month, are shown in the accompanying

WATER BALANCE FOR IZMIR, TURKEY[1]

	Jan.	*Feb.*	*Mar.*	*Apr.*	*May*	*June*	*July*	*Aug.*	*Sep.*	*Oct.*	*Nov.*	*Dec.*	*Year*
Potential evapotranspiration	13	16	51	54	97	148	179	163	104	67	35	18	945
Precipitation	115	96	63	47	33	9	4	1	20	62	75	112	637
Soil moisture utilization, or recharge	102	30	0	−7	−57	−88	−66	−35	−12	−1	40	94	
Soil moisture storage[2]	270	300	300	293	236	148	82	47	35	34	74	168	
Actual evapotranspiration	13	16	51	54	90	97	70	36	32	63	35	18	575
Water deficit	0	0	0	0	7	51	109	127	72	4	0	0	370
Water surplus	0	50	12	0	0	0	0	0	0	0	0	0	62

[1] In millimeters.
[2] Computed on the basis of 300 mm. capacity in the root zone according to the method of C. W. Thornthwaite and J. R. Mather: "The Water Balance," *Publications in Climatology,* VIII, No. 1, 1955.

WATER BALANCE FOR ISFAHAN, IRAN[1]

	Jan.	*Feb.*	*Mar.*	*Apr.*	*May*	*June*	*July*	*Aug.*	*Sep.*	*Oct.*	*Nov.*	*Dec.*	*Year*
Potential evapotranspiration	2	7	25	55	102	154	178	155	110	61	23	5	877
Precipitation	17	11	24	15	5	1	1	0	1	4	14	22	115
Soil moisture utilization or recharge	15	4	0	−5	−9	−10	−7	−3	−1	−1	0	17	
Soil moisture storage[2]	35	39	39	34	25	15	8	5	4	3	3	20	
Actual evapotranspiration	2	7	24	20	14	11	8	3	2	5	14	5	115
Water deficit	0	0	1	35	88	143	170	152	108	56	9	0	762
Water surplus	0	0	0	0	0	0	0	0	0	0	0	0	0

[1] In millimeters.
[2] See footnote under table for Izmir.

table.[1] Potential evapotranspiration represents the demand; when this does not correspond with precipitation, soil moisture is stored or depleted. At Izmir during February and March, the available soil moisture in the root zone exceeds its storage capacity of 300 millimeters (twelve inches), so that there is a water surplus in these months. At Isfahan there is rarely enough water to fully charge the soil, so that a water deficit persists throughout the year.

The monthly rainfall and withdrawals from soil moisture contribute to the actual evapotranspiration; the water deficit is the difference between the actual and potential evapotranspiration. On the basis of similar computations for 400 stations, Douglas B. Carter has prepared maps of Potential Evapotranspiration, Water Deficit, and Water Surplus for all of Southwest Asia.

The variation of average annual evapotranspiration with temperature as related to latitude is obvious; it is equally true with altitude. Near the Dead Sea the figure is 1,450 mm. (fifty-seven inches), whereas due west at Hebron, 4,200 feet higher, the amount drops to 850 mm. (thirty-three inches). A comparable situation is found in southwestern Arabia where the evapotranspiration decreases from 1,927 mm. (seventy-six inches) at Kamaran Island in the Red Sea to 824 mm. (thirty-two inches) at San'a in Yemen at an elevation of 8,000 feet.

The map of potential evapotranspiration may be divided into five main categories according to the energy involved: megathermal, mesothermal, microthermal, tundra, and frost. In general, megathermal climates, with their large energy potential, cover the lowlands south of latitude 35°N. In this area, the potential evaporation varies from 1,140 mm (forty-five inches) to a maximum of slightly more than 1,900 mm. (seventy-five inches) along the shores of southwest Arabia. The maximum monthly amounts in Iraq and interior Iran even exceed those for the Sahara. The dryness of these Asiatic areas is shown by the fact that the evapotranspiration figure for July exceeds 220 mm. (nine inches). This is only moderately more than that in January, so that aridity continues the year around.

Mesothermal climates characterize Turkey, the Levant, northern Iraq, and the highlands of Iran and Afghanistan. The moisture requirement varies from 570 mm. (twenty-two inches) to 1,140 mm. (forty-five inches). Since there is a cold winter, the January evapotranspiration is only ten to twenty mm. (0.4 to 0.8 inches). In contrast, peak requirements in summer are from 150 to 200 mm. (six to eight inches) per month.

Microthermal climates have rates of 285 to 570 mm. per year (eleven to twenty-two inches). Freezing temperatures are common in winter, so that the available energy for evapotranspiration is low, and most of the precipitation is stored as snow or as soil moisture.

Tundra type climates, with less than 285 mm. (eleven inches) of potential evapotranspiration, are found only on the highest mountain peaks of the Taurus, Elburz, and Hindu Kush, with elevations above 12,000 feet, 15,000 feet, and 16,500 feet, respectively. A snow cover persists for eight or nine months a year, although July may have up to 100 mm. (four inches) of potential evapotranspiration. True frost climates, with large permanent snow fields, occur only on Mt. Ararat and Mt. Demavend.

The pattern of water deficit shows that drought conditions are persistent and extreme throughout dry Asia. The work of Carter on water balance now makes it possible to understand its intensity and dura-

[1] This table and certain of the following descriptions are taken from Douglas B. Carter: "Maps of Water Requirements for Southwest Asia," Centerton, New Jersey: C. W. Thornthwaite Associates (1957), (Prepared for UNESCO, Advisory Committee on Arid Zone Research).

tion. Across Southwest Asia, water deficit ranges from less than 100 mm. (four inches) in the most humid areas near the Black Sea and in the adjoining mountains to over 1,852 mm. (seventy-three inches) in southwest Arabia.

Areas with a water deficit of under 200 mm. (eight inches) occupy a third of Turkey, largely in the north; a third of Afghanistan, chiefly in the highlands; the Elburz Mountains of Iran; and the Lebanese highlands. These are either regions of abundant precipitation or of low temperatures. Even in these areas with a satisfactory annual balance, several months may show a water shortage. On an annual basis, few localities have a water surplus.

Areas with deficits of 200 to 800 mm. (eight to thirty-two inches) generally lie at moderate elevations, largely north of latitude 30°N. which is near the heads of the Red Sea and the Persian Gulf. Soil moisture storage in winter provides a carry over for the maturing of winter sown crops, but summer cultivation is impossible without irrigation.

Areas with over 800 mm. (thirty-two inches) of water deficit are clearly to be classed as desert and steppe. In this area drought conditions continue for most of the year, although low winter temperatures during the rainy season may create a balance in some months. Agriculture is possible only with irrigation, usually to be supplied from outside the area, and vegetation for grazing is unreliable. The area with a water deficit of 800 mm. and over includes all of lowland Arabia, Israel, Jordan, Syria, Iraq, and Afghanistan. This area measures about a 1.5 million square miles. Here, aridity dominates all of life.

CLIMATIC REGIONS

The two leading schemes of climatic classification are those of Koeppen and Thornthwaite. These involve mathematical relations between rainfall and evaporation as related to temperature. The Koeppen and Thornthwaite systems differ somewhat, especially in the recognition of subhumid climates; moreover, the Thornthwaite system is more complex, involving several elements of the water balance. Although a greater variety of climate types is available in the Thornthwaite system, the broadest groupings are not essentially different from the conventional Koeppen regions.

None of Koeppen's tropical humid "A" climates are present in Swasia, and there are only limited highland areas of humid low temperature or microthermal "D" climates. Tundra "E" conditions prevail only on a few mountain peaks. Most of the realm is dominated by desert "BW," steppe "BS," or by Mediterranean-type dry summer mesothermal "Cs" climates.

In the Koeppen system, subtropical desert climates, "BW," cover all of eastern Arabia and a strip along the Red Sea. They extend north into Syria and include much of Iraq, the Iranian lowland along the Persian Gulf and the Arabian sea, eastern Iran, and both southern and northern Afghanistan. Desert climates are the most extensive of all climatic types in Swasia, accounting for almost half of the entire realm. The boundaries are drawn in terms of relations between rainfall and temperature, but almost everywhere the precipitation is under five inches. Since this occurs during the winter, and year-round temperatures are mild, the Koeppen symbols might be expanded to "BWCs."

Semiarid steppe conditions, Koeppen's "BS," are found in the uplands of western Arabia and in Oman, in central Turkey, and in an arc from Jordan through Syria and Iraq to western Iran. This last area accounts for the Fertile Crescent, thus forming a continuous grassland for nomadic travellers from Mesopotamia to Palestine.

Large areas of semiarid climate are also included in northern and southern Iran and

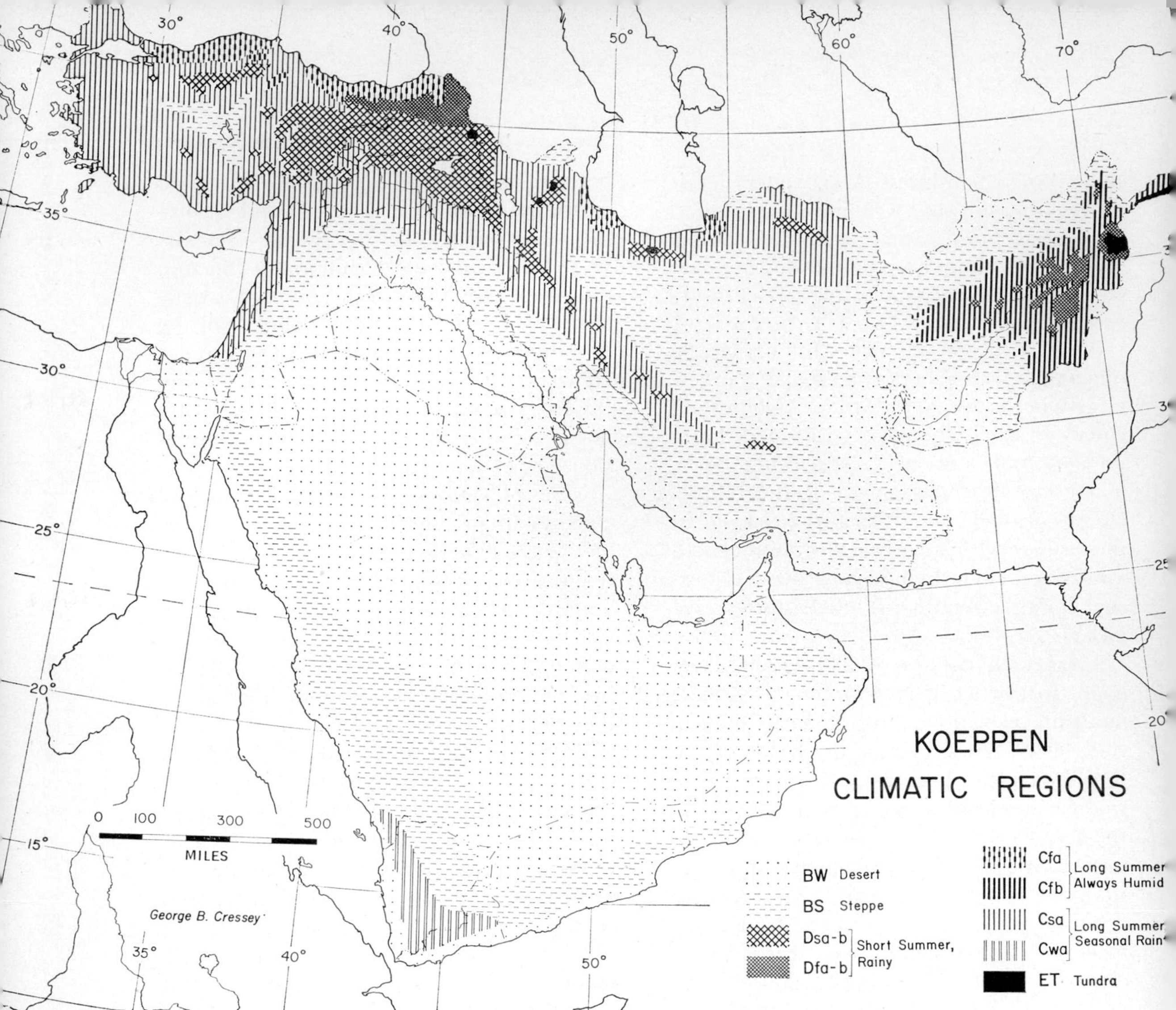

This map follows the Koeppen system of climatic classification, and suggests the great diversity of environments within the area. Mediterranean-type climatic conditions in Turkey, the Levant, and parts of Iran resemble those in the humid American southwest, while Arabia and interior Iran somewhat match the Mohave and Sonoran deserts.
"B" climates are dry, divided into BW for desert and BS for steppe. "C" and "D" are rainy climates with moderate temperatures and long or short summers, respectively. "E" represents high altitude or arctic conditions. Lower case letters are used as follows "a," hot summer; "b," cool summers; "f," always humid; "s," dry summer; "w," dry winter. (Compiled by Hassan Al-Khayat.)

in northern and southern Afghanistan, intermediate between the humid mountains and the desert basins. In total extent, "BS" steppe climates occupy about one-fifth of all Swasia. In practice, it is difficult to draw a precise boundary between "BW" and "BS" climates since they are gradational and meteorological data are limited. Some Koeppen-style maps class as steppe much that is otherwise mapped as desert.

Subtropical Mediterranean type climates with winter rain, "Cs," and either hot, "a," or cool, "b," summers are the characteristic types across much of inhabited Swasia. This is a delightful year-around climate, rarely uncomfortable in winter although rather hot in summer. In its distribution, it extends along the Aegean and Mediterranean to the

CLIMATIC TABLES[1]

Country and City	Years of Record	Elevation in feet	Jan.	Feb.	Mar.	Apr.	May	Jun.	July	Aug.	Sept.	Oct.	Nov.	Dec.	Year
			Monthly average temperature in °F., and precipitation in inches												
AFGHANISTAN															
Kabul	9	5,955′	27°	31°	44°	55°	65°	72°	77°	75°	68°	58°	48°	37°	54°
			1.2″	1.4″	3.7″	4.0″	0.8″	0.2″	0.1″	0.1″	0.0″	0.6″	0.8″	0.4″	13.3″
Kandahar	7	3,462′	44°	49°	57°	67°	75°	81°	84°	81°	72°	65°	55°	45°	64°
			3.1″	1.7″	0.8″	0.3″	0.2″	0.0″	0.1″	0.0″	0.0″	0.0″	0.0″	0.8″	7.0″
ARABIA															
Aden	6	22′	77°	78°	81°	83°	87°	91°	90°	89°	90°	84°	80°	78°	84°
			0.2″	0.0″	0.2″	0.0″	0.0″	0.0″	0.2″	0.1″	0.0″	0.0″	0.0″	0.2″	0.9″
Bahrein	16	18′	63°	65°	69°	77°	85°	89°	92°	93°	89°	83°	76°	64°	79°
			0.3″	0.7″	0.5″	0.3″	0.0″	0.0″	0.0″	0.0″	0.0″	0.0″	0.7″	0.7″	3.2″
Jidda	5	20′	75°	75°	76°	81°	85°	86°	89°	90°	87°	84°	81°	77°	83°
			0.2″	0.0″	0.0″	0.0″	0.0″	0.0″	0.0″	0.0″	0.0″	0.0″	1.0″	1.2″	2.5″
Kuwait	14	16′	55°	58°	66°	76°	86°	90°	95°	95°	91°	82°	70°	59°	77°
			0.9″	0.9″	1.1″	0.2″	0.0″	0.0″	0.0″	0.0″	0.0″	0.1″	0.6″	1.1″	5.1″
Muscat	23	15′	72°	72°	78°	84°	92°	94°	92°	88°	88°	86.5°	79.5°	73.5°	84°
			1.1″	0.7″	0.4″	0.4″	0.0″	0.1″	0.0″	0.0″	0.0″	0.1″	0.4″	0.7″	3.9″
Riyadh	3	1,938′	58°	61°	69°	77°	86°	92°	93°	91°	87°	78°	70°	60°	77°
			0.1″	0.8″	0.9″	1.0″	0.4″	0.0″	0.0″	0.0″	0.0″	0.0″	0.0″	0.0″	3.2″
IRAN															
Abadan	10	7′	54°	59°	66°	76°	89°	93°	97°	97°	90°	81°	69°	58°	77°
			1.5″	1.7″	0.6″	0.8″	0.1″	0.0″	0.0″	0.0″	0.0″	0.1″	1.0″	1.8″	7.6″
Bushire	53	14′	58°	59°	66°	74°	83°	87°	90°	91°	87°	80°	71°	62°	76°
			2.9″	1.8″	0.8″	0.4″	0.0″	0.0″	0.0″	0.0″	0.0″	0.1″	1.6″	3.2″	10.8″
Isfahan	22	5,817′	36°	41°	49°	59°	69°	77°	83°	80°	73°	62°	50°	41°	60°
			0.6″	0.4″	1.0″	0.6″	0.2″	0.0″	0.0″	0.0″	0.0″	0.1″	0.6″	0.8″	4.3″
Kerman	7	6,100′	43°	46°	52°	62°	74°	83°	83°	79°	72°	64°	53°	44°	63°
			0.5″	0.9″	0.9″	0.7″	0.1″	0.2″	0.0″	0.0″	0.0″	0.0″	0.5″	1.4″	5.4″
Meshed	25	3,104′	33°	38°	46°	57°	68°	75°	78°	75°	67°	57°	48°	39°	57°
			0.8″	1.0″	2.2″	1.8″	1.2″	0.3″	0.1″	0.0″	0.0″	0.4″	0.6″	0.7″	9.1″
Seistan	30	2,000′	46°	52°	60°	72°	81°	88°	92°	89°	81°	70°	58°	48°	70°
			0.4″	0.4″	0.6″	0.1″	0.0″	0.0″	0.0″	0.0″	0.0″	0.6″	0.5″	0.3″	2.9″
Teheran	22	4,002′	36°	41°	49°	60°	70°	80°	86°	84°	77°	65°	53°	42°	62°
			1.8″	1.5″	1.8″	1.4″	0.5″	0.1″	0.1″	0.1″	0.1″	0.3″	0.8″	1.2″	9.7″

CLIMATIC TABLES (*Continued*)

Country and City	Years of Record	Elevation in feet	Monthly average temperature in °F., and precipitation in inches												
			Jan.	Feb.	Mar.	Apr.	May	Jun.	July	Aug.	Sept.	Oct.	Nov.	Dec.	Year
IRAQ															
Baghdad	15	111′	50°	53°	60°	71°	82°	89°	93°	93°	87°	76°	64°	53°	73°
			0.9″	1.0″	1.1″	0.5″	0.1″	0.0″	0.0″	0.0″	0.0″	0.1″	0.8″	1.0″	5.5″
Basra	10	8′	55°	58°	65°	74°	86°	91°	93°	92°	87°	79°	69°	59°	76°
			1.4″	1.1″	1.2″	1.2″	0.2″	0.0″	0.0″	0.0″	0.0″	0.0″	1.4″	0.8″	7.3″
Mosul	26	730′	45°	48°	54°	63°	75°	84°	91°	90°	82°	70°	59°	48°	67°
			2.8″	3.1″	2.1″	1.9″	0.7″	0.0″	0.0″	0.0″	0.0″	0.2″	1.9″	2.4″	15.0″
Rutba	22	2,019′	45°	48°	53°	64°	74°	81°	86°	86°	80°	71°	58°	48°	66°
			0.6″	0.6″	0.6″	0.7″	0.3″	0.0″	0.0″	0.0″	0.0″	0.2″	0.4″	0.9″	4.3″
ISRAEL															
Eilat	7	7′	60°	63°	68°	76°	84°	88°	91°	92°	88°	81°	72°	64°	77°
			0.0″	0.3″	0.3″	0.2″	0.0″	0.0″	0.0″	0.0″	0.0″	0.0″	0.0″	0.3″	1.1″
Haifa	16	33′	57°	59°	62°	68°	74°	78°	82°	83°	81°	77°	69°	61°	71°
			6.9″	4.3″	1.6″	1.0″	0.2″	0.0″	0.0″	0.0″	0.1″	1.0″	3.7″	7.3″	26.1″
Jerusalem	19	2,485′	48°	49°	56°	62°	69°	73°	75°	76°	74°	70°	62°	52°	63°
			5.2″	5.2″	2.5″	1.1″	0.1″	0.0″	0.0″	0.0″	0.0″	0.5″	2.8″	3.4″	20.8″
JORDAN															
Amman	25	2,548′	47°	48°	52°	61°	70°	74°	77°	78°	75°	69°	60°	51°	63°
			2.7″	2.9″	1.2″	0.6″	0.2″	0.0″	0.0″	0.0″	0.0″	0.2″	1.3″	1.8″	10.9″
LEBANON															
Beirut	62	111′	57°	57°	60°	65°	71°	76°	80°	82°	80°	75°	67°	60°	69°
			7.5″	6.2″	3.7″	2.2″	0.7″	0.1″	0.0″	0.0″	0.2″	2.0″	5.2″	7.3″	35.1″
Ksara	10	3,018′	43°	45°	51°	58°	65°	71°	74°	76°	72°	65°	56°	47°	60°
			4.8″	6.5″	1.9″	1.7″	0.5″	0.0″	0.0″	0.0″	0.0″	0.7″	2.7″	4.2″	23.2″
SYRIA															
Aleppo	8	1,280′	42°	47°	52°	62°	71°	79°	83°	83°	77°	68°	56°	46°	64°
			3.5″	2.5″	1.5″	1.1″	0.3″	0.1″	0.0″	0.0″	0.0″	1.0″	2.2″	3.3″	15.5″
Damascus	13	2,362′	45°	48°	54°	62°	70°	76°	80°	82°	76°	68°	57°	48°	64°
			1.7″	1.7″	0.3″	0.5″	0.1″	0.0″	0.0″	0.0″	0.7″	0.4″	1.6″	1.6″	8.6″
Deir-ez-Zor	5	699′	44°	48°	56°	66°	77°	85°	92°	90°	84°	71°	59°	48°	78°
			1.6″	0.8″	0.3″	0.8″	0.1″	0.0″	0.0″	0.0″	0.0″	0.2″	1.5″	0.9″	6.2″

CLIMATIC TABLES (*Continued*)

Country and City	*Years of Record*	*Elevation in feet*	*Jan.*	*Feb.*	*Mar.*	*Apr.*	*May*	*Jun.*	*July*	*Aug.*	*Sept.*	*Oct.*	*Nov.*	*Dec.*	*Year*
			Monthly average temperature in °F., and precipitation in inches												
TURKEY															
Adana	21	82′	48°	50°	56°	63°	71°	78°	82°	83°	79°	71°	62°	52°	66°
			4.3″	4.0″	2.5″	1.6″	2.0″	0.7″	0.2″	0.2″	0.7″	1.9″	2.4″	3.8″	24.3″
Ankara	26	2,825′	32°	34°	41°	52°	61°	66°	73°	73°	65°	57°	47°	36°	53°
			1.3″	1.2″	1.3″	1.3″	1.9″	1.0″	0.5″	0.4″	0.7″	0.9″	1.2″	1.9″	13.6″
Erzurum	16	6,402′	16°	20°	27°	41°	52°	58°	66°	67°	59°	48°	37°	24°	43°
			1.4″	1.6″	2.0″	2.5″	3.1″	2.1″	1.3″	0.9″	1.1″	2.3″	1.8″	1.1″	21.2″
Istanbul [2]	50		41°	40°	45°	53°	61°	69°	74°	74°	68°	62°	54°	45°	57°
			3.2″	2.7″	2.5″	1.6″	1.2″	1.3″	1.2″	1.7″	2.0″	2.7″	3.6″	4.8″	28.8″
Izmir	39	92′	47°	49°	53°	60°	68°	75°	81°	81°	74°	66°	58°	50°	63°
			4.4″	3.3″	3.0″	1.7″	1.3″	0.6″	0.2″	0.2″	0.8″	2.1″	3.3″	4.8″	25.5″
Kars	18	5,741′	11°	14°	23°	39°	51°	57°	63°	64°	56°	46°	34°	19°	40°
			1.1″	1.1″	1.1″	1.7″	3.4″	2.9″	2.1″	2.1″	1.2″	1.6″	1.2″	1.0″	20.5″
Samsun	24	131′	44°	45°	47°	52°	60°	67°	72°	73°	68°	63°	56°	49°	58°
			2.9″	2.6″	2.7″	2.3″	1.8″	1.5″	1.5″	1.3″	2.4″	3.2″	3.5″	3.4″	29.1″
Trabzon	14	354′	45°	45°	46°	52°	61°	68°	73°	74°	69°	64°	56°	49°	59°
			2.8″	2.7″	2.3″	2.2″	1.7″	1.9″	1.8″	1.6″	2.7″	3.2″	4.0″	3.0″	29.9″
Van	9	5,682′	26°	26°	32°	43°	54°	63°	70°	70°	63°	52°	43°	30°	48°
			2.2″	1.6″	2.0″	2.3″	1.4″	0.6″	0.2″	0.1″	0.3″	2.0″	1.5″	1.3″	15.5″

[1] Data from: Air Ministry, Meteorological Office: *Tables of Temperature, Relative Humidity and Precipitation for the World, Part V, Asia,* London: H. M. Stationery Office (1958). Monthly temperatures derived from average of daily maximum and minimum temperatures.

[2] Data for Istanbul from: British Admiralty, Naval Intelligence Division: Turkey, Vol I. (1942).

Sinai Peninsula, thus including the bulk of western and southern Turkey and the coastal Levant. Farther east, "Cs" climates occur in northern Iraq and occupy large areas in the Elburz and Zagros ranges of Iran. Similar Mediterranean climates, but with shorter summers and colder winters, "Ds," are present in eastern Turkey.

While the area of proper Mediterranean "Cs" climate amounts to only one-sixth of Southwest Asia, if one adds the regions of "Ds," and includes areas of the "BW" and "BS" which also have a Mediterranean rhythm, the total extent of winter period rainfall occupies more than nine-tenths of the realm.

Several other climatic types are to be added. Along the shores of the Black and Caspian seas, rain may occur at all seasons so that the Koeppen symbol is "Cf." At higher elevations in eastern Turkey and central Afghanistan, the classification would be "Df."

An area of humid mesothermal climate with summer rain "Cw" is found in the highlands of Yemen due to the influence of the monsoon circulation which is derived from the Ethiopian Highlands.

In the Thornthwaite system of climate classification, five humidity categories and five energy, or thermal, provinces are represented. Neither the perhumid nor humid climates occur in the hottest or megathermal zone of Swasia. Although perhumid climates occupy small areas along the coasts of the Black and the Caspian seas in the milder mesothermal energy zone, most perhumid and humid climates are found in higher mountain regions where there is only enough energy for a microthermal or lower designation. Subhumid climates are excluded from the megathermal province, but they occupy mainly the Mediterranean shore area and an upper mesothermal and microthermal zone in the mountain ranges from Turkey to Iran.

According to Thornthwaite, the valley bottoms, especially in Turkey, Iraq, and western Iran, have semiarid climates, with either mesothermal or megathermal conditions. These semiarid climates occur at progressively higher elevations from central Turkey to the mountains of Afghanistan. Arid climates occupy nearly all the lowlands south of the Elburz and east of the Zagros in Iran, and the area east of the Levant Highlands extending southward to all of Arabia except the highest zone in the southwest. On the Thornthwaite maps of water balance prepared by Carter and previously described, arid climate is the dominant influence in Swasia. Wherever megathermal conditions exist, and wherever deficits are moderate or large (more than eight inches of deficiency) the climate is arid, according to the Thornthwaite system.

REFERENCES

* Air Ministry, Meteorological Office: TABLES OF TEMPERATURE, RELATIVE HUMIDITY AND PRECIPATION FOR THE WORLD, PART V, ASIA. London: H. M. Stationery Office (1958). [Useful compilation, used throughout this volume]

Biel, Edwin R.: "Climatology of the Mediterranean Area," Univ. of Chicago: *Institute of Meteorology Miscellaneous Reports,* No. 13 (1944); reviewed in *Geog. Rev., XXXV* (1945), 489–490.

Boesch, H.: "Das Klima des Nahen Osten," *Vierteljahrschr. Naturforsch. Gesellschaft,* XCII (1947), 20–31.

Butzer, Karl W.: "Late Glacial and Postglacial Climatic Variation in the Near East," *Erdkunde,* XI (1957), 21–35. [With bibliography]

Butzer, Karl W.: "Quaternary Stratigraphy and Climate in the Near East," *Bonner Geog. ABH.,* XXIV (1958).

Caponera, Dante A.: WATER LAWS IN MOSLEM COUNTRIES. Rome: U. N. Food and Agric. Organization (1954).

Carter, Douglas B.: MAPS OF WATER REQUIREMENTS FOR S. W. ASIA. Centerton, N. J.: UNESCO Advisory Com. on Arid Zone Research (1957).

* Cressey, George B.: "Water in the Desert," ANNALS ASSOC. AMER. GEOGS., XLVII (1957), 105–124.

Environmental Protection Division: ANALOGS OF YUMA CLIMATE IN THE MIDDLE EAST. Natick, Mass.: Quartermaster Research and Development Command (1955). [One of several studies]

Kramer, Harris P.: "Climatology of the Middle East and Central Asia; A Selected Annotated Bibliography," *Meteorol. Abstracts and Bibliog.,* II (1951), 453–480.

Kramer, Harris P.: "Selective Annotated Bibliography on the Climatology of the Near East," *Meteorol. Abstracts and Bibliog.,* II (1951), 373–404.

Loehnberg, Alfred: "Water Supply and Drainage in Semi-Arid Countries," *Trans. Amer. Geophysical Union,* XXXVIII (1957), 501–510.

Oppenheimer, H. R.: "Summer Drought and Water Balance of Plants Growing in the Near East," *Jour. of Ecol.,* XXXIX (1951), 356–362.

Peterson, A. Delbert: BIBLIOGRAPHY ON THE CLIMATE OF IRAQ. Washington: U. S. Weather Bureau (1956).

Peterson, A. Delbert: BIBLIOGRAPHY ON THE CLIMATE OF IRAN. Washington: U. S. Weather Bureau (1957).

Peterson, A. Delbert, and Stepanova, Nina A.: BIBLIOGRAPHY ON THE CLIMATE OF TURKEY. Washington: U. S. Weather Bureau (1957).

* Thornthwaite, C. W., Mather, J. R., and Carter, D. B.: THREE WATER BALANCE MAPS OF SOUTHWEST ASIA. Centerton, N. J.: Laboratory of Climatology (1958).

Trewartha, Glenn T.: "Climate as related to the Jet Stream in the Orient," *Erdkunde,* XII (1958), 205–214.

U. N. Flood Control Service: "Glossary of Hydrologic Terms used in Asia and the Far East," *Economic Survey Asia and the Far East,* IV (1956), 1–38.

VonWissmann, Hermann: "On the Role of Nature and Man in Changing the Face of the Dry Belt of Asia," in Thomas, W. L., Jr. MAN'S ROLE IN CHANGING THE FACE OF THE EARTH. Chicago: Univ. Chicago Press (1956).

* White, Gilbert F., Ed.: THE FUTURE OF ARID LANDS. Washington: Amer. Assoc. for the Advancement of Science (1956). [Excellent symposium]

CHAPTER 5

Rivers

Rivers in the Desert
The Zayandeh Rud and the Isfahan Oasis
Wadi Hanifah: A Sample from Arabia
The Jordan and the Dead Sea
The Menderes River in Turkey
The Helmand River in Afghanistan
The Shatt-al-Arab, The River of the Arabs
Qanats and Karez
References

RIVERS IN THE DESERT

THE RIVERS of Southwest Asia all bear the stamp of the alternately wet and dry climate which gives them birth. Following the winter rains and snows, they are swollen to flood proportions by concentrated runoff or by spring thaw in the mountains. In summer they shrink to a small stream or may even disappear. This fluctuation is most noticeable where rivers rise in lowland areas with seasonal precipitation. Only when streams come out of high mountains where moisture is stored up in the form of winter snows, or where there are limestone uplands which accumulate water in their cavernous bed rock, is there a year-round flow.

Few Swasian rivers continue to flow the year around or extend far unless they have their source in a mountain area. Desert streams are wet weather phenomena, flowing for a few days after the chance rains and then dying in the sunshine. If any water is to be found during the summer, it is only underground. So close is the relation to a highland source that one may judge the topography of a river's headwaters by examining the fluctuations in the discharge data at its mouth.

Widespread inundations are the inevitable result of concentrated runoff. Swasia is an area of young, steep-sided mountains, generally devoid of vegetation, which experiences occasional but intense downpours, with rain falling at the rate of several inches per day.

Flash floods are to be expected. They often sweep away cultivated fields and at

(Opposite) The Jordan River is short but historic. This view is near the Allenby Bridge in southern Jordan. (Courtesy Jordan Tourist Department.)

When the Tigris is in flood and overtops its embankments, large areas near Baghdad are inundated, as in 1954. Man occupies the flood plain at his peril. (Courtesy Iraq Petroleum Co.)

times destroy cities. Experience has shown the desirability of a proper location and solid foundations, so that "when the rains descend and the floods come and the winds blow and beat upon the house, it falls not" (Matthew VII:6). Where flood-free natural sites are lacking, as in Iraq, many cities have been built on artificial mounds.

Rivers the world around are subject to flood, but the range in flow is greater in dry lands. The St. Lawrence has a difference between low and high volume of 1:2; on the Mississippi the fluctuation is 1:25; the increase on the Columbia is 1:35. In comparison, the Euphrates at Hit has a range of 1:28, whereas the low and high water in the Tigris at Baghdad fluctuates between 1 and 80.

Peak floods at intervals of once in a decade or a century are best described as 10 per cent or 1 per cent possibilities. It is also likely that there are once in a millennium floods, but the fact that they have only a .001 probability does not mean that two of them may not occur within a decade. In terms of flood control, there is no such thing as assurance of complete protection against future conditions. All that man can do is to guard against calculated risks and reduce them by diversional and retentional works.

Since stream flow may be torrential for a brief period, it becomes an active agent of erosion. One has only to see or hear a wall of water descending a dry wadi to realize the geological work which can be accomplished in a day. There is no reason to search for other agents which caused the sculpturing of arid landscapes even if cloudbursts are known to be years apart or a desert area is

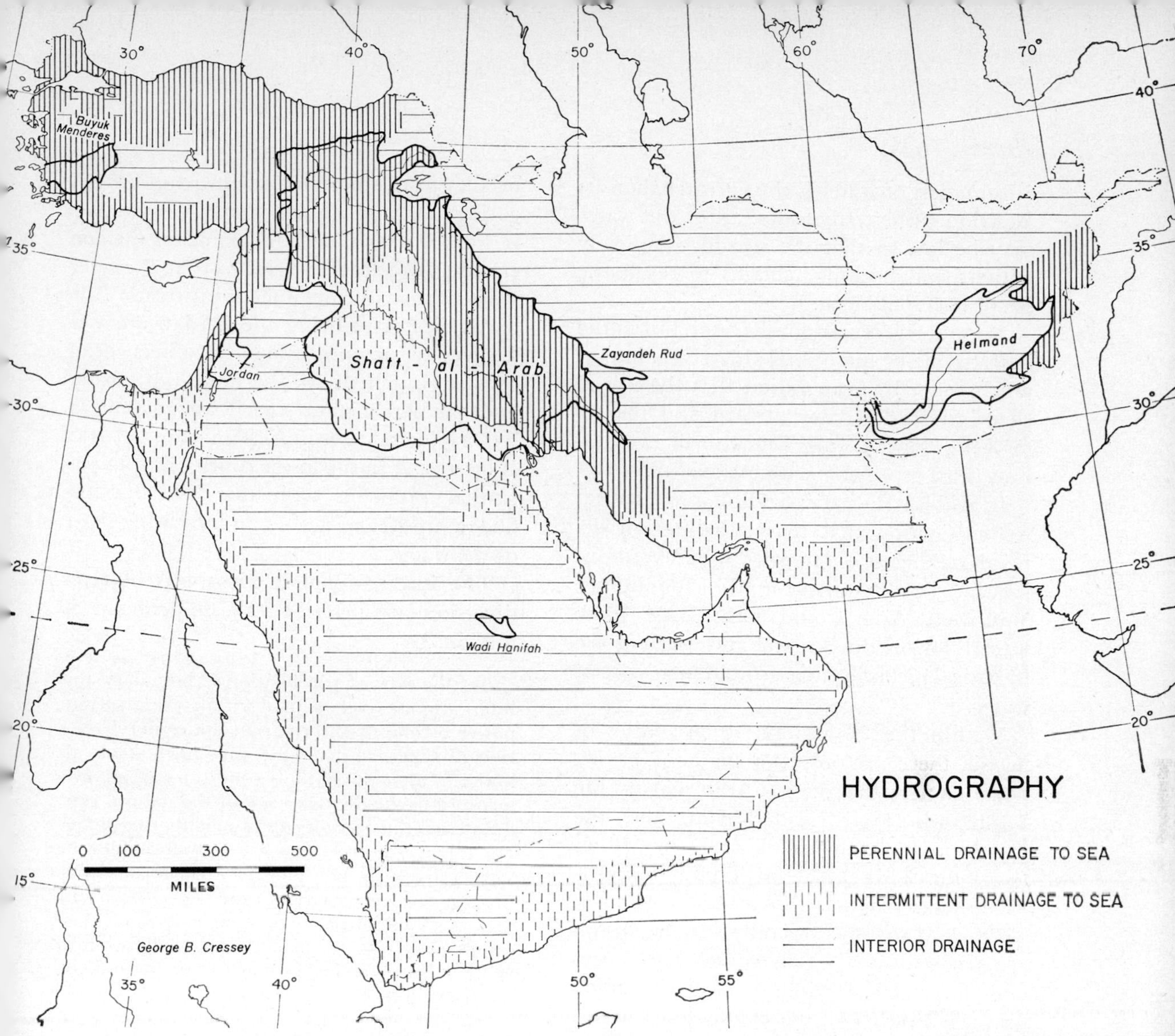

Large areas are so dry that there is insufficient run-off to reach the sea; many enclosed basins contain salt lakes. Only two major river systems are present, the Shatt-al-Arab and the Helmand. Each of the six drainage areas named above are described in this chapter.

assumed to be nearly rainless. Desert rivers may accomplish more erosion and transport of debris in a few days of flood than they can in several years of normal flow.

Rivers which change quickly from flood to a tiny flow usually fail to carry their load of sediments to their ultimate destination. Hence, desert rivers develop great alluvial fans; these represent material in transit which has been dropped temporarily. In many cases, this transported load never reaches the sea, for it is trapped in interior basins.

Many dry-land rivers have a regime which is the reverse of those in humid lands. Once they leave their feeding grounds in the highlands, they flow across arid lands and begin to wither. The maximum volume is not at the mouth, but at the head of their delta or alluvial fan. Since they flow through arid regions which fail to nourish them, losses by evaporation, seepage, or diversion for irrigation may exceed contributions by runoff.

Subtraction of water is thus greater than its addition. In extreme cases, all of the water may be lost so that the stream completely withers and nothing remains to reach the sea or terminal basin.

Normal rivers carry fresh water, but in the desert some of these shrinking rivers lose so much water by evaporation that the initial chemical load is concentrated and the remaining flow becomes brackish or even saline. This represents extreme aridity.

In arid landscapes, irrigation is so essential for cultivation that settled habitation depends on the use of imported water. Without melting snow in the surrounding mountains, Southwest Asia would have little food. Stream flow is thus critical and much of the historical record centers around man's use of water.

Within the 2.5 million square miles of Swasia there are only two major river systems, namely the Shatt-al-Arab, fed by the Euphrates, Tigris, and Karun, and the Helmand in Afghanistan. Only one other river, the Kizil Irmak in Turkey, exceeds 350 miles in length.

Much of the area has only a coarse drainage pattern, with widely spaced tributaries and large areas without clearly defined drainage lines. This reflects the low rainfall and limited runoff. Discharge figures for the various rivers thus represent small volumes per square mile. Since humid air masses deposit their moisture on windward slopes, the lee sides of the mountains normally have smaller and less persistent streams than those exposed to the rain-bearing winds.

Innumerable problems arise when rivers cross international boundaries. How much of the water is an upstream country entitled to divert for its own use, or how far is it permissible to modify the flow by the construction of reservoirs? Boundary control and navigation rights introduce further complications. Iraq depends on the water from the Euphrates, but what will happen when Syria decides to use more water upstream for irrigating new lands? Further up the same river is Turkey which has built dams for the generation of hydroelectricity so that the reservoirs change the regime downstream. The difficulties of utilizing the Jordan are well known; its potentials may have been exaggerated, but little can be done until Israel and the Arab states reach an agreement. The Helmand rises in Afghanistan, but Iran is interested in the lower course. Egypt faces similar problems with the Nile, for the Sudan, upstream, desires an increasing share of the water.

The international legal aspects of river diversion are described by Oppenheim as follows: [1]

> But the flow of pluri-national, boundary and international rivers is not within the arbitrary power of one of the riparian States, for it is a rule of International Law that no State is allowed to alter the natural conditions of its own territory to the disadvantage of the natural conditions of the territory of a neighboring State. For this reason a State is not only forbidden to stop or divert the flow of a river which runs from its own to a neighboring State, but likewise to make such use of the water of the river as either causes danger to the neighboring State or prevents it from making proper use of the flow of the river on its part.

Water is Swasia's most valuable resource. For the most part it is renewable, thanks to the hydrologic cycle, but in some places man is drawing upon underground reserves which required millennia to accumulate. Even in Southwest Asia the total amount of available water is considerable, but it is poorly distributed. Many uses compete; domestic requirements take top priority, but there is need for wise decision as to the relative use of rivers for irrigation, waste removal, navigation, hydroelectric power, and industry.

Great amounts are currently lost through

[1] L. Oppenheim: *International Law, Vol. I, Peace.* New York: Longmans Green (1948), 430. Quoted by permission.

The Isfahan oasis is the gift of the Zayendeh Rud which rises in the snow crowned Zagros and is spread across its alluvial fan in a series of distributary canals. (G. B. C.)

evaporation from lakes and reservoirs, often five to six feet per year. There is some evidence that this may be prevented through the use of a monomolecular film, formed by a nonpermeable substance floating on the surface which checks evaporation. Other water losses occur through seepage in unlined irrigation canals. Through proper infiltration methods it is often possible to recharge ground water aquifers. Eventually it may prove economically feasible to desalinize sea water; even if all the seas were fresh, there would still be the problem of pumping water onto the uplands. Nowhere is it now economically feasible to lift water more than a few hundred feet.

Most of the desert will remain desert, for there is little indication that man can change the climate. The basic problems lie in the field of economics rather than in meteorology or hydrology. Swasia needs an inventory and a program for the wise utilization of its water resources; assumptions as to their inadequacy are premature. The future will be limited not so much by the scarcity of water as by human ingenuity and resourcefulness.

This chapter deals with six representative streams, ranging from a tiny desert wadi to the great Shatt-al-Arab system. These are the Zayandeh Rud in Iran, the Wadi Hanifah in Arabia, the Jordan in Palestine, the Menderes in Turkey, the Helmand in Afghanistan, and the Shatt-al-Arab in Iraq and Iran. Only two of the six ever reach the ocean.

In addition to its rivers, Swasia secures an

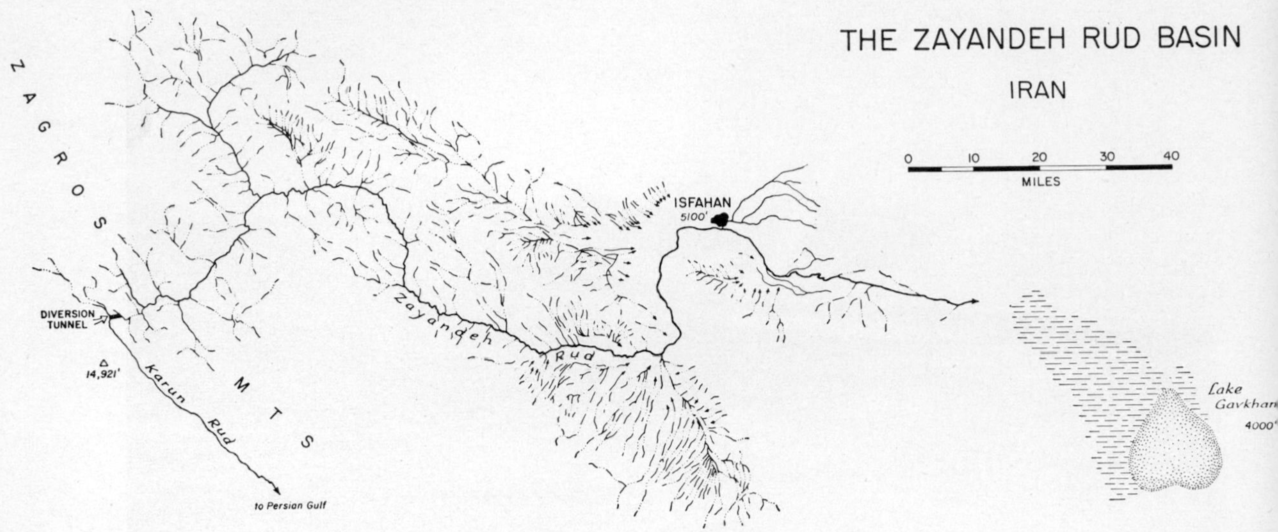

The Zayandeh Rud rises in the Zagros Mountains of southwestern Iran, where many elevations exceed 10,000 feet, and terminates in a salt marsh at 4,000 feet. In order to increase the summer flow, a tunnel diverts water from the west-flowing Karun drainage.

important part of its irrigation water from the underground infiltration tunnels known as qanats or karez, discussed in the final section of this chapter.

THE ZAYANDEH RUD AND THE ISFAHAN OASIS

SCATTERED ABOUT IRAN are hundreds of oases. The best of these are lovely garden spots, with tall poplar and pistachio trees, good crops of wheat and vegetables, and walled courtyards whose mud walls carry no suggestion of the flowers within. These sites are found where water is available through much of the summer; in places where the supply is limited or discontinuous, existence may become marginal for both vegetation and man.

Most Iranian oases lie within sight of high mountains; the higher these are, the more precipitation they receive, and where they rise above 5,000 feet, most precipitation falls as snow. From the mountains radiate scores of short rivers, many soon to be lost in the surrounding deserts. Only a few are more than 100 miles in length, and most of these are on the outer flanks of the ranges where snowfall is greatest.

One of the more significant of these streams is the Zayandeh Rud which waters the oasis of Isfahan. The river of Isfahan is variously known as the Zendeh Rud, or great river, and the Zayandeh Rud, the life-giving river. Both names are significant to those who live on its banks. The oasis measures some twenty miles in width by twice that distance down the slope.

The Zayandeh Rud rises on the interior slopes of the Zagros Range at a point where nearby peaks rise to 14,000 feet. Two hundred miles to the east, what is left of the river loses itself in the Gavkhaneh salt marsh, whose elevation is approximately 4,000 feet. During the hundred miles of its turbulent course through the subhumid mountains, the stream grows through the contribution of numerous tributaries; once it starts to cross its thirsty alluvial fan, water is progressively lost by seepage, evaporation, and diversion into a network of irrigation

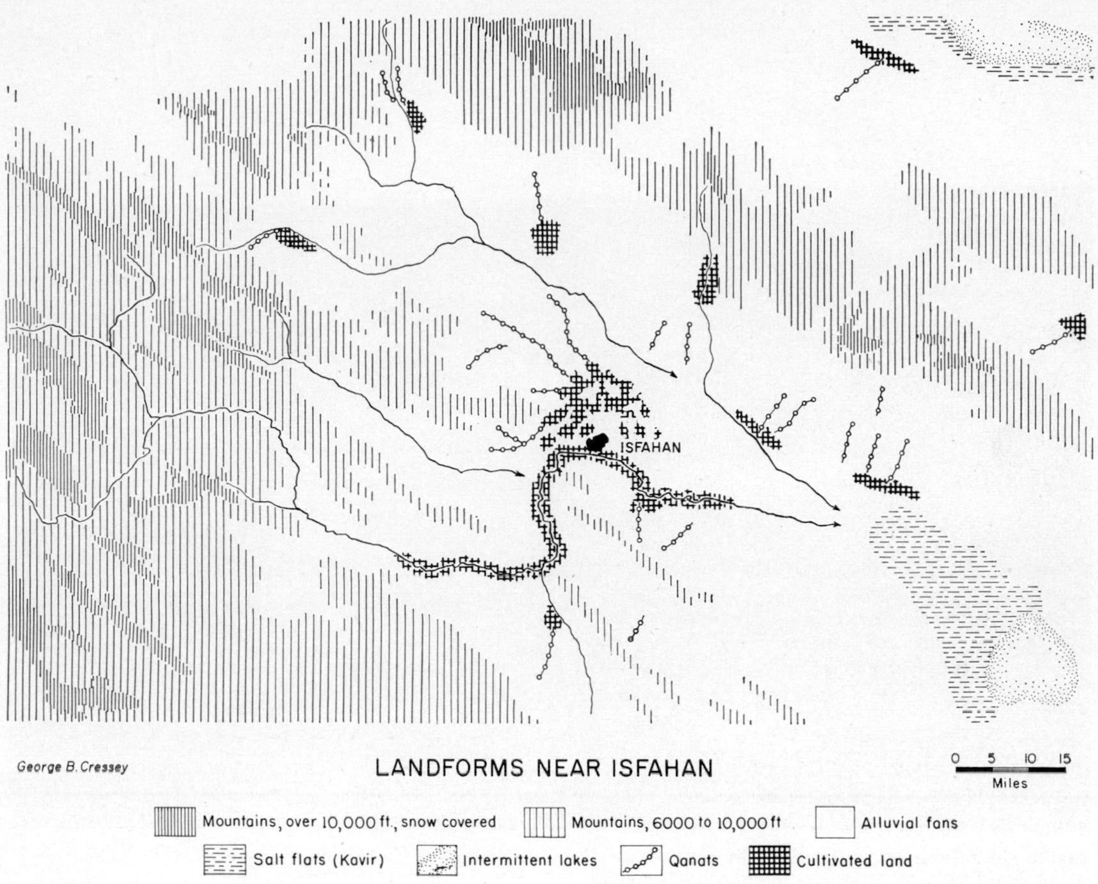

Alpine mountains surround the Zayandeh Rud basin, and their erosion supplies debris which has built compound alluvial fans around the desert oasis of Isfahan. Streams fed by melting snow flow the year around and help to convert the otherwise barren alluvial slopes to a garden. White, brown, and green are thus the landscape colors. Hundreds of "horizontal wells" known as *qanats* supply additional water for the cultivated areas.

canals. For the first fifty miles of its dwindling course, the Zayandeh Rud creates a fertile oasis; further down slope there is only wasteland.

The river drains a considerable area, perhaps 75,000 square miles. Precipitation ranges from thirty-five inches per year in the higher mountains of the west to less than five inches in the desert terminus. Isfahan averages four inches, but it has received an inch within twenty-four hours.

Precipitation is seasonal, so that a succession of flood and low water is the rule. In spring, the Zayandeh Rud usually carries 60,000 cubic feet per second, even more during high flood stages. In the autumn, the flow is greatly diminished since almost all the available water is used for irrigation. The extreme ratio between maximum and minimum flow may approximate 100 to 1.

In order to increase the water supply of the river, the kings of Persia, as long ago as the sixteenth century, attempted to divert the upper course of the Karun River, which flows to the Persian Gulf, into the Zayandeh Rud by means of a deep cut through the

The basin of the Wadi Hanifah in central Saudi Arabia has been carved in a sedimentary escarpment. This view east of Riyadh is representative of many dry valleys in interior Arabia. (Courtesy Standard Oil Co. of New Jersey.)

rocky ridge which separates the two systems (50° E., 32° 30′ N.). Although a 300-yard trench was made, the work proved impossible. In 1935 Iran completed the Kurang tunnel, ten feet in diameter and 9,250 feet in length, which diverts 1,050 cubic feet per second in summer, thus enabling the Isfahan area to irrigate an additional 25,000 acres. Snowfall in the Kurang area is so heavy that access to the control works is not possible until April.

The terminal basin occupied by Gavkhaneh Lake is the first of a series of structural depressions which continue for 150 miles to the southeast. Each depression is the site of an intermittent lake or a salt tamarisk swamp. After the rains, an aimless maize of channels makes such areas quite impenetrable. When dry and where these playas have a salt crust, the area is known as a *kavir*. While the lower slopes of these basins are water logged and salt encrusted, the upper slopes generally have adequate drainage.

Isfahan owes its prosperity to an elaborate irrigation system. There are more than 100 named canals with an aggregate length of thousands of miles. Since there are no dams or barrages along the river, these canals depend on its free flow or on low temporary weirs. Many canals receive water only when river levels are high. Proposed reservoirs near the headwaters and modern canal systems will regulate the flow and increase the agricultural acreage.

Some of the irrigation water which seeps into the soil, along with ground water derived from runoff from the mountain slopes, is recaptured by hundreds of qanat tunnels, to be described in a later section. This unique system of "horizontal wells" or infiltration galleries brings ground water to the surface by gravity, and the area irrigated by qanat water may equal that fed directly from the river.

WADI HANIFAH: A SAMPLE FROM ARABIA

IF ONE COULD FLY back and forth across the Arabian Peninsula, the dominant impression might be one of barren aridity. Here is a desert; and yet, aside from the areas of sand dunes, almost every surface shows signs of sculpture by running water. Rain is limited and infrequent, but it does its work and there is little to erase its signature. Since there are few mountains, there are no areas with sufficient precipitation to start rivers on a trans-desert course.

Innumerable wadis mark transient watercourses. Almost none carry permanent streams, for runoff lasts only a few days after the chance downpours. Whereas valleys in humid lands have well-marked beginnings and ends, most Arabian wadis are ill-defined. Some end in playa mud flats which form a salt-encrusted *sabkha* for 360 days of the year. Many wadis, however, lack a proper terminal basin; the stream withers and gradually disappears so that its length depends on the momentary volume. A few wadis occupy steep-sided canyons, but more commonly they merely flow across a broad linear depression.

In a few cases, several intermittent streams occupy a single long depression and may even flow in opposite directions within different parts of it. Such linear lowlands may mark ancient river valleys carved during a more humid period, or they may represent structural features now choked with debris brought in by tributary streams. Water flows so rarely that one cannot be sure as to the direction in which each channel slopes.

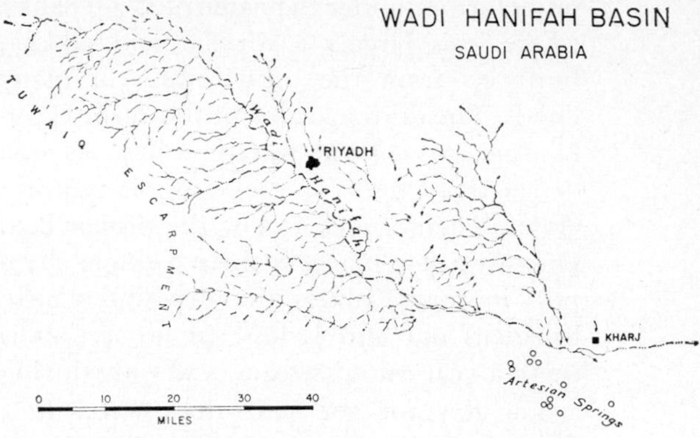

The drainage pattern of the Wadi Hanifa is similar to that of many streams in central Arabia. Stream beds carry water for only a few days a year following the occasional rains.

One such depression in the extreme northwest of Saudi Arabia is known as the Wadi Sirhan. This extends for some 200 miles and contains half a dozen intermittent streams, end to end, flowing in opposite directions. The few spot elevations along the floor of the Wadi Sirhan range between 400 and 700 feet above sea level, but the direction of the over-all gradient is not clear.

One of Saudi Arabia's typical wadis is that which flows past the capital city of Riyadh, the Wadi Hanifah. The wadi rises in the Tuwaiq Escarpment at an elevation of 2,400 feet and flows along its back slope, ending at around 1,200 feet. This section of Arabia has a number of escarpments formed by the outcrop of east-dipping sediments. The Wadi Hanifah rises near the crest of one such outcrop, flows down the dip, then along the strike, and eventually loses itself along the base of the next escarpment to the east.

The wadi has an airline length of 100 miles, but the lowland continues for fifty miles farther under the name of Wadi Sahba where it is largely a silt flat and sabkha, built up from the contribution of many floods. The drainage area of the Wadi Hanifah measures 1,850 square miles. As one drives the length of the wadi, it requires close observation to follow the proper bed. Only in a few places is there a single channel; in many places the dry watercourse broadens out and is lost. In no section is there a year-round stream, and only during a few days of the year does water flow throughout the length of the wadi. A local resident reports that only once in twelve years was there sufficient flow to continue through the Wadi Sahba.

The drainage regime reflects the climate. Precipitation records are available from the Riyadh Airport following 1948. They show that the rainy season commonly commences during December and usually ends late in May. For the first decade the annual rainfall averaged 3.5 inches, with a range from 9.4 to 1.1 inches. Data for some of these years are also available for Kharj, fifty miles to the east. These show the spotty character of desert rainfall since both the amounts and at times even the dates of the few showers vary between the two stations.

Only rainfalls of more than half an inch produce any runoff for it takes at least this much to wet the surface. Since years with only an inch or two of rain are common and because the bulk of the rain falls in light showers, the wadi may remain completely dry for several years at a time.

The largest measured flood along the Wadi Hanifah produced a flow of 450 hectare-meters (approximately 3,500 acre feet) during twenty-four hours, with a maximum flow of 1,700 cubic meters per second. Flows seldom last more than two days at a time and usually total less than 1,000 hectare-meters per year. Only rarely does the wadi carry water more than three or four times in any one season. It is not uncommon to have runoff in one portion of the wadi which disappears entirely after flowing a few miles.

When the wadi does carry water, some of it is diverted over the adjoining flood plain to moisten the soil and also to encourage recharge of ground water storage. An ancient dam below Riyadh once stored some of the flood flow for diversion into now-abandoned canals, but the reservoir is completely filled with sediment. In a few instances, the infiltration galleries known as qanats provide a small supply of water.

Since runoff is limited and uncertain, water was normally obtained from hand-dug wells. For centuries, these wells were of the donkey-lift type, reaching down a few tens of feet to saturated gravels in the wadi. In this arrangement, animals walk down an inclined plane while pulling a rope which leads, over a pulley, to the leather bucket which lifts water from the well. There were once 1,000 wells of this type. Beginning in 1938, scores of drilled wells and centrifugal pumps were introduced, and the level of the water table began to drop. Shallow wells have entirely dried up, and some of the date gardens once dependent on them have disappeared.

In 1935 the water level stood thirty feet below the surface; by 1958 it had dropped to 100 feet. Meanwhile, domestic demands in Riyadh increased phenomenally, for during the 1950's it was one of the fastest growing cities in the world.

Since the Wadi Hanifah, like most desert watercourses, flows "upside down," it is important to examine its subsurface flow and the prospects for the future for water supply. All of the ground water is derived from rainfall within the catchment basin. Infiltration rates are uncertain, but probably no more than 1 to 5 per cent of the rainfall reaches the underground storage. With a rainfall of four inches over the catchment area, and an infiltration rate of 5 per cent, the annual contribution to the ground water of the wadi gravels would amount to 2,150 hectare-meters.

The storage capacity of the alluvial sediments is a function of their volume and character. Near Riyadh the valley fill probably does not exceed 5,500 feet in width, and test borings show average depths of under 180 feet. On this basis, the total alluvial sand and silt has a volume of some 1,300 million cubic meters.

About half of the wadi fill is composed of nonwaterbearing silts and clays which yield no well water. In the remaining sands and gravels, pore space occupies 20 per cent of the volume, and it is here that effective storage takes place. Since the saturated thickness within the basin averaged 100 feet in 1958, the volume of water stored in these sediments was estimated as 5,000 hectare-meters. Unfortunately, this ground water has excessive amounts of dissolved minerals, averaging 950 parts per million or 200 parts above the desirable salinity limit for safe irrigation water.

For several decades, withdrawals for consumption have exceeded replenishment, and if this continues, the day will soon come when all storage accumulated over the centuries will be gone. Wells will then be at the mercy of the weather, and during dry years there will be no water at all.

The present water budget for the Wadi Hanifah area includes domestic needs in Riyadh and irrigation for gardens of dates, alfalfa, grain, and vegetables. The agricultural land totals 1,200 hectares and requires an average of one and one-quarter meters of irrigation water per year to balance evaporation and transpiration, plus water which reinfiltrates into underground storage.

On the basis of known rainfall and probable recharge rates, the safe yield of the Wadi Hanifah gravels appears to average 2,000 hectare-meters per year, with wide fluctuations from year to year. Against this is the annual consumption of 1,500 hectare-meters for agriculture and 1,220 hectare-meters for municipal use. This represents a total use of 2,720 hectare-meters, or a current overdraft of 700 per year. In view of the fact that the remaining water in storage was estimated at 5,000 hectare-meters in 1958, imminent depletion was in prospect.

Fortunately, Riyadh also has a few 3,500 foot wells, and additional supplies are derived from a nearby wadi, but these also represent overdrafts which cannot continue indefinitely. Unless there are drastic curtailments in agricultural use, the area faces serious consequences.

Richard S. Davis concluded his hydrographic study in 1958 with this paragraph:[1]

> The water supplies of the Wadi Hanifah Drainage Basin are already being used to capacity, and the time has nearly passed for taking action to preserve water from the Wadi Hanifa basin as a water resource for the city. Unless strong and positive governmental action is taken soon to evaluate the city's water resources from all possible sources, prevent waste, initiate conservation practices, establish water use priorities, and plan for periods of drought, the people of the capital of the Kingdom will one day find themselves without sufficient water to drink, to say nothing of water for rose gardens, air coolers, and washing of the streets.

The Wadi Hanifah is a poor site for a modern city, as it was for the ancient Wahabi capital at nearby Nasriyah. Unfortunately, interior Arabia offers nothing much better. So serious is the problem that far distant sources have been considered, even a $250 million pipeline from the Shatt-al-Arab. Both drought and excess water present problems. Large floods are so infrequent that the present-day builders have overlooked the probability that the city may be swept by flood at some future time. Such are the problems of desert cities.

[1] Richard S. Davis: *Review of Wadi Hanifa Water Resources,* Riyadh: Ralph M. Parsons Co. and Kingdom of Saudi Arabia, Division of Water Resources (1959). Quoted by permission.

The lower Jordan River flows through an inner valley known as the Zor, several hundred feet lower than the main depression or Ghor. This scene is near the Dead Sea. (Courtesy Iraq Petroleum Co.)

THE JORDAN RIVER AND THE DEAD SEA

THREE RIVERS flow parallel to the eastern Mediterranean shore. All lie in the same valley which, however, is not a true valley but rather, a long structural depression. From south to north these are the Jordan, the Litani, and the Orontes. None of these are large rivers, none have much to offer in the way of possible irrigation, and none are navigable; but each has a rich history.

The Jordan is a short river, only eighty-five miles in length. One may stand near its mouth and see the faint outlines of Mount Hermon, the snow crowned source of the river. The Jordan proper is formed by the junction of several tributaries which unite at an elevation of 260 feet above the Mediterranean. The chief tributary is the Hasbany, some twenty-five miles long, and in line with the main river so that it may be considered a part of the Jordan. In the 110 miles from Mount Hermon to the Dead Sea, the Jordan and its tributaries drop from an elevation of 9,232 feet to 1,286 feet below sea level.

The crest line of the western uplands—the hills of Judea—lies well back from the Mediterranean and close to the depression so that only short tributaries descend to the main river. In contrast, longer tributaries and more drainage comes from the Moab uplands on the eastern side where the fault block is tilted toward the Jordan. This structural condition is hydrographically unfortunate, because the uplands of Palestine rob the Mediterranean winds of their moisture leaving the valley floor and low eastern hills in the rain shadow.

Only one tributary of importance enters the Jordan, namely, the east bank Yarmuk with a length of sixty-six miles. Its normal flow nearly equals that of the Jordan above Lake Hule, known as the Waters of Merom.

Since the Jordan receives few other permanent streams, the Yarmuk contributes about a third of the water which enters the Dead Sea.

Two lakes provide local base levels. The first is the shallow Lake Hule, seven miles from the junction of the Jordan and the Hasbany, at an elevation of 231 feet. Part of the lake and the widespread papyrus swamps which formerly existed around it, have been drained for agricultural purposes, a total of some 10,000 acres. Nine miles farther on is Lake Tiberias, 696 feet below the Mediterranean. This is sometimes known as the Sea of Galilee but since it has an outlet and is therefore fresh, the term "sea" is improper. It is known as Lake Kinneret in current Israeli practice. The descent between the two lakes exceeds 100 feet per mile, resulting in a series of cascades which cut through a basalt gorge.

Below Lake Tiberias, the Jordan has a depth of three to ten feet and averages 100 feet in width except in the rapids where it may narrow to twenty-five feet. In places the river becomes incredibly sinuous. The air line distance to the Dead Sea is only sixty-five miles but the meanderings of the river measure fully 200 miles. In a few places, cascades and rapids make the river almost unnavigable, although expeditions have occasionally made the hazardous trip.

One of the earliest of these vogages was organized by the United States Navy in 1847 under Lt. W. F. Lynch. Two descriptions by Lynch from the area south of Lake Tiberias indicate the character of the river:[1]

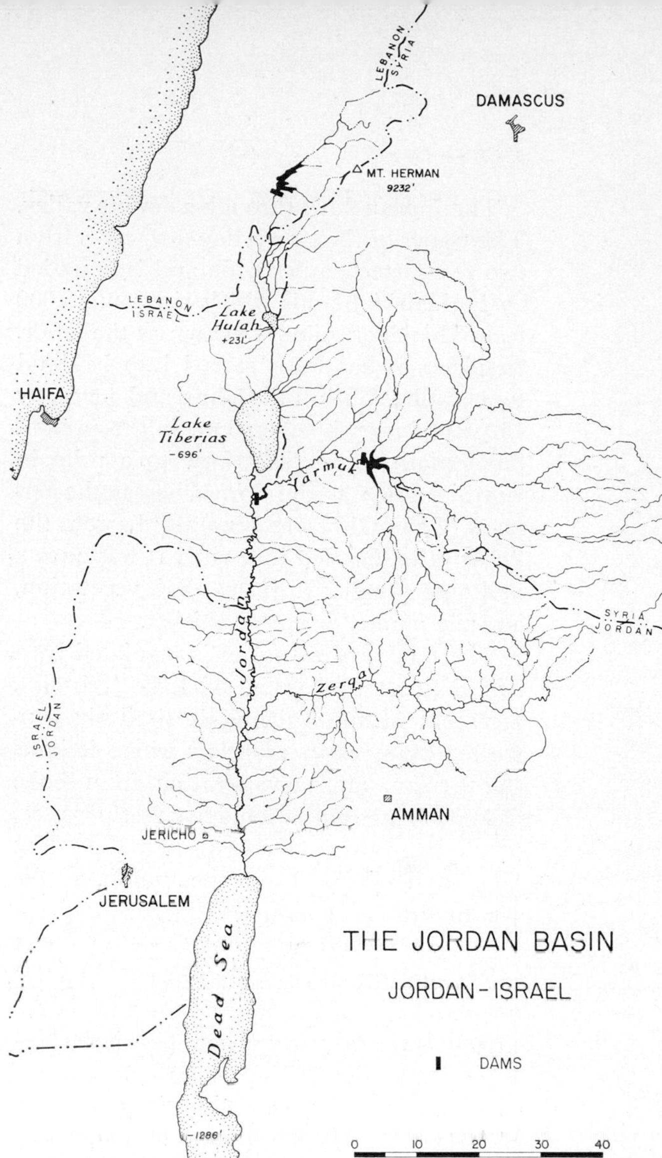

The Jordan River is short and offers only limited agricultural possibilities along its banks. The flow is never large, but in a dry land every stream is valuable. The upper valley lies in Israel, while the lower course and the major tributaries are in Jordan.

> The current at first [was] about $2\frac{1}{2}$ knots, but increased as we descended until we came to where the river, for more than three hundred yards, was one foaming rapid. The water was fortunately very deep to the first fall, where it precipitated itself over a ledge of rocks . . . . Below us were yet five successive falls, about eighteen feet in all, with rapids between. The boats had little need of the oars to propel them, for the current carried us along at the rate of four to six knots . . . . The river curved and twisted north, south, east and west, turning, in the short space of half an hour, to every quarter of the compass . . . . There was little variety in the scenery of the river today. The stream sometimes washed the bases of the sandy hills, and at other times meandered between low banks.

[1] W. F. Lynch: *Narrative of the United States' Expedition to the River Jordan.* London: Richard Bentley (1849) 177, 211–212.

The Jordan flows through a double valley. The upper of the two valley surfaces is from two to fourteen miles wide and is bounded by faulted highlands which rise some 2,000 feet. This depression is known as the Ghor. In places it has been carved into badland topography. Within the Ghor, and generally 150 feet lower in elevation, is the present flood plain, from 200 yards to a mile in width, known as the Zor. Whereas the terraces of the Ghor are generally barren, the Zor is often flooded in spring. It was once a veritable jungle with tropical vegetation, and the name Zor means thicket.

The flow of the Jordan is regulated by a low dam at the outlet of Lake Tiberias, and that of the Yarmuk is similarly controlled by a power reservoir where it joins the Jordan. Since evaporation from Lake Tiberias amounts to some five feet per year, it is worth noting that less water leaves the lake than enters. Near the mouth of the Jordan, at the Allenby Bridge, a decade of observations indicates that the river has a minimum discharge of sixteen cubic meters per second, a maximum of 660, and an annual average of thirty-seven. This is derived from a basin of 6,205 square miles.

In only a few places has it been feasible to irrigate much of the Ghor. Small tributaries leading to the Jordan have so dissected the old flood plain surface that canal systems fed by the main river involve expensive engineering work. Toward the Dead Sea especially the soil tends to be saline, and any use of the rather highly mineralized water of the Jordan creates irrigation hazards. The safest areas lie on the alluvial fans of tributary streams where there is porous soil and enough slope for natural underground drainage.

Elaborate schemes have been proposed for the development of the Jordan basin, some overly impressive through references to assumed parallels with the Tennessee Valley Authority. It should be obvious that the Jordan is a small river; therefore only modest amounts of water are available, and furthermore, the topography is unfavorable and evaporation losses are high. The water requirements of various crops differ, but in the Jordan Valley, several acre-feet of water must be added by irrigation to adequately counterbalance evaporation losses.

The most serious development problem is political, because several nations share the basin. Since the bulk of the water originates in the Arab lands, which have their own plans for its utilization, they will obviously not agree to any large diversion into Israel. Some Israeli proposals call for diversion of the Yarmuk into an enlarged reservoir in Lake Tiberias and for diversion canals leading west and then south along the Mediterranean Coast. Arab suggestions involve storage along tributaries such as the Yarmuk, with high level canals along the Ghor on both sides of the Jordan. Variations of these schemes forecast a six-fold increase in irrigated land, up to a maximum of 600,000 acres, including that along the Mediterranean. Such estimates should be taken with considerable reserve. The over-all unattractiveness of the Jordan lowland is shown by the fact that there is no town of importance along the river's banks; even Jericho lies some miles to the west.

The regime of the lower Jordan is regulated by the height of the Dead Sea. Since this elevation has fluctuated over the centuries through changing conditions of inflow and evaporation, the river has alternated between erosion and deposition. During the past century, the elevation has varied by seventy feet above and below its present level. Within recent millennia, the over-all climatic average has caused the Dead Sea to shrink. These long-range fluctuations are recorded in a series of ancient terraces and deltas, with elevations up to several hundred feet above the present water level. These elevations border the river upstream and

The fertile delta of the Buyuk Menderes provides an excellent area for grapes and general farming. A network of small canals supplies irrigation water. (Courtesy Turkish Information Office, New York.)

also extend south to encircle the Dead Sea.

Old shore lines make it evident that the Dead Sea was once 1,400 feet higher, and much larger, extending up the Jordan Valley almost to Lake Hule. During the more favorable climatic balance of the Ice Age, with lower evaporation and presumably higher rainfall, the Dead Sea probably overflowed to the Mediterranean. It was in this area, known today as Lake Jordan, that the sediments were deposited which now form the floor of the Ghor. Such a lake would have had fresh water, and the present salt content would have accumulated since it ceased to overflow. On the somewhat uncertain assumption that the chemical load of the Jordan has remained constant, this accumulation might have required 50,000 years.

The Dead Sea is one of the world's most remarkable bodies of water. It occupies 370 square miles of the earth's lowest land, with a length of forty-six miles and a maximum width of ten miles. The Dead Sea is as deep as its surface is below sea level, some 1,310 feet at a maximum. The average salinity is 24 per cent, seven times that of the ocean, so that boats or swimmers float as high as a cork. Most of the salts are magnesium and sodium chlorides. There is also a variety of other

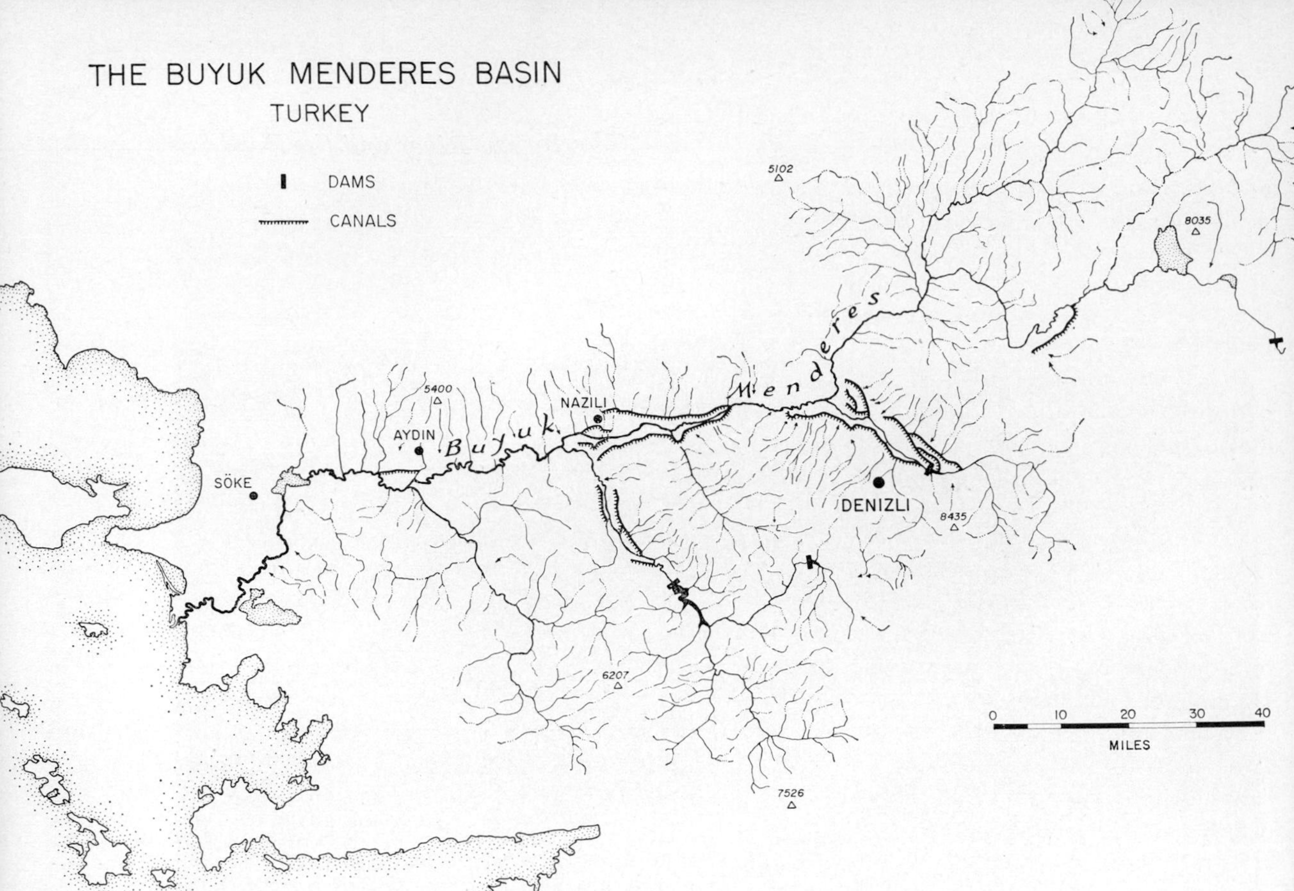

The basin of the Buyuk Menderes is the most humid of any of the rivers described in this chapter, so that its tributaries tend to be more permanent. Storage dams provide water for canals which irrigate considerable areas.

chemicals such as potash and bromine, whose commercial extraction by solar evaporation has led to a number of industries. If all of its salts could be concentrated, their volume would amount to four cubic miles.

THE MENDERES RIVER IN TURKEY

TURKEY HAS MANY RIVERS, certainly a greater mileage of perennial streams than any other country in Swasia and perhaps more than all others put together. The precipitation in the mountains is comparable to that in Iran, but the lowlands are considerably more humid. Since Turkey probably leads in the quantity of rainfall, it is not surprising that its river pattern is better developed.

The two greatest rivers of Southwest Asia, the Tigris and the Euphrates, both rise in Turkey. Other streams which lie entirely within the country are the 750-mile long Kizil Irmak and the 350-mile Sakarya, both draining into the Black Sea. To the south are the Seyhan and the Ceyhan rivers. Several others end in interior basins, for central Turkey is so dry that there are numerous unfilled depressions, partly occupied by salt lakes.

Turkish drainage is about evenly divided into three parts: that which reaches the Black and Mediterranean seas through a series of short rivers, that which drains to the Persian Gulf via the Tigris and Euphrates, and that which flows into interior land-locked basins.

The most important west-flowing river in Turkey is the Menderes, draining to the Aegean. This river is better known by its ancient name of Maeander since it has given us the classic example of a meandering river. The full name is the Buyuk, meaning greater, Menderes Nehri, meaning river; this distinguishes it from a smaller stream nearby.

The Menderes has an air line length of 200 miles and drains an area of mountain and plain covering 9,555 square miles. The source of the river lies at 3,000 feet, with nearby snow mountains rising to 8,035 feet. The precipitation is high for Turkey, and ranges from fifty inches on exposed slopes to fifteen inches in the interior plains. Evaporation measurements suggest an annual loss of forty-five inches, so that irrigation is generally necessary for successful crop production.

Stream flow varies widely with the season and from year to year. Higher elevations receive much of their precipitation in the form of snow, thus enabling the river to flow long after the end of the rainy season. Karst areas in parts of the basin provide underground storage for year-round springs.

The natural regime of the river is complicated by the fact that extensive withdrawals for irrigation take place on tributaries above their junctions. Upstream measurements show a low-water flow in August of eight cubic meters per second as compared with a March high of thirty-two. Farther downstream, below the last important tributaries and after most canal diversions, stream flows for the same months read three and 239 cubic meters per second. The annual runoff to the sea appears to average twenty-two cubic meters per second, or a total of 710 million cubic meters per year. If this could all be conserved in reservoirs and used as required, agriculture would benefit enormously.

The Menderes Valley has a human history which goes back for several thousand years. Ruins of ancient cities and irrigation works suggest its early importance, but its fertility has suffered from continued and uncontrolled exploitation. While many hillsides are almost denuded of their original soil cover, some terraced fields have been cultivated for 2,000 years. The basin represents 3 per cent of the total area of Turkey, and its population of 800,000 amounts to 4 per cent of the national total.

The valley has long been significant as a natural highway to the interior, but, unfortunately, the upper course of the river includes a succession of canyons, and the source lies 1,000 feet below the general level of interior Turkey. Roads must thus be built with a sharp incline in order to reach the central upland.

Three types of topography characterize the valley of the Menderes. The first lies in the steep upper course where the stream drops down from the Anatolian Plateau through a series of canyons interrupted by local basins. Here lies the Baklan Plain, some ten by thirty miles in extent. Most of the encircling mountains are rugged and steep-sided, almost devoid of soil and vegetation. Runoff is thus torrential. The central portion follows for a hundred miles, where the Menderes traverses a graben or "moat," seldom more than ten miles wide and close to sea level. Below this is the rapidly expanding delta.

The delta of the Menderes has grown so rapidly that the classic seaport of Miletus, "this most celebrated city of Ionia," is now eight miles inland. Strabo spoke of sediment in the Menderes and wrote, "by its deposition of silt, extending forty stadia, it has made Priene, which in earlier times was on the sea, an inland city." Lagoons and sand spits border the coast, and the river mouth is impractical for a seaport. Inland are two shallow lakes which were formerly part of the sea. Swamps once occupied much of the delta and the central valley, giving rise to malaria. Part of the area has been drained and the rich alluvium is intensively cultivated.

Across the delta and through the "moat," the river is so near tide level that it meanders elaborately. Floods are frequent, and water may stand for weeks after such flooding. Numerous low lakes and secondary channels attest to the shifting course of the stream. The bordering land is so low that no town lies near the river banks. The largest city is Nazilli in the central valley with a population of some 25,000.

This pattern is characteristic of several rivers which drain to the Aegean. A series of major fault lines cut across Turkey from west to east; several of them are still active earthquake zones. These parallel faults have created grabens, separated by highland massifs; along each of the former there is a more or less linear valley. The Aegean itself is a depressed area so that the coast line is embayed. Into these structural bays the heavily laden rivers are building deltas. So it is with the Menderes.

Extensive multi-purpose development works have partly brought the river under control. Several dams have been built on the southern tributaries for irrigation storage, hydroelectric production, and flood control, with others being planned for the main river. Electric power potentials exceed 100,000 kilowatts. The largest of these is the Kemer Dam, near Nazilli, 304 feet high, designed to aid in the irrigation of several hundred thousand acres during the summer months.

In addition to the large dams with their reservoirs, there are a series of low regulators which divert water into a network of canals. When fully developed, these will irrigate 225,000 acres of cropland in the flood plain and delta. Although there is a high water table, this is a dry area where irrigation is essential for summer crops. Ground water is available to supplement the supply from the river.

The Menderes and the Zayandeh Rud give rise to very different oases. Around Isfahan at any season one passes abruptly from irrigated land to desert. In western Turkey there is enough rainfall so that the entire landscape is green in winter; only in the dry season does the green-brown contrast appear. While the Menderes rises in the relatively dry interior and flows across a more humid delta, the Zayandeh Rud begins in humid mountains and ends in a dry alluvial basin. Qanat tunnels contribute an important amount of irrigation water to the Isfahan Oasis, but are unknown in western Turkey where ground water must be pumped. A large part of the summer flow in both rivers is diverted for irrigation, and there are ambitious plans for storing the now wasted winter and spring runoff in reservoirs in order to enlarge the irrigated areas. The future of both basins rests on the wise management of the available water.

THE HELMAND RIVER OF AFGHANISTAN

Afghanistan is drained by three river systems: one group lies north of the Hindu Kush and flows to the Amu Darya and the Aral Sea, another is the Kabul River in the east which leads to the Indus, while the third is the Helmand Rud (or river) which drains most of the south. Neither the first nor the third ever reaches the ocean since the runoff is all lost by evaporation.

The Helmand River has a length of about 600 miles, starting from mountains 12,000 feet high which lie twenty-five miles west of Kabul, and ending along the Iranian border in a series of ill-defined swamps in a lowland whose lowest elevation is 1,526 feet. This depression is known to the Persians as Seistan, and to the Afghans as the Chakhansur Basin.

For the first half of its course, the Helmand flows through rough barren highlands: essentially treeless, roadless, and uninhabited. Northwest of Kandahar it leaves the mountains and winds its way, in many places with a braided course, across the

The earth-fill Kajakai Dam rises 308 feet above the Helmand River in southern Afghanistan, conserving water for the irrigation of reclaimed desert and for generating hydroelectricity. (Courtesy Morrison-Knudsen-Afghanistan.)

nearly flat desert. Here irrigation supports a few expanding oases: green settings in a vast expanse of sand. Nowhere along the Helmand or its tributaries is there a town of much over a thousand people.

The central Helmand Valley receives from four to eight inches of rainfall, all of it in winter. Were it not for heavier precipitation in the mountains, much of it in the form of snow, the river would scarcely contain any water in summer. In fact, the lower course was dry for sixty-two days in 1902.

The Afghan area which drains into the Seistan-Chakhansur depression covers 139,537 square miles; the Iranian side adds a few tens of thousands more. Fully a third of the basin is "non-contributory" in that little or no runoff reaches the Helmand.

Along both the Helmand and its major tributary, the Arghandab, modern storage dams have been built where each enters the plain. On the Helmand, there is the 308-foot rock-fill Kajakai Dam and its thirty-six-mile long reservoir which has a capacity of 1,498,000 acre feet. The total annual flow at this point varies between 3,611,000 and 6,170,000 acre feet, but the seasonal range of the river has a ratio of 1 to 31. The dam has a power potential of 120,000 kilowatts. On the Arghandab, the 150-foot earth dam holds back a twelve-mile long reservoir which has a capacity of 388,000 acre feet; the

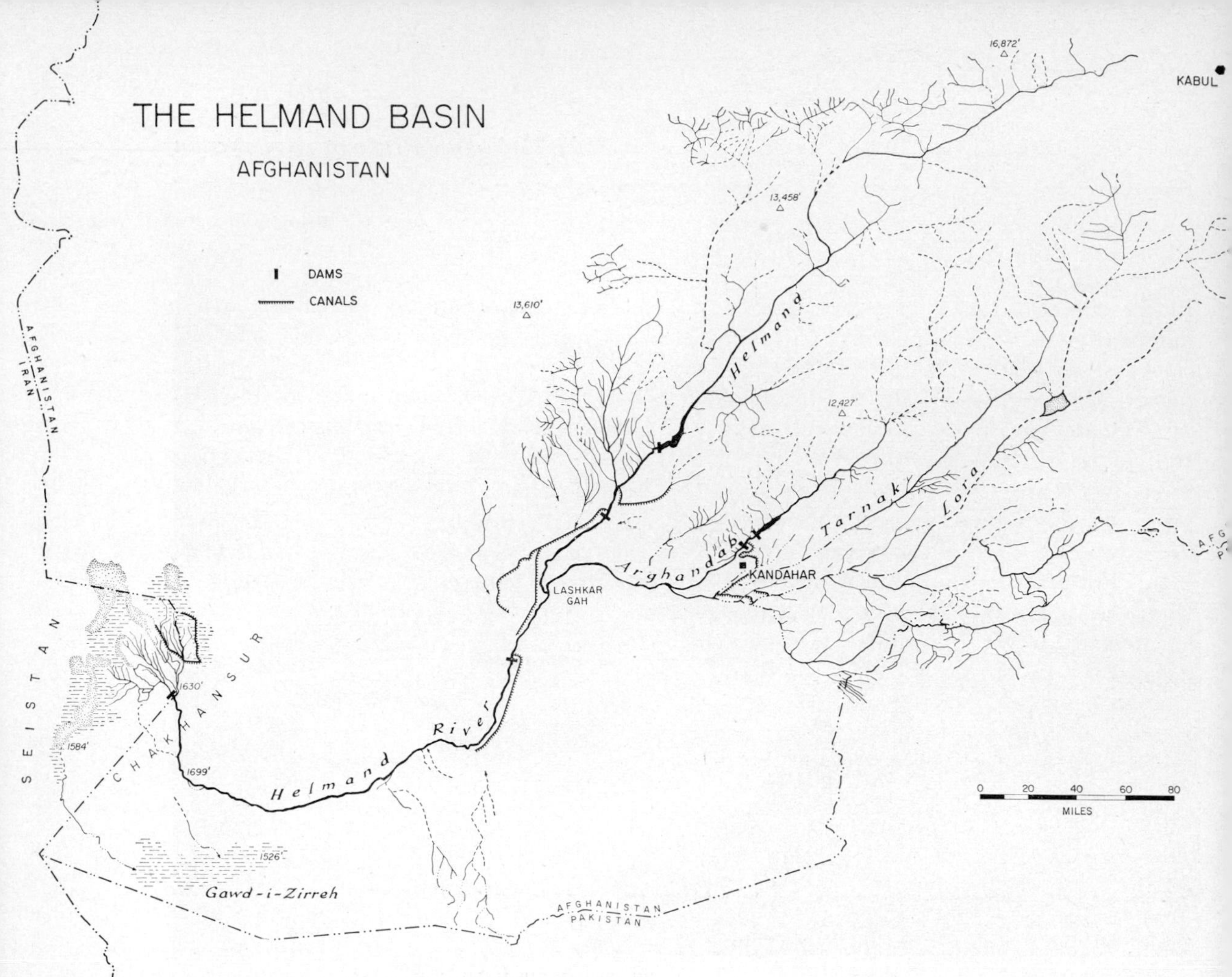

The Helmand is the major river of Afghanistan, flowing from the high Hindu Kush to the desolate Seistan basin. Modern dams store water for the irrigation of newly reclaimed desert areas. The scale of this map is half that of the preceding river systems.

annual river flow varies from 464,000 to 1,358,000 acre feet.

On the basis of available discharge records, it is estimated that the annual runoff of the entire Helmand–Arghandab system amounts to 7,065,000 acre feet, of which some 5 million acre-feet normally reach the terminal basin unused. This is only an average, for both dry years and heavy floods are recurrent. Monthly discharge averages for forty-one years show a range between 86,280 acre feet for September and 1,317,066 in May.

In the water of the Helmand River, the total salt content increases from 200 parts per million at the Kajakai Dam to 600 parts near the mouth. This results from evaporation losses and additions from saline soils. On the Arghandab the content increases from 300 parts of salts per million at the dam to 650 parts at the junction with the Helmand. In both cases, fortunately, the sodium content is low.

The Helmand River terminates in a series of reed-filled marshes and lakes, known as *hamuns*. There are half a dozen of these along the border between Afghanistan and Iran, with most of the water on the Iranian side. The size of the *hamun* fluctuates from year to year, varying in response to inflow and evaporation. Old shore lines indicate that the lakes were once much larger. Elevations have also been lower, as shown during the low-water period of 1902 when an old city was exposed.

Drainage patterns in the terminal area are ill-defined and variable; in general the flow moves from basin to basin in a counter-clockwise circulation. Where the Helmand turns north (latitude 30°20′, longitude 61°50′), its elevation is 1,699 feet; at the Iranian border, the height is 1,630 feet. Each successive lake is a few feet lower, until the lowest elevation appears to be 1,526 feet in the Gawd-i-Zirreh or Shela Marshes.

In addition to irrigation developments in Afghanistan, about 50,000 acres are more or less irrigated by the Helmand in the Seistan Basin across the border in Iran. A low diversion dam along the Rud-i-Seistan, the principal channel on the Iranian side, sometimes backs up water into Afghanistan and causes trouble. This may lead to further changes in the main course of the river, possibly diverting the entire Helmand southward over a low divide and through a former channel into the lowest of the depressions, the Gawd-i-Zirreh which lies in Afghanistan. Such a diversion might leave the irrigated lands in Iran waterless since only very limited drainage enters the Seistan depression from Iran. These problems have led to extensive international negotiations.

The Tigris at Baghdad is spanned by four modern bridges. This view looks west to the older part of the city. (Courtesy Iraq Petroleum Co.)

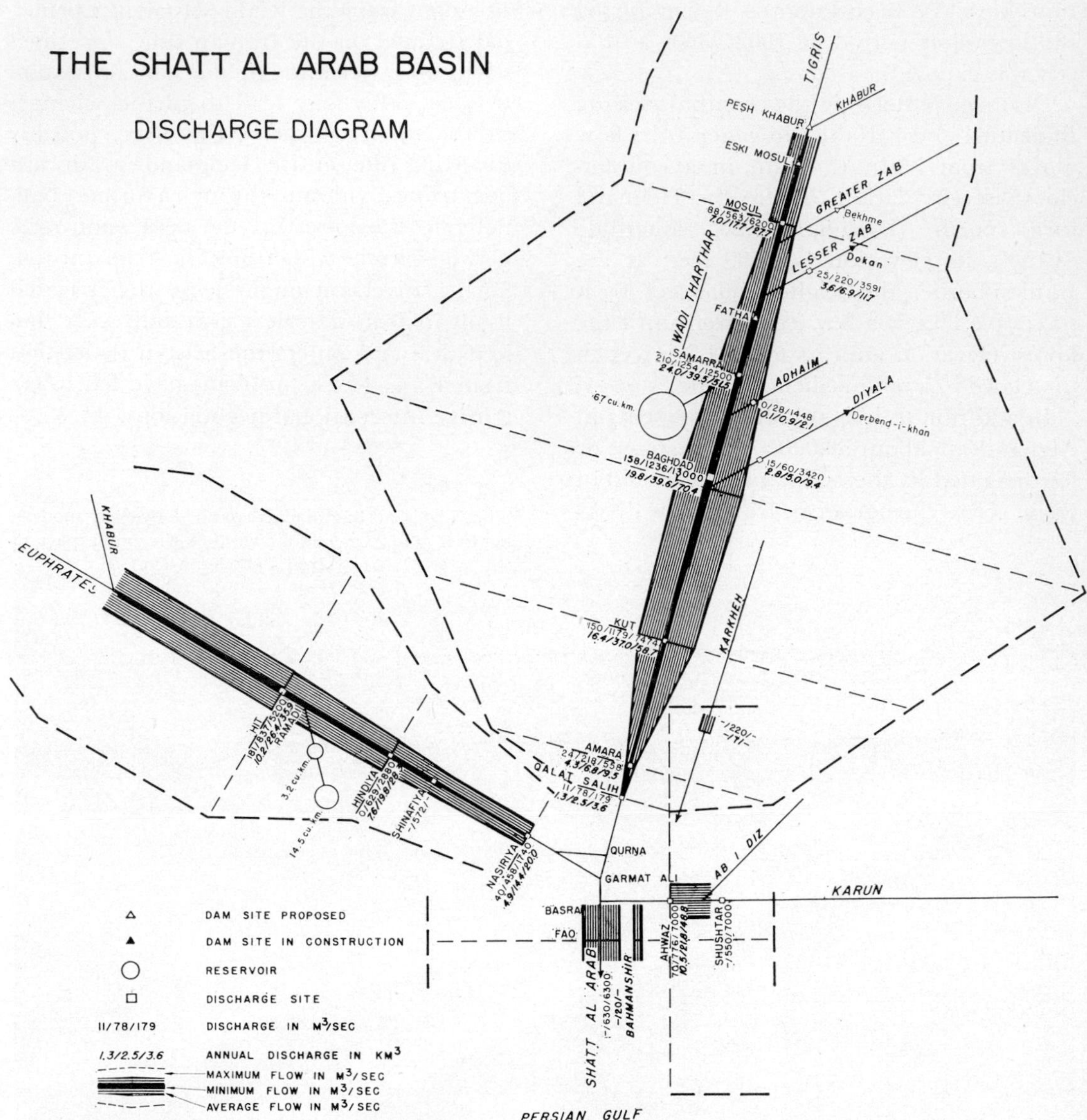

The three major tributaries of the Shatt-al-Arab vary widely in their seasonal flow, and in their volume from place to place. The volume of the recorded minimum flow is shown in solid black, the average flow is shaded, while the known maximum is shown by dashed lines. The most striking aspect of the Tigris and Euphrates is their loss of water downstream due to diversion for irrigation and evaporation in swamps. Discharge data refer to minimum, mean, and maximum flow in cubic meters per second (Cusecs).

THE SHATT-AL-ARAB, THE RIVER OF THE ARABS[1]

THREE RIVERS converge near the head of the Persian Gulf to form the Shatt-al-Arab. These are the Euphrates, Tigris, and Karun.

[1] For assistance in the preparation of this section I am indebted to Mr. Vahe J. Sevian, formerly Inspector General of Irrigation for Iraq.

The Karun is Iran's largest river and a major contributor to the Shatt-al-Arab. This scene is near Lali. (Courtesy Iranian Oil Participants.)

Together they drain 312,000 square miles. A third of this basin lies in the mountains of Turkey and Iran, and the rest is in the desert uplands of Syria and Iraq. This is by far the most important river system in Southwest Asia.

In the highlands, rivers have normal valleys and conventional hydrology; they grow larger as they flow onward. But as they cross the desert, they lose water through diversion for irrigation and by subsequent evaporation. As the flow diminishes, the river's carrying power is reduced, and silt is deposited. The bed is built higher and higher, so that after the rivers enter their delta, the channels must be controlled by dikes. As irrigation water evaporates, its chemical load is precipitated. Southern Iraq is thus a vast subaerial delta in which both sediments and salts are accumulating.

The Euphrates proper, sometimes known as the Nahr Frat, begins at the junction of the Kara Su and the Murat Suyu in central Turkey, and ends at Qurna where it joins the Tigris and becomes the Shatt-al-Arab. The river drains a basin which covers 101,950 square miles above the head of the delta at Hit. Of this area, 40 per cent lies in Turkey, largely mountainous, and another 15 per cent in Syria, largely hills and plains. Although half of the drainage area lies in Iraq, the river receives no important tributary and the only contribution is from nonperennial wadis.

The headwaters of the Euphrates system lie in the North Anatolian or Pontus Mountains of eastern Turkey at elevations of 10,000 feet, where much of the precipitation falls as snow. The river begins its delta near Hit at a low water elevation of 170 feet, some 460 miles from the mouth. The over-all length from its source to its junction with the Shatt-al-Arab is 2,100 miles.

The Tigris rises amid the snow-covered Taurus Mountains of eastern Turkey. Mountains and foothills each account for half of its basin of 43,110 square miles above the head of the delta near Samarra, where the elevation is 190 feet. The over-all length to the Shatt-al-Arab is 1,270 miles. Whereas the Euphrates receives no tributaries across the lowlands of Iraq, the Tigris is augmented by a number of major streams, all on its left bank, which descend from the Zagros Mountains. These are the Khabur, the Great Zab, the Little Zab, the Adhaim, and the Diyala. Farther south, the Karkheh loses itself in swamps but most of its water eventually enters the Tigris.

The third contributor to the Shatt-al-Arab is the longest river in Iran, the Karun, which rises in the 12,000 foot Zagros Mountains. Although the Karun is 515 miles in actual length, its course is so winding that the source is only 210 air line miles from the mouth. The drainage pattern reflects the folded geologic structures, with long sections parallel to the mountain ridges which are crossed in magnificent gorges as much as 8,000 feet deep. While the basin measures only 26,090 square miles, the Karun drains a mountainous area of moderately heavy precipitation so that it carries a large volume of water. The flow of the Karun at Ahwaz is greater than that of the Tigris at Samarra and nearly equal to the Euphrates at Hit. The upper half, above Shushtar, is sometimes known as the Kurang. The Karun's major tributary is the Ab-i-Diz.

In addition to these three tributary systems, the total basin of the Shatt-al-Arab includes several noncontributory areas. These are desert sections, so dry that little or no runoff reaches the main rivers. Even when some wadis are filled by local rains, the water may be lost before reaching a river. One such area is the great western desert of Iraq, extending into Saudi Arabia. Another is the basin of the Wadi Tharthar, midway between the Tigris and Euphrates, which covers 9,445 square miles. Still others include shallow depressions such as Habbaniya, Abu Dibbis, and Shari, partly filled by nonoverflowing lakes.

The Shatt-al-Arab is formed by the junction of the Euphrates and Tigris above Basra. The proper head of the river is in some question. The Tigris and Euphrates are usually said to join at Qurna, but at this point most of the so-called Euphrates actually consists of diverted Tigris flood water which has escaped through its right bank into marsh lands and joined the left bank of the Euphrates. The latter, in turn, contributes much of its volume into the Hammar Lake which flows into the Shatt-al-Arab at Garmat Ali, forty miles downstream.

If the junction is taken as Qurna, the river extends 113 miles to the bar, six miles below Fao. The Shatt-al-Arab is joined by the Karun forty-eight miles above its mouth. The bar below Fao once had a depth of only eleven feet below mean sea level, but dredging now makes it passable for ships drawing thirty feet.

The combined length of the Shatt-al-Arab, Euphrates, and Murat Suyu system is about 2,200 miles, enough to place it among the sixteen longest rivers in the world.

The composite delta is exceptionally flat. There are areas south of Baghdad where one may look to the full circle of the horizon and not see a hill, a tree, an irrigation canal, a person, or anything to break the imperceptible slope; nothing interrupts the unrelieved flatness. Elsewhere the delta is equally flat,

Most of the water in the Tigris comes from the mountains of Turkey and northern Iraq where it originates as winter rain or snow. This view of a tributary is near Dohuk. (Courtesy Iraq Petroleum Co.)

but cultivation makes it less austere. Parts of the erosional plain surrounding the delta are nearly as level; here one may drive across the unirrigated countryside almost at will.

The Euphrates and Tigris pass through marsh and lake areas near their mouths, and much of the flow is diverted. These water bodies change with the season, reaching a minimum of 3,200 square miles in the fall and increasing to 10,900 square miles in the spring. During the 1946 flood, the total inundated area in all of Iraq reached 35,000 square miles. Evaporation from these lakes amounts to about six feet per year.

It is obvious that there have been repeated shifts in river courses. Aerial photos reveal many old channels, and archaeological evidence suggests others. In central Iraq, the Euphrates is generally a few tens of feet higher than the Tigris, and the land on either side of both rivers is lower than their natural levees. The rivers thus flow on top of their flood plains, rather than in proper valleys. Although this requires dike control, it facilitates diversion for irrigation.

The lowlands of Mesopotamia have been an area of deposition since the early Cenozoic Era. The stratigraphic column includes many horizons laid down while the basin was landlocked, so that there are unusual amounts of gypsum, anhydrite, salt, and other evaporites. These ancient precipitants contribute abnormal amounts of dissolved material to the present rivers. Any examination of irrigation and its resulting problems must start with the initial high chemical content of the local ground waters.

Salt accumulation is a critical problem in

The Kut Barrage south of Baghdad raises the level of the Tigris River a few feet so that irrigation water may be diverted into gravity canals. A navigation lock appears at the far end of the dam. (Courtesy Iraq Petroleum Co.)

the irrigated lands of the lower valleys of the Tigris and Euphrates. The chemical content of the two rivers averages 250 and 445 parts per million, respectively. Not all of this is sodium chloride for there are considerable percentages of lime and gypsum. So much water is withdrawn for irrigation and then lost by evaporation that the Shatt-al-Arab carries 746 parts per million.

Since evaporation losses on the irrigated lands of Iraq amount to 30 billion cubic meters of water per year, this means an annual addition to the agricultural areas of 22 million metric tons of dissolved chemicals. The total accumulation of salt in the agricultural lands of Iraq amounts to billions of tons.

All the rivers carry large amounts of sediment. The Diyala, a left-bank tributary of the Tigris, is the most silty for its size, with some 11.5 million cubic meters of material a year derived from a catchment basin of 29,678 square kilometers. The Tigris itself annually moves 40 million cubic meters of sediment past Baghdad, but only a tenth reaches the Persian Gulf. The silt content in flood may reach 20,000 parts per million by weight; this is five times the flood load of

PRECIPITATION IN THE SHATT-AL-ARAB BASIN[1]

Rainfall average in millimeters	*Approximate elevation in meters*	*Area in square kilometers*	*Volume in cubic kilometers*
0–400	Lowlands	505,000	101
400–800	500 to 1,000	217,000	130
over 800	over 1,000	86,000	94
		808,000	325

[1] Data from George B. Cressey: "The Shatt-al-Arab Basin," *Middle East Jour.*, XII (1958), 448–460.

the Nile. On the Euphrates, the silt content at Hit has reached 6,100 parts per million, but the annual contribution is less than that of the Tigris. To this the Karun adds 29.7 million cubic meters of silt per year.

Since the three tributaries of the Shatt-al-Arab carry sediment amounting to millions of tons a year, it is natural to assume that the river is building new land at the head of the Persian Gulf, and that in earlier centuries the sea extended much farther inland. Some of the monuments at ancient Ur, now 150 miles from the Gulf, portray boat life and it has been assumed that the city once lay near the sea. Many articles on the history of early Mesopotamia are accompanied by maps which assume shore lines even north of Baghdad.

The evidence for this delta growth is questionable. Most of the sediment from the Euphrates and Tigris is deposited in the Inland Delta above Basra, so that the water which enters the Shatt-al-Arab is relatively clear. The Karun, however, pours its full load of mud into the main river, and the growth of the Karun delta may have cut off the former head of the Persian Gulf, thus forming Hammar Lake and the nearby swamps. Geological evidence as cited by Lees and Falcon[1] indicates that at the dawn of history, the head of the Gulf may even have been seaward of its present position. They conclude that "there is no acceptable historical evidence that the head of the Gulf was ever very far up-country from its present position."

Further indication that the delta front is not a thick lens of sediments may be found in the fact that test wells sunk by the Basra Oil Company south of Hammar Lake penetrate only a few feet of alluvium before reaching bed rock. Likewise, captains of dredging boats engaged in deepening the channel below Fao report coral and conglomerate within their operating depths.

Arnold T. Wilson writes:[2] ". . . the position of the seashore can have altered very little during the last sixty centuries, though no doubt very large areas formerly covered by brackish lakes have been reclaimed."

Within the combined basins of the Euphrates, Tigris, and Karun, the mean annual rainfall amounts to some 325 billion cubic meters, or 325 cubic kilometers. If spread evenly over the entire basin, this would be an average of about twelve inches or one acre-foot. In reality, many areas south and west of Baghdad receive but five inches, while the higher mountains have seventy inches and more.

About one-third of the precipitation falls above 3,000 feet, where much of the total comes as snow. Another third occurs between 1,500 and 3,000 feet. Areas below 1,500 feet represent five-eighths of the total surface but account for only a third of the rain.

[1] G. M. Lees and N. L. Falcon: "The Geographical History of the Mediterranean Plains," *Geog. Jour.*, CXVIII (1952), 24–39.

[2] Arnold T. Wilson: "The Delta of the Shatt-al-Arab and Proposals for Dredging the Bar," *Geog. Jour.* LXV (1925), 225–239.

With suitable meteorological conditions, a large area of the Tigris basin might receive ten inches of rain in a week, and this might even be repeated a few weeks later. While it is unlikely that flood peaks on the various tributaries would be simultaneous, this is a possibility. The Euphrates is less likely to receive such a rainfall, and its floods from Turkey are usually "ironed out" before reaching Iraq. Due to its longer course, Euphrates flood waters usually reach the delta a week later than those on the Tigris.

Should this concentrated rainfall coincide with a period of rapid snow melt, the resulting stream flow might set an all time record. The freezing isobase over the mountains of eastern Turkey in spring usually lies around 3,000 feet. On one occasion this freezing level rose to 10,000 feet and remained there for a week. This change in the isobase resulted in the melting of great masses of snow, with torrential runoff.

The account of Noah's flood may lack statistical data, but its magnitude is not surprising for a basin such as that of the Shatt-al-Arab. Measurements of flood levels at Baghdad have been kept for only a few decades, and it is highly probable that new records will still be set. No matter what floods the Tigris has experienced, there is a reasonable likelihood that future flood flow will be larger. Even Noah may need to be updated.

Gauge and discharge records along the Euphrates are available from several stations in Turkey, in Syria from Deir-ez-Zor, and at three dozen sites in Iraq. At Hit, near the head of the delta, the flow has ranged from a maximum of 5,200 cubic meters per second, (or cumecs) in May, 1929, to 181 cumecs in September, 1930; the mean annual flow is 837 cumecs. Downstream at the Hindiya Barrage, the discharge has varied between nearly zero and 2,880 cumecs, with a mean of 629 cumecs. At Nasiriya, farther south, the range is from 40 to 1,740 cumecs with a mean of 458 cumecs. The progressive downstream shrinkage reflects losses due to evaporation, especially in the rice growing areas, plus flood diversion into the Habbaniya Lake.

The regime of the Tigris shows a similar decline in flow downstream. At Mosul, readings have varied between a minimum of 88, through a mean of 563, to a maximum of 6,200 cumecs. At Samarra, at the head of the delta, the corresponding discharge figures are 210, 1,254, and an estimated 12,500 cumecs. The records at Baghdad, dating back to 1906, show a minimum discharge of 158 cumecs, a mean of 1,236, and an estimated extreme high of 13,000. The latter includes the total flood flow after the dikes were breached and large areas east and west of the city were inundated. River velocities in flood may reach ten knots.

Below Baghdad large amounts of water are withdrawn by irrigation canals and by hundreds of pumps, so that the river flow diminishes appreciably. At the Kut Barrage the minimum, mean, and maximum discharge figures are 150, 1,179, and 7,474 cumecs. At Amara, the corresponding data are but 24, 218, and 558, and still farther downstream near Qala Salih after much of the river is lost in the marshes, the figures are only 11, 78, and 179. One may wonder whether any other river in the world shrinks so amazingly.

Some of the irrigation canals withdraw so much water that they become rivers themselves. In fact, both the Hilla Canal below the Hindiya Barrage and the Gharraf Canal below the Kut Barrage were formerly the main channels of the Euphrates and Tigris, respectively. Each of these canals, in turn feeds many distributaries. The Hilla Canal supplies water to 1,735,000 *mesharas*[1] by gravity flow, plus 500,000 mesharas by pump lift, while the Gharraf contributes water by gravity to 1.4 million mesharas. The total

[1] One *meshara* equals 0.612 acre.

DISCHARGE DATA FOR THE EUPHRATES[1]

City	Low Water Elevation in Meters	Catchment Area sq. Km.	Discharge in Cubic Meters per Second Min.	Mean	Max.	Annual Discharge in Cubic Kilometers Min.	Mean	Max.
Deir-ez-Zor	—	—	—	—	—	—	24.	—
Hit	52.0	—	181	837	5,200	10.2	26.4	35.9
Hindiya Barrage	23.9	—	0	629	2,880	7.6	19.8	28.3
Nasiriya	1.7	—	40	458	1,740	4.9	14.4	20.0

DISCHARGE DATA FOR THE TIGRIS[1]

City	Low Water Elevation in Meters	Catchment Area sq. Km.	Discharge in Cubic Meters per Second Min.	Mean	Max.	Annual Discharge in Cubic Kilometers Min.	Mean	Max.
Mosul	212.6	54,898	88	563	6,200	7.0	17.7	27.7
Samarra	—	—	210	1,254	12,500	24.0	39.5	51.5
Baghdad	27.6	134,259	158	1,236	13,000	19.8	39.6	70.4
At junction of the Diyala	—	166,155	163	1,339	14,000	18.9	42.3	63.5
Kut	9.5	—	150	1,179	7,474	16.4	37.0	58.7
Amara	4.6	—	24	218	558	4.3	6.8	9.5
Qala Salih	—	—	11	78	179	1.3	2.5	3.6

DISCHARGE DATA FOR THE KARUN[1]

City	Low Water Elevation in Meters	Catchment Area sq. Km.	Discharge in Cubic Meters per Second Min.	Mean	Max.	Annual Discharge in Cubic Kilometers Min.	Mean	Max.
Shushtar	—	—	—	550	7,000	—	—	—
Ahwaz	—	67,579	70	766	7,000	10.5	21.8	48.8

DISCHARGE DATA FOR THE SHATT-AL-ARAB[1]

City	Low Water Elevation in Meters	Catchment Area sq. Km.	Discharge in Cubic Meters per Second Min.	Mean	Max.	Annual Discharge in Cubic Kilometers Min.	Mean	Max.
Fao	—	808,000	—	630	6,300	—	20	—

[1] Data from George B. Cressey: "The Shatt-al-Arab Basin," *Middle East Jour.*, XII (1958), 448–460.

area of Iraq irrigated by gravity flow, as contrasted to pump irrigation, amounts to 6,840,000 mesharas, about equally divided between Tigris and Euphrates basins.

Since much of this irrigation water has no proper drainage channel through which to rejoin the main rivers, vast areas are waterlogged. This is especially true near the head of the Persian Gulf where water accumulates in the Hammar, Suniya, and Sadiya lakes, and in the surrounding marsh lands. This is the home of the unique Marsh Arabs.

Less is known about the Karun. Where it enters its delta at Shushtar the mean discharge is 550 cumecs and the flood maximum reaches 7,000. At Ahwaz, downstream from the mouth of the Ab-i-Diz but above the various delta mouths, the minimum reads 70, the mean is 766, and the maximum is 7,000 cumecs.

All of these discharge figures, minus evaporation, should add up to the Shatt-al-Arab. Discharge data for tidal rivers are difficult to compute, but it appears that the mean figure for the Shatt-al-Arab at Fao, near the mouth, is 630 cumecs with an extreme flood flow of 6,300 cumecs. On an annual basis, the discharge amounts to 19.6 cubic kilometers.

To reduce the flood hazard, Iraq has developed a series of flood control works on the Euphrates and Tigris, and on the tributaries of the latter. Since the maximum flow is unpredictable, these dams will not entirely prevent floods but they will greatly reduce the hazard.

Along the Euphrates, a low dam or barrage at Ramadi raises the river level a few feet, so that a part of the flood flow may be diverted southward into the natural basin of Lake Habbaniya where dikes have enlarged it into a reservoir which provides a storage capacity of 3.2 cubic kilometers. If this is insufficient, water will pass southward to a similar natural depression at Abu Dibbis, with a potential capacity of 14.5 cubic kilometers. There is also an arrangement whereby surplus water in Habbaniya may return to the Euphrates for irrigation use, once the flood has passed.

Conditions along the Tigris are even more favorable for flood storage. To the west is the enclosed basin of the Wadi Tharthar which terminated in a dry playa with a floor below sea level. A barrage at Samarra and a sixty-kilometer canal diverts flood water into this depression, whose capacity is sixty-three cubic kilometers.

Two dams have been built along Tigris tributaries, the Dokan Dam on the Little Zab and the Derbendi Khan Dam on the Diyala, both with large storage capacities. Each of these dams, and the Samarra Barrage as well, are designed for both flood control and irrigation, and eventually for the generation of hydroelectric power as well. Such multi-purpose objectives raise problems as to whether the reservoirs should be kept empty until the end of April for spring flood control, or kept full to provide the maximum water for power and irrigation. Tigris dams are under consideration in Turkey, in Iraq at Eski Mosul and Fatha, and at Bekhme on the Great Zab.

The Samarra Barrage is designed to pass a flood flow of 9,000 cumecs, and the Wadi Tharthar diversion canal will carry 8,000 cumecs safely. This total of 17,000 cumecs is only 3,000 cumecs larger than the estimated record flood flow of the Tigris at this point, so that the safety margin is low. In order to provide for the security of the lower valley, no more than 7,000 cumecs should be allowed to pass Samarra.

The flood control problem lies in what to anticipate on rare occasions. Hydrologic estimates at Samarra by A. R. Thomas,[1] based on twenty-five years of records, place the flood expectations as follows:

FLOOD FREQUENCIES AT SAMARRA

11,680 cumecs	5 per cent frequency
15,350 "	1 " " "
18,990 "	0.2 " " "
20,550 "	0.1 " " "

These figures are smaller than for fan-shaped basins in other parts of the world since the Tigris has no right bank tributaries. Experience tables for basins of this general character forecast a theoretical peak of 41,000 cumecs. This may be compared with an estimate of 35,000 cumecs for the maximum possible flood as computed by the Iraq Hydrological Office.

Since there is abundant evidence, both historic and geologic, that the discharges observed during the past twenty-five years have been greatly exceeded in the past, the expectations of Thomas should be taken seriously.

[1] A. R. Thomas: *Report on Hydrologic Problems in connection with Wadi Tharthar Project, Iraq.* Baghdad: Development Board (1954).

Thomas adds, "It is possible that the flood risk may be greater than estimated, due to available flood data being unrepresentative. A failure of the Barrage or breach of the retaining banks might lead to catastrophic disaster."

While great floods are rare, they do occur, and since Baghdad lies downstream, the risk must be recognized. The city is surrounded on all sides by dikes, and has several times been seriously threatened. The new dams will greatly reduce the flood menace, but it should not be said that Baghdad is now "safe."

Two other low dams, one downstream on each river, provide take-off points for irrigation canals. On the Euphrates there is the Hindiya Barrage, while on the Tigris there is the Kut Barrage. A third dam, on the Diyala, distributes the entire summer flow to a large agricultural area.

Many sites are available in the Karun basin. The first large structure is a 620-foot dam near Ahwaz, designed to irrigate 375,000 acres and to generate 520,000 kilowatts of electricty.

The water budget of the Shatt-al-Arab presents some interesting figures. Within the drainage basin of the three rivers, the annual precipitation totals about 325 cubic kilometers. Where the Euphrates, Tigris, and Karun enter their flood plains, and after they receive the contribution of their last major tributaries, the combined annual flow amounts to 90 cubic kilometers. Thus, out of the original supply of 325 cubic kilometers, 235 cubic kilometers have been lost by evaporation upstream. Most of the precipitation disappears before it ever reaches a permanent stream.

Other evaporation losses take place in the lowlands. Subtractions in the irrigated areas account for thirty cubic kilometers. Losses from the lakes and swamps which make up the vast Inland Delta north of Basra amount to thirty-three cubic kilometers.

The Karun has two mouths; about two-thirds of the water enters the Shatt-al-Arab while the remainder reaches the Persian Gulf through the Bahmashir Channel to the east of Abadan. As already pointed out, the annual discharge of the Shatt-al-Arab proper is twenty cubic kilometers; to this may be added some seven cubic kilometers for the other mouth of the Karun.

The total water budget of the Euphrates, Tigris, and Karun thus reads as follows.

SHATT-AL-ARAB WATER BUDGET

Discharge to the Persian Gulf		27 km³
(from Karun:	22)	
(from Tigris and Euphrates:	5)	
Evaporation in the Inland Delta		33 km³
Evaporation in the irrigated area		30 km³
Evaporation losses above the head of the deltas		235 km³
Original supply from precipitation		325 km³

The above figures suggest that the average drop of rain has but one chance in twelve of flowing to the sea. Were it not for the contribution of the Karun, which loses little water by evaporation en route, the average would be even smaller. Water passing Baghdad has but one chance in thirty-five of getting to the Persian Gulf.

QANATS AND KAREZ[1]

ALTHOUGH RIVERS and wells supply irrigation water for the major oases, thousands of acres and hundreds of villages receive their sole supply from the underground infiltration tunnels or "horizontal wells" known as *karez* or *qanats* (pronounced kä'nŭt).

Qanats are present by the thousands in Afghanistan, Iran, and across the Arab world.

[1] Some of this material has appeared in an article entitled "Qanats, Karez and Foggara," *Geog. Rev.*, XLVII (1958) 27–44, and is reproduced here by permission.

Thousands of qanats or karez supply irrigation water in Iran, as in this scene near Shahrud. A windlass is used to lift earth from the excavation; where the tunnel is apt to cave in it is lined with tiles. (G. B. C.)

The essential idea is that of a gently sloping tunnel, often along the radius of an alluvial fan, extending upslope until the water table is tapped and emerging at the downslope end to supply an oasis. To give access to the tunnel, a number of vertical shafts are dug at closely spaced intervals. The length of the tunnel may range from a few hundred yards to tens of miles, and the shafts near the upper end may be several hundred feet deep.

The scheme is of Persian origin, dating back more than 2,000 years. The palace city of Persepolis is thought to have been supplied by qanats about 500 B.C. Near the Mediterranean, qanats are erroneously ascribed to the Romans. The term karez is a Persian word, but is used more outside the country than within where preference goes to the Arabic word qanat, meaning subterranean canal or conduit for water.

Qanats are limited to sloping lands, usually alluvial fans or outwash gravels at the base of a mountain. In the area to be irrigated, surface water is inadequate and local ground water may be too deep or too saline. By means of these nearly horizontal tunnels, water is brought by gravity from a distant underground source. Once the channels are dug and as long as they are periodically cleaned, the water flows freely.

Many deserts of Southwest Asia have a succession of mountains and sedimentary basins, with great alluvial fans encircling the depressions. Such rain as falls in the highlands quickly runs off and, on leaving the bed rock area of the mountain face, seeps into the gravels and sands of the encircling fans. From the margin of the basin, water moves underground toward the central playa or terminal lake.

The cross section of a typical basin shows a gentle surface slope from the mountain across the fan to the central playa, whereas the ground water profile will be more dish shaped. The water table rises near the bedrock of the mountain wall, but is flatter than the ground surface near the center of the basin, so that the central lake may mark the merging of the land surface with the water table. Ground water toward the center of the basin tends to be stagnant and highly mineralized, and only near the peripheral sources of intake is it fresh.

The yield of qanats varies widely, according to ground water characteristics, the porosity of the soil, and the season. A qanat in porous gravels near Meshed, one and one-half kilometers in length, which had a flow of 4,200 gallons per minute in April, declined to 400 gallons in July and was dry from August through the following March. Other qanats have nearly a constant flow throughout the year because they tap a dependable ground water source.

There are many variations in qanat systems. Where a single tunnel fails to yield an adequate supply, additional branch infiltration galleries may be added upslope. During dry periods when the water table is depressed, the tunnels may be lengthened to reach more dependable supplies.

In a few cases, notably east of Tehran, there are a succession of qanat systems down an alluvial slope, each drawing upon the water of the other as it seeps into the ground from irrigated fields. In many towns qanats terminate in the bazaar, or in a mosque, or in the house of the owner. Where a qanat passes beneath a residential area, some houses have a summer living room or *sirdab* alongside the flowing stream, two to six stories underground. The water is usually cool throughout the year, but may become poluted from similar rooms upstream.

Since qanats are the key to life in these arid lands, many laws have been developed to govern their construction and use. Some of these regulate the distance between new qanat tunnels and those already in existence. Thus, lines of qanat wells must be spaced at least twelve yards apart. Around each qanat entrance is a *harem* or reserved area. Other laws govern the distribution of the water, or the responsibilities of the owner. The title to empty land may be awarded to whoever supplies it with water, and on rented land the owner of the water may be entitled to as much as 80 per cent of the crop. One book of qanat laws, the Kitabi Qani, dates from the ninth century.

The aerial traveller near Tehran looks down on lines of shafts which lead to the nearly horizontal tunnels known as qanats. (G. B. C.)

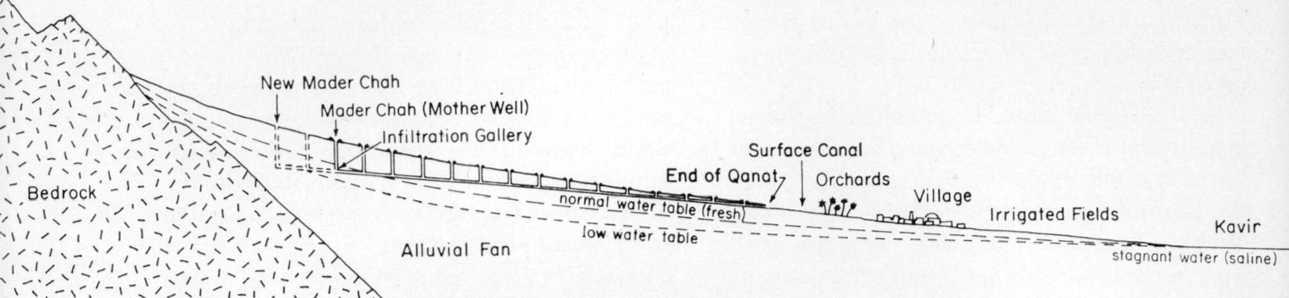

Qanats or karez are "horizontal wells" which tap ground water in the upper slopes of alluvial fans and bring it to the surface down slope by gravity. Many qanats are tens of miles long, and the mother well may be several hundred feet deep.

Iranian history records many invaders who conquered by filling in the qanat shafts, as when the city of Hamadan was captured by destroying its qanats. In describing the Persian wars, Herodotus advises that to destroy a town, one should fill the qanat wells.

Qanat construction is a specialized trade. The diggers are known in Iran as *moghani,* or in Afghanistan as *karezkan,* and often conduct their business as a family occupation, generation after generation. When a new qanat is to be dug, the moghani first locates a point on the surface beneath which it is hoped to find water. This is usually on the upper slope of an alluvial fan, perhaps near the mouth of a dry mountain valley. Sometimes an area marginal to a wadi may be selected if there is assumed to be a good underground flow.

First, an initial shaft is dug. When the water table is reached and it appears that there is an adequate supply of good water in porous gravels, it is then necessary to run a rough line of levels to see whether the water surface at that point is high enough above the desired outlet downslope for a gentle flow to reach the area to be irrigated. If not, other wells must be dug farther up slope. The most distant shaft upslope is known as the mother well, or *madar chah.*

To excavate the qanat, a line of shafts is then sunk, spaced thirty to a hundred yards apart. Several men often work together. Boys are commonly used in the smaller qanats. One man below extends the tunnel, which is just large enough to crawl through, another puts sixty pounds of earth into a small leather bag and drags it to the base of the shaft, while another operates a wooden windlass on the surface. Where wells are deep, two men may operate the windlass, lifting a bag every six minutes in a 240-foot shaft. The miners have small lamps which burn castor oil, and the quality of the air is judged by the flame.

In some cases, work starts from the lower end of the system, first as a shallow ditch, which is converted to a tunnel as the depth increases up slope. In other situations, the tunnel may start from the upstream end and work down hill from the mother well. The slope of the tunnel must be gentle enough to avoid erosion. In most cases the water in the tunnel is six inches to a foot in depth, flowing at the rate of a mile or two per hour.

Around each shaft a ring of earth accumulates. Where the openings are deep and widely spaced, and especially where the qanat tunnel caves badly, these circular piles may be six feet in height and thirty feet in diameter. More commonly, the dimensions are half these figures. As seen from the air, these piles of earth resemble small craters or

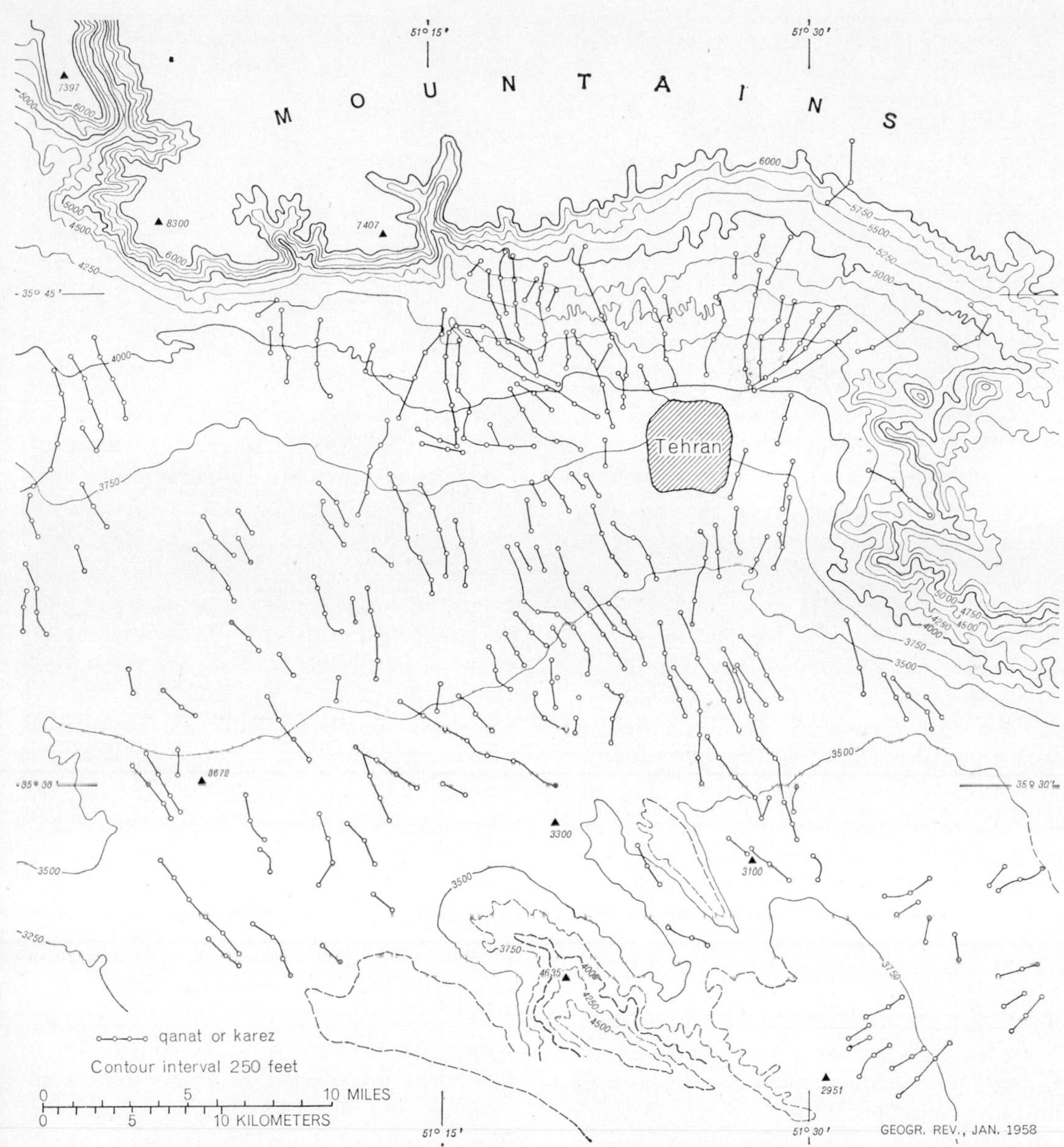

The alluvial slopes of the Elburz Mountains contain scores of qanats or karez, only the more important of which are here shown. Many qanats are miles in length, and the mother well may be several hundred feet deep. (Courtesy American Geographical Society)

huge doughnuts. One purpose of the circular pile is to keep out surface drainage which might flood the tunnel after a storm. This is especially important when the line of shafts follows a wadi or dry stream bed.

Qanat tunnels generally have widths of two to three feet, with heights of three or four feet. Soft earth presents a problem since it tends to cave in; under such circumstances, the tunnel may be lined with oval tiles. Since thousands of tiles may be required, they are

The combined flow of the Euphrates, Tigris, and Karun reaches the Persian Gulf through the Shatt-al-Arab which flows through the palm groves near Basra. (Courtesy Iraq Petroleum Co.)

often made on the spot in a kiln which uses local brush. If an area caves too badly, or if large boulders are encountered, a run-around may be necessary.

A long qanat system may have several hundred wells, so that the total amount of material to be excavated is considerable. If the cross sections of the tunnel and shaft each average one square yard, and the mother well has a depth of 50 yards, and the wells are spaced 100 yards apart, the total excavation of a one mile qanat would amount to some 6,160 cubic yards. Lengths of five and ten miles are common, with some tunnels of twenty miles and more. Such qanat systems may require three years to construct and inevitably cost large sums.

While qanats waste water by seepage along their channel and by continuing to flow when not needed, they have a great advantage since they derive their water from high up on the alluvial fan where the supply is fresh and continuously replenished. In contrast, local well water is derived from nearly stagnant sources and is inclined to be saline near the center of a basin.

With the introduction of drilled wells and diesel pumps, some qanat systems have proved to be uneconomical and have been allowed to fall into disrepair, but in other areas long, new qanats continue to be dug.

Many parts of Iran and Afghanistan still depend exclusively on qanat water for both domestic supplies and cultivation. Once in operation, the qanat flows night and day, and the only expense is for occasional cleaning. On the other hand, pumped wells require operators, fuel, and mechanical upkeep.

Some qanats have a flow of several hundred gallons per minute, but most are much smaller, and their flow usually varies somewhat with the season. One good qanat is sometimes thought adequate for 200 acres, but this would require an average flow of 120 gallons per minute to yield one acre-foot of irrigation water in the course of a year. Some qanats irrigate two square miles, so that their owners may well become wealthy.

Since desert land may be useless without water, the ownership of water is the deciding factor in agriculture. Most qanats are owned individually, but, in some cases, private ownership has been minutely subdivided through inheritance so that some qanats at Yezd have from fifty to 1,000 owners. Others are village property.

All qanats require maintenance. Where the tunnel passes through soft earth, cleaning must take place each year. During years of exceptionally heavy rain, the ground down to the tunnel level may become saturated, resulting in widespread collapse. Where owners are unable to keep a qanat in repair, the flow may decrease or entirely cease so that the cropland and even the village must be abandoned. Many of the ruined villages and dead fields seen so commonly in desolate areas owe their abandonment to a failure to keep the qanat in repair; no climatic change need be assumed.

Most qanat tunnels continue downslope until the gravity flow reaches the surface. In a few cases, pumps are installed in some of the shafts toward the end of the line. These may be hand or animal operated, or motor driven. Irrigation is thus made possible in upslope areas which do not have flowing water. If the tunnel is not continued to reach the surface, the qanat may terminate in an underground cistern, known as *birket* or *ambar,* from which water is lifted as needed; long flights of steps may lead down to this reservoir.

Where a qanat supplies water to several small irrigation canals, the water is divided by a weir. Allocation to various users is usually based on time rather than volume. Each part owner, or more commonly each renter, is permitted to use the flow of the canal past his field for so many hours on certain days. In some areas there is an eight-day rotation.

REFERENCES

* Cressey, George B.: "The Shatt al-Arab Basin," *Middle East Jour.,* XII (1958), 448–460.

Cressey, George B.: "Qanats, Karez and Foggaras," *Geog. Rev.,* XLVIII (1958), 27–44.

Harrison, J. V.: "The Shatt-el-Arab," *Jour. Royal Asian Soc.,* XXIX (1942), 43–51.

Ionides, M. G.: THE REGIME OF THE RIVERS EUPHRATES AND TIGRIS. London: Spon (1937).

Lane, Ferdinand C.: EARTH'S GRANDEST RIVERS. New York: Doubleday (1949).

* Russell, Richard J.: "Alluvial Morphology of Anatolian Rivers," *Annals Assoc. Amer. Geogs.,* XLIV (1954), 363–391.

Wilson, Arnold T.: "The Delta of the Shatt el Arab and Proposals for Dredging the Bar," *Geog. Jour.,* LXV (1925), 225–234.

CHAPTER 6

Land Use

Arable Land
Tenancy
Food Crops
Technical Crops
Livestock
Forests
References

ARABLE LAND

IN A CRITICAL STUDY on agriculture in Egypt, the Levant, and Iraq published by the Royal Institute of International Affairs, Doreen Warriner begins her introduction with the following words:[1]

> Near starvation, pestilence, high death rates, soil erosion, economic exploitation—this is the pattern of life for the mass of the rural population in the Middle East. It is a poverty which has no parallel in Europe, since even clean water is a luxury. Many incomes are low—£5 to £7 per head per year. . . .

Miss Warriner continues concerning,

> the tendency to see the Middle East, not as a poor region, with extra-ordinarily adverse conditions, in part heavily overpopulated; but as a land of promise, virtually empty and capable of vast agricultural development. . . . While there is undoubtedly scope for advance in agricultural technique, to regard such change as likely to cause a great or general increase in productivity means a complete loss of perspective. It must not be forgotten that ecologically the Middle East is not, and never will be, a good grain growing region. . . . Nor does irrigation really change the situation, since the costs of growing grain on irrigated lands are too high in relation to costs on non-irrigated land in more favored countries.

With the present conditions and prospects there can only be agreement with the above, though rural poverty is in general much less than in India, China, or Africa.

The Sixth General Conference of the Food and Agricultural Organization, meeting in Rome in 1951, recommended that its member nations should strive for "a well balanced increase of 1 to 2 per cent per annum in world production of basic foods and other agricultural products in excess of the rate of population growth." The Cairo regional

[1] Doreen Warriner: *Land and Poverty in the Middle East*. London and New York: Royal Institute of International Affairs (1948), 1. Quoted by permission.

(Opposite) Only 5 per cent of the land in Southwest Asia produces crops. This palm oasis is at Qatif in eastern Arabia. (Courtesy Standard Oil Co. of New Jersey.)

Irrigated fields surround this village west of Tehran. Southwest Asia has large areas of potential agricultural land where the soil is satisfactory but water is rarely adequate. (Courtesy U. S. Air Force.)

conference of 1953 reported that[1] "in the Near East the production of both food and non-food agricultural commodities had increased faster than population in the last few years. This expansion, however, was uneven, most of it being in the food surplus countries." The most outstanding increase was in Turkey, while the major food deficit country was Egypt.

Information as to the extent of arable or of irrigated land can only be an approximation. The United Nations Food and Agricultural Organization has published figures as supplied by each country, but accepts them without any attempt at evaluation.

[1] Food and Agricultural Organization: *Agriculture in the Near East*. Rome: United Nations (1953).

In some cases data on cultivated land involve large areas periodically left fallow, orchards may or may not be included, and the totals do not indicate how much land is actually harvested in any given year. The term "irrigated land" frequently refers to the entire area occasionally supplied with water. Many figures conflict, and in the general absence of census data or of precise maps, there is little basis to pass judgment.

On the basis of published data, cultivated land in all Swasia measures 162,800 square miles, or 7 per cent of the total area. Of this total, 27,190 square miles are reported to be irrigated, equal to 17 per cent of the cultivated area. However, the figure for the total cultivated area seems too high, so that the second percentage may be too low. It may be more precise to place the actual crop area at 5 per cent, say 125,000 square miles, and

Agricultural land covers no more than 125,000 square miles of Southwest Asia. Large areas lie fallow each year. Some additional land may be brought under cultivation through reclamation, but increased food supply rests largely on more intensive use of presently cultivated acreage.

to recognize that at least 20 per cent of it requires supplementary water.

The fact that Swasia covers almost 2.5 million square miles should not lead to an assumption that vast areas of undeveloped agricultural land are available. Most of the deserts and mountains in this corner of Asia appear permanently unproductive. Any increase in crop area will require large capital investments; this is no place for the individual pioneer farmer.

One key to agricultural expansion lies in good and inexpensive water. Even if the Shatt-al-Arab and the Helmand were used to the full, the total agricultural area would not increase enough to feed the expected population. Cheap processes for desalting sea water may some day become available, but even if all the ocean were fresh it would still be necessary to pump it onto the upland fields, and power costs might be prohibitive.

If the present crop area measures something like 5 per cent of the whole, it will require a major effort to increase this by

Large areas of semiarid land have been brought into cultivation by modern tractors, as in this scene near Ankara. Many of these areas of dry farming have good soil, but rainfall is low and erratic. (Courtesy Turkish Press, Broadcasting, and Tourist Department, Ankara.)

one or two percentage points per decade. Meanwhile population grows by nearly 2 per cent a year. Increased food supplies may need to come from the more intensive utilization of present crop land rather than from new acreage.

The distribution of agricultural land shows wide variation in pattern, generally diminishing in density as one moves southward into drier areas. Turkey and Syria report about a quarter of their land under cultivation, but whereas only about 8 per cent is irrigated in humid Turkey, 17 per cent is irrigated in more arid Syria. In Afghanistan cultivated land approximates one-seventh, of which irrigation accounts for 65 per cent. Iran, Iraq, and Jordan each credit themselves with one-tenth of their entire area in cultivation, of which 10 per cent, 5 per cent, and 3 per cent respectively receive irrigation. According to the Food and Agricultural Organization, Israel and Lebanon, both mountainous, have one-fifth of their total area in agriculture, with irrigation accounting for 28 and 18 per cent. In Saudi Arabia the crop area represents only one-hundredth of the whole, but virtually all of it requires extra water.

TENANCY

The progress of agriculture has long been retarded by the obscure and confused status of all land rights. Any increase in cultivated

LAND USE[1]

	Population In thousands	Area Total	Arable Incl. Orchards	Irrigated Land	Potentially Productive	Pasture	Forests
Aden Colony	152	21	—	—	—	—	—
Aden Protectorate	650	29,008	120	—	24	18,000	—
Afghanistan	13,000	65,000	9,015	—	2,327	3,214	1,000
Bahrein	124	60	—	—	—	—	—
Iran	19,253	163,000	16,760	1,600	33,000	10,000	19,000
Iraq	6,538	44,444	5,457	2,800	12,100	875	1,770
Israel	1,937	2,070	392	118	1,280[2]	805	66
Jordan	1,527	9,661	893	32	400	740	525
Kuwait	208	1,554	—	—	—	—	—
Lebanon	1,525	1,040	278	48	364	—	92
Muscat and Oman	550	21,238	—	—	—	—	80
Qatar	40	2,201	—	—	—	—	—
Saudi Arabia	6,036	160,000	210	—	—	92,760	400
Syria	4,082	18,448	4,590	583	2,561	5,951	449
Trucial Oman	80	8,360	—	—	—	—	—
Turkey	25,500	77,698	24,070	1,988	—	29,748	10,418
Yemen	4,500	19,500	—	—	—	—	150
All Swasia	85,702	623,303	61,785	7,169	52,056	162,093	33,950
Egypt	24,026	100,000	2,610	2,610	516	—	—

[1] Area given in thousand hectares. Data from Food and Agricultural Organization, PRODUCTION YEARBOOK, 1958.

[2] 1957.

area or in crop yields is handicapped by uncertainties as to ownership and lawful possession. Until the middle of the nineteenth century, much of the land had no regular system of private ownership, and there was no registration of title deeds.

The Ottoman Empire attempted to regularize the system by recognizing *miri* or state land, in some cases partly under private management comparable to a lease; *mulk* or fully owned private land, and *waqf* or land held as a religious endowment or trust, often under some measure of state control. Much of the agricultural area is ultimately owned by the state, in other words it is *miri* land, but is held under such variations as *tapu,* meaning tenure or fief land where the owner holds everything except title, or *luzma* which resembles perpetual leasehold such as tribal lands. Since *waqf* land involved lower taxes and since the rent can be assigned to individuals and inherited, much *waqf* land is held under collusion, and over the generations has been repeatedly subdivided. Land of this category presents a major obstacle to reform. Other lands are held as communal property, *masha,* perhaps registered in the name of one or several leaders, or a religious community.

Everywhere the conditions of tenancy are changing. In Syria, the rural scene was dominated by owners who lived in the cities and had little interest in farming other than to provide credit. In Iraq, considerable ownership resides with large sheikhs who no longer reside on the land, or with urban capitalists who provide money to operate irrigation pumps. Major revisions have occurred in Israel, but little of the land is owned by the individual who farms it. Prior to the revolution in Egypt, half the agricultural land was owned by wealthy farmers who actually lived

Water is the key to cultivation in the desert. These watermelons are being raised on the demonstration farms at Al Kharj near Riyadh in central Arabia. (Courtesy Standard Oil Co. of New Jersey).

on the land and employed laborers; the remainder of the land belonged to small peasant cultivators many of whom had but an acre for their family.

While conditions vary widely, most Swasian farmers are share-cropping tenants, in places almost serfs, living on a subsistence basis. Their income consists of a portion of the crop which may vary from 50 per cent down to 20 per cent depending on whether the owner supplies seeds, water, and draft animals, or merely leases the land. Farmers have little inducement to improve the soil, or the necessary capital in case they have the initiative. Land is a traditional form of wealth, and large areas are held by absentee owners who desire security for their investment but who seldom visit their farms.

This combination of wealthy owners, too often shortsighted, and poor and discouraged peasants provides a fertile field for social and political explosion. Even a wise government program of agricultural improvement faces many obstacles in its application. Shall new irrigation systems serve the present agricultural areas with their fragmentation of fields and perhaps of ownership, or shall they develop new virgin lands where there can be an efficient over-all design but where ownership rests with a single owner with political influence?

FOOD CROPS

WHEAT apparently originated in Southwest Asia, and many species of *Triticum* are still grown here. These include wild forms such as *einkorn* and *emmer,* known from Neolithic times and still raised in a few parts of Turkey. Durum wheat is found in western Turkey, the Levant, and Yemen. Club wheat originated in Afghanistan and Iran. Com-

A common device for lifting water from open wells is the Persian water wheel, a device where draft animals raise an endless chain of buckets through a gear arrangement. This well is near Kabul in Afghanistan. (G. B. C.)

mon bread wheat, *Triticum vulgare,* was first developed in an area extending from eastern Turkey across northern Iran and Afghanistan to northern India, and from there it has spread around the world.

Wheat is one of the world's best grains and the most versatile. Most varieties require a frost-free season of 100 days. While the largest yields occur with thirty inches of rainfall, wheat will also mature with as little as ten inches if the precipitation comes during the growing season. This means that in Swasia the crop is largely winter wheat. The harvest begins during May in Syria and Iraq, shifts to June in Lebanon and western Turkey, and moves into July in central Turkey and Iran. Highland areas, where planting is delayed, may have an August harvest.

Wheat cultivation is widespread in Turkey, with some concentration in central Anatolia and a decrease in the eastern highlands. In the Levant, wheat is the preferred crop in all humid lowlands. Iraq has two patterns, rain-fed wheat in the north, extending into northern Syria, and irrigated wheat in the south. In Iran and Afghanistan there are only a few places where rainfall is adequate; elsewhere wheat requires irrigation.

The annual harvest fluctuates widely because of variations in rainfall and world prices. Crop yields per hectare are modest, partly due to limited moisture and the lack of fertilizers.

Turkey is the major producer, with 7.5 million hectares under cultivation and a yield of around 8 million metric tons, about 250 million bushels. Iran and Afghanistan follow with about one third this area and yield. Next are Syria and Iraq, each with 1.5 million hectares, with yields of about a million metric tons of wheat. Lebanon, Jordan, and Israel each produce modest amounts,

This Turkoman farmer from Meshed in Iran holds a prize winning sheaf of grain.

and Saudi Arabia produces a small quantity. Some wheat is also grown in Yemen and Masqat.

Barley is the second most important food crop, long known in Swasia since it is found in Neolithic remains. Six-row barley is pictured in Sumerian and Babylonian inscriptions. Cultivated barleys appear to have developed in the highlands of Turkey and Iran, as well as in East Asia and East Africa. Barley matures more rapidly than wheat and thrives with lower temperatures and on lighter soils. In Mediterranean lands barley is generally a winter crop, but its resistance to heat and drought also qualify it as a summer crop.

The distribution of barley resembles that of wheat, namely a concentration in the northern part of the realm. Turkey leads by far, with over 2.5 million hectares and 3 million metric tons. Iran and Iraq follow, with 1 million hectares and about an equal tonnage. Syria and Afghanistan are also important producers. Every nation in the area lists some barley.

Most of the other grains are grown but are inferior to wheat and barley. Corn probably ranks third, especially in Turkey where its area measures 700,000 hectares and the yield is 800,000 metric tons. Afghanistan reports half as large an area for corn production, but elsewhere it is of little importance.

Rye is reported only in Turkey, where the area approaches that of corn. Oats are common in Turkey, but rare elsewhere.

Drought-tolerant crops such as millets and sorghums are important, as might be expected. While widespread, they dominate only in Yemen where *dhura* is the main crop.

AGRICULTURAL PRODUCTION[1]

	All grains		*Wheat*		*Barley*		*Corn*		*Millet and sorghum*		*Rice*	
	1956	*1957*	*1956*	*1957*	*1956*	*1957*	*1956*	*1957*	*1956*	*1957*	*1956*	*1957*
Aden Protectorate	29[2]	—	5[2]	—	4[2]	—	—	—	3[2]	—	—	—
Afghanistan	—	—	2,124[2]	—	283[2]	—	—	—	—	—	270[2]	—
Egypt	5,138[2]	5,371	1,547	1,467	129	131	1,652	1,498	594	566	1,573	1,709
Iran	4,169	4,279	2,700	2,800	1,000	980	14	—	17[2]	—	440	480
Iraq	1,965	2,589	776	1,118	1,066	1,305	6	5	6	7	111	154
Israel	209	234	74	83	85	74	23	38	26	38	—	—
Jordan	348	310	242	220	96	81	—	—	—	—	—	—
Lebanon	104	113	60	65	21	24	14	17	6	5	1	—
Saudi Arabia	170	—	37	—	23	—	—	—	13	—	4	—
Syria	1,613	2,151	1,051	1,354	462	721	15	15	75	52	6	2
Turkey	11,443	14,256	6,510	8,419	2,900	3,650	858	750	74	70	153	192

[1] In thousand metric tons. Data from Food and Agricultural Organization: *Production Yearbook.*
[2] Nearest year.

Rice is a favorite food, especially in the desert. Surprisingly large amounts are grown, all by irrigation. In Iran the area exceeds 250,000 hectares, much of it along the Caspian Sea, and the yield amounts to 500,000 metric tons. The marsh lands of lower Iraq are also a significant rice area, with some 70,000 hectares under cultivation and a normal yield of 150,000 tons. Turkey produces somewhat more rice, but from a smaller area.

The total area devoted to all grains, omitting Yemen and other small areas, as reported in the *Production Yearbook* of the Food and Agricultural Organization, amounts to over 25 million hectares. Yields fluctuate considerably but approximate 25,000 metric tons. Nearly half the reported area and considerably more than half the tonnage is in Turkey.

In most years, the area as a whole is a net importer of grain, in other words, Swasia does not feed itself. However, barley and rice are exported; roughly one-half million tons of the former and one-quarter million of rice. Regional wheat imports often amount to a million tons.

Afghanistan is normally self-sufficient. Turkey, Iraq, and Syria usually have a surplus for export. Iran is commonly deficient in grains and must import.

Tree crops form an important part of the agricultural picture. Olives and oranges are famous in all Mediterranean lands, while dates are characteristic of the desert. Irrigation is usually a profitable venture.

Olives are so representative of subtropical climates with mild humid winters that their northern limit is sometimes used to define the extent of Mediterranean conditions. Southwest Asia appears to be the original homeland, and cultivation goes back to prehistoric times. Many trees are centuries old, much gnarled, but still productive. Olives prefer light, well-drained soils and are often found on tiny, hill-side terraces. Irrigation

Date palms thrive around the Persian Gulf and provide for both local food and export. This grove lies in an oasis near Riyadh in Saudi Arabia. (Courtesy Arabian American Oil Co.)

is uncommon unless winter rainfall is under eight inches, for excessive water lowers the oil content. The harvest takes place at the beginning of winter, with a yield of twenty to forty pounds of olives per tree, which equals from two to four pounds of oil. A good grove will yield 200 gallons of oil per acre.

Turkey leads in the eastern Mediterranean, with nearly 2 million acres of olives. The leading areas are within fifty miles of the Aegean coast, where olives grow up to 1,500 feet above sea level. Coastal portions of Syria, Lebanon, and Israel also raise olives. Iran is a minor producer.

Citrus crops probably originated in Southwest Asia and were introduced into Europe by the Arabs in the eleventh century; they now grow throughout the northern half of Swasia. Commercial plantings of Jaffa oranges date from the eighteenth century. They once traditionally formed three-quarters of the export revenue from the original Palestine. While the Levant states lead in output, southern Turkey and northern Iran are also important producers. Oranges far outstrip lemons and grapefruit.

Dates are the one important crop in which Southwest Asia leads the world. The date palm is the queen among Arabian flora; with milk it forms the chief item in the diet of the Bedouin. The date palm matures its fruit only where summer climates are long, hot, and dry and where its roots have ample water. Dates are more tolerant of saline

Terracing is widespread on the humid slopes of the Lebanon Mountains, shown here, and in Yemen, but is uncommon elsewhere in Swasia. (Courtesy U. S. Operations Mission, Beirut.)

water than most other crops and are thus well adapted to desert conditions. There are several hundred varieties, of which *halawi* are the choicest, yielding forty pounds per tree. Other varieties may yield three times as much. Some trees bear for fifty years. The palm flower is bisexual and needs artificial pollination in order to give heavy crops; it is thus necessary to climb every female tree in the spring in order to fertilize the flowers. The harvest is in the fall.

Iraq produces three-quarters of the world's dates. The major area is along the Shatt-al-Arab below the junction of the Tigris and Euphrates, but dates are present along both rivers to and beyond the head of their deltas. The country is reported to have 24 million bearing palm trees with a total production of 350,000 tons, two-thirds of which is exported. Both alcohol and the native drink *arak* are made from dates; date stones are ground up as cattle or camel fodder; rope may be made from the fibers of the trunk, and the tree is an important source of domestic fuel.

About 7 million palms line the Shatt-al-Arab continuously for 100 miles, extending one or two miles from the river bank. Each tree is close to an irrigation canal, and as the tide rises and falls in the Persian Gulf and the estuary, river water flows in and out of each lateral canal. Although some of this water is brackish, the daily flushing prevents any accumulation of salt. Other date areas lie near Baghdad.

Bananas grow well in the warm and humid coastal areas. (Courtesy U. S. Operations Mission, Beirut.)

Dates have long played a role in this area. Stone reliefs in the Assyrian Palace of Khorsabad show the king carrying the symbol of date fertilization, and the former coat of arms of Iraq carried date palms.

In the Arabian peninsula, date palms occupy 90 per cent of most oases. Saudi Arabia ranks second to Iraq in date palm production. Iran raises dates in the southern third of the country, chiefly along the Persian Gulf and the Gulf of Oman where palms grow at elevations ranging to 4,000 feet. The country has some 10 million trees, more than one-third of which are along the Iranian side of the Shatt-al-Arab; production amounts to 150,000 tons, and it is an important export product.

Dates are not grown to any extent in Turkey or in the Levant, except in the drier and hotter areas.

Coconut palms are found only in Dhufar, a somewhat more humid coastal section of southern Arabia.

Nuts of many varieties are grown and exported. Almonds, walnuts, and pistachios are common from the Mediterranean to Afghanistan. Filberts or hazel nuts are exported from the western and northern parts of Turkey; in fact, Turkey supplies half of the world's commerce in these nutmeats.

Fruits are widely grown. Excellent apples are raised in the highlands of Lebanon and in Turkey which has 5 million trees. Apricots of superior size and flavor are found in Iran; many are dried for export. Figs are famous around Izmir in western Turkey, formerly known as Smyrna.

Grapes rank high in all Mediterranean lands. Large amounts are dried as raisins; some wine is made, but its use is prohibited

The drier areas of Southwest Asia are noted for their sweet grapes and melons. This farmer lives at Baquba in central Iraq. (Courtesy U. S. Operations Mission, Baghdad.)

Hemp is raised for its fibre in Turkey and Syria. This scene is in the Ghuta oasis near Damascus. (Courtesy Iraq Petroleum Co.)

for all faithful Moslems by the Koran.

Afghanistan raises some of the sweetest melons in the world, and the country's grapes are equally delicious. There is a considerable export of fruit to Pakistan.

TECHNICAL CROPS

THIS SECTION describes crops which normally require some processing before they are used. The group includes fibers such as cotton, flax, and silk; coffee and tea as beverages; sugar beets and sugar cane; tobacco; and opium.

Cotton is a hot-season plant, usually requiring 180 days or more to mature; in general, the longer the season, the longer the fiber. The plant requires at least moderate moisture, so that in many parts of Swasia it is necessary to provide irrigation. Planting is done in March or April, as in the United States, with picking in October. There are few large fields and most cotton is grown by local farmers.

Turkey leads in cotton production, with several hundred thousand bales, grown chiefly in the south near Adana and along the Aegean Sea. Syrian production, famous even in the Middle Ages, ranks second, followed by Iran and Iraq. With proper direction and adequate irrigation, each of these countries might become an important exporter.

Flax is widely raised in northern and western Turkey, in part for export both as fiber and linseed oil. The production of hemp is about equal to that of flax. In Iraq, flax is sometimes raised as a winter crop in place of barley. It can be grown either with or without irrigation; the quality of the fiber is poor, so that production for linseed oil predominates.

Silk is an ancient product across Swasia, where black mulberry trees are indigenous. White mulberry was introduced early from China following the ancient silk trade across Asia. In Iran, where Chinese artisans were once employed, mulberry trees are widely grown especially near the Caspian. Lebanon and Syria, originally under French guidance, still produce small amounts of silk. Mulberries grow well in Turkey where sericulture is an old industry, especially near Bursa. Iraq has a small silk output around Baghdad.

Coffea arabica is cultivated on the mountain slopes in Yemen, between elevations of 4,000 and 6,500 feet, probably the highest in the world. Production amounts to some 5,000 tons per year. The ancient port of Mocha, now little used, was once famous for its exports of coffee.

Tea is raised in the extreme north of the realm, with small production at the eastern end of the Black Sea coast in Turkey and along the Caspian Coast of Iran.

Sugar is produced from both beet and cane. The largest production of beet sugar is in western and northern Turkey, with smaller amounts of both varieties grown in Iran and elsewhere. The realm as a whole is a large importer of sugar; in order to reduce the need for foreign exchange, several countries have developed domestic sugar programs.

Tobacco is grown in each of the warm and humid countries. In hot and dry areas, leaves are smaller and nicotine content is higher. Turkish tobaccos are highly aromatic, burn easily, and have small leaves. The leading area lies near the Aegean Sea where summer temperatures are warm; tobacco is also raised along the Black and Mediterranean seas, including the coastal areas of Syria and Lebanon. Iran is likewise a producer.

Opium poppies are grown in Turkey and Iran, largely under government supervision and for export. Opium was raised in Yemen as early as the sixteenth century. The city of Afyonkarahisar in western Turkey means "opium-black-castle," in reference to its ancient specialty. Opium is obtained early in the summer when the poppy is in full flower and the petals are about to fall. The seed capsules are partly slit each afternoon and

Opium is obtained from the juice of poppy capsules which oozes out after the capsules are slit. (Courtesy U. S. Information Service, Ankara.)

Although camels may travel far from wells, they must be watered from time to time. These Bedouin have gathered around a government well near Jauf in Saudi Arabia. (Courtesy Standard Oil Co. of New Jersey.)

the drops of opium oxide which exude are collected the next morning.

LIVESTOCK

Camels are the distinctive animal of the desert; sheep are more numerous. Estimates of uncertain value, assembled by the Food and Agricultural Organization, suggest that the total in all Swasia is probably under a million. This compares with perhaps twice that number in the days when trade moved by caravan rather than by truck. Saudi Arabia, Iran, and Iraq each have several hundred thousand head of camels, with some representation in every other country. Even humid Lebanon reports two thousand. Their importance is suggested by the fact that the Arabic language has a thousand names for camels in various stages of growth, condition, and breed. All Swasian camels are of the one-humped, dromedary type.

Camels still have an important role in Bedouin life, for they are an effective converter of the scanty desert vegetation into products useful to man. From camels, the nomad obtains transport, food, and wealth; without the camel the desert would scarcely be habitable. Bedouins drink the milk, eat the flesh, weave the hair for their tents, burn the dung, use the urine as a medicine or hair tonic, measure a bride's dowry or a gambling wager in camels, employ camels to lift water from wells or even to plow the fields, and rate the importance of a sheikh in terms of his herds. No wonder that the Bedouin has been described as the parasite of his constant companion, the camel. He prospers only when the camel prospers. In dire emergency, when the nomad is completely without drinking water, a stick may be pushed down the camel's throat, forcing it to vomit. Camels are thus a special gift of Allah (Koran 16:5–8).

The ability of the camel to go without water is proverbial. In winter they may even obtain all their body fluids from the scanty vegetation; in summer they are able to undergo so much dessication that when watered, say once a week, they will drink thirty or forty gallons at one time. Camels walk slowly, usually two and one-half to three miles per hour. This means that they cover only twenty to twenty-five miles a day. Four hundred pounds represent a good load. While they may live to be forty or even fifty years of age, they are seldom used beyond the age of twenty-five.

Sheep and goats are usually grazed together and furnish fibers and milk as well as large amounts of meat. Goats have been called the poor man's cow. Many breeds are especially adapted to steppe and semidesert conditions, including the ability to stand long migrations. The mutton is inferior, and most wool is coarse though suitable for carpet making. Several types of sheep store surplus fat in an enlarged tail or rump. Goats thrive on pasture which is too poor to support sheep.

Both sheep and goats are widespread from Turkey to Afghanistan, absent only in the areas of continuous cultivation, the marshlands, and the absolute desert. Their numbers are uncertain, but total tens of millions.

In Turkey, sheep and goats are especially numerous in the western Anatolian uplands where considerable areas show a density of nearly 200 per square mile; farther east the ratio declines to fifty head per square mile. The total for the country numbers some 4 million head. Sheep outnumber goats by four to one, with goats concentrated in the drier areas. Turkey is especially famous for its Angora goats which have silky hair six inches long; each goat yields some four pounds of hair a year. The name comes from Ankara where they are most numerous.

Iraq reports 5 million sheep and half that number of goats. In Iran the number of sheep is estimated at 14 million, and goats at 7 million; thus there is a large supply of wool for export, some of it in the form of Persian rugs. In Syria, sheep and goats number about 3 million each. In Lebanon, the half million goats outnumber sheep, because the former is primarily a mountain animal.

Since sheep and goats can only go without water for two or three days, their grazing area is limited to a few tens of miles from a watering place. Good pasture may be available elsewhere, but water is inaccessible. To meet this problem, a few well-to-do nomads who own trucks now carry water to remote areas so that flocks are grazed in hitherto inaccessible districts.

Goats are notorious for the destructive way in which they eat grass down to its roots, so that the original natural vegetation may not be able to re-establish itself. Attempts at reforestation are doomed as long as goats are grazed in the same area. Even in dry steppe regions, fenced-in plots show a remarkable change in vegetation in a single season. One such governmental experiment plot in western Iraq became so green in three months that the local sheikh cut the fence, turned in his flocks, and ended the experiment.

In most areas, sheep and goats are shifted to different pastures with the season. This may involve a vertical migration from summer pastures on highland meadows to winter grasslands in the lowlands, or it may be a horizontal migration onto the stubble of crop lands near water supplies during the summer and, in winter, into the desert to take advantage of the scanty vegetation which accompanies winter rains. The Zagros Mountains are famous for the great seasonal

The warm seas which surround Swasia are not commonly rich in fish. These Turkish fishermen in the Sea of Marmara take advantage of the cooler waters and seasonal migrations which characterize the Straits. (Courtesy U. S. Information Service, Ankara.)

migrations, known as transhumance, where a hundred thousand nomads move up and down the slopes each year, in places crossing high passes and turbulent streams. For each person there are fifty animals, including sheep, goats, cattle, and horses.

Cattle are small in size and relatively few in number, in part due to the shortage of fodder crops. Through centuries of adaptation, they have become adjusted to the limited environment. Whereas sheep and goats are the property of the nomad, cattle are more commonly owned by settled farmers who pasture them on the stubble and stalks of fallow fields, or on the overgrazed vegetation of common lands. Cattle are used chiefly as draft animals. The yield of milk is low and little is drunk fresh; instead it is made into thickened and slightly fermented yogurt. In Iran, oxen slightly outnumber cattle, with about a million and a half of each.

Water buffalo replace cows as the preferred draft animal in the rice areas, such as the marsh lands of southern Iraq.

Donkeys are widely used, being the chief riding animal in many countries. Horses are less common, and the famous Arabian breeds are luxury items of declining importance.

Since Islam and Judaism prohibit the eating of pork, pigs are uncommon in the Moslem and Hebrew areas and are raised only by the few Christians.

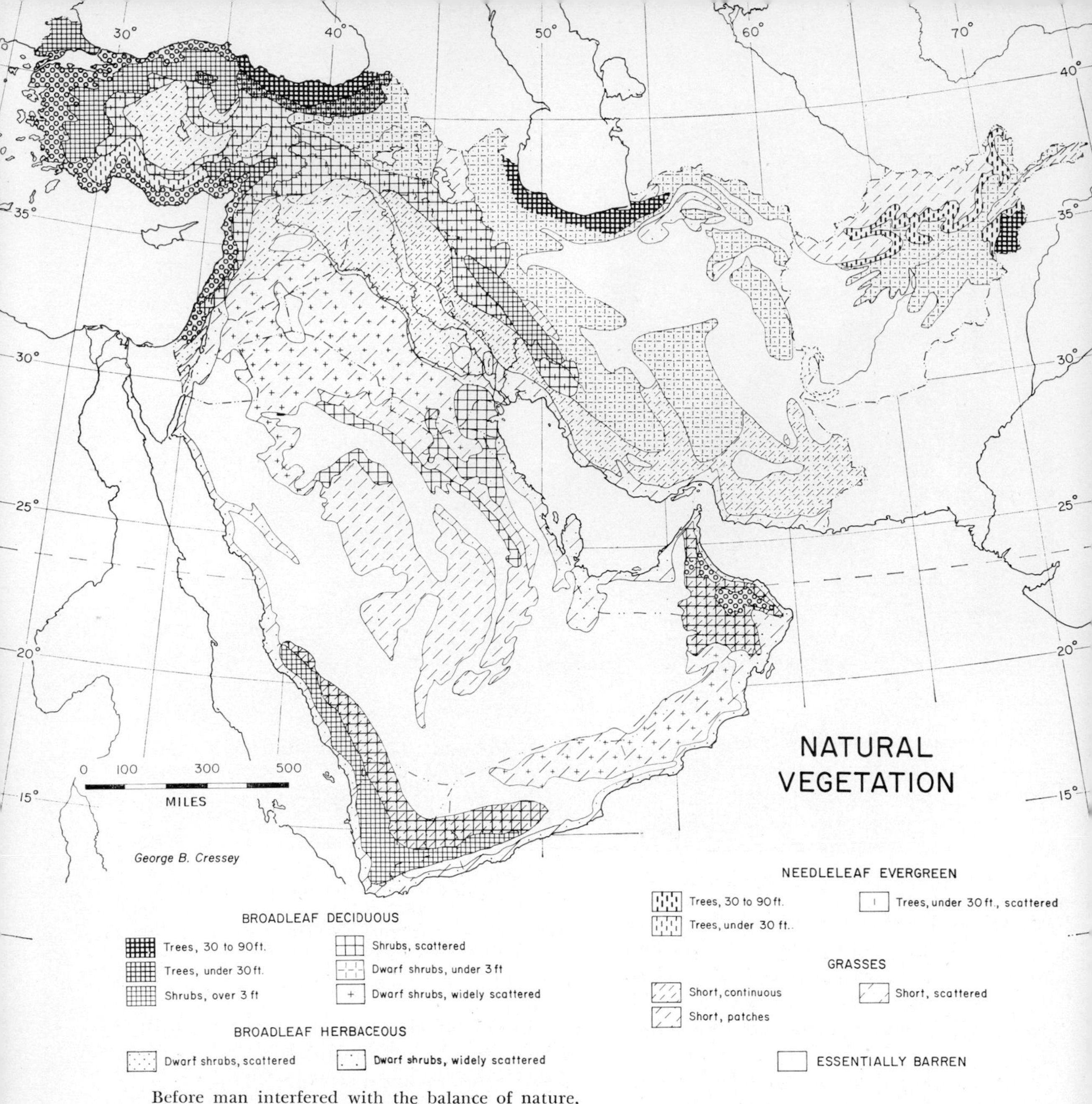

Before man interfered with the balance of nature, the cover of vegetation reflected climate and relief. Only traces of the original forests remain, and even in the deserts overgrazing has altered the natural cover. (Compiled by Charles Woolever.)

FORESTS

FORESTS are of limited extent, although once they were more widespread in the humid highlands. The northern mountains of Iran and Turkey receive moisture from the Caspian and Black seas and still contain splendid forests, with commercial lumber production. Lebanon's famed cedars now number but a few hundred trees, all in protected groves. The definition of forest land appears to differ widely, for even desert Arabia reports a considerable area. The accompanying table presents the available data.

FOREST LAND[1]

Country	Forests: Accessible forests	Forests: Inaccessible forests	Forests: Total	Nonforested Land: Agricultural land	Nonforested Land: Total	Forests as percentage of land area	Forest area per capita
Aden Protectorate	—	—	—	18,110	29,029	—	—
Afghanistan	700	300	1,000	15,000	59,000	1.7	0.08
Egypt	1	—	1	2,450	100,000	—	—
Iran	16,000	3,000	19,000	26,760	144,600	11.6	1.0
Iraq	895	645	1,540	6,338	42,904	3.5	0.3
Israel	89	—	89	347	1,952	4.4	0.06
Jordan	79	—	79	839	9,581	0.8	0.06
Kuwait	—	—	—	—	2,072	—	—
Lebanon	64	10	74	270	933	7.3	0.06
Muscat & Oman	80	—	80	—	21,160	0.4	1.0
Qatar	—	—	—	—	2,200	—	—
Saudi Arabia	350	50	400	92,970	154,200	0.3	0.07
Syria	444	5	449	6,591	17,935	2.4	0.13
Trucial Oman	—	—	—	—	1,500	—	—
Turkey	10,284	300	10,584	17,175	66,197	13.8	0.47
Yemen	120	30	150	—	19,350	0.8	0.03

[1] Food and Agriculture Organization of the United Nations, *World Forest Resources.* Rome: (March 1955), 66–67. Areas in thousand hectares.

Reforestation is actively under way in Israel and sporadically elsewhere. Several thousand square miles have a rainfall in excess of twenty inches and would again have a fair forest cover if sheep and goats might be kept out; with thirty inches or more of rainfall, excellent commercial timber production should be possible.

REFERENCES

Bonne, Alfred: "Land and Population in the Middle East," *Middle East Jour.,* V (1951), 39–56.

Crist, Raymond E.: "Land for the Fellahin," *Amer. Jour. of Economics and Sociology,* XVII (1957), 21–30, 157–166.

Dost, H.: BIBLIOGRAPHY ON LAND AND WATER UTILIZATION IN THE MIDDLE EAST. Wageningen, Netherlands: Agricultural University (1953).

Food and Agricultural Organization of the United Nations: AGRICULTURE IN THE NEAR EAST. Rome: FAO (1953).

Janssen, A. C.: "Key Problems of Agricultural Development in the Near East," *FAO Monthly Bull. of Argic. Economics and Statistics,* III (1954), 1–8.

Tannons, Afif I.: "Land Reform: Key to the Development and Stability of the Arab World," *Middle East Jour.,* (1951), 1–20.

VanValkenburg, Samuel: "Agricultural Regions of Asia, Part II—The Near East," *Econ. Geog.,* VIII (1932), 110–133.

* Warriner, Doreen: LAND AND POVERTY IN THE MIDDLE EAST. London and New York: Royal Inst. of Internat. Affairs (1948).

CHAPTER 7

Mineral Resources

Mineral Wealth
Sources of Power
The Metals
Nonmetallic Resources
References

MINERAL WEALTH

WHEN JASON AND THE ARGONAUTS set out on their quest for the Golden Fleece before the Trojan War (1230 B.C.), they were lured by the gold of northern Anatolia. Then, as now, placer gold dust was sometimes concentrated on greasy sheepskins. The names of Midas and Croesus bring to mind the wealth of antiquity, and the array of gold ornaments from Ur and other ancient capitals suggests a notable accumulation of treasure.

The ancient Hebrews were familiar with many of the common metals, some of which were obtained from the Sinai Peninsula, others by barter from a distance. One list mentions "the gold, the silver, the bronze, the iron, the tin, and the lead" (Numbers XXXI:22). Copper is known to have been obtained from the Red Sea area as early as 3700 B.C.; later on, the area supplied the Roman Empire.

The first recorded use of iron dates from 1250 B.C., in the Hittite Kingdom of Asia Minor. Later on, swords of Damascus steel were among the Assyrian spoils about 730 B.C. Silver and mercury were also early products. In no case, however, is there any suggestion of large mineral output. It may well be that the accumulation of the metals in early times represented great amounts of cheap labor operating on low grade deposits.

In the twentieth century, many resources are of critical importance. As a source of power, man needs coal, oil, and gas, fissionable material, and hydroelectricity. For construction purposes, we rely on iron, copper, aluminum, and a long list of other metals. The raw materials for cement, glass, and many other materials are equally important. Agriculture requires fertilizers such as phosphates, potash, and nitrogen. Chemical in-

(Opposite) Turkey's steel mill at Karabuk represents the foremost concentration of the metal industry in all Swasia. The two blast furnaces are supplied with hot air by the cylindrical ovens seen at the right. (Courtesy U.S. Information Service, Ankara.)

Cement is made by heating limestone, clay, and gypsum in a revolving kiln. This Lebanese mill produces 1,000 tons a day. (Courtesy Arab Information Center, New York.)

dustries require sulphur, salt, coal, and many raw materials.

The list of essentials is long and growing. Several of these commodities are required in tonnage quantities, so that freight rates may be a critical factor. National security and trade restrictions involve further considerations. Unless a nation has most of these commodities near at hand and unless it has the foreign exchange with which to buy others, its industrial development may be handicapped.

In evaluating present-day mineral assets, it is well to keep a sense of perspective. The world will never really run out of minerals; the problem is one of diligent search, and of economical utilization. Commercial deposits of iron ore should contain at least 40 to 50 per cent of metal, but when such deposits are exhausted, or if there is an easy access to coal and markets, 30 per cent ore may be used. A gold deposit with an ounce of gold per ton of rock may represent a bonanza; but when such lodes are depleted, we should remember that there is enough gold dissolved in sea water to make every person on earth a millionaire.

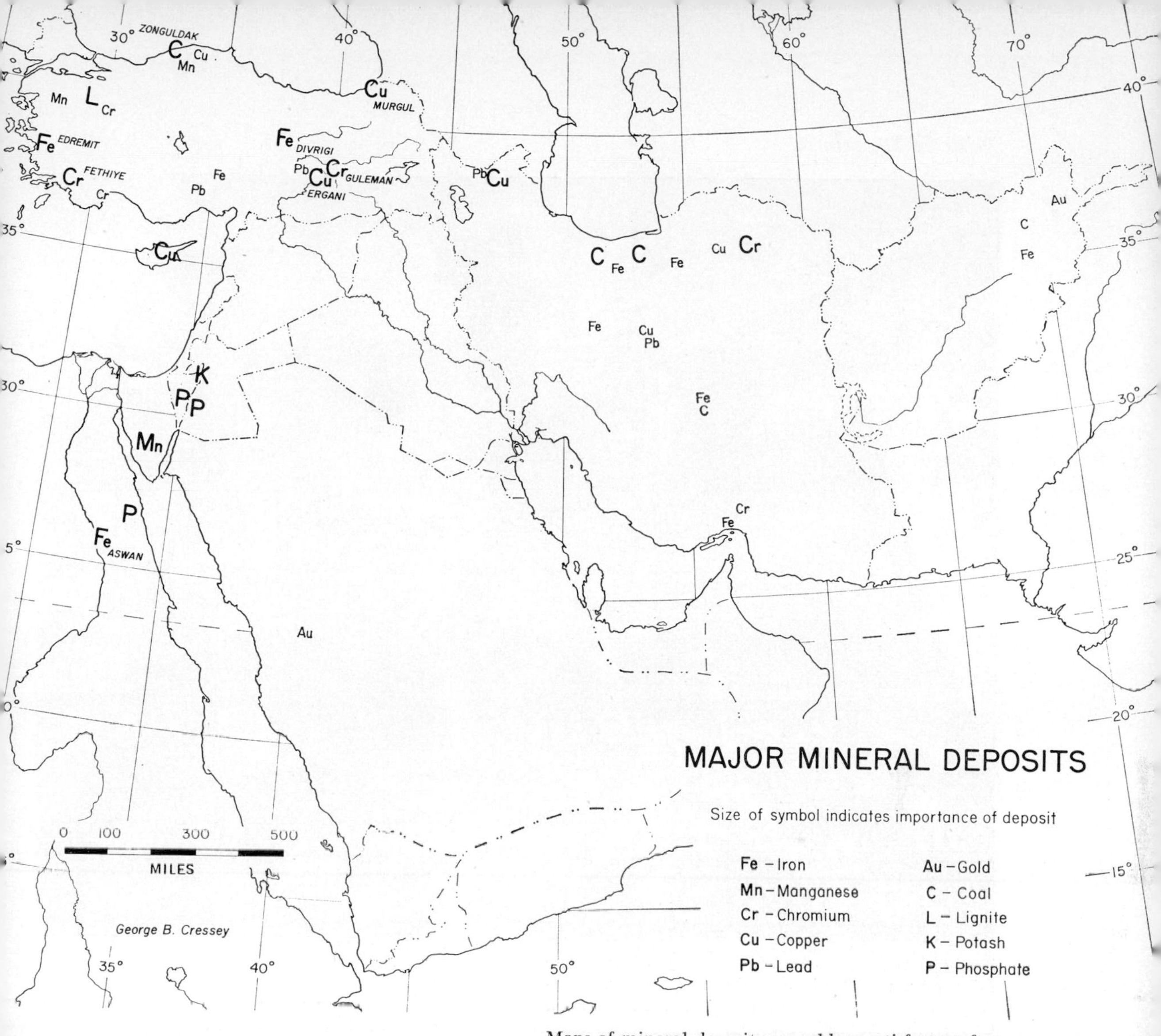

Maps of mineral deposits are seldom satisfactory for they may fail to distinguish between theoretical reserves and actual production and seldom suggest the amount. Changing technology, new accessibility, and fluctuating world price levels affect the importance of many deposits.

An "ore" is a rock which contains a valuable substance which may be extracted at a profit. New methods of mining or metallurgy, new accessibility, or new markets, may change a worthless mineral into a commercial deposit. Scores of mineral occurrences are reported across Southwest Asia; most are now uneconomic, but with further geological study and improved communications, some may prove valuable.

Any forecast as to the possible location and extent of mineral resources in Swasia must start with the geological map already presented on page 72. Each deposit is the result of unique conditions which nevertheless follow a pattern. The fact that gypsum occurs as a sedimentary rock means that it is never present in igneous or metamorphic areas; likewise, gold is commonly found in quartz veins or in placer deposits derived from them. Deep-seated magmas beneath some localities have given rise to mineralized zones, in contrast to adjacent areas.

Turkey leads Southwest Asia in coal reserves. These miners are working in one of the mines at Zonguldak near the Black Sea. (Courtesy U. S. International Cooperation Administration.)

In large areas of Southwest Asia, only the general outlines of geology are known; many mineral deposits hidden today will come to light with detailed field work. The veneer provided by alluvium, shifting sands, and broad lava flows doubtless conceals many mineral occurrences, but they are beyond our present reach.

Igneous and metamorphic rocks underlie large parts of western Arabia, a dozen scattered areas in Turkey, and a few patches in Iran. In these crystalline areas and around their margins there is the possibility of iron, copper, chromium, and manganese.

Sedimentary rocks provide a possible locus for coal and oil, if of the proper age and character, and for certain types of iron ore. They also are the site for evaporites such as gypsum and salt. While Swasia has many sedimentary areas, only limited sections contain rocks of the ages when coal accumulated elsewhere. The story of oil is quite different and will be considered in the next chapter.

Much geological work remains to be done, but it must be remembered that Southwest Asia is a land in which man has long been settled and long has known how to search for coal, iron, copper, and the simpler metals. The evidence to date suggests that this is a rather poorly mineralized area.

The mountains of Southwest Asia contain numerous potential locations for hydroelectric power. This is the site of the Diz River dam in the Zagros Mountains of southwestern Iran. (Courtesy Development and Resources Corp., New York.)

Only Turkey appears to have the basis for a rounded industrial development. Although workable deposits are present elsewhere, problems of transport, capital, market, and management may postpone industrialization into the future. Ore in the ground is not the same as refined metal fabricated into machinery. National aspirations will doubtless conflict with sound economics and in some countries may lead to subsidized exploitation of deposits which cannot yet be worked economically.

This chapter omits the assets of water and oil, discussed elsewhere, and evaluates the sources of power and minerals by commodity. Further details are available in the chapters which treat the separate countries.

SOURCES OF POWER

Coal is one of the resources with which Southwest Asia appears to be poorly supplied. Fortunately, oil is superabundant and can partly take the place of coal. In much of the world, the leading period for the formation of coal was the Carboniferous but rocks of this period are poorly represented here. If they ever were present, they have been largely removed by erosion.

The chief Carboniferous coal beds occur as scattered outcrops near Zonguldak in

COAL PRODUCTION[1]

	Iran	Turkey	
		Coal	Lignite
1937		1,615	116
1938		1,744	76
1939	75	1,881	92
1940	92	2,081	149
1941	90	2,125	177
1942	82	1,814	266
1943	69	2,212	420
1944	100	2,493	532
1945	150	2,524	523
1946	150	2,526	459
1947	188	2,623	604
1948	150	2,669	680
1949	170	2,706	778
1950	200	2,832	747
1951	170	2,988	751
1952	150	3,010	765
1953	155	3,664	942
1954	252	3,690	1,085
1955	180	3,498	1,188
1956	330	3,718	1,317
1957	330	3,969	1,726

[1] In thousands of metric tons. Data from *United Nations Statistical Yearbook,* (1958).

western Turkey and in northern Iran. Jurassic formations in Iran and Afghanistan yield inferior coal. Lignite is present in certain Tertiary beds and in some places is of high quality. Elsewhere, potential coal-bearing beds are absent or deeply buried.

These various coal beds occupy a discontinuous belt extending entirely across the northern part of the realm, almost all of them north of latitude 35°N. In the amount of reserves, present output, and perhaps in quality as well, there is a steady decline eastward from the major producing center along the Turkish Black Sea coast. The shortage of coal for coking purposes and its distance from mineral deposits poses a problem for metallurgy.

Very little is known with regard to uranium or other sources of atomic energy; it is entirely possible that commercial sources may be present somewhere, but their location and extent are so far unknown. However, Turkey contains a variety of acidic rocks which elsewhere contain uranium.

The development of water power is related to abundant precipitation and steep gradients. Swasia has rugged mountains but few large rivers, so that the hydroelectric potentials are limited to the more humid areas. There are numerous sites in the Taurus, Zagros, and Elburz mountains; Turkey and Iran thus hold the chief possibilities to develop this source of power. Several large dams were constructed during the late 1950's. Under existing conditions it is not practical to transmit electricity beyond a radius of a few hundred miles, so that several excellent hydroelectric sites are too far from present markets.

When the day arrives that the utilization of solar energy proves feasible, the deserts of Southwest Asia should provide ample sites for extracting power from the sun.

The accompanying tables are derived primarily from figures reported annually by the respective governments to the United

Copper is mined at a number of locations in Turkey. This is the open-cut operation at Ergani in the east. (Courtesy Turkish Information Office, New York.)

Nations. They may thus be readily brought up to date. Where official figures are missing, other sources are used. It cannot be repeated too often that much statistical data for this part of the world must be viewed with some reserve. Additional comments will be found in the regional chapters to follow.

THE METALS

COMMERCIAL IRON ORE deposits may occur in several ways. Some deposits are associated with igneous rocks as a result of magmatic differentiation; in such cases the mineral is often magnetite. Many deposits of hematite represent ancient sediments. High grade ores of both types are mined in central Turkey and in northern Iran, making iron the realm's most important metal. Scattered occurrences of unknown value are reported in eastern Afghanistan, central Iran, northwestern Arabia, and elsewhere. Central Turkey has an important steel center, but coal must be brought fifty miles while iron ore is carried over 550 miles, in both cases by rail.

Finely divided red iron oxide, used as a base for paint and rouge, is mined on Hormuz Island at the entrance to the Persian Gulf.

While the evidence is incomplete, it appears that Swasia's known reserves of iron ore are very small if measured in world terms. The fact is that the world around, the

Chromium is Turkey's unique metal, and the country may hold the world's largest deposits of high-grade chromite. These mine cars transport ore at the Guleman works. (Courtesy U. S. Economic Cooperation Administration.)

number of districts which have large amounts of high grade ore of suitable composition are near metallurgical coke, have cheap transportation and are close to a large market, number only a few dozen.

The second most valuable metal of the realm appears to be chromium, found widely in Turkey and mined also in Iran. In the former, mining dates from 1848, and reserves are very large. In the nineteenth century, Turkey led the world in chromium production, but it is now exceeded by the Soviet Union and several other countries. Estimates of world reserves for 1952, in millions of tons, credit the Union of South Africa with 150, Southern Rhodesia with fifty, Turkey and the Philippines with twenty each, and perhaps comparable figures for the Soviet Union.

Chromium is a very hard metal, nearly equal to the hardness of a diamond. Unlike many of the metals, it was unknown to the ancient peoples. It makes a refractory brick for lining furnaces; the chemical industry uses it for pigments; and in metallurgy it is employed for plating and particularly as an alloy in the manufacture of stainless and special quality steels where it imparts hardness, resistance to wear, and useful magnetic properties. The ore is called chromite, with a theoretical composition of 68 per cent of chromium sesquioxide (Cr_2O_3). Commercial grades should contain at least 40 per cent.

Chromite occurs as a segregation from

ultra basic igneous rocks such as peridotite, or in serpentines derived from them. Such rocks are present in many parts of both eastern and western Turkey. Occurrences of chromite are reported in western Syria, northern and southern Iran, and eastern Afghanistan.

Other metals in production include copper, manganese, lead, zinc, antimony, mercury, and silver. In no case is the output of world-wide importance. Occurrences are reported for nickel, tungsten, molybdenum, and gold.

Arabian gold has been known for centuries and it was an early item of trade. Dozens of primitive mines were in operation, some of them during the days of King David and King Solomon. The "cradle of gold" at Mahad Dhahab, 250 miles north of Jidda, was developed into a modern mine by the Saudi Arabian Mining Syndicate in 1934,

GOLD PRODUCTION [1]

	Saudi Arabia
1939	497
1940	994
1941	1,136
1942	975
1943	1,326
1944	270
1945	1,181
1946	1,493
1947	1,620
1948	2,300
1949	2,079
1950	2,059
1951	2,274
1952	2,158
1953	2,537
1954	1,067

[1] In kilograms. Data from *United Nations Statistical Yearbook.*

Iron ore for the large Turkish steel mills at Karabuk is brought from the mines at Divrigi, 550 miles distant. (Courtesy U. S. Economic Cooperation Administration.)

Mineral Resources

IRON ORE PRODUCTION [1]

	Turkey		Turkey
1938	50,000	1948	121,000
1939	155,000	1949	136,000
1940	85,000	1950	143,000
1941	38,000	1951	143,000
1942	12,000	1952	305,000
1943	59,000	1953	315,000
1944	59,000	1954	301,000
1945	82,000	1955	479,000
1946	73,000	1956	577,000
1947	95,000	1957	722,000

[1] Data from *United Nations Statistical Yearbook*. In metric tons.

LEAD AND ZINC PRODUCTION [1]

	Iran		Turkey	
	Lead	Zinc	Lead	Zinc
1930			10,500	5,800
1931			1,900	900
1932				2,000
1933			2,100	4,200
1934			4,900	8,600
1935			3,000	8,800
1936			6,100	12,500
1937			7,600	14,800
1938			7,300	17,300
1939			6,600	13,700
1940				
1941				
1942				
1943				
1944				
1945				
1946				
1947				600
1948			2,600	2,400
1949			300	200
1950	2,000		100	
1951	17,500		400	400
1952	16,300	12,000	900	900
1953	8,000	5,000	4,400	4,000
1954	18,000		6,100	5,400
1955	18,200		2,600	2,300
1956	31,600		3,800	2,200
1957	30,400		2,900	5,600

[1] In metric tons. Data from *United Nations Statistical Yearbook*.

CHROMIUM PRODUCTION [1]

	Turkey		Turkey	Iran
1930	14,100	1944	89,200	
1931	12,700	1945	71,900	
1932	27,600	1946	50,600	
1933	37,700	1947	50,000	
1934	59,900	1948	139,800	
1935	75,200	1949	216,800	
1936	80,200	1950	207,000	
1937	96,300	1951	295,000	15,000
1938	106,500	1952	395,400	14,400
1939	91,600	1953	438,000	3,000
1940	83,200	1954	270,000	17,700
1941	66,500	1955	312,000	17,700
1942	57,000	1956	400,000	32,800
1943	75,700	1957	470,000	38,600

[1] Cr_2O_3 content, in metric tons. Data from *United Nations Statistical Yearbook.*

OTHER METALLIC PRODUCTION [1]

	Copper		Manganese		Antimony		Mercury
	Turkey	Iran	Turkey	Iran	Turkey	Iran	Turkey
1930			400		17		19.0
1931			400		26		8.0
1932			1,100				
1933			3,100		351		1.0
1934					35		1.0
1935			3,700		122		1.0
1936			1,800		562		28.1
1937	700		200		643		16.6
1938	2,200		1,100		580		20.6
1939	6,700		200		661		13.6
1940	8,800		400		372	1	16.6
1941	10,500		700		77	19	12.2
1942	8,300		1,700		40		9.3
1943	9,700		1,300		8	18	6.4
1944	11,000		900		56	2	3.3
1945	9,900		2,500		29		5.4
1946	10,000		1,200		31		
1947	10,100		2,800		93		3.4
1948	11,000		4,100		526		0.9
1949	11,300		11,100		462	175	
1950	11,700		15,800		1,386	230	
1951	17,500	400	24,700	4,000	2,166	160	
1952	23,300	2,200	39,400	3,200	928	240	
1953	23,800	700	43,900	600	690	100	
1954	25,200	3,800	24,400	14,200	713	100	0.3
1955	23,800	3,800	24,600	9,700	893	100	1.0
1956	24,800	5,100	29,800	18,100	2,400	102	1.3
1957	24,400	5,100	27,800	18,200	800		0.9

[1] In metric tons. Data from *Unitea Nations Statistical Yearbook.*

Salt has long been mined in northern Afghanistan and is widely distributed by caravan. These mines in Badakshan were mentioned by Marco Polo. (Ewing Galloway.)

but the ore shoot bottomed at 540 feet and operations were suspended in 1954. Production was divided about evenly between the underground workings and old dumps and tailings. Silver was present in equal amounts with gold.

NONMETALLIC RESOURCES

SALT IS SWASIA's most widespread mineral and is produced in every country. The total output probably exceeds the combined tonnages of every other resource except coal and lignite. Some of this is marine salt, evaporated along every sea coast; other supplies come from inland salt lakes or salt springs. With a long rainless season and high summer temperatures, the evaporation of sea water is a simple operation. Rock salt occurs in eastern Anatolia, in Yemen, and particularly in scores of huge salt domes in southern Iran, most of which are as yet untapped. Export for industrial uses far outstrips the domestic demand.

Sulphur is one of the chief chemicals for industry. It occurs with volcanic activity, in mineral combination with substances such as iron, in pure form, and in limited amounts with petroleum. A small output is reported in Iran and Iraq as a by-product from

SALT PRODUCTION [1]

Nonmetallic Resources

	Aden	*Afghanistan*	*Iran*	*Jordan*	*Lebanon*	*Iraq*	*Israel*	*Syria*	*Turkey*	*Yemen*
1930									146,000	
1931									170,000	
1932									218,000	
1933									154,000	
1934									182,000	
1935									215,000	
1936									200,000	
1937	361,000								252,000	
1938	283,000								262,000	
1939									240,000	
1940									234,000	
1941									251,000	
1942									241,000	
1943									266,000	
1944									257,000	
1945									254,000	
1946									206,000	
1947									276,000	
1948	275,000					13,300	5,000	20,300	266,000	
1949	308,000		100,000		2,500	9,200	9,300	21,600	318,000	
1950	260,000		100,000		6,500	11,200	7,200	19,200	310,000	
1951	309,000	24,700	76,252	2,712	7,000	15,700	9,800	4,000	273,000	
1952	382,000	17,100	200,000	7,377	3,500	19,300	12,500	14,300	323,000	100,000
1953	245,000	16,700	220,000	7,100	4,000	18.700	21,000	20,400	350,000	
1954	214,000	25,900		10,400		20,300	20,600	21,500	484,000	
1955	279,000	22,200				30,800	20,300	16,000	373,000	
1956	252,000	22,600		7,700	1,200	19,200	26,000	32,700	378,000	
1957	201,000			10,100		20,000	31,600	25,000	421,000	
1958				10,100						

[1] In metric tons. *United Nations Statistical Yearbook* and other sources.

OTHER NONMETALLIC PRODUCTS [1]

	Phosphate		*Potash*	*Asbestos*	*Boracite* [3]	*Magnesite*	*Sulphur*	*Emery* [3]
	Israel	*Jordan*	*Palestine*	*Turkey*	*Turkey*	*Turkey*	*Turkey*	*Turkey*
1931			3,000					
1932			6,000					
1933			7,000				100	
1934			7,000				300	
1935			10,000				2,200	
1936			10,000				3,200	
1937			15,000	200		1,400	2,800	
1938			24,000	700	4,100	900	3,900	8,500
1939			32,000	100	15,200	500	2,600	10,000

OTHER NONMETALLIC PRODUCTS *(Continued)*

	Phosphate		*Potash*	*Asbestos*	*Boracite*[3]	*Magnesite*	*Sulphur*	*Emery*[3]
	Israel	*Jordan*	*Palestine*	*Turkey*	*Turkey*	*Turkey*	*Turkey*	*Turkey*
1940			45,000	100	5,300	800	3,700	8,600
1941			51,000	100	2,200	1,900	2,200	5,100
1942			52,000	300		100	2,700	9,300
1943			47,000	100		100	3,400	7,800
1944			53,000	200		800	3,400	100
1945			47,000	100	5,000	800	4,200	2,200
1946			45,000	100	2,200	100	3,000	8,500
1947			40,000	200	3,600	900	2,700	11,800
1948			30,000	200	5,300	3,600	2,600	7,900
1949					7,100	6,400	3,100	8,900
1950				200		400	6,000	
1951		6,600		100		500	7,400	
1952	17,200	23,800				900	8,400	
1953	23,100	40,000	3,000[2]			400	9,800	
1954	58,200	75,000	11,000[2]			1,100	10,000	
1955	71,800	163,600	11,000[2]	200			11,500	
1956	115,600	208,400	28,000[2]	600		900	13,900	
1957	152,000	261,900	45,000[2]			1,300	13,100	

[1] In metric tons. *United Nations Statistical Yearbook.*

[2] Israel

[3] Turkish Central Statistical Office.

Salt is obtained by the evaporation of sea water along the shores of the Mediterranean and Red seas and the Persian Gulf. This is a scene among the salt pans at Aden. (Courtesy British Overseas Airways Corp.)

The Dead Sea is a vast treasure house of soluble minerals. In addition to common salt there is production of potash and bromine. This is an evaporation deposit of carnalite, the potassium-magnesium chloride, at Sodom in Israel. (Courtesy Israel Office of Information, New York.)

the oil fields. West central Iraq has deposits of 40 to 60 per cent sulphur which yield a few thousand tons a year. Turkey is the largest commercial producer.

The Dead Sea is a vast store house of minerals in solution, with extraction plants at each end of the sea. Potash and bromine are the chief commercial products. Output is expanding.

Other nonmetallic production includes phosphate rock for fertilizer; boracite, a borax mineral; emery, used as an abrasive; meerschaum or sepiolite, employed for lining the bowls of pipes; and semiprecious stones such as turquoise and lapis lazuli.

REFERENCES

Nahai, L.: *"The Mineral Industry of Turkey,"* U. S. Bureau of Mines, INFORMATION CIRCULAR 7855 (1958).

Reichestelle fur Bodenforschung: *"Die Bodenschatze des Nahen Osten,"* DIE WICHTIGSTEN LAGERSTATTEN DER ERDE, IX (1941).

U. S. Bureau of Mines: *"Preliminary Survey, Mineral Resources and Industries of the Middle East,"* FOREIGN MINERALS SURVEY, I (1944).

CHAPTER 8

Oil

Retrospect and Prospect
A Preface from Geology
Reserves and Production
Pipelines and Refineries
Country Descriptions
References

RETROSPECT AND PROSPECT

THE MAGIC OIL of Aladdin's lamp takes on new meaning with the discovery of petroleum in Southwest Asia. These oil fields appear to contain two-thirds of the world's reserves, and they produce one-quarter of its current consumption. Recent decades have seen spectacular drilling developments, but these are only a preface to the profound economic consequences which are transforming this corner of Asia. The exploitation of petroleum in Swasia has been called one of the great industrial developments of our time; whether or not this is true, it is certainly one of the most spectacular local achievements anywhere.

Petroleum has assumed an irreplaceable role in our modern world, not only as a source of fuel and lubricants but also for an increasing array of petrochemicals. Requirements rise yearly. Oil spells power and without assured access to oil, a great nation can scarcely exist; therefore, dependable supplies have a vital place in foreign policy. The problem of oil is global. Reserves within the United States are very large, but are being consumed at alarming rates. Fortunately for the Americas, there are great deposits in Latin America and possibly western Canada.

Several questions arise. To what extent should American supplies be conserved and replaced by imports, and if so from where? To what extent is it in America's interest to see that Europe has assured sources of supply? Are overseas oil companies purely commercial concerns, or do they have a role in national policy? Would United States security be endangered if the countries which contain oil should be controlled by strong nationalistic policies, or if the Persian Gulf should come under Soviet domination? Since the answers to these problems are important, it is clear that America has a vital interest in the oil of Swasia.

Geography has a role in these affairs, be-

(Opposite) This 30-inch pipe carries oil from the Persian Gulf a thousand miles westward to the Mediterranean. The desert surface has the characteristic veneer of residual pebbles. (Courtesy Trans-Arabian Pipe Line Co.)

The sun-dried bricks of ancient Ur were cemented by bitumen obtained from natural seeps. Bitumen was also used for waterproofing boats. (Courtesy Iraq Petroleum Co.)

cause it is concerned with the distribution of supplies, the routes of transportation, the location of potential markets, and the human results. These are matters of both economic and political geography. In its relationship to oil, geography stands midway between geology and economics.

Southwest Asia has long been significant because of its strategic position between East and West. Oil now puts it at the crossroads of the world and assures the realm a new importance in international economics and military power.

Oil and gas seeps have been known in many parts of Southwest Asia for millennia. The sun-dried bricks of Babylon and Ur are held in a bitumen mortar. Early sickles used for harvesting grain were made with small flints cemented to jawbones with bitumen. Writing in the fifth century B.C., Herodotus described the oil seeps at Hit on the Euphrates, and near Susa in Iran, in terms which are applicable today. In numerous places, oil and gas come to the surface in springs of sulphur water; the oil then forms a scum which may be collected like thick cream on milk.

A British traveler named George Rawlinson visited Hit on the Middle Euphrates in 1745 and wrote as follows:[1]

> Having spent three days or better among the ruins of Old Babylon, we came into a town called Hit, inhabited only by Arabians, but very ruinous. Near unto this town is a valley of pitch, very marvelous to behold and a thing almost incredible, wherein are many springs throwing out abundantly a kind of black substance, like unto tar and pitch, which serveth all the countries thereabouts to make staunch their barks and boats. Every one of which springs maketh a noise like a smith's forge in puffing out the matter, which never ceaseth night or day, and the noise is heard a mile off, swallowing all the weighty things that come upon it. The Moors call it the Mouth of Hell.

Natural gas seeps, when ignited, have led to the creation of temples for the worship of fire, such as the so-called Altar of Solomon at Masjid-i-Sulaiman in Iran and the fire temples at Baku. The fiery furnace of Shadrach, Meshach, and Abednego may well have been the eternal fire which still burns near Kirkuk (Daniel III: 8–30) . A parallel to the story of Moses is found in the legend that King Sargon, ruler of Assyria in the third millennia, B.C., was placed as a small boy in a cradle of rushes waterproofed by bitumen, and entrusted to the river.

Only in modern times, however, have the vast resources of petroleum been known and properly exploited. Large scale production in Iran started just prior to World War I, and the great Arabian fields have only been discovered since the end of World War II.

The oil companies of two outside nations now dominate production in Southwest

[1] G. Rawlinson: *Collection of Travels and Voyages.* London: (1745), II, 752.

NOTE: The preparation of this chapter has been made possible by extensive travel assistance in the field from The Iraq Petroleum Company, The Arabian American Oil Company, The Trans-Arabian Pipe Line Company, The Kuwait Oil Company, The Bahrein Oil Company, and the Iranian Oil Consortium.

Bitumen is brought to the surface along with gas and sulphur waters and may be skimmed off like cream and used in crude form for many purposes. This oil seep is at Hit in Iraq. (Courtesy Iraq Petroleum Co.)

Asia: Britain and America each have investments in excess of a billion dollars. The Netherlands and France have also been represented for many years. Other countries are interested in securing dependable supplies, or in gambling for profits. Italy has secured development rights for new Iranian fields, and Japanese interests hold an offshore concession opposite the Kuwait–Saudi Arabian Neutral Zone. The Soviet Union also has strategic concerns, and though its reserves are large, it does not have enough oil. Soviet goals for oil have been directed to the northern parts of Iran and Afghanistan, but, so far, they have not met with much success.

British capital was responsible for the initial developments in Iran and in Iraq, which later became the Anglo-Persian Oil Company and the Iraq Petroleum Company respectively. In the former, the government of Great Britain was the largest stockholder.

American companies did not become interested until the 1930's, first in Bahrein and later with great success in Saudi Arabia and Kuwait. Although no United States government funds have been involved, diplomatic pressures from the Department of State were instrumental in some of these developments. Just as Winston Churchill recognized the military importance of dependable supplies from Iran, so it became clear that America, too, has strategic interests in Persian Gulf

Oil

MAJOR OIL FIELDS AND CONCESSION OWNERSHIP

Country, company, and base of operations	*Area in sq. miles*	*Concession ownership*	*Main fields*	*Discovery year*
IRAN				
Iranian Oil Producing Consortium, Tehran	100,000	Owned by National Iranian Oil Co. operated by 17 concessionaires [1]	Masjid-i-Sulaiman	1908
			Haft Kel	1928
			Agha Jari	1937
			Gach Saran	1928
National Iranian Oil Co., Teheran		Iranian Government	Qum	1956
IRAQ				
Iraq Petroleum Co., Kirkuk	32,000	British Petroleum [2] 23.75%	Kirkuk	1927
		Royal Dutch Shell [3] 23.75%		
		Cie. Francaise des Petroles 23.75%		
		New Jersey Standard 11.87%		
		Socony Mobil 11.87%		
		Gulbenkian 5%		
Mosul Petroleum Co., Mosul	46,000	Same as Iraq Petroleum Co.	Ain Zalah	1939
			Butmah	1951
Basra Petroleum Co., Basra	93,000	Same as Iraq Petroleum Co.	Zubair	1949
			Rumaila	1953
KUWAIT				
Kuwait Oil Co., Kuwait	6,000	British Petroleum 50%	Burgan	1938
		Gulf 50%		
SAUDI ARABIA				
Arabian-American Oil Co., Dhahran	365,000	California Standard 30%	Dammam	1936
		Texaco 30%	Abqaiq	1940
		Jersey Standard 30%	Qatif	1945
		Socony Mobil 10%	Ain Dar	1948
KUWAIT–SAUDI ARABIAN NEUTRAL ZONE				
American Independent (for Kuwait)	2,200	Ten American Companies	Wafra	
Getty Oil Co. (for Saudi Arabia)		J. Paul Getty		

MAJOR OIL FIELDS AND CONCESSION OWNERSHIP *(Continued)*

Country, company, and base of operations	*Area in sq. miles*	*Concession ownership*		*Main fields*	*Discovery year*
IRAQ–SAUDI ARABIAN NEUTRAL ZONE					
Basra Oil Co. (for Iraq)		See Iraq		None	
Arabian American Oil Co. (for Saudi Arabia)		See Saudi Arabia			
BAHREIN					
Bahrein Petroleum Co., Awali	200	California Standard	50%		
		Texaco	50%	Awali	1932
QATAR					
Petroleum Development Ltd., Doha	4,500	See Iraq		Dukhan	1940
PERSIAN GULF OFFSHORE					
Several		British Petroleum, Shell, IPC, French, Cities Service, Japanese		None	
TRUCIAL COAST AND MASQAT					
Petroleum Development Ltd.	88,000	See Iraq		None	
DHUFAR		Cities Service, Richfield			1957
SYRIA					
Iraq Petroleum Co.	41,700	See Iraq		None	
TURKEY					
Several		Various Concessions		Raman Dag	

[1] Iran Consortium: British Petroleum-40%, Shell-14%, Cie. Francaise des Petroles-6%, Jersey Standard-7%, California Standard-7%, Texaco-7%, Gulf-7%, Socony Mobil 7%, eight other U. S. Companies-5%.

[2] British Petroleum: British government-53%, Burman Oil-25%, Individuals-22%.

[3] Royal Dutch Shell: Dutch-60%, British-40%.

Natural gas seeps, escaping from deep-seated pockets, supply "eternal flames" which have burned for millennia. This scene is at Kirkuk in Iraq. (Courtesy Standard Oil Co. of New Jersey.)

oil. American companies now have interests in almost every area in Southwest Asia, and the investments exceed those of any other country. Oil operations are fantastically expensive, and while the profits may appear large, so too are the risks.

The major producing fields, with their concession arrangements are shown in the accompanying table.

Three concession areas are entirely under American ownership. In Saudi Arabia, the Arabian American Oil Company, often known as Aramco, is owned by California Standard, New Jersey Standard, Socony-Mobil, and Texaco. In the Bahrein Petroleum Company, the ownership is divided between California Standard and Texaco. The Neutral Zone has two oil companies, both American owned. The Gulf Oil Co. owns one-half interest in the Kuwait Oil Company. The situation in southwestern Iran is complex, but 40 per cent of the stock is held by American oil companies, principally Jersey Standard, California Standard, Texaco, Gulf, and Socony Mobil. Indiana Standard holds an offshore concession from Iran for part of the northern Persian Gulf. Nearly one-quarter of oil development operations in Iraq has been through capital from the United States.

Royalties from oil production have

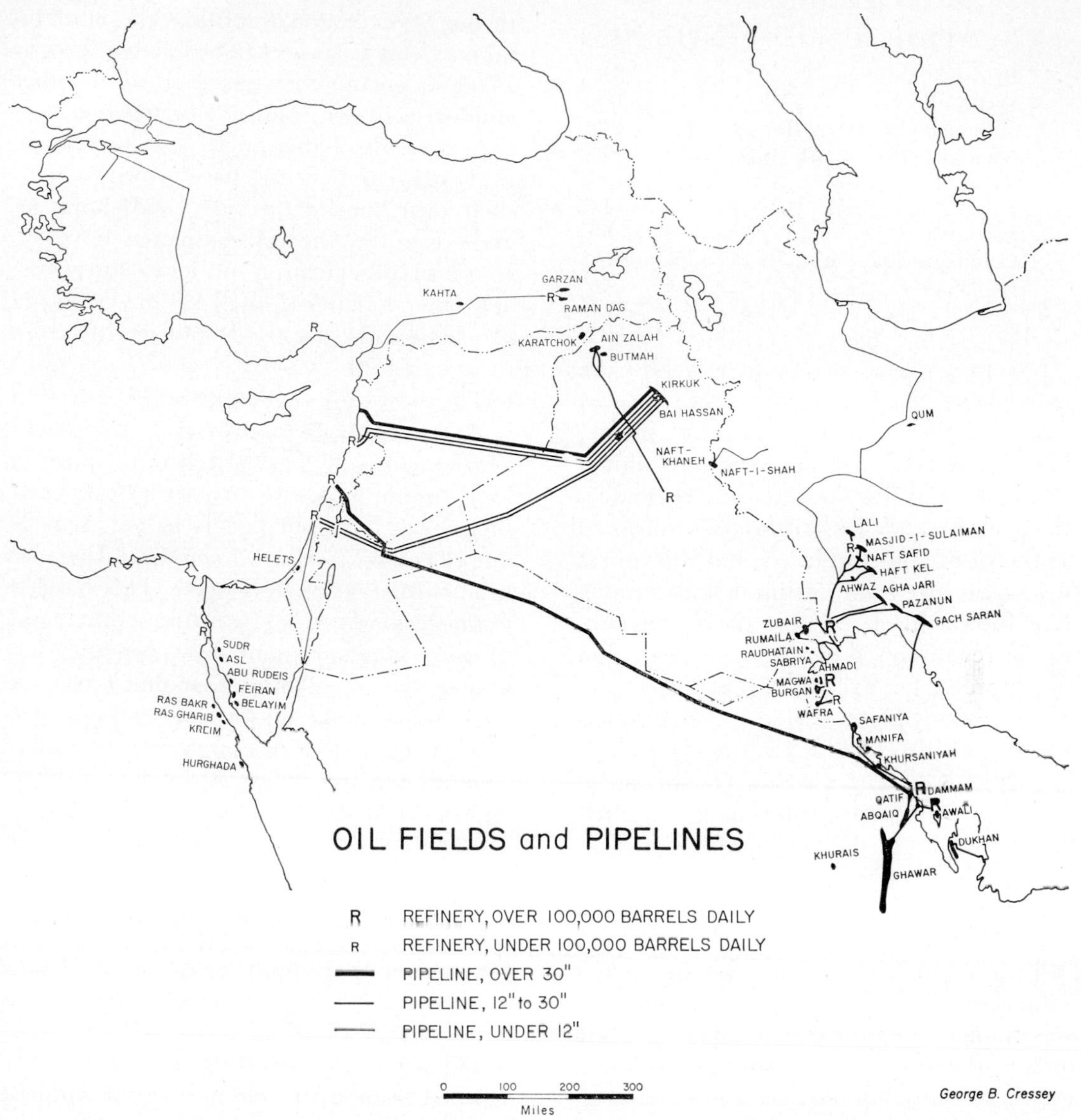

Most of Southwest Asia's petroleum occurs in fields on either side of the Persian Gulf or the Mesopotamian trough where ancient oil-bearing marine sediments accumulated under favorable structural conditions. All important producing fields are named above.

brought a fabulous income to a few fortunate areas. In several countries this exceeds a million dollars a day, and by 1960, the total for Swasia was $1.5 billion a year. Constitutional nations such as Iran and Iraq allocate the bulk of this income to development projects; in absolute monarchies such as Saudi Arabia and Kuwait, there is little budget control and the income is the personal property of the ruler, although in practice large sums are devoted to welfare.

Production by companies is shown by the following figures.

PRODUCTION BY COMPANIES, 1958

British Petroleum	30%
Gulf Oil	18%
Standard Oil of New Jersey	11%
Standard Oil of California	9%
Texaco	9%
Royal Dutch Shell	7%
Socony Mobil	6%
Compagnie Francaise des Petroles	6%
Others	4%
	100%

The proportions of the new wealth are truly phenomenal in barren areas such as Kuwait, Bahrein, and Qatar, tiny sheikhdoms in desert lands previously inhabited for the most part by poverty-striken Bedouin. Bahrein and Kuwait were traditional centers of the pearl industry, but this source of income had been declining for decades. The income from oil has started an economic revolution everywhere. Kuwait and Qatar probably have the highest per capita incomes of any place outside of North America, well over $1,000 for each man, woman, and child, if divided pro rata. On the political side, impoverished rulers have cemented their control, but the new wealth is also an occasion for rivalries and revolutions.

In addition to huge royalty payments to the governments, large amounts have been spent by the industry on local purchases and employment. On tiny Bahrein Island, the oil company spends $5 million yearly, while in Iraq the annual expenditure on salaries, wages, and supplies purchased in the domestic market exceeds $20 million; the Saudi total is at least as large. Aramco's labor force of 25,000 is greater than the total of all other employers in the country put together.

As a result of this purchasing power, entirely new communities have grown up with their own housing, services, and shops. In every country, the oil companies have encouraged the creation of local enterprise, and the companies purchase an increasing proportion of their goods and services from these new firms.

The most elaborate effort in this direction is Aramco's Arab Industrial Development Department which gives technical advice to local people who wish to start a business of their own. The purpose is to get Aramco out of non-oil industrial activities wherever local skills can be developed. This has led to the development of furniture shops, metal working plants, cement works, engineering plants, truck gardening, soap and food processing, and local import-export firms.

This does not mean that every oil field has come to be surrounded by an Arab equivalent of Tulsa, but it does suggest the trend. Striking examples are found in the cities of Damman and Khobar in eastern Arabia where one may purchase goods from all over the world, or the commercial towns which have arisen in the midst of the empty desert alongside the pump stations of the Trans Arabian Pipe Line.

The oil fields of Southwest Asia have developed with little reference to previously

OIL ROYALTIES [1]

	Saudi Arabia	*Kuwait*	*Iraq*	*Iran*	*Bahrein*	*Qatar*
1940 [2]	1.5	nil	8.1	16.0	1.0	nil
1950 [2]	112.0	11.65	13.96	44.9	1.98	.99
1955 [2]	270	280.0	223.37	85.1	8.40	36.75
1958 [3]	310.7 [4]	415.0	235.0	246.0	.... [4]	57.0

[1] In millions of dollars.
[2] Institute of Petroleum Review, June, 1956.
[3] William S. Evans, First National City Bank of New York.
[4] Saudi Arabia and Bahrein combined.

Oil wells reach thousands of feet into ancient marine sediments, in places to depths of three miles. This well is Lali Number One in Iran. (Courtesy Iranian Oil Participants.)

existing transport facilities, and as a result, new roads, railways, air terminals, and seaports have had to be constructed. The oil industries have built thousands of miles of highways and imported great numbers of trucks and cars. Private industry is now developing bus and freight services. Another source of annual revenues brought in by the petroleum industry is nearly $3 million in tolls paid to Iraq by oil tankers serving Iran through the Shatt-al-Arab. At Suez, transit charges on tankers form the largest source of canal revenue.

Even more striking than these economic items are the social changes introduced by the oil business. These include widespread familiarity with technical skills, the emergence of a new middle class, the upsurge of nationalism, and the awakening of political consciousness. Company standards of employment have been uniformly high with generally good labor relations.

Geography has been changed by the development of oil. This becomes obvious in the aerial photograph, the pattern of communications, or the growth of nearby towns.

A PREFACE FROM GEOLOGY

THE PHYSICAL GEOGRAPHY of Southwest Asia which we see today is unlike that of the geological past. The distribution of land and water formed a different map, and the hills and mountains were not those of the present. As the continent of Asia has experienced a slow alternate rising or depressing of the land surface, ancient shallow seas have repeatedly spread far inland and then withdrawn. Such advances and retreats have continued since the earliest Paleozoic period, 550 million years ago, and are recorded in the sandstones, limestones, and other marks of the geological record.

It is in the marine sediments laid down in these ancient seas, that we find our supplies of petroleum, sometimes in a single horizon, sometimes in three or four. In this part of the world, most oil-bearing formations belong to the Mesozoic Era and the early part of the Cenozoic Era, but there is no intrinsic reason why oil may not have accumulated at other times.

For millions of years, these shallow water and nearshore environments around the fringe of Asia have periodically been the site of oil formation. Here microorganisms flourished and under favorable conditions were buried and transformed into the complex substances which we call oil. In most cases, the amount of oil per cubic foot of flat lying rock is too small for extraction. It is not enough that oil be formed. In order to make development possible, the petroleum and associated gas must have been concentrated by slow migration through pore space and tiny openings until trapped in a closed pressure system, such as in an anticline or stratigraphic trap.

Where thick layers of marine sediments have accumulated in gradually sinking troughs or geosynclines, subsequent pressures may squeeze the rocks so that they are folded and faulted, sometimes building great mountain ranges. This is the case in the oil areas along the foothills of the Zagros Mountains of Iran and Iraq. In the oil fields of eastern Arabia, close folding is replaced by broad domes, usually elongated but with gentle dips.

Oil fields are generally small and often narrow, with a length of only a few tens of miles. The actual extent of productive oil horizons, concentrated in the proper structures, covers far less than 1 per cent of the potentially petroliferous area of the great Mesopotamian-Persian Gulf trough.

The search for commercially profitable deposits of oil often involves a geographical reconstruction of ancient shorelines, especially where shallow water was within 100 miles of land or in nearly enclosed gulfs and where the right kind of marine life was entrapped with the proper sediments, later to be gradually altered into hydrocarbons.

If the oil reservoir is not tight, that is to say if there are fissures which lead to the surface, the accumulated oil and gas will escape. Thus the occurrence of natural oil seeps and gas springs in Swasia may mean, in places, that the underlying accumulation has largely escaped or that all the lighter fractions are gone leaving only heavy residues. While commercial deposits have been developed near some seeps in Iran and Iraq, others have failed to yield oil.

Oil is not always found in the same formation in which it was originally deposited; instead it may have migrated into some nearby porous horizon, usually a sandstone or a fractured limestone. In such a reservoir rock, gas, oil, and water have separated according to gravity. Thus the oil lies midway in elevation between the water below and the gas cap above. Both may exert pressures on the oil so that it is lifted to the surface when reached by drilling.

Observation wells are usually drilled to both gas and water zones, thus making it possible to measure the changes in pressure and to schedule oil production programs accordingly. In some fields, most of the pressure comes from the underlying water. Elsewhere gas is the dynamic agent. If the oil pressure drops and yields decline, waste gas and surface water may be pumped back into the reservoir to maintain pressure on the oil. At Bahrein, 75 per cent of the oil flow is due to the pressure of re-injected gas, while 25 per cent results from the lift of the underlying water.

About one-third of Southwestern Asia is underlain by sedimentary formations of one kind or another. The sediments of the

WORLD OIL RESERVES AND PRODUCTION[1]

	Producing wells, 1958	Proved reserves, 1958	Production, 1958
United States		30,535,917,000	2,488,837,000
Venezuela		16,800,000,000	951,079,040
Western Hemisphere		56,004,525,000	3,836,124,941
Bahrein	147	170,000,000	14,873,111
Egypt	160	900,000,000	21,997,988
Iran	105	32,000,000,000	301,525,712
Iraq	110	21,800,000,000	266,102,000
Israel	23	16,000,000	650,000
Kuwait	297	60,000,000,000	509,382,593
Neutral Zone	141	2,500,000,000	29,310,000
Qatar	50	1,650,000,000	63,910,000
Saudi Arabia	195	45,000,000,000	370,485,585
Turkey	36	60,000,000	2,268,551
Southwest Asia		163,196,000,000	1,558,508,000
Free World		232,076,075,000	5,680,183,000

[1] In barrels. Data from *World Oil,* Aug. 15, 1959. One barrel of oil contains forty-two U. S. gallons or thirty-five Imperial gallons; this is equal to 0.159 cubic meters. The gravity may range from 28° (heavy) to 44° (light) on the scale of the American Petroleum Institute (specific gravity equivalents: 0.887 to 0.809). Where oil is measured in tons, as is the custom in Iraq and Iran, these may be short tons (2,000 pounds), long tons (2,240 pounds), or metric tons (2,204.6 pounds). To roughly convert barrels to metric tons, divide by 7.5 (7.10 for 28° gravity to 7.81 for 44° gravity). To convert barrels per day to tons per year multiply by about 50.

Persian Gulf–Mesopotamian geosyncline attain a thickness of 50,000 feet and cover an area of 600,000 square miles. Favorable signs of oil are widespread, and this appears to be one of the greatest oil basins in the world. Every few years, new discoveries are made. So rich and permeable is the Kirkuk reservoir that six wells were able to produce a total of 80,000 barrels per day for several years.

RESERVES AND PRODUCTION

As LONG AGO as 1944, one of the world's leading petroleum geologists, Everette de Golyer, wrote: "The center of gravity of world oil production is shifting from the Gulf–Caribbean area to the Middle East and is likely to continue to shift until it is firmly established in that area." Reserves in Swasia amounting to 22,175 million barrels had by then been discovered through the drilling of fewer than 100 exploration wells. By comparison, it took 40,000 new wells to increase American reserves by 10,925 million barrels.

Since Dr. de Golyer's forecast was made, additional fields have been discovered and vigorous development programs have enlarged the prospects still further. By 1958, the reserves of Southwest Asia had reached the incredible total of 163,196 million barrels.

It is clear that Southwestern Asia is rich in oil, but it appears to be the nature of oil operations that final answers as to quantities are seldom available until fields are nearly exhausted. Even then new potentials may be discovered in old fields, as through repressuring by gas or water which revives old structures.

Estimates of petroleum reserves must be understood for what they are. Unlike coal and some minerals where it is possible to block out unmined accumulations with reasonable accuracy, the amount of recoverable oil involves uncertain predictions and changing techniques. In areas where numerous wells have been drilled and production has been under way for some time, allowing changes in pressure and yield to be studied, the life expectancy of a field may be forecast with reasonable confidence. This is the category of "proven reserves." Nearby areas with only partial drilling and less evidence come under the heading of "probable reserves." With still greater uncertainty, and often no more than a generalization based on analogies, estimated figures are described as "possible reserves."

In the United States, the total proven reserves for several decades have amounted to about twenty times the annual consumption. This could mean that the known oil would be exhausted within two decades, provided that no new deposits are found. But each year, fortunately, exploration has found about as much new oil as has been used. Since it is unlikely that we shall continue to make new discoveries indefinitely, American oil reserves are clearly limited. Hence the importance of the vast deposits around the Persian Gulf.

At the beginning of 1958, the proved crude oil reserves of the Free World amounted to 232,076,075,000 barrels, of which 70 per cent or 163,196 million barrels were assigned to Southwest Asia. Data for the Soviet Union, Romania, and the People's Republic of China would somewhat reduce the percentage for Swasia. Proven reserves in these Communist areas are estimated at 26 billion barrels.

Production for the Free World in 1958 totaled 5,680,183,000 barrels, of which the United States accounted for 2,448,837,000 barrels, or about half, while Swasia produced 1,558,508,000 barrels, or nearly one-quarter.

During the middle of the twentieth century, the world demand for oil and its by-products increased at the rate of 6 to 8 per cent per annum. This meant that the demand doubled with each passing decade. About half of this increase was accounted for by needs in the United States.

By 1960, daily production in Southwest Asia had reached almost 5 million barrels, and the known reserves and potential markets indicate that this output may double by the late 1970's. Such production is of overwhelming importance to areas like Europe which have negligible oil and of future significance to areas of dwindling reserves such as the United States. Whereas Europe has previously met some of its needs by imports from Latin America, this output may soon be diverted largely to the United States, leaving Europe almost exclusively dependent on Persian Gulf supplies.

Oil produced in Swasia moves to several destinations. In 1958, 7 per cent was used locally, 19 per cent went to other parts of Asia, 3 per cent was moved to Africa, 3 per cent to Latin America, 11 per cent to North America, while 54 per cent of the production was consigned to Europe.

Statistics of production change so rapidly that they can only be of historical interest. In 1945, Southwest Asia accounted for 8 per cent of the world's total; by 1955, it had risen to 21 per cent. Given normal conditions, the share may rise to half the world total. Some of the pertinent data are presented in the accompanying table.

It is especially noteworthy that the output in Southwest Asia comes from fewer than 1,200 wells, many of them averaging over 5,000 barrels per well per day. This may be compared with a yield of some twenty barrels per day per well for the 450,000 active wells in the United States. The entire output of Kuwait is derived from a dozen wells. Some wells in America are partly shut down through pro-rata agreements, but the comparison clearly points out the limited and nearly worn-out character of American fields. Their total output is only kept high through

TOTAL CRUDE OIL PRODUCTION [1]

	Iran	*Iraq*	*Kuwait*	*Neutral Zone*	*Saudi Arabia*	*Bahrein*	*Qatar*	*Turkey*
1930	6,036	121						
1931	6,440	120						
1932	6,549	122						
1933	7,200	115				4		
1934	7,658	1,030				39		
1935	7,608	3,664				173		
1936	8,330	4,011			2	635		
1937	10,331	4,255			8	1,061		
1938	10,359	4,298			67	1,133		
1939	9,737	3,963			539	1,038		
1940	8,765	2,514			700	967		
1941	6,711	1,566			590	929		
1942	9,550	2,595			620	853		
1943	9,862	3,572			650	899		
1944	13,487	4,146			1,063	918		
1945	17,110	4,607			2,872	999		
1946	19,497	4,680	800		8,200	1,095		
1947	20,519	4,702	2,200		12,300	1,287		1
1948	25,270	3,427	6,400		19,078	1,492		3
1949	27,237	4,086	12,378		23,239	1,502	100	12
1950	32,259	6,584	17,291		26,649	1,506	1,636	17
1951	16,844	8,592	28,226		37,122	1,503	2,370	19
1952	1,360	18,251	37,637		40,313	1,505	3,297	23
1953	1,489	28,186	43,286		41,173	1,501	4,062	27
1954	3,500	30,625	47,723	849	46,455	1,503	4,779	58
1955	17,070	32,705	54,756	1,266	47,042	1,502	5,438	179
1956	26,481	31,322	54,982	1,672	48,201	1,506	5,877	306
1957	35,129	21,980	57,286	3,328	48,361	1,599	6,611	298
1958	40,590	35,670	70,217	4,258	50,128	2,035	8,222	328
1959	45,500	41,700	70,000	6,000	53,600	2,250	8,150	330

[1] In thousand metric tons, 000 omitted. Data from *United Nations Statistical Yearbook.*

intensive and unremitting search, as compared with the new and phenomenally productive nature of the Persian Gulf deposits.

Several factors contribute to the high yields of the Persian Gulf area. In the first place, the source rocks are exceptionally thick and unusually rich in organic matter. Some horizons are hundreds of feet thick. Secondly, stratigraphic conditions are very favorable. Third, the reservoir structures are unusally large, with upslope oil drainage from a wide tributary area. Most structures are simple, even ideal, although not always visible from the surface. Fourth, the cover or cap rock formations are impervious and generally tight so that gas pressures are high and the wells flow freely.

Additional advantages apply in most fields. Since subsurface property rights belong to the government, each concession covers a wide area. Operations may be planned on a large and efficient scale, thus avoiding wasteful drilling. Wells may be properly spaced for the largest long-range yield. Except for inland fields as at Kirkuk, most wells are fortunately situated within a few miles of tidewater. Gravity flow through pipe lines may be all that is needed to reach coastal terminals.

Against these aids to high production are the obvious difficulties of operating in the desert, far from sources of supply and in many cases without suitable water. In many places, in fact almost everywhere at times, there has been political insecurity and trouble with bandits. Central governments have frequently been unable to enforce law and order in areas remote from the capital, so that oil operators have had to come to terms with local tribal chiefs. Political changes have also led to the cancellation of contracts, or demands for revision. Even when oil is produced, Swasia is far removed from markets.

PIPELINES AND REFINERIES

PIPELINES FORM the arteries of oil operations, essential if oil is to move. Every field has thousands of miles of pipe; some lead to plants which separate the oil from the gas, other pipes serve refineries which may be a hundred miles or more from the wells, and still others lead to tank farms and loading terminals. The tonnage of steel required for these pipelines is impressive.

Since most of the petroleum is exported, marine loading facilities are needed. At some terminals, the shores are so shallow that long piers are required. Elsewhere, ships load offshore from submarine pipelines. Furthermore, the major terminals for Iraq and Iran lie in the estuary of the Shatt-al-Arab where ships are limited to a draft of thirty feet, a length of 600 feet, and 20,000 tons displacement. Since the largest tankers carry 100,000 tons and require more than fifty feet of water, deep-water sites are now required.

Several overland pipelines lead to the Mediterranean Sea. The necessity for those serving wells in inland Iraq is obvious. The first trans-desert lines were built by the Iraq Petroleum Company; two twelve-inch pipes were laid down, one across Syria to Tripoli in Lebanon, the other farther south across Jordan to Haifa in Palestine. These lines were completed in 1934 and were 534 and 620 miles long, respectively. Later on, two sixteen-inch lines were installed, parallel to the above, but Arab–Israeli difficulties prevented the completion of the second line to Haifa and have since closed the southern twelve-inch pipe. A fifth pipeline, thirty to thirty-two inches in diameter, completed in 1952, follows the northern route but reaches the coast at Baniyas in Syria.

These five Iraq lines share a common alignment from Kirkuk to the Euphrates, with pump stations known as K1, K2, K3. Farther west, on the separate Haifa and Tripoli lines, are pump stations H1 through H5, all inactive, as well as T1, T2, T3, and T4. With the installation of larger pumps at T3, stations T2 and T4 have been abandoned. All of the oil shipped to the Mediterranean is in stabilized crude form, in other words minus its original gas content. The combined capacity of the Iraq Petroleum Company's three northern lines amounts to 500,000 barrels per day. The amount delivered to the Mediterranean might be increased if the old Haifa lines should be rerouted around Israel to a new terminal in Lebanon.

Within Iraq, a twelve-inch line leads south 262 miles from the Ain Zalah field near Mosul, past K2, to the government refinery at Daura opposite Baghdad. Other lines connect the Basra fields with loading terminals in the Shatt-al-Arab and the Persian Gulf.

The longest desert line is the Trans-Arabian Pipe Line, known as Tapline, which provides an alternative outlet for Aramco's fields in Saudi Arabia. Tapline proper has a length of 754 miles, to which should be added 314 miles of Aramco pipeline, making a total of 1,068 miles from the

The thousand-mile pipe line across Arabia reaches the Mediterranean at Sidon in Lebanon where four tankers, anchored offshore, may be loaded simultaneously. (Courtesy Trans Arabian Pipe Line Co.)

Abqaiq field to off-shore loading facilities at Sidon in Lebanon. The system was completed in 1950 at a cost of $230 million. Its construction required 325,000 tons of steel, enough to make 200,000 automobiles, and it took 4,850,000 barrels of oil merely to fill the pipe. This is a thirty to thirty-one-inch line with six pump stations, plus six unattended booster units operated by remote control. The capacity is 450,000 barrels per day.

Almost every country has its pipelines. Israel has constructed a 175-mile line from Elath on the Gulf of Aqaba to Haifa, but it has no present international importance. Turkey has a 400-mile pipeline from the Batman refinery to Iskenderun, as well as several shorter lines which lead inland from the Mediterranean. In addition to short Iranian lines to the Persian Gulf, there is a 510-mile, ten-inch pipe from Ahwaz to Tehran, with extensions to Isfahan and Resht on the Caspian Sea, and a ninety-mile, twenty-six to thirty-inch pipe from the Gach Saran field to the deep water terminal on Kharg Island in the Persian Gulf.

It is obvious that trans-desert pipelines shorten the distance to European markets as compared with shipment by sea and also avoid canal tolls. However, this is not the entire picture. On a basis of costs per mile, water transport is always cheaper than by pipe. Tankers of over 35-foot draft cannot pass through the Suez Canal, but the large super tankers are so efficient that they can carry oil from the Persian Gulf around the Cape of Good Hope to Europe cheaper than any combination of pipeline and Mediterranean tankship. In the case of oil shipments to the east coast of North America, this route around Africa is definitely more economical. The Suez Canal seems to be approaching capacity use, and even if enlarged, may not be able to handle the prospective oil trade.

Shipping charges by tanker fluctuate with world market demand and new efficiency, while pipeline costs are determined by overhead charges and can be lowered only by efficiency or increased volume. The difference between the posted price for oil on the Persian Gulf and at Mediterranean terminals has averaged around fifty cents per barrel. This differential represents pipeline charges, but when these become too high in comparison with tanker costs, buyers prefer to take delivery at Gulf ports with the result that Mediterranean pipe shipments drop off until the cost differential is in balance.

On the basis of fluctuating economics, it is uncertain whether the trans-desert pipelines can always operate at a profit; perhaps they should not have been built. On the other hand, pipeline operation becomes cheaper as the volume is increased and as pump stations are made more fully automatic, thus reducing expensive payrolls in the desert.

One major difficulty confronting all pipeline operations to the Mediterranean is political. Every alignment must cross one or more frontiers, and it is possible for each sovereign country to stop the flow or to impose higher and higher duties until the charges become almost prohibitive, as has happened several times. Pipelines thus become a hostage to changing political forces. The problem becomes acute if lines cross the territory of rival states or where some have little or no oil of their own and see in the pipeline the possibility of lucrative income from taxes to match the royalties of their oil-rich neighbors.

It probably represents wise policy for the oil industry to continue the alternatives of pipelines and tankers, since the political and economic factors are variable and remain in doubt. The availability of the Trans-Arabian pipeline enabled Aramco to continue production despite the closure of the Suez Canal in 1957. On the other hand, the Kirkuk field in Iraq had no alternative outlet and was obliged to shut down when Syria destroyed the pump stations in the same year.

There are many proposals for additional pipelines. One would be a line from Kirkuk south to the Gulf. An ambitious line would lead from Kuwait and the Persian Gulf to the Mediterranean via Turkey and Iraq thus entirely avoiding the Levant states. The new Qum field in Iran needs an outlet, such as a line through Turkey to a port on the Mediterranean.

Refineries present another problem. There is a growing tendency for importing countries to buy crude oil and refine it themselves, thus providing employment and extra profits at home. Increasing percentages of Persian Gulf petroleum thus go abroad in crude form. On the other hand, a great refinery as at Abadan in Iran can efficiently tailor its output to the current world demand by changing the percentage of crude oil made into kerosene or into high octane gasoline in terms of the market need. The Aden refinery, in contrast, is designed to draw on crude supplies from various fields, wherever cheapest, and to be somewhat free from national restrictions. Both of these situations are an advantage, but national policies often override economics.

Most oil from Southwest Asia contains large amounts of "sour" gas, high in hydrogen sulphide. At some fields, as in Iran, sulphur is extracted commercially. Since sulphurous gases tend to corrode pipes and are unsatisfactory for shipment, all crude oil is first passed through stabilizers or gas-oil separators. The gas is then pumped back into the ground to maintain pressures, or is burned in great flares. Kuwait, for example, has several flares which burn 50 million cubic feet a day.

The gas reserves of Swasia are very large but at present lack a market. The distance from the Persian Gulf to Berlin or Paris is some 2,500 miles, not much longer than pipelines across the United States. Such a line would cross half a dozen international boundaries, so that the political hazards seem insuperable. It has also been suggested that compressed gas might be carried to Europe by special gas tankers. In Kuwait and elsewhere, some of the waste gas is used to distill sea water for domestic use. Local petrochemical industries are just getting under way.

The major refineries and their rated capacities in barrels per day are shown in the accompanying table.

The combined capacity of all refining operations amounts to less than one-quarter of the crude oil output.

In addition to loading facilities at each of the coastal refineries, several other terminals are important, chiefly for crude oil. Along the Persian Gulf, these include Fao in the mouth of the Shatt-al-Arab and the new offshore artificial island in Iraq, Bandar Mashur and Kharg Island for the Gach Saran field in Iran, Mina Saud in the Kuwait—Saudi Arabian Neutral Territory, and Umm Said in Qatar. There are four Mediterranean pipeline terminals: Baniyas in Syria, Tripoli and Sidon in Lebanon, and the facilities at Haifa in Israel, each with offshore loading arrangements via submerged pipes.

REFINERY CAPACITY [1]

Aden	120,000
Bahrein	186,500
Egypt	87,200
Suez	81,000
Alexandria	6,200
Iran	495,000
Abadan	415,000
Masjid-i-Sulaiman	75,000
Iraq	55,830
Baghdad	30,000
Khanaqin	10,250
Israel	87,000
Kuwait	220,000
Mina-al-Ahmadi	190,000
Mina Abdullah	30,000
Lebanon	24,500
Tripoli	11,550
Sidon	12,500
Neutral Zone	50,000
Saudi Arabia	
Ras Tanura	189,000
Turkey	
Batman	6,950
Mersin (planned)	65,000

[1] In barrels per day. Data from *Oil and Gas Journal*, Dec. 28, 1959.

COUNTRY DESCRIPTIONS[1]

SINCE THE various oil fields are so closely related, it seems best to describe them in the following paragraphs rather than in the chapters devoted to specific countries. Data as to ownership, reserves, and production have already been given.

Iran

Oil and gas seeps have been known in Iran since the earliest times, long before the Chrisian Era. Scientific studies date from the middle of the nineteenth century, and the first wells were drilled unsuccessfully in 1884. In 1901, an Australian financier, William Knox D'Arcy, obtained a concession, but the several wells bored in subsequent years proved to be failures. A million dollars

[1] Information on current developments throughout Swasia may be found in the magazine *World Oil*, especially in its annual "International Outlook Issue," or in the *Oil and Gas Journal*.

were spent before D'Arcy was successful. He then organized the Anglo–Persian Oil Company with the government of Great Britain as a major stockholder.

The first oil was struck in 1908 near Masjid-i-Sulaiman opposite the head of the Persian Gulf. The story of this first successful well has an element of drama for the official in charge, Mr. G. B. Reynolds, apparently ignored a telegram from his supervisor ordering him to cease operations and ten days afterward reached oil. Because of the inaccessible nature of the area, it was necessary to build roads, towns, and pipelines so that production could not get under way until 1913. By the mid 1950's, the output from the Masjid-i-Sulaiman field had totaled a billion barrels of oil. The success of this and other Iranian fields led to the building of the refinery at Abadan in 1913, later to become the world's largest.

The Zagros Mountains in southwestern Iran are a sharply folded and overthrust area, deformed by pressures from the northeast, so that the structures are asymmetrical. The western foothills have elevations of 1,000 to 2,000 feet and include a number of long, narrow, and closely folded anticlines with individual dimensions up to five by twenty miles and with beds which dip from 20° to 50°. Several of these folds involve the oil-rich Asmari limestone, up to 1,500 feet thick, which ranges from Lower Miocene to Oligocene in age. This is the producing horizon except at Masjid-i-Sulaiman, where oil also comes from Eocene limestones.

Above the oil-bearing Asmari, the reservoir is sealed by cap rock composed of massive anhydrite and other evaporites. While the Asmari has simple "text book" folds, the overlying Fars formation, more plastic, has been intricately folded so that surface outcrops often have little correspondence with buried structures, even reversing the Asmari folding. These features have immensely complicated the search for oil.

The producing area extends for a distance of a hundred miles, with seven distinct fields. Masjid-i-Sulaiman dates from 1908. Haft Kel came into production in 1928, and its output soon exceeded that of Masjid-i-Sulaiman. Gach Saran field, five by twenty-eight miles in size, was discovered in the same year. The Agha Jari field, three and one-half by thirty miles in size, was proven in 1937, and in two decades became the leading Iranian field with a daily average yield of 19,000 barrels per well.

Petroleum in this part of Iran has a parafin-naptheline base, with some asphalt. On the gravity scale of the American Petroleum Institute, it ranges from 38° API at Masjid-i-Sulaiman and Haft Kel, to 35° at Agha Jari, and 32° at Gach Saran; with 1 to 2 per cent sulphur. The ratio of gas to oil varies from 40 to 1 at Masjid-i-Sulaiman, to 165 to 1 at Agha Jari.

The fields of southwestern Iran are notable for their great production per well and for the very large reserves. Thus Masjid-i-Sulaiman has averaged a million barrels per well per year, while at Haft Kel the annual output of each of the eighteen producing wells has averaged over 2 million barrels. Yields such as this are virtually unknown outside the Persian Gulf fields. Gach Saran has 1,500 feet of oil-bearing limestone at a depth of only 3,000 feet, in a dome twenty miles long. Since the production of the entire area is under a unified control, it has been possible to regulate the output in such a way as to conserve pressures and obtain the maximum yield.

Two other areas have been developed in Iran. One structure is an eight-mile anticline which lies astride the Iraq border east of Baghdad, with Naft-i-Shah in Iran and Naft Khaneh inside Iraq. The first successful well was dug in 1923. Production is also from the Asmari limestone with a gravity of 43° API, highest in Southwestern Asia. The output amounts to a few thousand barrels a day and

Crude petroleum is a mixture of many organic components which must be separated and reconstituted by elaborate processes. This view covers a part of the Abadan Refinery in Iran. (Courtesy Iranian Oil Participants.)

is refined at Kermanshah, 158 miles to the east.

In 1957, a new field was discovered at Qum, south of Tehran, where there is a promise of large production from Oligocene and Miocene formations. The initial well came in at the rate of 80,000 barrels per day from a depth of 8,782 feet, in the Asmari limestone. This is part of the Alborz structure which extends forty miles from east to west with a width of six miles. The nearby Sarajeh structure appears similar. Only a limited amount of drilling has taken place, and production must await the building of a long pipeline, but reserves appear very large. This is a purely Iranian development with no foreign capital.

The Persian Gulf along southern Iran is bordered by large salt domes, Cambrian in age, which form glistening peaks of rock salt up to 3,000 feet in height. Unfortunately, they are not yet productive.

Extensive off-shore exploration suggests the possibility of oil beneath the gulf floor.

Production figures for Iran have steadily increased. In 1920 the daily output averaged 35,000 barrels. By 1930 the rate was 125,000 barrels per day, in 1940 it amounted to 188,000 barrel daily, in 1950 the average exceeded 700,000, and by 1960 the daily capacity was about 1 million barrels. Some of the output is refined at Abadan; the balance is shipped as crude from the port of Bandar Mashur or from the new deep-water terminal on Kharg Island, twenty-three miles offshore.

The early development of Iranian oil was under the Anglo–Persian Oil Company, which later became the Anglo–Iranian and is now known as the British Petroleum Company, in which the government of Great Britain secured a controlling interest shortly before World War I. In 1951, the Iranian government cancelled the concession and expropriated its holdings. For several years, production nearly ceased but an agreement in 1954 provided that, while ownership resided with the newly created National Iranian Oil Company, operations in the former concession area were placed under two foreign owned corporations; one for oil production, the other for the Abadan refinery. These are the Iranian Oil Producing Consortium and the Iranian Oil Refining Consortium, each with similar international control involving seventeen companies in four countries; incorporation is in the Netherlands.

Whereas the Anglo–Iranian Oil Company had been almost exclusively British, the new consortiums included 40 per cent of American capital. The American interests are Standard Oil of New Jersey, Standard Oil of California, Texaco, Gulf, and Socony Mobil, each with 7 per cent, and eight other companies who collectively own 5 per cent. While the Iranian government agreed in principle to payment for all expropriated Anglo–Iranian properties above ground, it was unwilling to provide compensation for the subsurface oil reserves which the company had blocked out. The final complex agreement called for gradual compensation to the original owner for these subsurface discoveries by the new partners.

From time to time, the Russian government has endeavored to secure permission to work in northern Iran, where geological conditions near the Caspian Sea may resemble the oil fields of Baku; no concession now exists.

New arrivals among the foreign interests are the Italians. In 1957, the Societe Irano-Italienne des Petroles was set up as a joint stock company under Iranian law to operate in three districts: an offshore area in the northern Persian Gulf, an area east of the central Zagros Mountains, and an area along the Gulf of Oman both on land and under water.

Offshore rights were secured in 1957 by a subsidiary of Standard Oil of Indiana. So attractive were the prospects, that the concession involved a cash payment of $25 million, and an agreement to spend $34 million on drilling operations during the first four years.

Iranian sedimentary basins in which the environment appears favorable for the accumulation of petroleum cover 312,000 square miles, with an additional 39,000 square miles beneath the continental shelves of the Persian Gulf and the Gulf of Oman. By 1960, about one-third of this area was covered by foreign operating agreements, while the balance was being explored by the National Iranian Oil Company.

Iraq

Oil concessions in Mesopotamia date from the end of the nineteenth century when the Turkish government, then in control, gave a contract to German interests, although this never became operative. In 1914, the government granted oil rights for what is now Turkey, Iraq, and the rest of the old Ottoman Empire to the Turkish Petroleum Company, whose name was changed in 1929 to the Iraq Petroleum Company.

Following World War I, the old German interests were allocated to the Compagnie Francaise des Petroles, while British interests were represented by the Anglo–Persian Oil Company, later named the British Petroleum Company, and by joint Dutch–British capital in the Royal Dutch Shell group. In 1922, two American shareholders were admitted: The Standard Oil Company of New Jersey and the Socony Mobil Oil Company. A small block of stock for the original concession has remained with heirs to the Armenian intermediary, who was Mr. C. S. Gulbenkian.

The present concession territory of the Iraq Petroleum Company includes all the area east of the Tigris River within the old Turkish vilayets of Baghdad and Mosul, ex-

Every oil field calls for thousands of miles of pipe, usually laid underground after being coated and wrapped in tar paper. This pipe leads from the Ain Zalah field in Iraq. (Courtesy Iraq Petroleum Co.)

cept for a small area around Khanaqin. In 1933, the remaining area of northern Iraq west of the Tigris and north of 33°N. was allocated to the Mosul Petroleum Company, with the same ownership, while southern Iraq was assigned to the Basra Petroleum Company in 1938, also a part of the I.P.C. group. The owners of the Iraq Petroleum Company are also the concessionaires in several areas around the edge of the Arabian Peninsula.

The rich Kirkuk field lies 140 miles north of Baghdad. It was developed in 1927, but production could not begin until the completion of the Mediterranean pipelines in 1934. The initial well at Baba Gurgur was a gusher which flowed at a rate of 95,000 barrels per day, and it soon became apparent that the reservoir was of giant size. Reserves are estimated at 7.5 billion barrels, enough to last until the year 2000. Kirkuk oil has a gravity of 36° API, with 2 per cent sulphur.

Oil is found in a simple anticline of coral reef limestone which ranges from the Miocene to Middle Eocene Period in age. Like the fields farther south in Iran, this fold is an outlier of the Zagros Mountains amid foothills which range in elevation between 500 and 2,500 feet. The structure of the Kirkuk anticline stands out strikingly when seen from an airplane, for Miocene and Pliocene sandstones and conglomerates make a distinct rim around an elongated basin which forms the core of the anticline. The structure is sixty-three miles long and two and one-half miles wide, with three separate domes. Oil is found in complex reef deposits, once populated with a diverse microfauna. Current

One of the world's largest oil refineries is at Abadan, on the Iranian side of the Shatt-al-Arab. The entire river belongs to Iraq. (Courtesy Iranian Oil Participants.)

production is from a horizon at 3,000 feet, but there are also rich oil accumulations at 6,000 and 11,000 feet.

Kirkuk is unique in several respects: the reservoir is of great extent; the upper zone has an oil column in excess of 2,000 feet; oil is found at shallow depths; there is easy intercommunication throughout the reservoir rocks; and oil occurs in several zones. Many of the early wells came in at a rate of 20,000 barrels per day, but with the drop in pressure throughout the field, the average of current wells is now lower. In order to maintain pressure in the Kirkuk reservoir, gas is pumped back into the top of the anticline and water injection has been installed around the margins. Since oil floats on the water, the most effective way to maintain yield is to increase the water level as fast as oil is withdrawn.

By-product plants utilize the waste gas for the production of sulphur, to make ammonium sulphate as fertilizer, and to operate cement kilns.

Two smaller fields lie near Kirkuk, Bai Hassan and Jambur, each with several producing wells.

Developments in northern Iraq have been disappointing, and production by the Mosul Petroleum Company is limited to the small fields of Ain Zalah and Butmah. At the former there is an anticline, trending east-west, which is eight miles long and two miles wide. Oil occurs in an Upper Cretaceous limestone, considerably older than the producing horizon at Kirkuk. The average depth is 5,000 feet, and the oil has a gravity of 32° API.

Another proven field is at Qaiyara, near the central Tigris, but the oil is so heavy, 17° API, that it cannot be moved through pipelines. Refining is difficult since the sulphur content is 5 to 10 per cent, but there is some production for making road bitumen in a plant owned by the Iraq Government.

The Basra Petroleum Company, in the south, has been more successful, with a large and promising output at Zubair, southwest of Basra, discovered in 1949. The oil is among the best around the Persian Gulf, with a gravity of 36° API. The structure is a broad dome, similar to occurrences in Arabia, except that the oil is Lower Cretaceous in age. Reserves are very extensive. The large Rumaila field came into operation in 1953, and both it and Zubair produce from depths of 10,000 to 12,000 feet. Another field has been discovered at Nahr Umr, of Middle Cretaceous age, but there is no production. Oil from the Basra area is shipped from Fao in the Shatt-al-Arab, and from a deep-water terminal for super tankers, sixteen miles offshore at the head of the Persian Gulf.

In addition to the three major companies in Iraq, there is a small field next to Iran, in the "Transferred Territory," once Turkish but later Persian, where oil was found in 1923. It has been owned since 1952 by the Iraq Government but was operated by the former concessionaire, the Khanaqin Oil Company. Production amounts to 13,000 barrels per day.

Production figures in Iraq have risen rapidly, generally as fast as pipeline facilities were available. In 1935, production averaged 71,000 barrels per day. This rose in 1945 to 87,000 barrels and in 1955 jumped to 654,000 barrels daily. This represents a cumulative output of over a billion barrels from the forty-four producing wells of the Kirkuk field alone. In tonnage terms, Kirkuk had produced 150 million tons of oil by 1955. Revenues to the Iraq Government have risen accordingly, and in 1956 exceeded $200 million. Of this income, 70 per cent was devoted, by law, to development operations such as irrigation and highways.

Large scale drilling and pipeline operations will enable Iraq to reach 1.4 million barrels per day by 1962. Improvements on the pipelines to the Mediterranean will raise their capacity to 960,000 barrels a day, while new pipe facilities in the Basra area will provide for a flow of 440,000 barrels daily. A portion of the latter will supply the new offshore marine terminal near the mouth of the Shatt-al-Arab.

Kuwait

Oil developments in Kuwait date from 1934 when a concession was granted jointly to The Anglo–Iranian Oil Company and The Gulf Oil Company, of British and American ownership, respectively. The first well was unsuccessful, but in 1937 the Burgan field was discovered thirty miles south of the town of Kuwait.

Unlike the closely folded anticlines of the Zagros fields, oil to the west of the Persian Gulf occurs in open structures with gentle dips. The Burgan area occupies a broad dome, covering about seventy-five square miles. Oil is present in an extraordinarily thick Middle Cretaceous sandstone reservoir at depths of around 4,000 feet. The structure is so simple that there are virtually no unsuccessful holes, and the average well yields several thousand barrels daily. As is the case in Iran and Iraq, the interpretation of the stratigraphy is based on the study of microfossils.

Oil

The oil is asphaltic, contains 2 per cent sulphur, and has an average specific gravity of 32° API. Large amounts of gas are present, as much as 475 cubic feet per barrel of oil; but unlike most Persian Gulf gas, it is low in sulphuric acid and hence "sweet." The gas is removed in gas-oil separator plants and then burned.

The Burgan producing sands aggregate one thousand feet. Reserves are thought to be no less than 30,000 billion to 40,000 billion barrels, so that the prospects are enormous. The Burgan pool is probably the richest single reservoir in the world, and it may contain as much oil as the entire United States.

In addition to the fabulous Burgan oil pool, other fields are located nearby at Magwa and Ahmadi. In northern Kuwait there is a field at Raudhatain, discovered in 1955, where oil occurs at 7,500 feet in producing sands which have the remarkable thickness of 1,500 feet.

Petroleum developments in Kuwait are only to be described as phenomenal. During 1946, the daily output reached 40,000 barrels. By 1949, this rose to 240,000, and by 1956 the figure was in excess of a million barrels a day. Royalty payments have brought an amazing change, for the Sheikh of Kuwait is receiving well over a million dollars a day. The inhabitants thus have a theoretical per capita income of something like $1,500 per year.

Most Kuwait oil is shipped in crude form, minus the separated gas. There are two deep-water tanker terminals at Mina al Ahmadi, served by gravity from the oil fields, with a loading capacity of a million and a half barrels daily of crude oil, plus smaller amounts of by-products. A new pier with a depth of sixty feet serves tankers of 100,000 tons, and there are several submarine lines to sea berths. Eighteen tankers can be loaded simultaneously. These make up the world's largest loading facilities. Kuwait ranks third among world producers and second only to Venezuela as an exporter.

Fresh water is unavailable in Kuwait either from wells, springs, or rivers and was formerly brought in barges from the Shatt-al-Arab. There are now distillation plants using natural gas both at the oil field and in Kuwait city.

The Neutral Zones

Two neutral zones border Kuwait. In the diamond-shaped area to the west, owned jointly by Iraq and Saudi Arabia, oil rights are shared by the Basra Oil Company and the Arabian American Oil Company, but no oil has been found.

In the Neutral Zone to the east, under Kuwait and Saudi Arabia ownership, there is the productive Wafra field with several dozen wells and large reserves. Production is under two separate concessionaires, the American Independent Oil Company, known as Aminoil, with ten participants on behalf of Kuwait, and the Getty Oil Company, which holds the Saudi concession. Each company holds an "undivided half"; both are American in ownership. Reserves and production are far smaller than in Kuwait, but the output is growing.

Interest in the eastern Zone did not arise until after the developments in Kuwait. As an illustration of the value of concessions in unexplored areas, it may be of interest to cite the terms involved. The American Independent Oil Company received its rights from Kuwait in 1948 to run for sixty years. This involved a payment on signature of $750,000, and an annual rental of $600,000 until the discovery of oil, and then a royalty of thirty-five cents per barrel with guaranteed minimum annual payments of $600,000. In 1949, the Saudi Arabian government sold its half rights to what is now Getty Oil Company for a down payment of $9.5 million, an annual rental of $1 million until discovery, and royalties of fifty-five cents per barrel with an annual guaranteed minimum of $1 million. No oil was discovered until 1953.

Offshore rights beneath the Persian Gulf were obtained in 1958 by Japanese interests, for even larger payments. For the first time in Southwest Asian oil concessions, these provide for Arab membership on the Board of Directors and a share in the profits from the transportation and retail sale of the oil.

Saudi Arabia

The oil of Saudi Arabia is found in several broad domes. In some cases these structures are scarcely visible on the surface, either because the dips are very low or because all bedrock is veneered by sand dunes. Several domes are exceptionally large; in general they are associated with an east-dipping monocline. Whereas the oil of the Zagros foothills is of early Tertiary age, that in Arabia is largely of the Jurassic and Cretaceous periods. Most oil occurs in four limestone formations known as the Arab Zone A, B, C, and D. All of the associated gas is sour, namely sulphurous, except at Safaniya.

The first production in Saudi Arabia occurred in 1938 at the Dammam field, but it had required extensive exploration to find the rich Upper Jurassic limestones. There are now several other fields, among them Abu Hadriya (1940), Abqaiq (1940), Qatif (1945), Fadhili (1948), Ain Dar (1948), Haradh (1949), the offshore pools at Safaniya (1951), Kharsaniya (1956), Manifa (1957), and Khurais near Riyadh (1957). Fadhili, Ain Dar, and Haradh all form part of the giant Ghawar field which is 152 miles long and one of the most extensive fields in the world.

The original Dammam field was brought in by a subsidiary of the Standard Oil Company of California but control is now shared with Texaco, the Standard Oil Company of New Jersey, and the Socony Mobil Oil Company. All operations are under the Arabian American Oil Company, often known as Aramco.

The Dammam dome around the company's base at Dhahran measures about four by five miles, with a productive area of about thirteen square miles. This is a broad anticline of unknown origin, although it may be draped over a deep-seated salt dome, similar to structures known in Iran. Oil is obtained from rocks, largely limestone, which are Upper Jurassic in age. Depths average 4,500 feet. The oil has a gravity of 35° API, and contains considerable amounts of sulphur which must be removed before shipment. Gas is found in the Cretaceous formation.

A larger field is at Abqaiq, thirty miles south of Dhahran. This is a huge anticline at least forty-three miles long and twelve miles wide, with proven oil beneath 136 square miles. Depths average 6,000 feet. Known reserves exceed 6,000 million barrels, and the API gravity is 37°. The gas is sour and averages 800 cubic feet per barrel of oil.

The Abqaiq field is comparable in area to the famous East Texas pool, but whereas the latter has a productive sand thickness of forty feet, the Arab D zone at Abqaiq averages 210 feet; and in place of 26,000 wells in the Texas area, this Arabian field produces from about forty wells. The production at Abqaiq had yielded a billion barrels by 1954. In order to maintain the yield, repressuring plants inject 150 million cubic feet of gas as well as 300,000 barrels of water daily.

Ghawar is the giant among the oil fields of Southwest Asia, with few equals anywhere for size. The extent of the proven area is still uncertain, but it covers at least 1,200 square miles. The average depth to oil is 6,000 feet and the yield from eighty-eight wells in 1957 amounted to 620,000 barrels per day. Ghawar produced its billionth barrel of oil on December 25, 1956. The gravity ranges from 32° API in the south to 36° in the north.

No oil area is more desolate than that in the Qatar peninsula. These valves control the degassing station in the Dukhan field. (Courtesy Iraq Petroleum Co.)

Aramco has two offshore fields in production, Safaniya and Manifa, with API gravities of 27° and 31° in the former, according to the zone, and 28° at the latter. Safaniya has two wells on shore and thirty out in the Persian Gulf, where the depth of water reaches forty-five feet and the farthest wells are fifteen miles from the shore. The proven area covers 100 square miles and is said to be the largest offshore pool in the world, with a 1958 output of 175,000 barrels per day. Oil is found in two Cretaceous horizons, known as the Zubair and Bahrein zones.

Saudi Arabian production has risen phenomenally. From a daily average of 500,000 barrels in 1949, output increased to nearly 1 million barrels daily in 1956, derived from only 184 wells. Reserves in 1957 were estimated at 34 billion barrels. All of this represents a total investment of $600 million.

The agreement between Saudi Arabia and Aramco provides that the Company must periodically relinquish a part of its concession area. This requires active exploration in order to discover where oil is presumably absent. Field work is difficult in all parts of Arabia, but especially in the vast sand deserts of the Rub-al-Khali. Tens of millions of dollars have been invested here in basic geological studies, but with no assurance of oil. Those who look at the profits of successful wells should realize the risk; a single wildcat well may represent a million dollar gamble. The Safaniya field required an investment of $21 million in order to start production.

Bahrein

The island of Bahrein lies twenty-five miles off the coast of Arabia. It contains a broad dome with ideal structures of Middle Cretaceous limestone, but since these formations are older than any previously known oil-bearing rocks in the Persian Gulf, the concession was at first thought unattractive. There is a single anticline thirty miles long by ten miles wide, with dips of 3° to 6°. Only a part of the dome is oil bearing, approximately fifteen square miles. The average wells are 2,300 feet deep, and the gravity is 33°–35° API.

Oil was found in 1932 by the Standard Oil Company of California and the Texas Company, but, since the Sheikhdom of Bahrein is under British protection, the Bahrein Petroleum Company, known as Bapco, is incorporated in Canada. Its products are marketed under the name of Caltex, derived from those of the joint owners. Both Bapco and the Kuwait Oil Company operate largely with British personnel and equipment.

Bahrein production began in 1933, grew to 967 tons in 1940, and reached 1,506 tons in 1950. The reserves appear modest.

Qatar

Qatar is a barren peninsula which juts into the Persian Gulf south of Bahrein. In 1935, the Sheikhdom granted a concession to a subsidiary of the Iraq Petroleum group known as Petroleum Development (Qatar) Ltd. Oil was found in 1939 in a long anticline of Jurassic limestones, five by fifty miles in dimensions, at depths of around 6,000 feet. The gravity is 41° API. This is known as the Dukhan field. Since the oil lies near the west coast where it is impractical to provide loading facilities, there is a twelve-inch pipeline across the peninsula to the terminal at Umm Said.

Reserves and production are important, ahead of Bahrein, but a poor third to Saudi Arabia and Kuwait. Production did not begin until 1949. In 1950, it averaged 32,340 barrels per day, rising to 162,000 barrels in 1958.

The Persian Gulf

The eastern shores of the Persian Gulf and the southern coast of Arabia are dotted with tiny sheikhdoms and local states. Kuwait, Bahrein, and Qatar have already been described; with the exception of Masqat the others had been of little economic or political importance until the possibilities of oil appeared.

Undefined boundaries and dubious sovereignties have added to the legal problem, but oil concessions have now been granted in all areas. The fact that some of these overlap has been the cause for local wars, with one sheikh or the other supported by rival concessionaires. Both onshore and offshore concessions are involved. Very little production has taken place. Even where oil prospects are very dubious, the local rulers have usually been granted handsome advance royalties for signing the contract.

Oil developments are no longer limited to wells on the land, for the shallow waters of the Persian Gulf are thought to overlie oil.

Offshore oil deposits have been discovered beneath the shallow water of the Persian Gulf. This floating rig, known as the "Queen Mary," is in the Manifa field. (Courtesy Arabian American Oil Co.)

Billions of dollars have been invested in the search for petroleum; single wells may cost a million dollars and yet fail to find oil. This well is in the Raman Dag field in Turkey. (Courtesy Turkish Press, Broadcasting, and Tourist Department, Ankara.)

The ownership of the Gulf floor adds further political complications, since Iran claims sovereignty over the entire Persian Gulf, plus its western shores including Bahrein Island. Little is known about actual subsea oil reserves, but they may well match those on shore. Drilling has taken place in depths of 150 feet of water.

Between the Qatar peninsula and Aden, most of these consessions belong to companies of the Iraq Petroleum group. In Dhufar, where oil was found in 1957, the concession is held by the Cities Service Company and Richfield Corporation. The oil has a gravity of only 12° API, exceptionally heavy, and comes from a depth of 3,200 feet.

Syria, Lebanon, Jordan, and Israel

Oil seeps occur in various parts of the Levant states. The Dead Sea has long been known for its lumps of bitumen which occasionally rise to surface and may be collected on the shore. Most of the area appears to lie within a sedimentary basin so that oil may be present.

In Israel, there are several small producing wells in the Helets field near the Mediterranean Sea in the south, with a combined yield of 1,000 barrels a day.

Syria has a few wells at Karatchok in the northeast, not far from producing fields in Iraq and Turkey. The first well was discovered in 1956 at a depth of 6,650 feet; the oil is heavy with a gravity of 20° API.

Numerous wells have been drilled in Lebanon and Jordan, but with only limited success. Although not producers themselves, these states have an interest in oil since pipelines pass through each country.

Turkey

Interest in Turkish petroleum goes back to the beginning of the century when concessions were granted for various parts of the Ottoman Empire. Some of these went to German interests, in part under the proposed Berlin-to-Baghdad Railway Convention of 1903. British, Dutch, and American interests also sought concessions, but in 1925 all foreign firms were debarred. Scores of wells have been drilled by the government's Mineral Research and Exploration Institute, but almost entirely without success. In 1953, concessions were again offered to a number of foreign corporations.

Production within present day Turkey has been disappointing. In 1940, a small field was developed near Raman Dag, east of Diyarbekir and 100 miles from the Ain Zalah field of northern Iraq. The oil comes from a massive Cretaceous limestone, at a depth of 4,500 feet, and is heavy with a 20° API gravity and 4 per cent sulphur. The structure measures twelve by one and one-half miles. Oil has also been found at nearby Garzan. There is a small refinery nearby at Batman, as well as one for imported crude oil at Mersin.

Oil may also be present around Adana and Iskenderon near the Mediterranean and along the Black Sea Coast.

Egypt

Egypt has oil on both sides of the Gulf of Suez and has become self-sufficient, with a small surplus for export. The first production dates from 1913, but most of the dozen fields were discovered about the middle of the century. Five hundred and fifty-five wells had been drilled to the end of 1958, most of them into Eocene and Miocene formations.

REFERENCES

Arabian American Oil Co.: REPORT OF OPERATIONS. (annual), New York and Dhahran.

Carol, Olaf: WELLS OF POWER. London: Macmillan (1951).

Elwell-Sutton, L. P.: PERSIAN OIL. London: Lawrence and Wishart (1955).

Eyoub, Djevad: "Petroleum Possibilities of Turkey," *Bull. Amer. Assoc. of Petrol. Geols.*, XV (1931), 629–669.

Finnie, David H.: DESERT ENTERPRISE: THE MIDDLE EAST OIL INDUSTRY IN ITS LOCAL ENVIRONMENT. Cambridge: Harvard Univ. Press (1958).

Iraq Petroleum Co.: IRAQ OIL. (annual), London.

Lees, G. M.: THE GEOLOGY OF THE OILFIELD BELT OF IRAN AND IRAQ. London: Oxford Univ. Press (1938).

Lees, G. M., and Richardson, F. D. S.: "The Geology of the Oil Field Belt of S. W. Iran and Iraq," *Geol. Mag.*, LXXVII (1940), 227–252.

Lenczowski, George: OIL AND STATE IN THE MIDDLE EAST, New York: McGraw-Hill (1959).

* Longrigg, Stephen H.: OIL IN THE MIDDLE EAST. London: Oxford Univ. Press (1954).

Melamid, Alexander: "The Geographical Pattern of Iranian Oil Development," *Econ. Geog.*, XXXV (1959), 199–218.

Melamid, Alexander: "The Oil Fields of the Sinai Peninsula," *Middle Eastern Affairs*, X (1959).

* Pratt, Wallace E., and Good, Dorothy: WORLD GEOGRAPHY OF PETROLEUM. New York: American Geog. Soc. (1950).

Shwadran, Benjamin: "The Oil of Iraq," *Middle Eastern Affairs*, III (1952), 360–380.

Shwadran, Benjamin: THE MIDDLE EAST, OIL AND THE GREAT POWERS, New York: Praeger (1959).

Sinclair, Angus: "Iranian Oil," *Middle Eastern Affairs*, II (1951), 213–224.

Van der Meulen, Daniel: THE WELLS OF IBN SA'UD. New York: Praeger (1957).

CHAPTER 9

International Contacts

Land of the Six Seas
New Avenues by Air
International Trade
Recent History
Political Problems
American Policy in Swasia

LAND OF THE SIX SEAS

THE SIX SEAS which partly envelop Swasia make it an irregular peninsula and also give it some of the qualities of an island. The isolation is especially obvious when one looks at a map and notes that mountains and deserts reinforce the insularity. Nowhere are there overland connections to the outside world across fertile plains.

Much of the contact of the realm with Europe, Africa, and the rest of Asia has been by way of the Mediterranean, Aegean, Black, Caspian, Red, or Persian seas. The Mediterranean Sea has been by far the most significant, but we should not overlook the historic importance of the others. Many cultural ties link western Arabia with the Sudan and Ethiopia across the Red Sea. Numerous families along the coast of southern Arabia and in the Hadhramaut made their fortunes in India and even ruled provinces there. Modern Persian Gulf commerce was developed from Bombay, which is still an important base for trade with Swasia. Native dhows Kuwait have long traded with Zanzibar.

The Mediterranean Sea enjoys several advantages. Its great size is obvious; so too is the productivity of its hinterland. Along its shores, and beyond Gibraltar, are rich civilizations with great commercial potentials. With its eastern links through the Bosporus and Suez, the Mediterranean and its arms form a coastline around Southwest Asia which measures 3,400 miles from Trabzon in eastern Turkey to Aden.

This is not all, for now that the Caspian Sea is linked with the Black Sea through the

(Opposite) The American University at Beirut, seen in the foreground, is one of the most international institutions in the world, with students from every country in Swasia as well as overseas. (Courtesy U.S. Operations Mission, Beirut.)

COAST LINE RELATIONS

Country		*Coast Line miles*	*Area square miles*	*Ratio coast to area*	*Commercial Seaports*
Iran		1,400	628,060	1:464	9
Persian Gulf	1000				
Caspian Sea	400				
Iraq		30	171,600	1:3888	2
Israel		110	8,000	1:71	3
Mediterranean	100				
Red Sea	10				
Jordan		10	37,500	1:3750	1
Kuwait		150	5,800	1:60	1
Lebanon		120	3,400	1:33	3
Saudi Arabia		1,400	870,000	1:621	3
Red Sea	1100				
Persian Gulf	300				
Southern Arabia		2,400			2
Syria		85	72,234	1:777	1
Turkey		2,000	296,185	1:148	8
Black Sea	750				
Aegean Sea	650				
Mediterranean	600				
Yemen		300	75,000	1:250	1
All Swasia		8,000	2,300,000	1:300	34

Volga-Don Canal, seagoing vessels can continue eastward to the shores of Iran. When the Soviets complete the North Turkmenian Canal between the Caspian and the Amu Darya, it should be possible for water-borne cargoes to reach northern Afghanistan.

Along Swasia's southern coast, the Arabian Sea and the Persian Gulf provide ready access. The Indus River is scarcely navigable, but it might be theoretically possible to start by boat from a point somewhere east of the Khyber Pass and almost encircle Southwest Asia, ending along the Soviet frontier of Afghanistan less than 300 miles from the starting point.

The entire coastline of Swasia measures some 8,000 miles, or much more if irregularities are included. This provides a ratio of one mile of coast to each 300 square miles for the realm as a whole. Such comparisons need to be qualified in terms of ports and accessibility, but they suggest the sea–land ratio. The orientation of Swasia is far more maritime than that of India with Pakistan, where the ratio is one to 5,000.

The accompanying table presents coastline relations for each littoral country in Swasia. Lebanon, Kuwait, and Israel have the longest frontage on salt water per square mile of total area and certainly are the most maritime conscious. Turkey's 2,000 miles of coast line, bordering three sides of the country, are served by eight commercial seaports. At the other extreme are Jordan and Iraq, with barely a window on the sea.

Scheduled services across several of the six seas from one side to the other are limited or absent. No shipping operates from the south coast of the Black Sea to the U.S.S.R. One or two boats on the Caspian Sea link Baku with Pahlevi in Iran. There is no service across the Persian Gulf, except as vessels bound for the north may call en route at Bahrein or Bushire. On the Red Sea, there

The Bosporus is one of the world's historic seaways, once guarded by the fort of Rumeli Hisar built in the fifteenth century. Although Turkey receives some snow, the Bosporus rarely freezes. (Courtesy Turkish Information Service, New York.)

are limited connections between Jidda and Port Sudan, largely to serve pilgrims bound for Mecca. The story on the Mediterranean is quite different, for there ample connections are available.

Four nations have the advantage of facing at least two of these seas. Iran may look north to the Caspian Sea or south to the Persian Gulf and the Arabian sea. Israel has an extra coast line on the Red Sea. Saudi Arabia has both an east and west coast. Turkey is equally interested in the Black, Aegean, and Mediterranean seas.

While Iraq has only a tiny frontage on the Persian Gulf, it is fortunate that this includes Basra and the Shatt-al-Arab. Jordan's coast line is equally short, but unfortunately Aqaba is poorly linked with the interior. Both of these seaports are "around the corner" from Suez so that, if time is important, shipments move overland through Beirut. Afghanistan is the only country which is completely nonmaritime, and would naturally welcome a free-trade zone or transit rights at the port of Karachi.

As one travels eastward from the Mediterranean there is a marked gradation from sea-minded Lebanon to the continental isolation of eastern Iran and Afghanistan. The ocean is the world's great commercial highway, and every country wants a gateway. Each country in Swasia with any port possibilities is thus actively engaged in development operations.

Several straits or narrow seas form bottle-

Through sleeping car services link Baghdad with Istanbul via the Taurus Express, but only limited amounts of freight pass between Turkey and Iraq. (Courtesy Iraq Petroleum Co.)

necks along the circum-Swasian sea routes. The Dardanelles and Bosporus guard the entrance to the Black Sea, and until 1910 carried more shipping than Suez. The Suez Canal forms one of the world's key avenues, but of equal importance is the Bab el Mandeb, the strait at the south end of the Red Sea. Access to the Persian Gulf is through the Strait of Hormuz. Several of these straits have nearby islands or control points. On either side of the Bab el Mandeb are Kamaran and Socotra islands, both British. To reach the Dardanelles from the south, ships must pass Crete and the many Greek islands of the Aegean.

Just as there are significant bottlenecks, so there are key terminal ports at the head of bays where ships cannot go farther and cheap water transport must give way to more expensive overland shipment. In the Gulf of Aqaba this means Elath in Israel and Aqaba in Jordan. At the end of the Persian Gulf are Basra in Iraq and the Iranian ports of Abadan, Khorramshahr, Bandar Shahpur, and Bandar Mashur. Trabzon and Iskenderon in Turkey fulfill a similar function for the eastern Black Sea and northeast Mediterranean. Trabzon has long served as an entrepot for northern Iran. It lies much closer to Europe than ports on the Persian Gulf, but has the disadvantage of customs problems. Most European automobiles consigned to Tehran are driven overland from Trabzon. In the southern Caspian lie Pahlevi and Bandar Shah. Soviet water-borne commerce bound for Afghanistan moves up the Amu Darya as far as Termez.

Several other gateways are important. Istanbul accounts for nearly half of Turkey's foreign trade. The various oil terminals involve large tonnages, but in terms of general cargo, Beirut occupies the leading place among all Swasian ports. Lebanon itself accounts for only nominal commerce, but Beirut is the chief trans-shipment point for Syria and Jordan, and also handles large overland freight movements with Iraq and even Iran.

Few railroads and not many highways cross international borders. From Turkey one line leads south to Aleppo and another extends southeast to Mosul. Istanbul has one connection with Europe. Proposed extensions of Turkish and Iranian railways will link the two countries. Iran has two trans-frontier railways; one connects Tabriz with the Soviet system in the Caucasus, and the other leads to Zahidan from the Pakistan border.

Four railways touch the edges of Afghanistan; one leads over the Khyber Pass east of Kabul, another Pakistan line terminates at Chaman opposite Kandahar, and two Soviet lines extend to the border on the north, opposite Herat and Mazar-i-Sharif respectively.

In the Levant, ineffective railways connect Syria with Lebanon and Jordan, and once led south to Saudi Arabia. The historic line from Egypt across Palestine has been inoperative since the creation of Israel.

International roads somewhat take the place of railways, but in many cases they are poorly paved. No road of any character crosses the Turkish frontier with Iraq, and only one leads to Iran. Turkey and Syria are linked by four roads but they carry little commerce. The major international highway of Swasia is an east-west route from Beirut over the mountains to Damascus, across the desert to Baghdad, and through the Zagros to Tehran. Trucks have largely replaced camel caravans and now operate in any direction across level areas, even in the absence of improved roads.

NEW AVENUES BY AIR

THE ADVENT of the airplane has brought a marked change in the transportation map. Half a million passengers a year use the Suez Canal, but at least as many fly across Swasia on their way from Europe to India and beyond. The great east-west airway starts with London or Paris, stops at Rome or Athens, and then includes Beirut on its way to Karachi and eastern Asia. Some planes follow routes which involve a stop at Cairo; others fly across Turkey.

The port of Beirut is of no importance for through passengers by sea, since ships bound for Suez and the Indian Ocean would need to detour to reach it; instead they call at Alexandria. Now that travelers no longer need to follow waterways, Beirut, Cairo, and Istanbul have come to be on the main lines. A similar change has taken place at Aden where all vessels pause for a few hours; in the air age, Aden is off the beaten path. Previously isolated places at the head of the Persian Gulf, such as Basra, have now become easily accessible by air. The change is even more striking at Baghdad or Tehran, which were once hard to reach, but today have several major air services daily.

Whereas the interior of Swasia was once relatively inaccessible and commerce moved around the periphery of the realm, the new aerial Main Street cuts directly across the heart of the area. Airlines easily hurdle the former barriers of mountain and desert.

The changes brought by air travel are dramatic. Planes serve areas which do not

COMMERCIAL AIRPORTS

Saudi Arabia	25
Turkey	23
Iran	16
Aden and Protectorate	8
Afghanistan	6
Iraq	4
Jordan	4
All Swasia	101

even have improved roads. Pilgrims to Mecca now fly instead of traveling by camel caravan, geological exploration parties in the most isolated deserts enjoy fresh vegetables and frozen foods flown in from Beirut, and valuable furs from Afghanistan reach London in a couple of days. Many parts of Southwest Asia appear to have skipped the railroad age.

In terms of direct routes to Europe from India or eastern Asia, Swasia enjoys only a temporary advantage. Few flat maps actually show great circle courses as straight lines. A great circle flight from London or Paris through Beirut leads to nowhere but the Indian Ocean. The great circle route from London or Paris to Karachi or Bombay misses most of Swasia but does pass over Tehran. A flight from Europe to Singapore and Australia could use the new jet base at Kandahar in Afghanistan. Any direct route to a destination east of India would pass well north of Swasia and far inside the U.S.S.R.

While planes seek the quickest route, this is not always the most direct. High level jet streams offer tail winds of more than a hundred miles an hour, so that it may be worth while to make considerable detours to take advantage of, or to avoid, conditions in the upper atmosphere. Our knowledge of three dimensional meteorology in Swasia is just in its beginning.

Great-circle routes cut far to the north of what some maps suggest as straight lines, but so long as Soviet air space remains forbidden, long distance traffic will detour southward. Current patterns may continue in any event, for while planes can fly long distances without refueling, there must be business at their necessary stops. Along the airways from the Mediterranean to India, there is a growing volume of traffic, and Beirut seems to provide the best intermediate airport.

MIDDLE EAST EXPORTS[1]

Intra Middle East	540
United Kingdom	505
United States	495
Western Germany	300
Italy	140
France	135
Japan	100
Egypt	50
Soviet Union	40
World total	2,995

[1] Data from *United Nations Yearbook of International Trade Statistics,* 1956. The Middle East as here defined omits Turkey and Afghanistan and includes Egypt, the Sudan, Libya, and Ethiopia. Figures in table represent millions of dollars.

The map of scheduled air services, as it appeared during the late 1950's (page 24), included 101 commercial airports in Swasia. Freight and charter services are not included. Companies such as the Arabian American Oil Company operate a dozen planes and serve a score of their own stations.

Three airports stand out in the west: Beirut, Cairo, and Istanbul, each served by more than twenty scheduled airlines. These are followed by Damascus, Baghdad, Tehran, and Ankara. Even Basra, Kuwait, Dhahran, and Bahrein have an average of ten companies apiece.

INTERNATIONAL TRADE

TRADE STATISTICS are influenced by many factors, including domestic politics and world prices, so that they change rapidly. Only general conclusions seem appropriate here.

In terms of export business for the entire Middle East, intra-realm trade leads with about 20 per cent of the total. Exports to the

Jaffa oranges have long been famous in coastal Palestine. This shipment is being loaded in the harbor at Haifa. (Courtesy Israel Office of Information, New York.)

United Kingdom and the United States follow, each with some 15 per cent, followed by Western Germany, Italy, and France. The share of the Soviet Union is about 1 per cent. The largest part of the export trade is in oil, both crude and refined. Comparable information as to the origin of imports is not available.

Foreign trade figures for the separate countries reveal striking differences in commercial development. Statistics are unfortunately lacking for Saudi Arabia, Kuwait, and other areas, but the prosperity of oil-rich Iraq and Iran is obvious. Turkey does a large international business but the considerable excess of imports indicates the unbalanced character of its foreign trade. The absence of a balance of trade is most noticeable in Israel and Jordan, and is made possible only by large grants and loans from overseas. Lebanon's trade appears equally out of balance, but other factors apply since it derives much of its income from services and imported capital. The volume of trade in Aden reflects its trans-shipment services.

The details of Iraq's trade illustrate the role of petroleum. During the mid 1950's, export totals averaged 175 million dinars (one dinar equals one pound sterling or $2.80). Oil accounted for 160 million, barley for something over 5 million, dates for 3 million, and wool was valued at about 1 million dinars. In return, imports averaged 100 million dinars, divided among more than a dozen commodities, each valued at over a million; machinery, automobiles, and steel were far in the lead, followed by sugar, tea, other foodstuffs, and textiles. The United Kingdom took first place as a source of imports, with more than a quarter of the total, and also received the largest share of the nonpetroleum exports. The United States was easily second in imports, but shared second place in exports with a number of European countries. Taiwan supplied the bulk of Iraq's sugar. Comparable differences between the character of exports and imports are present in Iran and Saudi Arabia.

The over-all picture is that of raw material exports and of manufactured imports. In addition to oil, the export list includes chrome from Turkey, karakul from Afghanistan, dates from the Persian Gulf, citrus fruits and vegetables from the Levant states, wool and hides from nomadic lands, and cotton from Syria.

Three dozen ports have something in the way of commercial facilities, but not all of them are adequately modern. Exports of crude or refined petroleum far exceed all other trade combined. Turkey leads in the total volume of dry-cargo imports and exports, but Beirut surpasses Istanbul in tonnage. Aden handles the largest number of ships, but most of these are in transit.

Imports far exceed nonoil exports. As a rough approximation, all of Swasia receives sea-borne freight amounting to some 10 million tons a year, but dry cargo exports are less than half this figure.

The following paragraphs indicate the principal ports, by country, with comments on their significance. References to cargo are in metric tons, which is of little significance in suggesting value.

Aden receives an average of 5,000 ships a year, with a total net registered tonnage of 25 million; many of these vessels take advantage of the extensive oil bunkerage facilities.

Bahrein is an entrepot for local trade in the Persian Gulf, and exports petroleum products.

Iran divides its trade between Caspian Sea and Persian Gulf ports. A thousand vessels call each year, representing 5 million net registered tons. Import freight weighs a million tons but exports, largely oil, are four times as large. Pahlevi and Bandar Shah handle Soviet trade, but this amounts to under 200,000 tons annually; the latter is a rail terminus. Abadan and Khorramshahr are ports on the Shatt-al-Arab; the former is a major shipper of refined petroleum products. Neither port has rail connections. Bandar Shahpur and Bandar Mashur are rail heads on the Gulf; the former is the principal import center; the latter ships crude oil. Kharg Island is the new deep-water terminal near the oil fields. Bushire and Bandar Abbas are old but insignificant ports on the Persian Gulf.

Iraq's only sea outlet is at the head of the Persian Gulf. Incoming freight amounts to a million tons a year, but is far outdistanced by oil shipments. Basra is a modern commercial port, handling all of Iraq's dry cargo. It is supplemented by oil terminals at Fao and the offshore deep-water facilities.

Israel has a frontage on both the Mediterranean and the Red Sea. Imports of dry cargo average 1.5 million tons; exports are about half this figure. Fifteen hundred ships call each year, with a total net registered tonnage of nearly 3 million tons. Haifa and Tel Aviv are the chief harbors, with the former handling nine-tenths of the traffic. Elath is Israel's back door on the Gulf of Aqaba.

Jordan is nearly landlocked, but has a small frontage on the Gulf of Aqaba. Seaborne imports at the port of Aqaba amount to a quarter of a million tons, with exports,

INTERNATIONAL TRADE [1]

	1955		1956		1957		1958	
	Imports	Exports	Imports	Exports	Imports	Exports	Imports	Exports
Aden	210	176	200	180	205	183	201	178
Afghanistan	—	—	55	57	47	78	37	48
Egypt	538	419	534	407	524	493	684	470
Iran	278	386	278	575	314	785	412	847
Iraq	271	518	321	478	343	360	307	567
Israel	325	88	367	104	435	138	434	136
Jordan	76	7	78	12	85	12	95	9
Lebanon	241	37	256	45	286	48	236	35
Saudi Arabia	196	657	225	797	232	914	217	868
Syria	196	132	205	145	172	153	204	118
Turkey	498	313	407	305	397	345	315	264

[1] In millions of U.S. dollars. Data from United Nations, *Direction of International Trade,* X, No. 8 (1959).

largely phosphate rock, at half that amount. Three hundred ships call annually.

Kuwait has almost no commerce other than petroleum. Mina-al-Ahmadi is the world's largest crude oil terminal.

Lebanon serves as the major gateway along the eastern Mediterranean. Beirut handles 3,000 ships a year. Import cargo amounts to nearly 2 million tons, but exports are approximately one-half million tons. Sidon and Tripoli are oil terminals for pipelines from Saudi Arabia and Iraq, respectively. All vessels are loaded from offshore submarine facilities.

Saudi Arabia faces both the Red Sea and the Persian Gulf; commerce is limited, except in oil. Jidda serves western Arabia and is the gateway for pilgrims to Mecca. Its annual trade is under 500,000 tons. Dammam, with rail facilities, is the port for eastern Arabia and its oil fields, handling around 500,000 tons of freight a year. Ras Tanura is a nearby oil terminal.

Syria has only limited frontage on the Mediterranean. Latakia handles a thousand ships a year with a third of a million tons of imports and half a million tons of exports. Baniyas is the terminal for a thirty-inch oil line from Iraq.

Turkey has the longest sea frontage, the most developed interior, and the largest number of modernized ports. The annual maritime imports amount to 2.5 million tons, while exports average 2 million tons. Istanbul handles two-thirds of Turkey's imports but only one-quarter of the export trade. The total net registered tonnage of ships entering the port amounts to 5 million tons. Izmit is nearby on the Sea of Marmara. Iskenderon and Mersin dominate the foreign trade of southern Turkey. Together they handle well over half a million tons of imports, with somewhat larger exports. Izmir leads in trade along the Aegean Sea with a quarter of a million tons of imports and nearly half a million tons of exports. Two and a half million net registered ship tons are involved. Zonguldak, Samsun, and Trabzon are the chief Black Sea ports. The first port ships coal, while the third provides a gateway to northern Iran. Numerous small ports handle coastal trade.

Yemen has very little foreign trade, but coffee is shipped from the open roadstead of Hodeida.

Qatar has a large oil terminal at Umm Said.

Several nations have transit problems due to inadequate port facilities of their own or a poor location with respect to major sea lanes. Turkey, Saudi Arabia, Lebanon, and Israel have no need to route shipments across international borders. On the other hand, a large part of the commerce of Syria and Jordan moves through Beirut; Yemen similarly depends on Aden. Their respective alternatives are the underdeveloped ports of Latakia, Aqaba, and Hodeida. Iraq and Iran look to Lebanon for a short route to Europe. Hundreds of trucks fan out into the interior from Beirut.

The transit complications of international pipelines have already been discussed.

While Iran has two coasts, both are poorly located. Even the oil terminal at Abadan does not have free access to the sea since the entire width of the Shatt-al-Arab is claimed by Iraq. As already indicated, some trucking trade enters Iran from Trabzon on the Black Sea, as well as from Beirut. One railway reaches Tabriz from the U.S.S.R., and another line enters the country from Pakistan in the far southeast.

Landlocked Afghanistan is particularly concerned over access to the outside world. Soviet trade comes from two railroads in the north. European and Indian commerce must cross Pakistan, either via the railroad from Quetta or from the railroad west of Peshawar. Only very poor roads lead to Iran, but here is the aerial avenue to Europe. Transit concessions are thus a vital element in Afghanistan's foreign policy.

Overland trade routes from Europe to India and China have attracted travelers since before Marco Polo's time. Early in the century, Germany had hopes for a Berlin-to-Baghdad railroad. No line yet leads across Swasia, but plans have several times been drawn up to connect Iranian railways with those in Turkey and Pakistan. Road conditions vary from fair to very poor, but it is possible to drive across every frontier except that of Israel. Through bus service sometimes operates from Paris to Bombay.

RECENT HISTORY

THERE IS NO SINGLE starting point for an historical understanding of modern Swasia, since many current problems trace back to events of earlier centuries. Some minority peoples owe their present location and relationships to events of a thousand years ago.

During the sixteenth century, Turkey ruled 40 million people. Its area was spread across 1.7 million square miles of Asia, Africa, and Europe. Present day boundaries only date from 1923. In all of the former Turkish lands, souvenirs remain, some involving railway or oil concessions, or special guarantees and semiautonomy for minorities.

The decline of the Ottoman Empire opened the way for a succession of intrusions by European powers, climaxing in British, French, Italian, and Russian territorial claims in Anatolia during World War I. All such ambitions eventually collapsed, but they would have reduced Turkey to a small area in the north central part of the present country. Proposals called for the internationalization of the Straits, a Greek area around Izmir, Italian control in the southwest, French occupation of southern Anatolia and the Levant, with an area of influence into northern Iraq, Russian control in Armenia, and British domination in southern Iraq and the Gulf area plus a zone of influence across northern Arabia. Palestine was to be internationalized.

Turkey is now free, but within its former areas are a series of new and artificial states.

Southwest Asia has long been a crossroads area. This Crusader castle at Sidon in Lebanon is a reminder of the successive waves of conquest. (Courtesy Iraq Petroleum Co.)

Since the boundaries are arbitrary, it is not surprising that the political units have proven unstable. Present day Iraq, Syria, Lebanon, Jordan, and Israel lack historic or geographic validity.

The political status of Palestine presents a series of problems with repercussions far beyond its borders, since it is the spiritual homeland for nearly half the world. To Christians, this was the target of the Crusaders, whose kingdoms lasted, off and on, for 200 years. The last period of Jewish rule ended before the time of Christ, but this has been the only area where there has ever been a Jewish national state. Palestine is equally sacred to Islam, for Noah, Abraham, Moses, David, and Jesus are all Moslem prophets, and Jerusalem ranks next to Mecca and Medina as a holy city. During the nineteenth century Palestine was overwhelmingly Arab. At the beginning of the present century, Jewish inhabitants in Palestine numbered only a few thousand in comparison to the Arab population of half a million. Between 1918 and 1941 the former increased by 380,000, largely by immigration, but during the same period the Arab population rose by 356,000, largely through natural increase.

The passing of Turkish rule was accompanied by the rise of Arab nationalism. During World War I the Allies sought the help of the Arabs in pushing back Turkey, then on the side of Germany, on the basis of specific promises that there would be an all-Arab sovereign state.

In 1915, Britain signed the McMahon-Hussein Agreements in which it promised to

> recognize and uphold the independence of the Arabs within the limits demanded by the "Sharif of Mecca," namely the territory that is now the Hezaj of western Arabia, Trans-Jordan, Syria, and Iraq, excluding only the non-Arab districts of Mersin and Alexandretta and portions of Syria lying to the west of the districts of Damascus, Homs, Hama and Aleppo (which) cannot be said to be purely Arab.

Palestine was not specifically mentioned, but the Arab text implies that it was not excluded.

On the strength of these promises, the

Arabs revolted in 1916 and defeated Turkey, contributing substantially to the Allied victory. An Arab state was set up in 1919 but was terminated shortly after by the Treaty of Versailles which established a series of mandates. President Wilson protested but was overruled.

In 1917, Britain issued the Balfour Declaration with regard to Palestine, presumably announced as a gesture to secure worldwide Jewish assistance in the war. This somewhat ambiguous statement reads:

> His Majesty's Government view with favor the establishment in Palestine of a national home for the Jewish people, and will use their best endeavors to facilitate the achievment of that object, it being clearly understood that nothing shall be done which may prejudice the civil and religious rights of existing non-Jewish communities in Palestine or the rights and political status enjoyed by Jews in any other country.

These two apparently conflicting statements have led to a head-on clash between two nationalisms, both reborn about the same time and both focused on the same area. Arab nationalism arose late in the nineteenth century as part of a cultural renaissance. Zionism was not at first political but became such following the oppression of Jews in Europe.

In 1939, the British government, fearing another world war in which Swasia would be involved, issued a White Paper which stated,

> His Majesty's Government therefore now declare unequivocally that it is not part of their policy that Palestine should become a Jewish state. They would indeed regard it as contrary to their obligations to the Arabs under the Mandate, as well as to assurances which have been given to the Arab people in the past, that the Arab population of Palestine should be made the subjects of a Jewish state against their will.[1]

Following the creation of Israel in 1948, the United Nations sought to establish boundaries, but these have not been accepted by either side. The Armistice Agreement of 1949 provided for truce limits, the option of repatriation or compensation for all Arab refugees who had left their homes, and the internationalization of Jerusalem and Bethlehem. None of these has been effected.

The Isthmus of Suez lies outside the geographical limits of this volume, but since the completion of the canal in 1869, its influence has profoundly affected all of Asia. Some of the resulting problems will be considered in Chapter 12 on Egypt.

The historical problems of Iran, once known as Persia, are scarcely less complex than those of former Turkish domains. The present official name dates from 1935. In the eighteenth century, Persia ruled much of Afghanistan and extended into northern India. On the north, control reached into the Caucasus and into what is now Soviet Middle Asia. During the nineteenth century, Iran was buffeted from the north, with equal pressure from the south by France and later by Britain. The most that nineteenth century Iran could hope to achieve was a stalemate between Russia and Great Britain.

Zones of foreign influence proposed early in the present century allocated all Iran north of Isfahan and Yezd to Russia, and an area in the south, east of Kerman and Bandar Abbas, to Britain, with a neutral zone in between. These were never given legal status, but the Soviet Union still has considerable influence in the north. Troops of both nations, plus Americans, were stationed in Iran during World War II. Revolts among the mountain Lurs, the Kurds, and the Arabs of the southwest have several times called for military action.

Afghanistan has been another contest area, with Persian, Russian, and Indian interests contending for control. During the decades when Britain was in India, it fought

[1] Cmd. 6019, 1946, p. 4.

The harbor of Samsun on the Turkish Black Sea Coast is the main port for the shipment of coal from the Zonguldak fields.

three wars in Afghanistan: 1839–42, 1878–80, and 1919. Upon the withdrawal of Great Britain, Afghanistan became a contest area for American and Soviet economic aid.

POLITICAL PROBLEMS

POLITICAL INSTABILITY has characterized every country in Southwest Asia during the twentieth century. Each nation has had its internal revolution and its border problems. Nowhere is there an international frontier without shifts in location or tensions or alliance. Even the sea has not provided a clear boundary, for there are disputes over territorial limits and offshore oil rights.

The midcentury map merely represents the momentary pattern of changing history. Tensions will remain so long as there are unsatisfied loyalties and untenable economic conditions. Ambitious dictators create additional uncertainties.

Several of Swasia's political problems relate to the presence of minority groups; some ethnic, some linguistic, others religious. Many people have had to flee from their original homes to compatriots in bordering countries. Latent political feelings frequently erupt into action.

In addition to the main blocks of Arabs, Turks, and Persians, each of whom has outlying minorities of their own people surrounded by other cultures, five ethnic groups number more than a million people. The Pushtuns or Pathans in Afghanistan amount to 7 million, and they, along with their relatives in Pakistan across the border, hope to create the new state of Pushtunistan. The Kurds, totaling 3 million, are scattered through Turkey, Iraq, and Iran and have at times agitated for political independence as the state of Kurdistan. The Jews of Swasia number some 2 million. Not all are Zionists, but the state of Israel represents the national sentiment of many. Two million Azeri or Azerbaijani live in Iran, and they are an object of Soviet interest. Afghanistan and Iran have at least a million Baluchi.

Numerous other people number over a hundred thousand each. Near the Soviet border of Iran and Afghanistan are large groups of Turkmen, Uzbek, Tajik, Kirghiz, and Hazar people. Some of these are old residents, others were pushed southward by Czarist advances. The Iranian frontier toward the Caucasus contains many Armenians, also with migration problems and trans-border relatives. Other Caucasian refugees include the Circassians of Syria and Jordan. Nomadic tribes in Iran may total as many as a million people in all; chief among them are the Qashqai, Lurs, and Bakhtiari. Greeks were once numerous in Turkey, but they are now largely confined to Istanbul. Religious minorities include the Maronites, Assyrians, Druse, and Azedi. Millions of people whose homeland was in Swasia have migrated overseas, notably the Jews.

Each refugee group has experienced tragic persecution and even partial liquidation; it is thus understandable that political consciousness remains. So ingrained is this fear that some Christians hesitate to accept a convert from Islam because of the suspicion that he may be a spy, who will later turn against them. Divisions within Islam between Sunni and Shia Moslems have often led to warfare.

The world may expect many things to develop in Swasia during the next few decades, but what it cannot expect is calm and peace. The basic fact of life in every country is revolution in the most profound sense of the word. This involves a complete overturn of the political, economic, and social structure as it formerly existed. Some revolutions appear to represent domestic change but all have international complications. In most cases, some aspect of geography is involved.

If every country in Swasia were to receive even a part of the territory which it once held or wants to add, boundaries would hopelessly overlap; and if all frontier areas where potential tensions exist were to be examined, scarcely a stable line would remain. Flux has been the rule for hundreds of years, and it continues into the present century. Every country within the realm faces tense problems, with results which affect even distant world powers.

The following paragraphs review country by country some aspects of past or potential tensions which have international or geographic implications.

Turkey does not have a single mile of stable or unchanged boundary other than the sea, and wherever there are offshore islands they too have been in dispute. Most of the Aegean Archipelago is now in Greek hands. Cyprus was once Turkish, and the transfer to Britain was with the understanding that no third power would be given control; hence Turkey's opposition to domination by Greece.

Russian pressure for a larger voice in Turkish matters is of long standing and reappears every few years. The present legal arrangements for the international use of the Bosporus and Dardanelles were only established in 1936 under the Montreaux Convention. Turkish control over Batumi and adjoining areas in what is now the Soviet Union was terminated in 1882. Russian forces have several times penetrated eastern Turkey, so that Turkish fear of the Soviet Union is deeply ingrained. All of Iraq was once Turkish, and while there is no dream of reacquisition, the bitter controversies over the inclusion of Mosul will not soon be for-

Native vessels compete with modern steamers for the coastal trade of the Persian Gulf and Red Sea. This is a Yemenite dhow in the Shatt-al-Arab. (Courtesy Iraq Petroleum Co.)

gotten. One of Turkey's most sensitive boundaries is that next to Syria which will be considered in a later paragraph.

Three large groups of minority peoples once lived in Turkey; 1.25 million Armenians, 1 million Greeks, and 1.5 million Kurds. Only the latter now remain in any numbers. The Armenians formerly lived in eastern Turkey but have disappeared through widespread massacre and migration; the presence of the adjoining Armenian Soviet Socialist Republic is a part of the picture. The Greeks who once lived in western Turkey were either massacred or repatriated in 1923 in exchange for Turks then living in Greece.

Kurds still occupy a large area of the upper Tigris basin where Turkey, Syria, and Iraq meet, numbering 3 million in all. The Treaty of Sevres in 1920 provided for a Kurdish national state, but the provisions were not implemented. Nationalistic Turks resent any use of the terms "Kurdistan" or "Armenia" as implying potential sovereign rights.

Iranian problems of political geography are scarcely less difficult. Persian control once extended well into the Caucasus and into what is now Soviet Middle Asia, but the present boundary dates from 1830 and 1880–85, respectively. Although the frontier has been demarcated, tensions continue. Minority difficulties have also been serious. Kurds, numbering 600,000, look across the border to their relatives in Turkey and Iraq. Armenians and Azerbaijanians are also numerous; each with an adjoining Soviet Socialist Republic. Soviet pressures have several times sought to detach the northwestern corner of Iran, with a period of military occupation in 1946.

The Persian Gulf presents a number of geopolitical problems. At one time, Persia controlled a part of the western shore of the Gulf, including Bahrein and Kuwait which are still claimed as Iranian territory. In the current search for offshore oil, Iran asserts her ownership to the line of deepest water, which is well to the west of the geographic center of the Gulf. The Shatt-al-Arab lies entirely in Iraq, which claims sovereignty to the high water mark on the eastern side. This denies Iran free access to her refinery at Abadan and is a source of irritation.

If Afghanistan appears remote, and perhaps unimportant, its problems are nevertheless real to the Afghans. It is well to remember that this country, along with Turkey and Iran, represents almost the only section of the entire Soviet frontier where there is no cushion or buffer of satellite Communist states. Afghanistan's significance to the free world should not be undervalued.

The people of Afghanistan are more diverse ethnically than those of any other country of Swasia. Some are Pushtuns, some Persians, others represent each one of the races found in the nearby Soviet Republics. This leads to varied political loyalties and problems of cohesion.

Afghanistan is vividly aware of the steady advance of Czarist territory during the late nineteenth century and naturally feels that its northern frontier is insecure. The country has accepted large amounts of economic aid from the Soviet Union but has been suspicious of any political alliance.

British penetration and occasional occupations date back to the beginning of the nineteenth century. Afghanistan has repeatedly served as a buffer between the Russian bear and the British lion. The withdrawal of Great Britain from the Indian peninsula has changed the relationship and has altered any ability of Afghanistan to play one side against the other. The country's willingness to accept aid and support from the United States may represent the desire to find an alternative against Soviet pressures.

Afghanistan's border next to Pakistan has long been unstable, with large "unadministered" areas where neither country is able to exercise police force. The Durand Line, drawn in 1893, was an attempt to fix a boundary but it was not based on clear ethnic, historic, or geographic factors. There is thus some agitation for a major boundary shift, or for a new border nation to be called Pushtunistan. When endorsed by Pakistani, it is assumed that the territory would be carved out of Afghanistan; where pressed by Afghans, the future state is thought to lie entirely in Pakistan. Ill-feeling has repeatedly closed the Afghan–Pakistan frontier.

Difficulties with Iran are of long historic standing, and northwestern Afghanistan was claimed by Iran until 1935. The Helmand River ends in the Seistan Basin, partly within Iran, and the amount of water to be used for irrigation on each side of the frontier is a matter of dispute.

As a land-locked nation, Afghanistan naturally wishes unrestricted and custom-free access to the outside world. One partial solution would lie in transit rights across Pakistan with a free port zone at Karachi. Still another solution could be found in the annexation of a corridor to the sea through Baluchistan.

Syria's problems look back to the days when it included most of the Levant and parts of Iraq and to the temporary Arab kingdom in 1919, as well as forward to dreams of leadership in a Greater Syria or in an Arab Union. In 1958, Syria joined Egypt

The port of Basra is the only maritime gateway into Iraq. Its docks are continually lined with more than a dozen vessels. (Courtesy Iraq Petroleum Co.)

to become a province of the United Arab Republic, but one may suspect that the union will not be too happy, for many Syrians have traditionally looked down on the Egyptians. Difficulties with Iraq center around rivalries for political domination, transit tolls on oil pipe lines, and a possible increase in the use of Euphrates water for irrigation.

Syria's relations with Turkey are a heritage from the period of the French Mandate in 1939 when Syria's main seaport, now Iskenderon but formerly known as Alexandretta, was transferred to Turkey, along with the vilayet, or province, of Antakya or Hatay. Various political factors were involved, along with the fact that many of the inhabitants were Turkish. Syria was not consulted, and many Syrian maps still show the area as rightfully Syrian. Iskenderon thus remains as an Irredentist problem.

Lebanon's international relations stem in part from her domestic religious composition. The population is about evenly divided between Christians and Moslems. Both of them are Arab in race and loyalties; but whereas the former have sent several hundred thousand emigrants overseas and are Western oriented, the latter favor closer ties with other Arab states. This brought on the troubles of 1958 which led to the landing of American troops. While the United States intervened at the request of the Lebanese

President, ostensibly to preserve the integrity of the country against international communism, history will have to decide whether this was the reason or whether American forces were requested in order to ensure the integrity of the government in power.

Lebanon cannot remain economically viable without international trade. At those times when her border with Syria has been closed, business stagnates. An isolated Lebanon might resemble an isolated Israel, the one Christian and other Zionist, both able to keep going only through outside aid.

Jordan's problems are particularly acute, for the country lacks resources as well as unity. During the period of the British Mandate, the Hashemite Kingdom of Trans-Jordan had a population of 375,000, all on the east bank of the Jordan River. With the partition of Palestine, the Kingdom took over a considerable area on the west bank and added 460,000 residents plus 500,000 refugees from Israel. What is now the western part of the country has traditionally been more advanced and prosperous than the semi-Bedouin East, so that internal coherence and economic development raises many difficulties.

Jordan may well be too small and poorly situated to form a proper state. The temporary union with Iraq in 1958 was based on the fact that both kingdoms had Hashemite rulers rather than any basic community of interests. Anyone who has driven the long desert road which links the two capitals will realize the technical problems of a federation which involves only these two nations. Given ideal political conditions, plus good will, Jordan might well merge in a larger Arab state, presumably to be centered on Damascus.

While Iraq dates only from modern times as a sovereign nation, it does have relative coherence. The 800,000 Kurds present a minority problem but agitation for a separate Kurdistan is quiescent. Another domestic problem stems from the fact that the country has been administered by a group of Sunni landlords dominating the rural Shiites who form the majority. Boundary problems do not appear serious, though there is need for clarification of the frontier next to Saudi Arabia, as well as at the head of the Persian Gulf.

The problems which surround Israel are clearly the most baffling in all Swasia. Some aspects have already been mentioned; still others will be discussed in Chapter 15.

Although the State of Israel enjoys full United Nations status and is recognized by almost all the world, the Arab lands still contest its legality. The present limits are de facto armistice lines rather than treaty boundaries, for Israeli territory extends well beyond the United Nations allocations. The Egyptian-occupied Gaza Strip is a further border problem.

Whereas Jerusalem is now divided between Israel and Jordan, the provisions of the United Nations called for an international city; neither the United Nations nor the United States has recognized Israel's use of it as a capital. The diplaced Palestinians, about a million in number, create a serious humanitarian problem as well as an explosive political situation. No real alternative of return to their homes or compensation through resettlement elsewhere has been provided.

Israel has a window on the Gulf of Aqaba at the port of Elath. The United Nations has ruled that the Gulf is an international waterway, but the Arab states which control the Strait of Tiran, at the southern entrance, have at times contested passage.

The conflict over Israel is not a matter of Arab opposition to Jews as such, for both people are Semites and thousands of Jews live peacefully throughout Swasia. Moslem treatment of Jewish minorities averages better than that of some Christian states. Instead, Arab opposition to Israel is a resentment against the creation of a foreign-supported intruder which has dispossessed most of the former inhabitants. Israel is also regarded as the arm of European and American imperialism in a new guise.

The impasse is not only a domestic problem within Swasia, but it presents a serious barrier to any good will between the Arab world and the West. In so far as the United States is regarded as the dominating force behind Israel, Arab cooperation is difficult. Should the Arab world find its only recourse in alliance with the Soviet Union, Europe and America would have only themselves to blame.

Both sides have basic suspicions of the other. Arab nationalism developed in a desire to eliminate outside colonial control. Arabs see in Zionism a renewed attempt on the part of the West, in this case primarily the United States, to intrude into historic Arab lands. The fears of further territorial expansion are heightened by Israel's plans to double her population, by references to the area "from the Nile to the Euphrates," and by Israel's invasion of the Sinai Peninsula in 1957. Israel is equally concerned by Arab exhortations to "drive the Zionists into the sea," by Egypt's refusal to allow Israeli commerce to move through the Suez Canal, and by international boycotts set up by the Arab League.

The present unity in Saudi Arabia was not established until 1925, and sectional rivalries remain. As one Arab of the Persian Gulf Coast remarked to the author, "By what right do the Saudis come out of the interior and take *our* oil?"

Many Saudi boundaries remain undefined. The northwest frontier next to Jordan has never been surveyed, and there are uncertainties along the Iraq border. The two neutral zones reflect the inability to reach a decision. Few of Saudi Arabia's southern limits are settled. This includes the border along eastern Yemen, the Aden Protectorate, Masqat, and the Trucial States of the Persian Gulf. The oasis of Buraimi is but one of several contested areas.

Yemen is plagued by border problems. In 1933, it lost the northern province of Asir to Saudi Arabia, and only parts of its present limits have been fixed. Sharp differences of opinion have arisen between Yemen and the various small states which make up the British-dominated Western Aden Protectorate, at times breaking out into border warfare. Two British islands on the Red Sea, Perim and Kamaran, are coveted by Yemen.

A series of small sheikhdoms line the Persian Gulf, each more or less independent in their domestic affairs but under the international protection of Great Britain. The traveler wishing a visa must thus apply at a British Consular office. Jurisdictional problems are especially uncertain in the area from Qatar to Masqat. Bahrein Island, and to a lesser extent Kuwait, are claimed by Iran.

The Sultanate of Masqat, in the extreme southeast, is more fully independent, but also has "treaty relations" with Britain. The Sultan, ruling the coast, maintains uncertain control over the Imam of Oman in the interior.

The Arab League, founded in 1945, represents an attempt to give political expression to nationalistic feelings. For the most part, it has remained ineffective. Three countries contest for leadership; Saudi Arabia, guardian of the Holy Places of Islam and wealthy but inexperienced; Iraq, off-center and undeveloped but with large oil royalties; and Egypt, populous, energetic, and poor but developed.

Other groupings have brought together Turkey and Iran, though all have been short-lived due to conflicting interests.

Many European countries have long had interests in Southwest Asia. Since the days of the Crusades, France has regarded herself as a protector of the Christian minorities, hence

Tobacco forms one of Turkey's famous exports, more than half of it raised near the Aegean Sea. This shipment at Izmir is consigned to the United States. (Courtesy U. S. Economic Cooperation Administration.)

her insistence on a mandate over Syria and Lebanon. In the same way, many Eastern Orthodox Christians still look to Moscow as the defender of the faith. Imperial Britain once regarded Suez as a key point along its colonial lifeline. Aden is Britain's only remaining possession, although she has treaty relations in the Aden Protectorate and the Persian Gulf. Italy had a period of partial control over Yemen which lasted until 1943. Russian ambitions are of long standing, with interests in the Bosporus as well as in access to the Indian Ocean. It has already been emphasized that Turkey, Iran, and Afghanistan represent the only significant part of the Soviet frontier which abuts directly on the free world.

AMERICAN POLICY IN SWASIA

WHILE AMERICAN political interests in Southwest Asia were once only nominal, some cultural relations are of long standing. For a century there have been religious and education contributions through organizations such as Robert College outside Istanbul (1863), the American University of Beirut (1866), or the American University of Cairo (1919). American missionaries have lived in Syria since 1823.

Political concern developed at the close of World War I when President Wilson sent out the King-Crane Commission to ascertain Arab wishes concerning an independent kingdom. The United States became directly involved with President Truman's support of Israel, and political relations acquired great economic significance with American investments in the oil industry.

In order for the United States to develop a sound foreign policy, it is necessary to clarify what it is that America seeks abroad and also what other countries desire for themselves. Where the two goals fortunately coincide there is little difficulty; where they conflict some accommodation is desirable if tensions are to be avoided.

It is obvious that America desires a peaceful world; it should also be obvious that the United States earnestly wishes a prosperous world, one in which every country enjoys the highest possible standard of living. Above all, America believes in people and in their potentials.

If the United States is to develop satisfactorily itself, it cannot live alone on an island. Some way must be found to narrow the gap between its expanding prosperity and that of less developed countries. This calls for assistance, when invited, to agriculture, resource development, industry and communications, and education. If this comes through international agencies, so much the better, but irrespective of its origin America should welcome all aid which improves the welfare of other lands anywhere.

Economic assistance is not enough. The great ambitions of the less advanced parts of the world are psychological, for they wish to regain their lost stature and achieve recognition in the family of nations. This calls for the elimination of any vestige of colonial dependence, including cultural imperialism.

To be specific, while the United States desires to strengthen its European friends, it should disassociate itself from any objectionable aspects of their foreign policy which seem counter to our concepts and which alienate us from our would-be friends elsewhere.

America's history has been characterized by change and flexibility; the country should equally welcome change in Southwest Asia. Too often American foreign policy has seemed to emphasize the status quo, and talk of freedom has conflicted with support of reaction. Instead of alliances with governments which may be unpopular and due for change, the best interests of America may be served through the support of continuing institutions and programs which contribute to public welfare and which may survive in any political overthrow.

Too many of America's actions in Southwest Asia seem designed more to check the Soviet Union than to further local welfare, and they fail because of this negative aspect. The United States should place its belief in democracy ahead of its opposition to totalitarianism. If America wants friends and allies, it must demonstrate that the friendship is genuine and that aid is without political strings.

Each sovereign nation has the right to make its own decisions, subject to international law and morality. The United States should clarify its hopes and explain its way of life, but it cannot impose its ideas on others. If some nations desire to be neutral, America might recall its own position two centuries ago. All this suggests that America and Europe should avoid over-activity in intra-Swasian alliances and not take sides in political disagreements. One of the chief difficulties with the American-inspired Baghdad Pact was that it created a division within the Arab World. Where there are basic conflicts, as over Israel, solutions are best sought through the United Nations. Where alliances are desirable, the initiative should come from within the area.

The island of Bahrein is a focal point for trade in the Persian Gulf. Here merchants from India meet customers from Arabia. (Courtesy Standard Oil Co. of New Jersey.)

When in Afghanistan, the author was told, "If you are our friend, you would oppose our enemy," meaning Pakistan. In Pakistan, he was told, "Why do you not compel India to give us Kashmir?" The Arabs contend that the creation of Israel is America's fault, while the Israelis desire the United States to bring pressures on the Arab states.

These are all generalizations, basic, but in need of specific implementation. In the case of Turkey and Iran, the United States has extended massive economic and technical assistance. Israel has also received large grants and loans. Jordan formerly had British support, later replaced by American aid. The oil-rich Arab nations have received technical assistance but only small amounts of financial or military aid. Afghanistan and the oil-less Arab states, including Egypt, have had only limited support.

Long-range aspects of American policy might well include the support of development programs, regional banks or funds, increased United Nations activities in the technical field, programs of health and education, advice when invited with regard to wise land use and general economic planning, encouragement of regional political cooperation and union when clearly desired by the majority of the people, counsel in border tensions and international disputes, support for orderly political evolution rather than any stabilization of the status quo, and efforts to create greater good will through mutual understanding. While there may be many changes which seem desirable, unilateral action is seldom productive.

If some of these items appear remote from geography, such is not always the case. Geography is concerned with all those factors, physical or cultural, which contribute to the personality of place. Many of these problems directly affect the landscape and are mapable. What is more, if the United States is to proceed wisely, the nation needs a far clearer understanding of Swasian potentials. We cannot make suggestions as to proper land tenure until we fully understand the use of the water. A wise program of highway development calls for knowledge of resource potentials.

Geography deals with inventory and here is, or should be, the beginning of planning. A significant part of geography's task is comprised in the question of "How much of what is where?" To this basis for formulating foreign policy, whether Turkish, Persian, Arab, or American, this volume attempts to provide a preface.

CHAPTER 10

Turkey

Istanbul and Ankara, Old Turkey and the New
History, Then and Now
Six Profiles
Agriculture and the Food Supply
Raw Materials for Industry
Patterns of People and Land
Turkey's Prospects
References

ISTANBUL AND ANKARA, OLD TURKEY AND THE NEW

BOTH ISTANBUL AND ANKARA have a long history; each in its way sums up the story of Turkey. Both cities are old but in the process of modernization. Old Turkey with its capital at Istanbul on the exposed Straits was vulnerable to outside political pressures, and the city was off-center and out of tune with the interior. The move to Ankara in 1923 symbolized the desire to make a firm break with the past, to insure a balanced national development for the country as a whole, and to be free from any possibility of foreign dictation. The revolution of 1923 which overthrew the Ottoman regime and set up the republic needed a symbol; this came with the change from the name Constantinople to that of Istanbul and the removal of the capital to the interior, coupled with the rediscovery of Turkey's ancient cultural roots in Anatolia.

(Opposite) The Galata Bridge at Istanbul crosses the Golden Horn, an arm of the Bosporus. Ferry boats lead to the Asiatic suburb of Uskudar. (Courtesy Turkish Information Office, New York.)

Istanbul

"If one had but a single glance to give the world, one should gaze at Istanbul." Few cities on earth have a more commanding site or skyline. Here two continents and two seas meet, and here has been the center of an empire for sixteen centuries.

"The Straits," that is the Dardanelles, the Sea of Marmara, and the Bosporus have played a double role throughout history. They are both a passageway from the Mediterranean to the Black Sea and a connecting link between Europe and Asia. The Sea of Marmara owes its existence to the fault pattern of northwestern Turkey and the submergence of linear segments; earth movement still occurs. Both the Dardanelles and

Modern Istanbul is a mixture of old and new. This is a glimpse of the Karakoy district near the Golden Horn. (Courtesy Turkish Press, Broadcasting, and Tourist Dept., Ankara.)

the Bosporus are the drowned valleys of ancient rivers, as shown in their winding courses.

The course of the Bosporus lies in ancient crystalline and volcanic rocks, and its shores are steep. A variety of bays and headlands give charm to the sixteen-mile passage. At one point, opposite the ancient fort of Rumeli Hisari, the waterway is only 660 yards wide. Nearby lies the American-founded Robert College. Surveys have been made for a bridge north of Istanbul, with a 3,100-foot suspension span.

While the Straits are tideless, there may be variations of as much as a foot according to winds and the seasonal differences in level between the Black and Aegean seas. Surface currents up to six miles per hour flow out from the Black Sea, due to the contribution of the Danube and other rivers, as compared with losses from excessive evaporation over the Mediterranean. There is also a deep counter current of heavier salt water. In severe winters the Bosporus freezes over. Although the Bosporus is less than a mile in width, its waters are sometimes so stormy

NOTE: Additional material on Turkey may be found in each of the preceding chapters, especially: Chapter 2, Turkish Empires: The Ottoman, page 59; Chapter 5, The Menderes River, page 134. I am especially indebted to Prof. Cemal Alagoz, Chairman of the Department of Geography at the University of Ankara, and to Mrs. Alagoz, for guidance in the field.

TURKISH DATA[1]

Area				
Thrace		23,485 sq. km.		9,065 sq. miles
Anatolia		743,634 sq. km.		287,033 sq. miles
Total		767,119 sq. km.		296,503 sq. miles
Arable land		240,700 sq. km.		92,100 sq. miles
Dimensions				
East-West		1,605 km.		1,003 miles
North-South		700 km.		430 miles
Population	1927	1940	1950	1955
	13,648,270	17,820,950	20,936,524	24,111,778
Students	1923–24	1943–44		1956–57
	358,548	1,118,517	—	2,485,125
Frontiers				
Bulgaria		200 km.		124 miles
Greece		204 km.		127 miles
Syria		789 km.		490 miles
Iraq		378 km.		234 miles
Iran		470 km.		292 miles
Soviet Union		591 km.		367 miles
Total		2,632 km.		1,633 miles
Sea Coasts				
Black Sea		1,546 km.		966 miles
Aegean		2,377 km.		1,486 miles
Mediterranean		1,560 km.		975 miles
Islands		520 km.		325 miles
Total (incl. Straits)		7,126 km.		4,454 miles
Mountains				
Ararat		5,165 meters		16,946 feet
Suphan		4,434 meters		14,540 feet
Resko		4,168 meters		13,671 feet
Cilo		4,119 meters		13,510 feet
Erciyas		3,916 meters		12,844 feet
Rivers (within Turkey)				
Kizil Irmak		1,151 km.		715 miles
Euphrates		1,107 km.		688 miles
Sakarya		790 km.		491 miles
Seyhan		516 km.		320 miles
Ceyhan		474 km.		294 miles
Tigris		452 km.		281 miles
Araks		435 km.		270 miles
Yesil Irmak		416 km.		258 miles
Buyuk Menderes		215 km.		135 miles

Lakes	Area		Elevation	
Van	3,764 sq. km.	1,460 sq. miles	1,720 meters	5,640 feet
Tuz	1,620 sq. km.	625 sq. miles	899 meters	2,949 feet
Bey	651 sq. km.	252 sq. miles	1,116 meters	3,660 feet

[1] Office Central de Statistique (Ankara): *Annuaire Statistique* (metric data only).

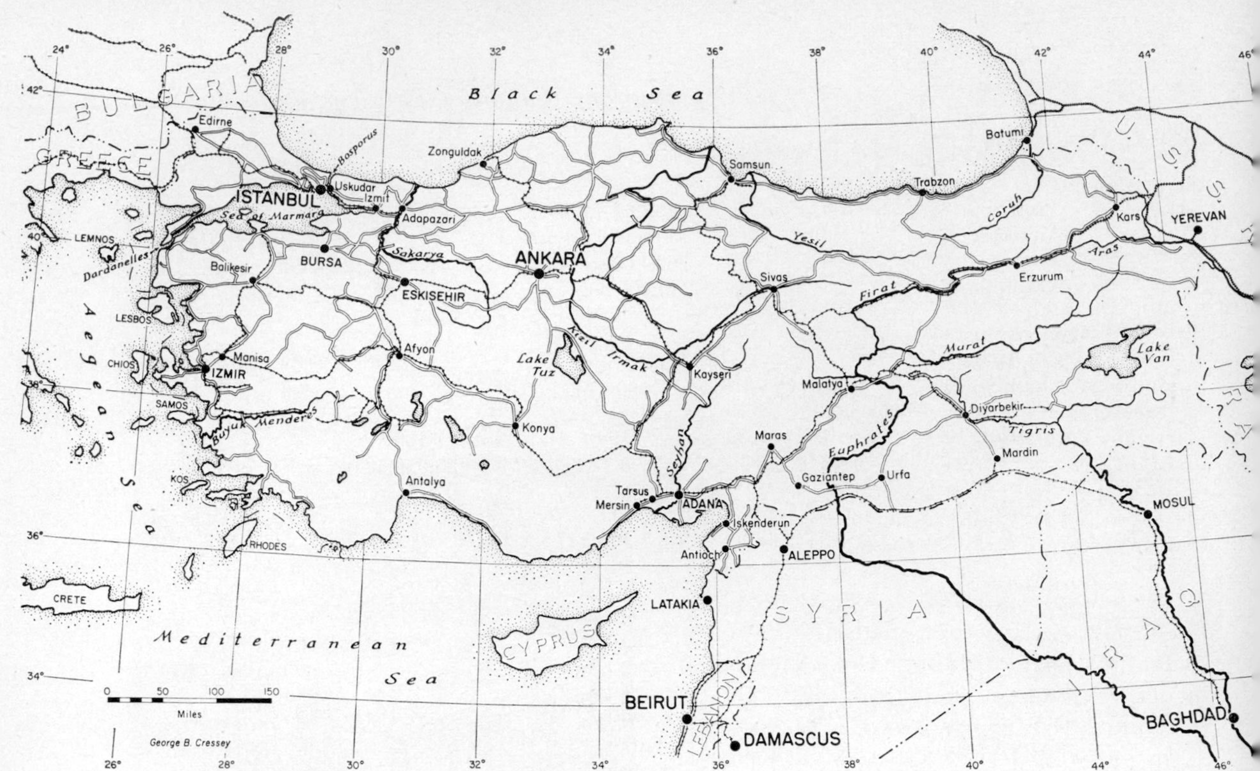

This reference map is on the same scale as those which accompany each of the regional chapters which follow. This uniformity provides a basis for a comparison of size and urbanization.

that vessels must seek shelter in protected bays. One such harbor is near the southern entrance to the Bosporus where the mouth of a tributary river is drowned, forming the Golden Horn. Here is the site of Istanbul.

Metropolitan Istanbul has several centers. The ancient city, with its five-mile wall, lies on a promontory to the south of the Golden Horn. To the north, and connected by two floating bridges, is Galata, while on the heights above is Beyoglu. Across the Bosporus is the suburb of Uskudar, once known as Scutari. Many other villages and residential areas surround the urban core.

The beginnings of Istanbul are obscure, but Pliny informs us that there was a small settlement here in the ninth century B.C. In 658 B.C., the Greek city of Megara founded a town which later became known as Byzantium from their leader, Byzas. Later on, the city was in turn conquered by Persia, Athens, Rome, and Alexander the Great. In A.D. 328, Constantine I chose Byzantium as his imperial capital and later renamed the city after himself, inaugurating the "New Rome." The city was frequently attacked by Huns, Russians, Goths, Arabs, and Turks and sometimes plundered, but it grew steadily. The First, Second, and Third Crusades (1096, 1147, and 1189) passed through the city. During the Fourth Crusade (1203) it was seized and largely destroyed. In 1453, the city was captured by the Turks under Mohammed II, the Conqueror, who made it the capital of the Ottoman Empire. In the decades which followed, the city became the greatest center of art, learning, and commerce in the Islamic World.

The heritage of Istanbul makes it one of the richest cities in the cultural sense to be visited in the world, along with Peking, Moscow, and Paris. Unfortunately, the city grew with little planning and there are many narrow, winding streets. One traveler writes of the city as [1]

> . . . squalid, smelly, disorderly, exciting and magnificent. The streets are narrow, crooked, dirty and without system . . . . The countless architectural and archaeological wonders are for the most part hidden away . . . ; an urbanist's nightmare; a reformer's dream. And yet what marvellous color and variety, what a superabundance of life! . . . Crowds . . . This is the kind of life that Johnson must have observed at Charing Cross and which he called the "full tide of human existence."

The new meets the old as one passes along broad new avenues from modern buildings such as the Istanbul Hilton Hotel to monumental St. Sophia or Aya Sofia. This great structure was built by Constantine in 347 as the imperial church. Following its partial destruction by fire, it was restored by Justinian in 552, and in subsequent centuries it was elaborately decorated with mosaics. In 1453 it was rebuilt as a mosque, and in 1935 it became a national museum.

Istanbul has hundreds of mosques, 444 by one count, so that graceful minarets dominate every skyline. One of the most famous is the Suleiman Mosque which dates from 1557; its dome rises 174 feet and has a diameter of 105 feet, and it is said to be one of the five finest religious structures in the world. When the tourist tires of mosques, he may turn to museums, one of which contains one of the largest collections of Chinese porcelains to be found outside of China.

Something of the grandeur of old commercial Constantinople is described by Robert Walsh, writing about 1850: [2]

> The Great Bazaar was erected by Mehmet II when he took possession of Constantinople. . . .
>
> It consists of long avenues covered over with lofty arches of brick lighted by apertures in the roof and branching off in various directions. The ceilings of the vaults and other parts of the walls are painted with various flowers and devices. Under cover at all times, and protected from wind, rain, and sun, this bazaar is the resort of crowds everyday and all day long. In the heat of summer it is particularly agreeable—crowded with a busy population of many thousand persons bustling, buying, and selling in the cool and dim twilight. But the fair sex form the majority by far. The first attraction is generally a perfume stall. Here attar of roses, essence of lemon, extract of jasmine are presented to your choice. But by far the most attractive display is the pipe department. It is here the fancy of a Turk luxuriates and loves to exhibit itself with a dexterity shown in nothing else.

The Istanbul Hilton Hotel brings modern architecture to ancient Constantinople. (Courtesy Hilton International.)

The ancient covered bazaar with its 3,000 shops is gone, but small merchants continue to offer goods, old and new, from all the East.

[1] J. B. Jackson: "Southeast to Turkey," *Landscape,* VII, #3 (Spring 1958), 21.

[2] Thomas Allom: *Constantinople and the Scenery of the Seven Churches of Asia Minor.* London: Fisherson and Co. (about 1850).

The streets of Ankara mirror the rapid urbanization of all Turkey. Since the city became the capitol in 1923, it has grown severalfold. (Courtesy Turkish Information Office, New York.)

Istanbul enjoys a pleasant climate, although winters may be snowy and raw. July temperatures have never exceeded 100°F., and the mean daily maximum is 82° in both July and August. Winter temperatures never drop below 17°F. The February mean daily minimum is 36°F. Every month has at least an inch of rain, with a maximum in December; the annual total is twenty-nine inches, reflecting the inter-sea position.

Ankara

Ankara is different. When it became the capital in 1923, it had a population of only 30,000; within three decades this figure had increased tenfold. The city lies at an elevation of 3,000 feet in a broad steppe, now irrigated. The temperature range is greater than that of Istanbul, with extremes of 100°F. and —13°F. The precipitation averages fourteen inches. The latitude is similar to Madrid, with which there are some climatic similarities. While the site has few advantages, it now appears that the area was once a center for the ancient Hittite culture, glamorized by modern Turkey as its spiritual progenitor.

Aside from its ancient ruins, Ankara is modern. Fine buildings line Ataturk Boulevard and give the city the most European atmosphere of any city in Swasia. On one of the highest hills in the city is the Mausoleum of Kemal Ataturk, founder of the republic. Broad avenues and public gardens are in contrast to crowded Istanbul. The city is a

TURKISH CITIES

	1935 [1]	1950 [1]	1955 [2]
Istanbul	741,143	1,000,022	1,214,616
Ankara	122,720	286,781	453,151
Izmir	170,959	230,508	286,310
Adana	76,473	117,799	172,465
Bursa	72,187	100,007	131,336
Eskisehir	47,045	88,459	122,755
Gazientep	50,965	72,743	97,144
Konya	52,093	64,509	93,125
Kayseri	46,181	65,489	81,127
Erzurum	33,104	54,360	69,499
Sivas	33,890	52,269	66,350
Malatya	27,296	48,621	64,880
Diyarbekir	—	—	63,180
Samsun	32,482	44,019	62,648
Izmit	—	—	56,702
Adapazari	—	—	55,116
Mersin	—	—	51,251

[1] Office Central de Statistique (Ankara): *Annuaire Statistique.*
[2] United Nations (New York): *Demographic Yearbook.*

day's ride by train from Istanbul or an hour by air. Ankara is also the location of the United Nations Middle East Technical University, founded in 1959.

HISTORY, THEN AND NOW

ALTHOUGH MAN is known to have lived in Turkey for 4,000 years, indigenous culture was slow to develop. The story of the Hittites, Byzantines, and Ottomans has already been reviewed in Chapter 2. Unlike Mesopotamia, Turkey lacks a focal center with adequate resources to dominate the whole. A dozen cities have served alternately as the capital. Only rarely has all of what is now Turkey been under one rule.

Prehistoric pottery is known in central Anatolia and elsewhere, but the Taurus Mountains apparently limited contact with stone age areas to the south, while Aegean cultures did not reach far inland. Skeletons suggest that the first people were of long-headed Mediterranean types, but round-headed Alpine people arrived from the east in the Bronze Age.

The Hittites were dominant from 2000 to 1200 B.C., centering on Capadocia in central Turkey. Their language was Indo-European with many Babylonian additions. In 1400 B.C. the Hittites became the chief cultural force in western Asia and were frequently at war with both Syrians and Egyptians.

Then came fresh invaders from the northwest who overthrew the Hittites and set up the Phrygian and Lydian dominions, 1200–546 B.C. These people, and groups from Greece, brought their language and culture from Europe. Persian rule followed from 546 B.C. to 334 B.C., at first under Cyrus. During this period Turkey included the satrapies of Ionia, Lydia, Phrygia, Cilicia, Moschi, Armenia, and Matiene.

In 334 B.C., Alexander the Great of Macedonia defeated the Persians near the Sea of Marmara and soon became master of the lands once ruled by the Persians, as far east as the Indus River. After Alexander's death, a series of successor kingdoms arose, and Greek influence continued to dominate western Asia until Roman rule was established in 133 B.C. While Rome intervened, it did not fully incorporate Turkey into its do-

Ancient Greek culture has left many souvenirs, as in this theatre at Antalya. (Courtesy Turkish Press, Broadcasting, and Tourist Dept., Ankara.)

mains. Rome in the east later became the Byzantine Empire, which in turn paved the way for the Ottomans, who ruled for over six centuries.

The conquests of Arab tribes, known to the West as Saracens, reached Armenia in 654 A.D. Although Constantinople was repeatedly attacked, and numerous raids penetrated the interior, Byzantine Turkey never came under Arab rule, but Islam did conquer and brought with it some of its culture.

The Turks did not reach Turkey until the twelfth century, when they arrived from the east, already converts to Islam. They first appear in history as the Hiung-nu, one of the nomadic Central Asian tribes against whose wanderings the Chinese built the Great Wall. Waves of these Turks, under various tribal names, and certainly of diverse ethnic stock though with a common language, overran Turkey and eventually developed the Ottoman Empire, 1299–1922. At its height, the Empire pressed against the gates of Vienna and even as late as 1908, bordered on the Adriatic.

For centuries, Byzantium was the great bulwark of eastern Christianity. Later on it became the center of Islam, and Constantinople remained the seat of the Caliph or "successor of Mohammed" until 1924.

As Bernard Lewis has written: [1]

> Let us look back for a moment over the best centuries of Turkish rule, from the rise of the Seljuks in the eleventh century to the beginnings

[1] Bernard Lewis: "The Ottoman Empire and Islam," London: *The Listener* (Oct. 2, 1952).

of the Ottoman decline in the seventeenth. The first thing that strikes us is the immensely important contribution of the Turkish period to Islam itself. The Arabs had given Islam its prophet, its book, its faith and its law—the Turkish dynasties, if one may misuse a western phrase, established its church. It was Turkish rulers who first created a regular hierarchy in Islam. . . .

In other fields, too, the age of Turkish domination in Islam saw notable achievements. Arabic literature was declining into its silver age, but Persian literature was reaching new heights of achievement, and a new Moslem literature in the Turkish language contained much that is of interest and value, especially as one would expect from an imperial people—in history. Perhaps the finest flower of Ottoman culture was in architecture and the fine arts—and in the superb mosques that still grace Turkey and the former Ottoman provinces, in the splendid products of the minor arts, and in the characteristic art of caligraphy, often underrated by western observers, but capable of reaching high levels of artistic self-expression.

It is in visual art and statecraft that we can see most clearly the three main streams of tradition that have combined to form Ottoman civilization: the high culture of classical Islam, with its religious and legal foundations; . . . finally, the truly Turkish tradition, brought by the first Turkish invaders from the steppes of Central Asia. It was this new Turkish element that remoulded the inherited traditions of older cultures into something new and distinctive, that reached its full flower in Ottoman civilization . . .

The Republic of Turkey is a by-product of World War I. It owes its creation and momentum to Mustafa Kemal Ataturk, under whose leadership dramatic cultural changes soon took place. One symbol of the new Turkey, already mentioned, was the removal of the capital from exposed Constantinople to interior Ankara. Another change was the decree requiring all public servants to wear "the clothes ordinarily in use among the civilized nations of the world." Whereas the medieval Turks took over Arabic characters, the new Turkey uses the Latin alphabet.

With all this attempt to be modern and Western, there is an interesting appeal to the past. Hence the interest in the glories of the Hittites as the founders of the country. In a discussion as to the title for this volume, one Turk remarked that any reference to Southwest Asia was inappropriate since they were now a part of Europe.

Minority problems have long brought suffering to the people of the area. For more than a century, local fighting led to the liquidation or migration of Greeks, Kurds, Armenians, Assyrians (or Nestorians), Circassians, and many others. Under the Ottoman regime, non-Moslem, national, and religious communities were administered as

This view of the interior of the Sultan Ahmet or Blue Mosque in Istanbul shows the great pulpit. (Courtesy Turkish Press, Broadcasting, and Tourist Dept., Ankara.)

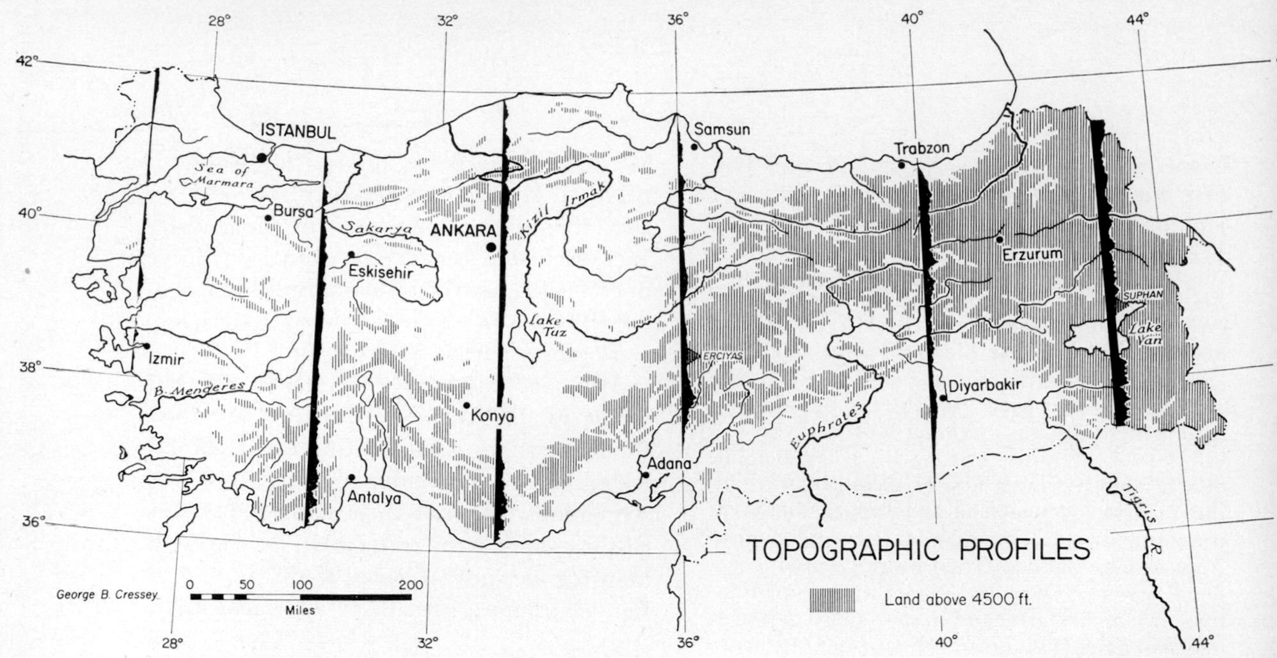

Turkey is rimmed by rugged mountains, and large parts of the country are above 4,500 feet. The cross section profiles are described in the accompanying text.

separate groups; this was known as the *millet* system. Most of these people have now been eliminated so that present-day Turkey is largely unified in nationality and language. Any use of place names with ethnic implications is resented, such as Armenia or Kurdistan. On one occasion, when the author saw a number of obviously Kurdish women in their characteristically bright clothing, an ethnic Turk repeatedly insisted that they were merely "Turkish women of the district." Legislation prohibits the importation of literature which carries the word "Kurdistan."

SIX PROFILES

THE FOUR DISTINCTIVE COLORS of the Swasian landscape are each present in Turkey, but in special proportions. While there is little which might be classed as desert, the brownish color of the steppe is characteristic throughout most of the year. Winter snows cover the mountains, and snow falls on the higher plains. Green fields are more extensive in Turkey than in any other country in Swasia, although agricultural land occupies only a quarter of the whole. Some oil is present, but one must look carefully at a map in order to identify the black of the oil fields. Here, as elsewhere, the pattern of the first three colors changes with the season, for geography is a moving picture.

Both the geology and the topography of Turkey are complex, possibly more so than in other parts of Southwestern Asia. Ancient mountains of pre-Cambrian crystalline rocks were worn down to a rolling landscape which was later buried deeply beneath Tertiary sediments. Folding, faulting, igneous intrusions, uplift, and erosion then provided the basis for the present mountain topography.

Several of the interior areas represent peneplains, recently uplifted half a mile at the same time that subsidence produced the straight Black and Mediterranean coasts, the grabens which lead to the embayed Aegean with its drowned shoreline, and the interior basins or *ova* occupied by salt lakes and linear valleys. Mountain building continues, as evidenced by the frequent earthquakes and many giant volcanoes such as Ararat.

Nearly half of the country lies above the

5,000-foot contour line. Large areas in the east have average elevations of 7,500 feet, and only small coastal sections are below 1,000 feet.

Rugged mountains, high enough to be humid and forest covered, lie to the north and south of the Anatolian Plateau. These chains merge into a highland complex marked in the east with great volcanoes. Along the Black Sea is the Pontus system, named from the ancient kingdom of the same name, and now known to Turkish geographers as the North Anatolian Mountains. Some elevations exceed 6,000 feet in the west, and many mountains exceed that height in the east. Linear east-west valleys separate local ranges, reflecting fault and structure patterns. In many places, the only roads leading inland from the Black Sea follow the antecedent valleys of streams which predate the mountain uplift.

Southern Turkey is also bordered by mountains, higher but less regular than those to the north. The name Taurus may be applied to the entire system, but it is more properly limited to the serpentine section from Antalya to Adana. East of this lies the Anti-Taurus, a range which extends inland in a northeasterly direction and then curves southward to join the Iranian Zagros.

Since the essentials of terrain and climate for Swasia as a whole have been considered in earlier chapters, it may be better here to examine detailed conditions along six north to south transects, spaced at roughly equal distances from the Aegean to the eastern frontier.

Longitude 27° E.

The westernmost profile follows along longitude 27°E., thus passing near the Sea of Marmara and Izmir. This, the shortest of the transects, is only 250 miles in length. At the northern end, this line crosses the rolling lands of Thrace in European Turkey. Along the Bulgarian border, the country is hilly and the rainfall reaches forty inches, so that forests are widespread. In the flat but dissected alluvial and lacustrine plains of the Ergene River, rainfall drops to twenty inches, and the country is a monotonous treeless steppe.

Western Turkey is marked by a series of parallel faults which trend east to west and divide the country into alternate strips of sunken lowland and narrow mountains. Some of the dislocations are as recent as the Pleistocene Period. One of these blocks is occupied by the Sea of Marmara, midpoint in the great sea-river which links the Black and Mediterranean seas. Depths exceed 4,000 feet. Around its shores, maritime and land routes have met for millennia.

South of the Sea of Marmara the transect leads over a succession of low mountains, generally with a parallel east-west orientation. Most elevations are below 3,000 feet. Level land is limited to deltas, interior basins, and flood plains. The width of the latter is often defined by bordering faults rather than by normal valley development. One of the more important of these lowlands is the basin west of Bursa; another is the valley of the Buyuk Menderes River.

Toward its southern end, the transect leaves the mainland and crosses a series of promontories and islands, some of which are Turkish and others Greek.

At Izmir, the profile touches the head of one of the many embayments which characterize the Aegean shore. Here a drowned valley provides a magnificent harbor for Turkey's second port. As an indication of the hilly terrain around Izmir, the only site for an airport is a raised coastal terrace, some miles inland and surrounded by half-buried hills.

The precipitation in western Turkey is a matter of altitude and exposure, ranging from fifty inches on higher west slopes to twenty inches in interior basins. All areas experience a long summer drought.

The city of Bursa lies at the base of one of the many peaks known as Mount Olympus. The Ulu Cami Mosque appears in the center of the picture. (Turkish Press, Broadcasting, and Tourist Dept., Ankara.)

Vegetation and land use show a similar zonation. The highest peaks have a humid grassland near the snow line, the goal of summer herders. Below this is a conifer landscape and farther downslope are broadleaf trees which remain green even in the dry summer; characteristic forms include poplar, sycamore, and mulberry. These trees provide charcoal for lowland villagers. Few forests have survived the centuries. Steppe vegetation covers the drier lowlands. Typical Mediterranean vegetation is a combination of short grasses and bush, with low, scattered trees, so that many areas have an open parklike landscape.

Longitude 30°E.

The second profile follows longitude 30°E. and reveals a succession of hills and low mountains. Elevations are generally below 4,000 feet, except in the extreme south. This is a transitional area between the faulted and dissected Aegean coastlands and the rolling plains of central Anatolia. In climate as well, humid coastal conditions give way to the interior steppes.

Near this transect flows the north-flowing Sakarya River. Like many Turkish rivers, it carries a heavy load of sediments, in part a reflection of excessive erosion in the recently-faulted highlands. Where rivers cross grabens or enter the sea in drowned valleys, deposition has built alluvial plains. Where the Sakarya crosses the Izmit graben, the alluvium has constructed an inland delta

Snow-crowned Mount Olympus is representative of the higher peaks of western Turkey. The summit rises to 9,476 feet and provides a site for winter sports. (Courtesy Turkish Press, Broadcasting, and Tourist Dept., Ankara.)

so rapidly that it has impounded the Sapanca Lake.

Longitude 33°E.

The third profile lies near longitude 33°E. and extends from the Black Sea to the Mediterranean along the line of Ankara. This crosses the widest part of Turkey and measures 375 miles; in some ways it is the most representative of the six sections.

The Pontus mountains meet the Black Sea abruptly, without a coastal plain. Elevations rise to 7,500 feet within a few miles of the coast. The streams are torrential where they cross the structure, and receive right angle tributaries which follow the strike. Great thicknesses of folded Cretaceous and Eocene rocks make up the mountains, with andesite and other lavas farther inland.

Two well-defined zones characterize these mountains. Next to the sea is a deeply dissected area of strong relief. Since the prevailing winds are from the north, this maritime zone receives fifty inches of rain or more, some of it during the summer. The exposed slopes are covered with luxurious forests of beech, chestnut, and fir. Where land forms permit, the population is dense. Farther inland is a more rounded upland, in part an uplifted peneplain a mile in height, with isolated monadnocks. The east-west structure is revealed in the deep valleys, linear mountains, and lines of structural basins known as *ova*. In other cases the term ova is used for the more open portions of normal valleys. In the area of these interior mountains, forests are limited to the valleys and to north-facing slopes. Elsewhere there is a steppe vegetation.

Ankara lies in a rolling basin, at 3,000 feet elevation. Miocene and Pliocene formations appear between areas of alluvium. Here rainfall drops to fourteen inches so that steppe vegetation prevails. Good crops re-

Ankara receives its hydroelectric supply from the Cubuk Dam in the mountains of central Anatolia. (Courtesy Turkish Press, Broadcasting, and Tourist Dept., Ankara.)

quire irrigation, or one takes the risks which accompany dry farming. Ankara has summer temperatures which have reached 100°F., as compared with the daily mean maxima for July and August of 86°F. In January the mean daily minimum averages 17°F., and the extreme low temperature has dropped to −13°F.

South of Ankara lies Lake Tuz or Tuz Golu, at an elevation of 2,985 feet. This salt sea measures some twenty by forty miles, but fluctates widely with the season. Its shores are either a tangle of reeds or a salt-crusted flat. Lake Tuz occupies one of the many enclosed basins of Anatolia, some of which have developed outward drainage as the result of stream piracy. A few basins owe their origin to lava flows which have blocked earlier valleys; most others are the result of faulting. In both cases hot springs may have developed.

Lake Tuz is in the most barren part of Anatolia, hence the ancient Greek name for the district meant "treeless." Several dune areas are nearby, and one is reminded of interior Iran or Syria.

Farther south are extensive lava fields with a number of fresh volcanic cones. One of them, near Karapinar, has a crater lake at the summit, and also a ring lake which makes a complete circle between the base of the cone and the surrounding collapse escarpment.

Along this transect, the snow-covered Taurus Mountains form the southern margin of the Anatolian uplands and mark a startling change from the dreary plains of the interior. There are four separate ridges in these mountains. The trends are from northwest to southeast and appear to plunge beneath the Mediterranean where they form

Along most of the Mediterranean coast, the mountains meet the sea without a coastal plain. This is a view of Alanya. (Courtesy Turkish Press, Broadcasting, and Tourist Dept., Ankara.)

a ragged coastline. Elevations reach 9,770 feet. Deep valleys lie between them, and in a few places there are small, fresh-water lakes. Extensive areas of Eocene and Oligocene limestone are characterized by lines of dolines or sinks along the strike. Elsewhere there are thick masses of yellow to reddish sandstone of the same ages, now very much eroded.

The steep Mediterranean shore leaves virtually no room for level land so that the coast road, constructed with great difficulty, is one of scenic grandeur. Earthquakes are recurrent, and some recent shore terraces are now fifty feet above sea level. This uplift has not erased the effects of earlier drowning for most valley mouths have an estuarine indentation. Thus the Bozyazi Valley has a delta which measures sixteen square miles, on which subtropical crops such as peanuts, rice, taro, and bananas are raised.

Longitude 36°E.

The fourth of the profiles is that which extends from Bafra through Amasya and Kayseri to Adana, roughly along longitude 36°E. Conditions resemble those of the previous section except for a less level interior and with the addition of delta plains both north and south.

The principal north-flowing river of Turkey is the Kizil Irmak, or Red River. Where it enters the Black Sea near Bafra, it has built a delta which projects a dozen miles northward to form 100 square miles of flat land. This intensively cultivated plain, with rice and tobacco, is in striking contrast to the uninhabited and almost impassable canyons and mountains to the south.

The course of the Kizil Irmak reflects the

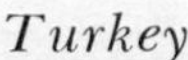

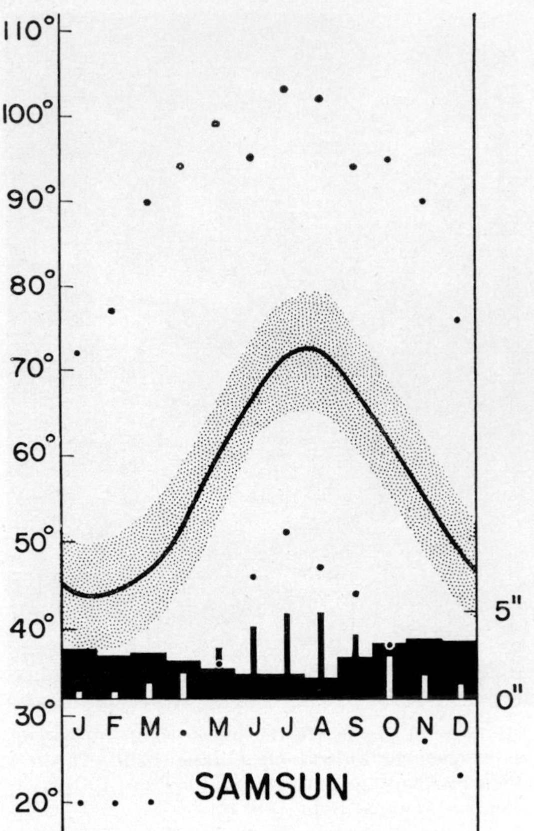

Samsun is the largest Turkish port on the Black Sea. Elevation 131 feet, annual precipitation 29.1 inches. See descriptive note on page 270.

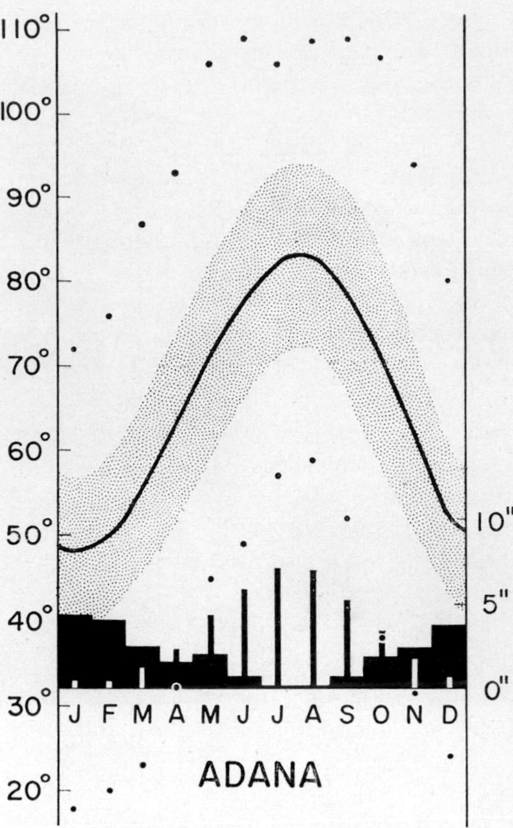

The city of Adana lies in a fertile plain near the northeastern corner of the Mediterranean. Elevation: 82 feet, annual precipitation: 24.3 inches.

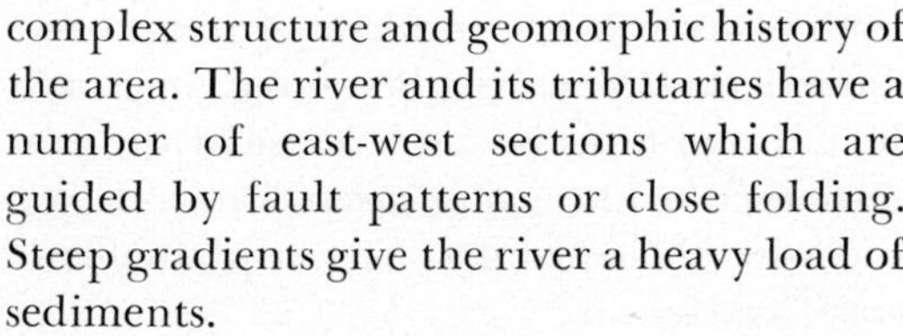

complex structure and geomorphic history of the area. The river and its tributaries have a number of east-west sections which are guided by fault patterns or close folding. Steep gradients give the river a heavy load of sediments.

The landscape of the Pontus Mountains in this area resembles that already described in the third transect. The coastal belt, which rises steeply, is rainy and heavily forested. Inland is a zone traversed by deep valleys which follow sunken blocks along the fractured plateau margin, to some extent in the rain shadow of the coastal range. In addition to the open folding of Cretaceous and Eocene beds, there are extensive areas of closely folded and altered Paleozoics. Many interior scenes resemble parts of Switzerland, even to wooden houses with stone roofs, raised on stilts, while the coast has some similarity with the shores of Italy near Naples.

Thick coniferous forests are present below 3,300 feet, composed mainly of black pine and some oak and beech. Above 5,000 feet, there are only scrub forests which merge into summer pasture above.

Along this line, Central Anatolia has more hills and less level land than around Ankara. Elevations are around 3,000 feet. Some rolling country represents ancient lava flows; elsewhere soft sedimentaries have given rise to hill lands. The chief cities are Amasya and

Kayseri; the latter lies in the center of a broad and rather dry basin with salt marshes. Several great volcanoes, such as Erciyas, 12,848 feet, lie near this traverse.

The Taurus system is locally represented by the Anti-Taurus, here developed with a northeast to southwest trend, with five recognizable ranges. Several summits exceed 9,000 feet. Forests cover the more remote middle slopes, but the lower levels have only scattered scrub. Higher elevations are bare in summer and covered by snow in winter. The gorge of the Cilician Gates, one of the main passes of antiquity, leads through these mountains from inner Anatolia to the Mediterranean.

One Britisher, J. H. M. Cornwall, who crossed the mountains, writes as follows:[1]

> To the traveller journeying from the dreary wastes of the central plateau, the glittering snow peaks of the Taurus come as a refreshing change of scene. On the morning after our arrival at Eregli, we plunged into one of the little ravines cut into the granite mass of the Bulghar Dagh, 10,000 to 12,000 feet high. Our road turned into a winding lane, bordered with poplars, walnuts, and fruit trees, and ended in a narrow cleft in the rock concealing the village of Ivriz, perched above a small trout stream and embowered in masses of cherry blossoms . . . .
>
> The next evening saw us at Ulu Qishla, a wretched village of mud hovels . . . about 5,000 feet above sea level, . . . and at night bitterly cold. We pushed on the next day to visit the historic pass of the Cilician Gates . . . we rode over the Tekir Beli Pass and down through the narrow defile which has witnessed the passage of so many armies. The Roman Emperor Marcus Aurelius has left an inscription . . . The scenery is magnificent, the steep mountain sides being covered with stately pines, while wild flowers peeped out everywhere from the crevices in the grey limestone cliffs.

The Seyhan River provides the chief southward drainage in this area, and around Adana it has built up Turkey's largest coastal alluvial area. The shoreline is low, in part backed by sand dunes, behind which are marshes and lagoons. Elsewhere, the delta is particularly fertile and intensively cultivated, though apt to be flooded when the river overtops its meandering course. Since the rainfall is only twenty-four inches, an elaborate irrigation system provides water from a mountain reservoir.

Splendid forests cover the humid slopes of the eastern Pontus near Coruh, one of the few good forest regions in Swasia. (Courtesy Turkish Information Office, New York.)

In some aspects of its climate, the Seyhan delta resembles the French Riviera. In winter, this is the warmest part of Turkey with daily maxima near 60°F. and minima about 40°F. Freezing temperatures occur on only sixteen days per year. Summer, however, is quite hot, with mean daily maxima in excess of 90°F. While snow is uncommon around Adana, there is a heavy fall in the Taurus, where the snow cover is important as the

[1] J. H. M. Cornwall: "A Journey in Anatolia," *Geog. Jour.*, LXIV (1924), 216–217.

The snow-crowned Taurus adjoin the palm lined Mediterranean coast. This view is near Antalya. (Courtesy Turkish Press, Broadcasting, and Tourist Dept., Ankara.)

source of summer irrigation water. Cold winds, known as the *bora,* move down from the mountains in winter, while hot *foehn* winds descend from the mountains in summer.

In comparison with this Seyhan area along the Mediterranean, the delta of the Kizil Irmak and the Black Sea coast have slightly more rain, much more evenly distributed throughout the year. The Pontus receives its moisture from the Black Sea, with heavy precipitation when the year-round north winds are cooled as they rise over the mountains. When these same north winds continue southward across the arid Anatolian interior and are forced to rise against the north slopes of the Taurus Mountains, they yield less rain.

Longitudes 40° and 43° E.

The fifth and sixth profiles cross the mountainous areas of eastern Turkey. Both the Pontus and Taurus systems merge here into the East Anatolian or Armenian complex, so that the terrain is rugged and level land is present only in limited areas. Profile number five extends from the Black Sea port of Trabzon southward along longitude 40°E. past Diyarbekir to the edge of the Mesopotamian plains. The sixth profile passes through Kars and Lake Van, from the Soviet Union to Iraq, near 43°E.

Trabzon is the major seaport of northeastern Turkey. Because of its maritime position, it has a milder climate than other places to the south. The mean daily minimum in January is 38°F. while the mean daily maximum in July is 81°F. The rainfall averages thirty-three inches, well distributed throughout the year. Near Trabzon, the coast rises abruptly and the shore is so regular that the only sheltered anchorage is behind a breakwater.

Trabzon is rich in history, for here is the area of ancient Colchis, famous as the land of the Golden Fleece, and of the kingdom of Pontus. At one time this was a Greek colony. Writing in 1877, James Bryce described the city as follows: [1]

> Trebizond dwells in my memory as a sort of enchanted city . . . . Its situation is wonderfully beautiful, with the serrated range of Lazistan on the one side, a group of snowy peaks plunging into a deep blue sea; and on the other the bold bluff cape on whose top tradition places the encampment of the Ten Thousand Greeks.

Several parallel ranges lie inland with intervening ova. Near the coast, elevations reach 6,000 feet, while farther inland, many peaks are more than double that figure. Over these mountains leads the Zigana Pass, 6,675 feet, on the classic road to Persia.

As elevations increase, temperatures drop, precipitation increases, and forests become more luxuriant. Snow measurements are unavailable; but the fall is heavy on north slopes, and the snow cover continues for five or six months. The permanent snow line lies at 12,000 feet, and many peaks carry a record of former glaciation. Several mountain roads tend to be closed during the winter. When winter winds occasionally shift to the south, air which descends over the mountains produces warm and dry foehn effects which rapidly melt the snow.

The general east-west trend of the country is revealed equally in the mountain pattern and in river alignment. Although the Kelkit and Coruh flow in opposite directions, the two rivers lie end to end in the same structural valley. The two branches of the upper Euphrates also have a westward trend.

The southern limit of the highlands is reached where the Taurus system, actually the Anti-Taurus range, swings in a broad curve around the north of the upper Tigris basin before turning southeast to join the Iranian Zagros. Here the mountains descend abruptly from peaks of 10,000 feet to a rolling lowland. The south slopes of the Taurus receive heavy snow fall, so much that nomads must find lower pastures in winter.

Farther south, toward Diyarbekir, the country becomes more flat and broad plains appear, in some places sharply cut by local drainage. Unfortunately, the rainfall is limited. Diyarbekir exhibits its interior lowland position by having a daily mean minimum of 26°F. in January, with an absolute low of 0°F., in contrast to a daily mean maximum of 99°F. in July, and an all-time high of 108°F. The annual precipitation amounts to eighteen inches, barely enough for unirrigated agriculture. Most of this falls in November and December, with eight to twelve days of snow or sleet each month.

Volcanic formations are extensively developed at both ends of the profile, that is near the Black Sea as well as next to Syria.

Farther east, the section which links Kars and Lake Van crosses a broken lava plateau above which towers a series of giant volcanic cones. Mount Ararat, 16,946 feet, lies to the east, but along this transect are Suphan and Nemrut. Mount Suphan rises to 14,540 feet in a symmetrical snow-crowned cone on the north shore of Lake Van. On the western shore of the lake is the ruined cone of

[1] Quoted in *Geographic Magazine,* XVIII (1945), 124.

Parts of interior Anatolia are a dry steppe, where water is at a premium. These mud houses are near Nigde. (Courtesy Turkish Press, Broadcasting, and Tourist Dept., Ankara.)

Nemrut or Nimrud, which rises to 9,900 feet and contains a superb explosion crater, six miles in diameter and one of the largest in the world; its last eruption was in the fifteenth century. Other volcanoes border the lake, among them one which has a breached rim with a circular lagoon that fills the crater.

Lake Van is the result of lava flows from Nemrut which blocked a tributary of the Euphrates and drainage toward the Tigris as well. It lies at an elevation of 5,640 feet and lacks an outlet. The water is noted for its sodium carbonate rather than for salt; the total sodium content is 2 per cent. The lake covers an area of 1,460 square miles, but the presence of old shore lines shows that it was once larger. One traveler has described it as "fabulously blue, an enamelled desert of water surrounded by a barren landscape of snowy ranges and extinct volcanoes." [1]

The vicinity of Lake Van is rich in history, for here was the homeland of the Armenians, and here still live nomadic Kurds who move up and down the slopes with the seasons. Only limited areas are under cultivation, for the rainfall is limited.

The rugged landscape of southeastern Turkey has many features in common with areas eastward in Iran and central Afghanistan. Vegetation is scanty at both lower and upper levels, the result of aridity below and cold above. Forests appear only at intermediate elevations. Increasing continentality is reflected in the climate of Kars which has a January minimum of —32°F. and a summer absolute maximum of 91°F.

[1] P. H. Davis: "Lake Van and Turkish Kurdistan: A Botanical Journey," *Geog. Jour.*, CXXII (1956), 157.

AGRICULTURE AND THE FOOD SUPPLY

THE LAND and its products have long formed the basis for Turkish livelihood. Turkey has over 3 million farm families, plus many hundred thousand pastoralists. Only 30 per cent of the population is urban. As in other countries, population is rapidly expanding, but unlike some others, food supply is growing even more rapidly. In two decades, Turkey was able to almost double its agricultural acreage; no similar growth, however, has been possible in total yield. Mechanization must be given some of the credit, for the number of tractors increased from 1,000 in 1944 to over 40,000 in 1955. Most of these were used in the wheat lands around Ankara and Konya, and in the cotton fields near Adana.

Land Use

Large parts of Turkey can not be used for any agricultural purpose. Steep slopes, poor soils, and unsatisfactory climate characterize a hundred million acres. Even with the maximum reclamation, not much more than a third of the country is potentially arable.

About a quarter of Turkey is now under some cultivation, but a third of this lies fallow every year. In view of the low rainfall and high evaporation over much of Turkey, the water balance in the soil is marginal. In order to store up moisture, many fields must lie fallow in alternate years. The harvested land thus amounts to less than 20 per cent, perhaps no more than 15 per cent in poorer years. Tree crops add 2 per cent to the plowed area. Nowhere is there much more readily usable land. Irrigation and drainage will add limited areas, and dry farming techniques will push agriculture farther into the arid margins; but, in general, additional food must come from intensification of the presently harvested areas. Fortunately, Turkey feeds itself.

Pasture lands are of limited value. High mountain meadows have rich grasses in summer, but most grazing lands are restricted to the dry steppe. The total area of "pasture" amounts to nearly half of Turkey, but this is decreasing as the tractor and plow invade the grass lands.

Rural Turkey, away from the cities and modern lines of communication, tends to remain backward. Many of the 35,000 villages are isolated, so that the average peasant earns a meager livelihood along traditional subsistence lines. Wooden plows, ill-fed livestock, poor seeds, and the lack of money for fertilizers and machinery keep down crop yields per acre. So much cattle dung is used for household fuel in the drier areas that there is an inadequate supply of manure as fertilizer. The majority of all farms are under ten acres in size.

Extensive land reform has somewhat changed the pattern of tenancy, but economic problems remain. Research stations and government aid programs have made significant contributions. Thousands of tractors have enabled agriculture to push into the dryland margins.

Soils are obviously varied. Rich alluvium is present in the few deltas and along flood plains. Many volcanic areas have good soils. The poorest conditions are found in the saline soils of the drier areas, in leached limestone soils, and in many crystalline areas. Where the natural cover of vegetation has been removed, excessive erosion has stripped off the hillside soils. In many areas, soils are deficient in phosphorus and nitrogen.

Central Anatolia leads in acreage and total output. Some sections are rather dry, but no other part of the country has such a large area of good level soil. Agriculture is more intensive in the various delta areas along the Mediterranean, Aegean, and Black seas, but the total extent is limited.

Irrigation is desirable in many areas, but the water is not everywhere available. Dur-

LAND UTILIZATION IN TURKEY [1]

	1934 Area in 1,000 hectares	%	1949 Area in 1,000 hectares	%	1952 Area in 1,000 hectares	%
Grains	5,903	7.6	7,527	9.7	9,868	12.7
Legumes	477	0.6	387	0.5	436	0.6
Vegetables	143	0.2	151	0.2	175	0.2
Industrial Crops	497	0.6	814	1.0	1,158	1.5
Other Crops	6	0.0	284	0.4	309	0.4
Fallow	3,674	4.8	4,274	5.5	5,608	7.2
Total Cultivation	10,700	13.8	13,437	17.3	17,554	22.6
Fruit Trees	286	0.4	544	0.7	464	0.6
Olive Trees	347	0.5	272	0.4	382	0.5
Vineyards	345	0.5	521	0.7	641	0.8
Tree and Vine Crops	978	1.4	1,337	1.8	1,487	1.9
High quality grasslands	3,421	4.4	3,676	4.7	1,650	2.1
Pastures	2,877	3.7	2,715	3.5	4,741	6.1
Meadows	38,032	49.2	36,510	47.0	28,384	36.6
Total Pasture	44,330	57.3	42,901	55.2	34,775	44.8
Forests	9,170	11.9	11,892	15.3	10,418	13.4
Lakes and Swamps	960	1.2	953	1.2	950	1.2
Other areas	11,097	14.4	7,178	9.2	12,514	16.1
Total Area	77,235	100.0	77,698	100.0	77,698	100.0

[1] Republique Turque, Office Central de Statistique: *Annuaire Statistique.*

ing the 1950's about 5 million acres were receiving some supplementary water, roughly 10 per cent of the total agricultural area. About a quarter of this irrigation was for wheat with one-eighth each for cotton and barley. With proper engineering, the irrigated area might be doubled and more since Turkey has many snow-fed rivers.

Dry-farming techniques are the standard practice throughout all the drier parts of Anatolia, including many coastal areas where rainfall during the growing season is inadequate. Two procedures are involved, fallowing and cultivation techniques. In humid lands, fields are sometimes allowed to lie fallow in order to replenish the nitrogen; in dry lands, fallowing is necessary in order to build up the accumulation of soil moisture. While cultivation in alternate years is the rule, it is sometimes desirable to accumulate the carry-over of two rainy seasons. In some dry lands, plowed furrows or low check dams at right angles to the slope help the runoff to sink into the soil. These are rare in Turkey. While some dry-farming procedures accumulate moisture through fallowing, others conserve it against evaporation. This usually involves harrowing or shallow plowing in order to decrease the size of capillary openings near the surface and thus reduce evaporation. Here is where Turkish farmers can learn better procedures.

Products

Crops are of many kinds. Cereals predominate, accounting for over half the cultivated area. Wheat is the principal grain, chiefly of winter varieties, grown almost everywhere. When it fails to germinate until spring, the crop is usually reduced by 25 per cent. The highest yields per acre are in the interior plains. The harvest season ranges from June to August, starting on the south coast and ending in the higher plateaus. Whereas Tur-

Mechanization has been responsible for a large increase in agricultural yield. These fields are near Izmir. (Courtesy U. S. Information Service, Ankara.)

key was once an importer of wheat, it has been producing a surplus during recent years. Wheat production amounts to half the total cereal output.

The second crop is barley, raised in part for fodder. Although much less important than wheat, barley is gaining in importance. Rye, oats, and corn are of minor importance, the first two especially in the drier areas. Rice is a favorite food of those who can afford it.

Turkey raises a wide variety of fruits and nuts, several of which form important exports. The long sunny summers are ideal for ripening, harvesting, and drying. Sultana raisins and Smyrna figs are especially famous. Other fruits include plums, cherries, apricots, peaches, apples, pears, mulberries, and citrus fruits. There are over a million trees for each variety of fruit.

Grapes occupy over 1.5 million acres, especially in the fertile soils of the western coastlands up to an elevation of 3,000 feet.

Olive trees are more numerous than in any other country of the eastern Mediterranean, occupying a million acres in Turkey. The chief areas lie within fifty miles of the Aegean and Mediterranean coasts, with most groves below 2,000 feet elevation. Irrigation is unnecessary, for olives will grow in areas with as little as eight inches of winter rain.

While olive trees thrive on the damp alluvial plains, most are grown on dry, thin, stony limestone soils. Most of the olive crop is converted into oil and is consumed within Turkey.

Figs are an important Turkish export, and the trees, like olives, require practically no irrigation. The most productive area is around Izmir, formerly known as Smyrna. More than 5 million trees produce well over 100,000 metric tons of figs.

Many nuts are grown in the west and north. Turkey leads the world in hazelnuts or filberts, of which there are 150 million trees on half a million acres. Export centers are Izmir, Istanbul, Samsun, and Trabzon. Walnuts, chestnuts, pistachios, and almonds each number several million trees.

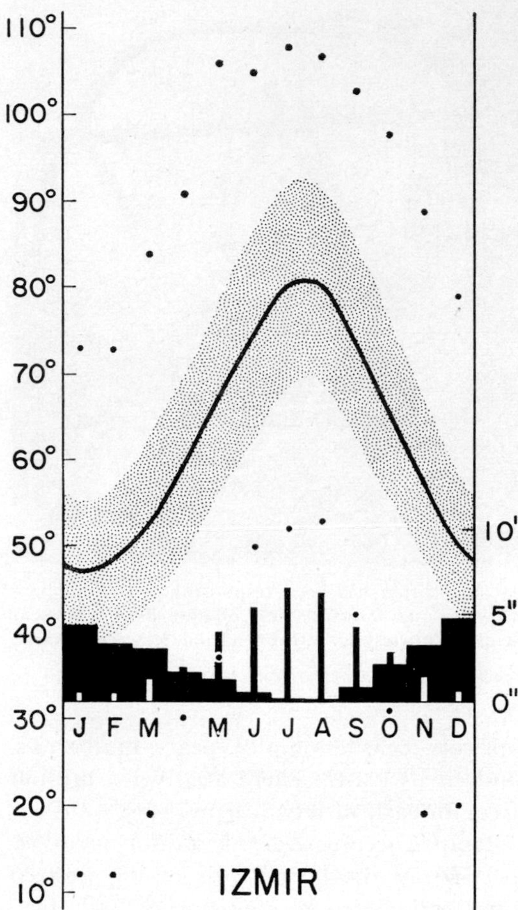

Coastal Izmir enjoys a climate which is moderated by the Mediterranean. Elevation 92 feet, precipitation 25.5 inches.

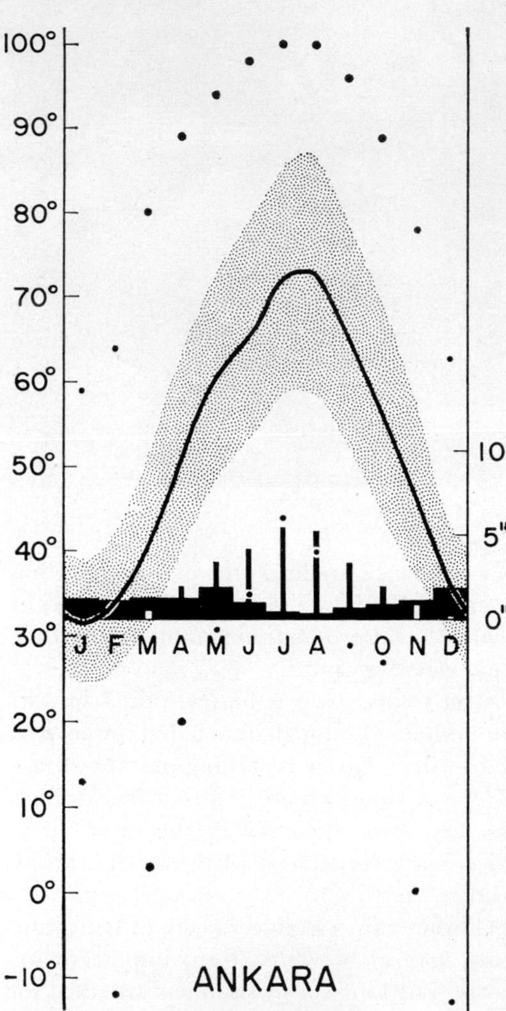

Ankara's climate is representative of dry interior Anatolia. Elevation 2,825 feet, annual precipitation 13.6 inches.

These graphs present monthly average temperature and rainfall, plus the daily temperature range, shaded, and the extreme recorded temperatures, in dots; as well as the monthly potential evapotranspiration, in thin bars.

Industrial crops are raised for export as well as for domestic processing. Cotton leads, with the principal production around Adana and Izmir. The area is expanding and approximates 2 million acres, so that cotton is the third most important crop in terms of area sown. Most of the cotton is irrigated. Some silk is still produced in the Bursa area.

Tobacco has been grown in Turkey for four centuries, especially in the damp coastlands along the Aegean and Black seas. Bafra is reputed to produce the world's finest tobacco. Exports, chiefly to the United States, contribute substantial amounts to the national economy.

Erzurum is representative of the high eastern interior. Elevation 6,402 feet, annual precipitation 21.2 inches.

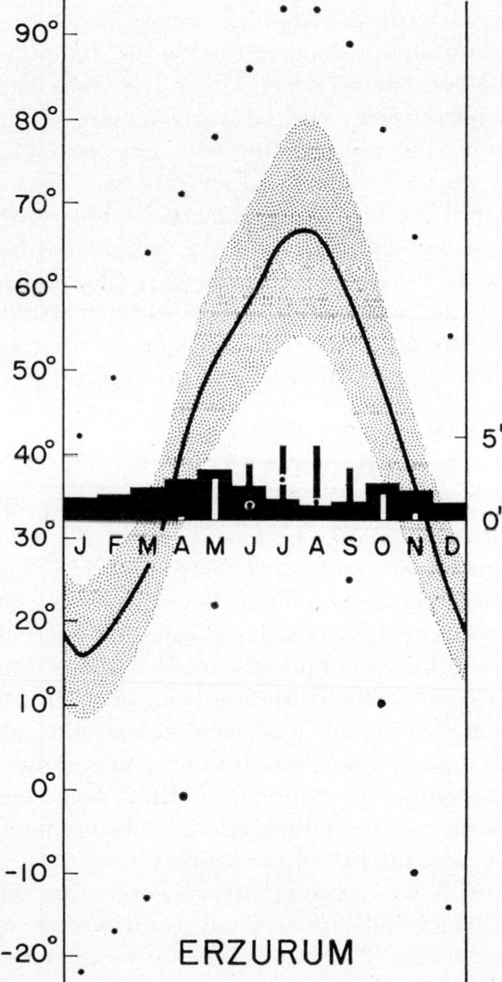

TURKISH CROPS[1]

	Area in 1,000 hectares	*Production in 1,000 metric tons*
Wheat	5,400	6,447
Barley	2,312	3,189
Rye	587	670
Oats	356	405
Corn	642	837
Millet	76	78
Rice	49	95
Total cereals	9,868	12,242
Total legumes	436	478
Cotton (fiber)	675	165
(seed)	—	338
Flax (fiber)	38	3
Hemp (fiber)	11	11
Tobacco	130	92
Potatoes	102	873
Sugar Beets	48	1,069
Opium	43	0.5
Olives		
Total cultivated area plus fruits and tree crops	19,024	

[1] Republique Turque, Office Central de Statistique, *Annuaire Statistique,* (data for 1952).

Sugar beets rank third among industrial crops. This is a new development, and Turkey is now self-sufficient in sugar. Most of the beets are grown in the interior. A small amount of sugar cane is raised along the Mediterranean.

Other industrial crops are sesame for its oil, opium for medicinal purposes, hemp and flax for fiber, acorns for tanning, silk from worms fed on mulberry leaves, and licorice. As a reflection of the varied climates of Turkey, 3 million pounds of tea are raised on 17 million acres in the extreme east along the Black Sea.

Stock raising and pastoral activities provide the livelihood for many people, both settled farmers and wandering herdsmen. The chief animals in order are sheep, goats, cattle, horses and mules, and camels. The total exceeds sixty million head, of which sheep and goats account for roughly two-thirds. In terms of the weight of the meat eaten, mutton slightly exceeds beef.

The most distinctive animal product is mohair, obtained from the fleece of some 5 million Angora goats which thrive in the dry plateau, hence their name is that of the capital. Mohair is silky, fluffy, and about six inches in length; the average goat yields some four pounds a year. Cows, buffalos, sheep, and goats are each a source of milk, usually drunk in the fermented and thickened form known as yogurt.

Turkish tobacco is among the world's finest. Each leaf is strung separately for drying. (Courtesy Turkish Information Office, New York.)

Here, as elsewhere in Swasia, nomadism is on the decline. However, many thousand Kurds engage in transhumance, migrating up and down the slopes of the eastern Taurus with the seasons.

Fishing is concentrated around Istanbul, where it takes advantage of the seasonal migration of fish through the Straits. The annual catch amounts to 100,000 tons. Caviar is obtained in the eastern Black Sea.

Forests are reported to cover one-sixth of Turkey, but fully half of this represents scrub growth. The best forests lie on the humid north slopes of the Pontus and in the higher Taurus. Much larger areas once had a good forest cover, but careless cutting, erosion, and the nibbling of young shoots by goats have taken a heavy toll. Most forest lands are now state property so that, with systematic reforestation, the country may become sulf-sufficient in lumber. Charcoal is widely employed as a domestic fuel. Hardwoods and softwoods are about equal in area, but the latter lead in production.

RAW MATERIALS FOR INDUSTRY

In industry, and probably in mineral wealth other than oil, Turkey is far in the lead among the nations of Southwest Asia. Remarkable developments have taken place in recent decades, especially since 1948, most of them through Turkey's unaided efforts, but in part with assistance from the United States. Progress has been noteworthy, although in some cases at the expense of overextending the national credit. Turkey has been impatient for material advancement, even at the risk of bankruptcy.

It is well to recognize, however, that the mineral industry is small, contributing no more than 2 or 3 per cent to the gross national product, and some 10 per cent of all

Sugar beets are an expanding crop, here processed in a mill at Adapazari. (Courtesy Turkish Information Office, New York.)

exports. Half of the output is represented by coal and lignite. The future of the mineral industry is uncertain but it is probably modest. Export minerals help Turkey's foreign exchange but are subject to the fluctuations of the world market. Even in the most favorable years, overseas sales are inadequate to pay for essential raw material imports.

Turkey has a diverse array of minerals.[1] Coal, lignite, iron, sulphur, and salt are consumed domestically. Chrome leads in export value, followed by copper, manganese, and a variety of commodities such as boracite, emery, antimony, meerschaum, lead, and mercury. To make up for her deficiencies, Turkey imports several of the above plus steel, aluminum, tin, zinc, phosphate rock, and petroleum. In world-wide terms, the only mineral of major significance is chromite, valuable as a ferro-alloy.

The geological knowledge of Turkey is well-developed. Igneous rocks of various types are widespread, and the genetic and structural relations of their mineral occurrences are becoming known. Ancient and now-metamorphosed granite massifs occur in the Menderes and Kirsehir areas. Later on, basic intrusions took place during the mountain building period from the Jurassic to the Eocene. More igneous activity accompanied the subsequent faulting, often pouring out great amounts of basalt. It is

[1] Some of the information and most of the tables in this section are based on L. Nahi: "The Mineral Industry of Turkey," *U. S. Bureau of Mines,* Circular 7855 (1958), (with extensive bibliography).

Mohair is one of Turkey's distinctive exports, produced from the fleece of Angora goats, especially in the dry area around Ankara. (Courtesy Turkish Information Office, New York.)

the last of these episodes which brought most mineralization.

In general, the most important metalogenic zones occur along the borders of the Pontus and Taurus systems rather than in their central folded zones, possibly since the folds represent the deepest parts of the ancient geosynclines where intrusive rocks are not presently revealed. To these sterile zones may be added the border folds along the Syrian and Iraq frontiers. For example, most of the important occurrences of iron lie within a few miles of the Taurus margins.

Coal is Turkey's major mineral resource, and reserves appear adequate for many years. The Eregli-Zonguldak field along the Black Sea was discovered in 1829, and by 1848 production amounted to 50,000 tons a year. Unfortunately, this is the only source of good bituminous coal or of metallurgical coke in all Turkey. The coal is of Carboniferous age, and resembles that of the Donets field north of the Black Sea; however, some of the coal is fragile and needs to be briquetted. By 1960, the field capacity had reached 5.8 million tons of marketable coal. The Zonguldak area has over fifty seams, varying in thickness from two to twenty feet. Many seams dip steeply, even to 90°, and are cut by faults, so that machine operations are made difficult; most mines use longwall methods. The total reserves are estimated at 1,076 million tons; of this 363 million are "measured" or in sight, 460 million are "inferred," while 253 million are "indicated." Since the mines are near the port of Zonguldak, distribution to western Turkey can be by ship. It had been hoped that Turkey might export coal to other countries in the Mediterranean, but increased domestic re-

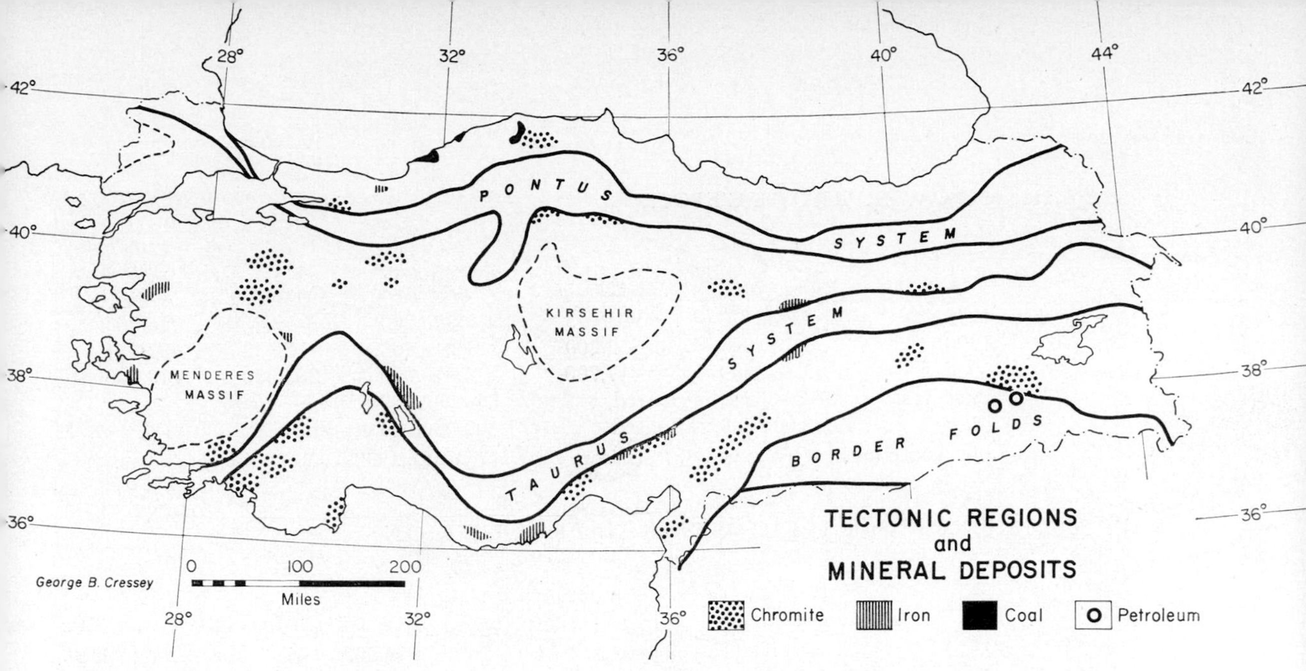

The major zones of mountain building have produced both surface land forms and deep-seated mineral deposits. (Based on L. Nahi, "The Mineral Industry of Turkey.")

quirements have outstripped production.

About a quarter of the output is used by the railroads, and an equal amount is consumed in steel mills and copper refineries. Production data for coal and other resources are found in the accompanying tables and also in Chapter 8 (page 177).

Lignite of Tertiary age is widely distributed, especially in western Turkey. There are two dozen mining districts, and the production almost equals that of coal. Reserves of all types may exceed a billion tons. The largest deposits appear to be in Kutahya province in the western interior, followed by European Turkey, Manisa, Bolu, and Corum provinces. The availability of lignite in the interior provides a cheap source of power and fuel for areas too remote from Zonguldak coal.

Petroleum production amounts to only one-fifth of the annual consumption, so that the country must use large amounts of foreign exchange for its imported oil. Production began with the Ramandag field in 1940, near Diyarbekir in the southeast. There is a refinery nearby on the railroad at Batman. The Ramandag area is characterized by a series of anticlinal folds along the foredeep between the Arabian shield and the Tethys geosyncline. In a sense, they represent an east-west continuation of the Zagros folding. The rocks range from Eocene to Permian and older, with oil present in Cretaceous limestones. A similar field is at Garzan, fourteen miles from Batman.

Favorable structures occur elsewhere, but hundreds of wells have been drilled with little success. Areas of possible oil outside the Syrian borderlands include the vicinity of Adana, Iskenderon, the Sea of Marmara, Antalya, Lake Tuz, and Lake Van.

In the event that Turkey fails to develop large amounts of oil at home, a new source of supply will be available after the completion of the pipeline from central Iran to a Turkish port on the Mediterranean.

Hydroelectric potentials are considerable, and, since more power for industry is a major goal, dam construction has received high priority. Five power dams completed by 1960 added over 400,000 kilowatt capacity and almost doubled the country's power supply. The Keban Dam on the Euphrates will be even larger, with an eventual million kilo-

Turkey

TURKISH POWER PRODUCTION[1]

	Coal				Installed electricity,
	Run of Mine	*Marketable*	*Lignite*	*Crude Oil*	*kilowatts*
1940	3,019,458	2,064,045	229,200		216,965
1950	4,360,600	2,832,200	1,214,460	17,532	407,781
1956	5,888,300	3,717,700	3,010,000	286,000	610,000 (1955)
Reserves	363,000,000 measured		200,000,000 proven		
	1,076,000,000 estimated		1,500,000,000 estimated		

[1] In metric tons except as noted. Data from Central Statistical Office, Republic of Turkey.

TURKISH NONMETALLIC MINERAL PRODUCTION[1]

	Asbestos	*Boron Minerals*	*Emery*	*Magnesite*	*Meerschaum (boxes)*	*Rock Salt*	*Brine Salt*	*Sulphur*
1940	100	5,000	8,600	840	260	19,600	193,200	3,700
1950	240	9,800	1,400	450	260	23,100	287,100	6,000
1956	600	33,500	6,400	850	850	30,000	350,000	13,950
Reserves								1,000,000

[1] In metric tons except as noted. Data from Central Statistical Office, Republic of Turkey.

TURKISH METAL PRODUCTION[1]

	Antimony Ore	*Chrome Ore*	*Blister Copper*	*Iron Ore*	*Lead-Zinc Ore*	*Manganese Ore*	*Mercury (flasks)*
1940	580	169,800	8,750	130,300	3,640	500	480
1950	3,220	422,530	11,700	233,590	110	31,180	—
1956	1,400	833,100	24,800	930,500	14,420	59,800	1,080
Reserves	10 to 20,000,000	3 to 4,000,000	350 to 400,000	75 to 100,000,000			

[1] In metric tons except as noted. Data from Central Statistical Office, Republic of Turkey.

watt installation. Scores of other projects are under consideration, with as many as five sites and 1,500 feet of head on the Sakarya River, and nine sites on the Kizil Irmak.

Iron ore is widespread, but high grade deposits of adequate size are limited to the east. Reserves are sufficient to meet Turkey's needs for many decades, although modest in world terms. The leading producer is at Divrigi, discovered in 1937 near the railway east of Sivas. The ore, a high grade magnetite of contact metamorphic origin, contains 65 per cent iron, but also has objectionable sulphur. The reserves are placed at 39.5 million metric tons, and by 1960 the output capacity amounted to 1 million tons per year.

Other iron deposits are worked around Edremit near the Aegean Sea, but the ore contains objectionable amounts of arsenic. Some of the production is exported. If the metallurgical problems can be solved, this may become an important steel center. Reserves at the leading mine amount to 11.5 million metric tons. Few other occurrences have been adequately surveyed but for Turkey as a whole the reserves may approximate 100 million metric tons.

Although Turkey has good iron ore and adequate coking coal, the deposits are 600 miles apart by rail; this is the main problem of the steel industry. Limestone and refractory clays are in adequate supply, and Turkish manganese is more than abundant. The only integrated steel plant is at Karabuk, fifty miles south of the Zonguldak coal field. At the site are coke ovens, a sintering plant to remove sulphur from the ore, three blast furnaces with a total capacity of 600,000 tons a year, five open hearth furnaces, rolling mills, founderies, and a sulphuric acid plant. The installation employs 5,000 persons. The usual blast furnace charge consists of 6,600 kilograms of iron ore, 1,500 kg. limestone, 4,000 kg. coke (derived from about twice this weight of coal), and 125 kg. manganese. From this total of 16,100 kilograms of raw materials, about 4,000 kilograms of pig iron is produced.

Expressed in metric units for 1956, Turkey produced 219,400 tons of pig iron and 192,500 tons of steel, and used 120,200 tons of straight iron ore, 204,000 tons of sintered or de-sulphured ore, about 8,000 tons of manga-

This transmission line carries electricity to Istanbul from a thermal power station in the Zonguldak coal field. (Courtesy U. S. Economic Cooperation Administration.)

LARGE TURKISH DAMS

Dam	*River*	*Nearest city*	*Height in feet*	*Construction*	*Purpose*	*Planned capacity, kilowatts*
Elmali		Istanbul (E)	135	concrete	urban water	
Seyhan	Seyhan	Adana (N)	175	earth	flood control irrigation power	67,500
Sariyar	Sakarya	Ankara (W)	356	concrete	power	160,000
Hirfanli	Kizil Irmak	Ankara (S)	270	earth	power	160,000
Kemer	Buyuk Menderes	Izmir (SE)	360	concrete	flood control irrigation power	60,000
Demirkopru	Gediz	Izmir (E)	250	earth	flood control irrigation power	69,000
Keban	Euphrates	Diyarbekir (NW)	490	concrete	power	1,000,000

The Karabuk Steel Mill is the largest metallurgical plant between Hungary and India. Turkey is well supplied with coal and iron ore, but they are far apart. (Courtesy Turkish Information Office, New York.)

nese, 77,100 tons of limestone, about 12,000 tons of scrap, and 212,500 tons of coke.

Production costs at Karabuk are high even though Zonguldak coal prices are subsidized by the government, for freight charges on the iron ore are considerable. Other iron deposits are closer, but are of unsatisfactory composition. In terms of national welfare, however, the operation is important. Production has increased steadily, as shown by the accompanying totals for all Turkey.

Chromite is Turkey's unique mineral, with production which dates back to 1860. Prior to World War I, the country supplied about 60 per cent of the world's requirements; due to competition from South Africa and elsewhere, the figure has dropped to 20 per cent. Very little chromite is used domestically; instead it is exported for use as a ferro alloy and a plating agent. The United States is by far the largest purchaser, and receives a quarter of its supply from Turkey.

Chromite deposits are associated with ultrabasic rocks such as peridotite and serpentine, which resulted from magmatic differentiation. Reserves of at least several million tons are scattered through two dozen areas. Southwest Turkey around Fethiye leads in production, and exports are through Izmir and Antalya, as well as from Gocek, nearby. In second place for production is the east, where the Guleman mine is the largest single producer in the country; unfortunately its top-grade deposits of 50 per

The Murgul Copper Works has a capacity of 10,000 tons of blister copper a year. This landscape shows the eastern Pontus Mountains. (Courtesy Turkish Press, Broadcasting, and Tourist Dept., Ankara.)

cent Cr_2O_3 are nearing exhaustion. Weather conditions generally close the open-cut operations in January and February. The northwest around Eskisehir is in third place, with Bursa as Turkey's oldest chromite area. Still other mines are in production in the vicinity of Adana.

Other ferroalloys include manganese, molybdenum, and tungsten, each produced in modest amounts and largely for export. Manganese is obtained between Eskisehir and the Aegean, near Zonguldak, and elsewhere. Most of it is of low grade, from 35 to 45 per cent manganese.

Nonferrous minerals are represented by antimony, aluminum, copper, lead, zinc, mercury, and gold.

Antimony production has fluctuated widely, according to the world demand, but never amounts to more than a few thou-

TURKISH IRON PRODUCTION[1]

Year	*Iron Ore*	*Pig Iron*	*Steel Ingots*	*Imports*
1940	130.3	83.4	37.5	142.2
1950	233.6	113.5	90.8	185.3
1956	950.5	219.4	192.5	145.8

[1] In thousands of metric tons. Data from Central Statistical Office, Republic of Turkey.

sand tons. The chief area is south of Samsun.

Bauxite for aluminum is present in the western Taurus near Antalya, the Amanus range east of Iskenderon, and near Zonguldak. Reserves probably amount to over 10 million tons, but the quality is poor and there is no production.

Copper output on an industrial scale began in 1936 at the Ergani deposit on the Tigris north of Diyarbekir. Production is now supplemented by the Murgul mine south of Batumi where reserves amount to 7.5 million tons of 2.5 per cent ore. At Kure, on the central Black Sea coast, there are 1,620,000 tons of 1.9 per cent ore. Exports are divided between Germany, the United States, and the United Kingdom. Primitive copper mining at Ergani dates back to the time of the Assyrians, 2000 B.C.

Lead and zinc occur together here as elsewhere. Production has been irregular. Reserves near Keban on the Euphrates are estimated at 150,000 metric tons with 10 per cent lead ore. There are also 285,000 metric tons of ore with 5 per cent lead and zinc each at Bolkerdag west of Adana. Numerous other mines are worked from time to time, depending on the world price level.

Mercury production in Turkey suffers by competition from richer deposits in Spain and Italy.

Gold has been known since antiquity, but the modern production is largely as a by-product from copper and lead ores. Small placer deposits are also occasionally operated.

The nonmetallic minerals include several in which Turkey is self-sufficient, such as salt and sulphur, or in which it has a surplus for export as with boron minerals, emery, and meerschaum. Apparently the country is deficient in potash and phosphate fertilizers, and in ceramic and refractory clays.

Boracite production in Turkey usually ranks third in the world, following the United States and Chile. The chief production is from underground mines between Izmir and Istanbul.

Emery was discovered more than a century ago, and at one time Turkey and the nearby Greek islands held a world monopoly on this aluminum oxide abrasive. Production now suffers from competition with artificial abrasives such as carborundum. The largest output is in the extreme southwest.

Meerschaum occurs as small lumps in residual clays weathered out of serpentine rocks and is used for lining pipe bowls. Turkey has almost a world monopoly.

Salt production is more than adequate, leaving a considerable amount for export. Rock salt occurs in eastern Anatolia, in the same group of beds which carry lignite, and accounts for 10 per cent of the total. Elsewhere, especially in central Anatolia, there are salt springs and lakes, with the chief production at the Yavsan Salina on the shore of Lake Tuz. However, the largest production is obtained by the evaporation of sea water, notably at the Camalti Salina near Izmir on the Aegean where the evaporating pans measure 5 million square yards. Because of its location, this is the source for export salt.

Sulphur mining dates from World War I. The principal deposit is at Keciborlu in the southwest. The bulk of the output is used for dusting vineyards, but there is some surplus for export. The sulphur is of volcanic origin and occurs in faulted rhyolite. Reserves are estimated at a million tons of ore with a sulphur content of 10 to 60 per cent. Pyrite ores also yield sulphur, as at Kure.

Cement has been in increasing demand to assist in general development. Although production tripled during the 1950's, imports also rose. Raw materials are widely available, although generally far from fuel.

Industry is both underdeveloped and highly concentrated. Aside from the steel mill at Karabuk, the seven cement plants, the arsenals, railroad and ship yards, and small chemical plants, heavy industry scarcely exists. With the development of hydroelectric power and better transport, important changes are to be expected. The 1950 census of manufacturing recorded a total of 98,228 establishments, but only 1,595 had as many as ten workers and only 2 per cent employed more than ten horsepower. Istanbul is overwhelmingly in the lead for light industry, with more than twice the "value added" of Izmir, and sixfold more than the Eskisehir, Ankara, or Tokat districts. In fact, Istanbul leads in all items except food where first place goes to Izmir by a slight margin.

PATTERNS OF PEOPLE AND LAND

THE COMPLEX PATTERNS of terrain and climate find their reflection in the map showing where people live. Turkey's rural population is strikingly adjusted to the capacity of the land to support life. The numerical land-man ratio varies from fewer than five people per square mile to over 250, yet the pressure for subsistence is everywhere roughly the same. The humid slopes bordering the Black Sea yield more food, but there one finds a dense population. Interior Anatolia is dry, and man has learned that it can support fewer people. Nature does not compel; it does not even guide, but man misreads its potentials at his peril.

Population Patterns

A population map is as valuable for showing where people are not found as for indicating where they are. Each area poses a problem. How is it possible for hundreds to earn a livelihood in certain square miles while a short distance away the number drops toward zero? To know all the answers is to understand the complex of history, custom, and nature.

Sparse populations characterize dry interior Anatolia, the mountainous Mediterranean Coast, the dry Syrian borderlands, and the cold mountains of the east. There are some 50,000 square miles, or one-sixth of the country, where the average density does not rise above twenty-five people per square mile; in area and density this resembles the western half of Colorado. At the other extreme, a somewhat smaller area has rural densities in excess of 100 people in each square mile, which compares to Ohio.

Turkey as a whole, cities included, averages nearly 100 people per square mile. This is almost twice the world average, but not excessive if all of Turkey were productive. Whether or not this represents overpopulation depends on technology. Even with its limitations of terrain and climate, Turkey could feed twice its present population provided that capital and skill were available. Costs are quite another matter.

Thirty per cent of the total population is classed as urban. Most cities lie around the periphery of the country, either on the sea or in coastal lowlands; Ankara is the major exception.

Just as electrons do not fill all the space of the atom, so people do not occupy every square foot of the earth (except perhaps in tall buildings!). Maps of population density cannot be on a 1:1 scale, just as it is impractical to map atoms to scale. When one examines the pattern of Turkey, it is well to be reminded that all dots or isopleth lines are generalizations. Even within a small valley there are differences in habitability, and Turkey has many mountain valleys. This implies an uneven population distribution considerably greater than that which any map can show.

Two areas of concentration stand out: the valleys of the west which lead to the Aegean or the Sea of Marmara, and the eastern coast along the Black Sea. Both reflect satisfactory growing conditions, but in neither case is topography too favorable. Neither of these areas is continuous. In the west, population matches the pattern of deltas, flood plains,

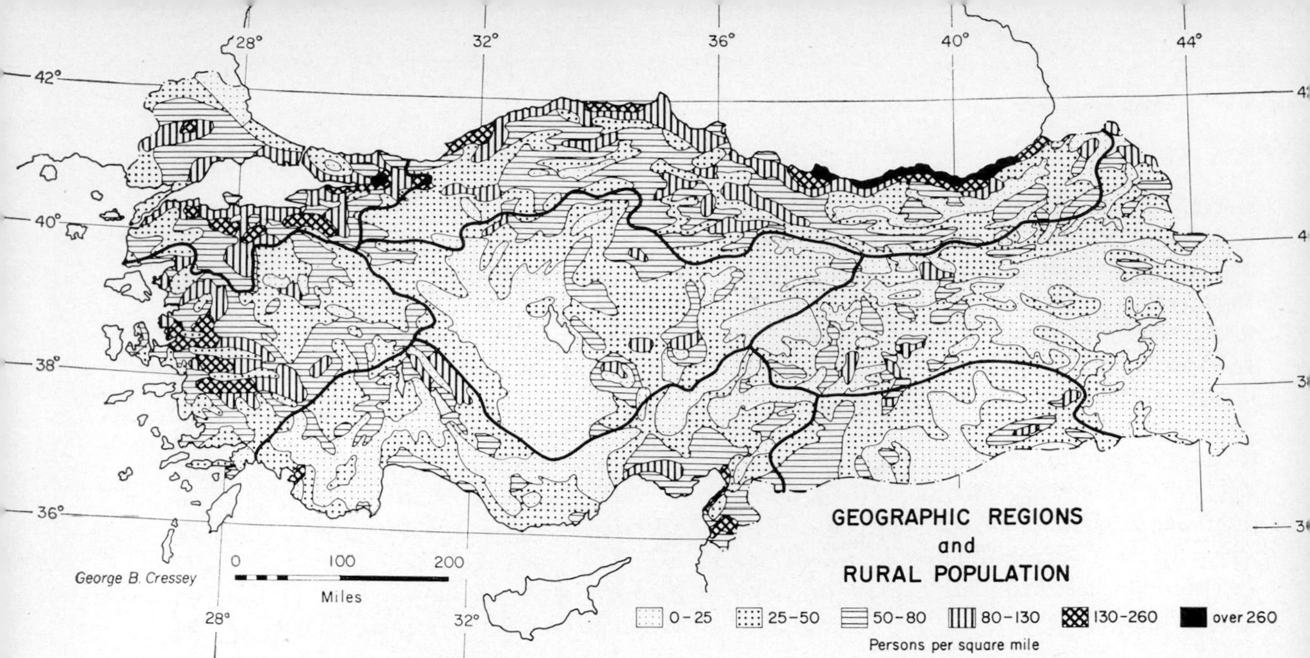

Rural population is strikingly concentrated in a few favored sections, thus reflecting the assets of terrain, climate and soil. The geographic regions are those discussed in the following pages. (Population data after Herbert Louis)

alluvial basins, and low hill lands. Along the Black Sea, people live close to the shore on a discontinuous coastal plain.

In both the Pontus and Taurus systems, linear topography prevails. Narrow valleys match structural trends and have ribbon patterns of settlement, paralleled by linear emptiness in the mountains. A similar linear arrangement prevails in the grabens which lead to the Aegean.

Most of the older cities in the interior lie in the midst of semioases where snow-fed streams supply water for good soil which has led to agriculture and in turn has built up a city. Such is the case with Eskisehir, Kayseri, or Erzerum. Modern Ankara, however, is an artificial development with rural population following rather than preceding its growth.

Along the Mediterranean, local population concentrations reflect the deltas around Antalya and Adana. Small-scale maps emphasize the discontinuous coastal population, with its contrast between congestion around river mouths or on uplifted fragments of coastal terraces, and the complete absence of any settlements where the mountains abruptly meet the sea.

The sparseness of population in the dry interior is obvious, but high mountain areas have even fewer people. Several months of snow cover and a short growing season preclude agriculture or forestry, and the only inhabitants are a few seasonal shepherds.

It is difficult to define a Turk in anthropological terms for racial mixing has gone on for a long time. In legal aspects, the word includes all citizens; linguistically it is those who speak Turkish. Roughly 10 per cent of the people belong to ethnic minorities, living largely in the east. Kurds make up about 7 per cent, while Arabs account for 1 per cent. Other groups in order are, the Greeks, Circassians, Armenians, Lazis, Jews, and Georgians. Greeks in the west and Armenians in the east were once much more numerous. Except for the Kurds, Turkey now has a relatively coherent population. Sharp contrasts in economic status still remain, especially between the west and east. Ninety-eight per cent of the people are Moslems.

One of the cultural and political problems which should be apparent from the material

Inner Anatolia is dry, much of it a short grass steppe. This is the Cokgoz Bridge at Kayseri. (Courtesy Turkish Information Office, New York.)

in this chapter relates to the lack of a common geographic focus. Istanbul is not centrally located and never was attuned with the country as a whole. Ankara is better but is rather artificial. The pattern of mountains and good land fails to provide any logical center of habitation.

Geographic Regions

Since geography is concerned with the totality of place, both cultural and physical, geographic regions are designed to show areas of over-all coherence. Complete internal unity or similarity is impossible; rather a geographic region is one where people and objects interact in the same relationships.

Turkish geographers have defined seven geographic regions, with boundaries as shown on the accompanying population map.

Marmara Region
Aegean Region
Black Sea Region
Inner Anatolian Region
Mediterranean Region
Eastern Anatolian Region
Southeastern Anatolian Region

The Marmara geographic region is one of the smallest in the entire country, but the historic significance of the Straits and the favorable condition of life give it the highest over-all density of population in Turkey. Here lie Istanbul with its suburb of Uskudar across the Bosporus and several cities with more than 50,000 people, notably Bursa. In total, the Marmara region accounts for half the country's urban population. The same situation probably holds for the concentration of light industry. Communications are also the best developed. The presence of three seas gives the area a marked maritime influence, and the many harbors have stimulated international contacts. History runs deep, and the past is obvious everywhere. This is the only area of Turkey which still has a Greek and Armenian population. A part of classical Thrace lies in European Turkey, while Mysia and the site of ancient Troy were in Asia Minor.

The Aegean area includes the basins of the Gediz and Buyuk Menderes rivers, which enter the sea to the north and south of Izmir respectively. The population exceeds 100 persons per square mile in many areas, though in large interior mountainous districts the density drops below fifty. Winds from the Mediterranean bring adequate rainfall to the lowlands, with higher amounts on exposed slopes. The region is dominated by Izmir, Turkey's third city, which lies at the head of a magnificent drowned valley. Here was ancient Lydia and Caria, the coastal parts of which formed Ionia.

The Black Sea region takes in all of the Pontus mountain system, with its variations in land usability. The eastern coastal belt, on either side of Trabzon, averages more than 250 people per square mile and is the largest continuous area of dense rural population in all Turkey. In contrast, mountainous areas thirty miles to the south have a density of only five people per square mile. Exposed mountain slopes near the Soviet border receive more than 100 inches of rain. The Black Sea region includes some of the best forest areas of the country, with a transition from drier Mediterranean types in the west to humid Caucasian forms in the east. Vertical zonation is notable in both cases, with high mountain pastures above 6,000 to 7,500 feet. The principal cities are the seaports of Zonguldak, Samsun, and Trabzon. Ancient Bythnia and Pontus lay in this area.

Inner Anatolia is the classic homeland of the Ottoman Turks, and the steppe environment mirrors their nomadic traditions. Encircling mountains reduce the rainfall to ten or fifteen inches so that agriculture is marginal and population sparse. Large areas have only five to twenty-five people per square mile and even around Ankara, Kayseri, and Eskisehir, the figure rises to only twenty-five to fifty per square mile. The ancient caravan centers of Konya and Sivas are other cities. The few areas of greater rural concentration represent higher elevations, with more rain, or favorable valleys with irrigation. The removal of the capital to Ankara has focused attention on the interior, but the future of the region is modest. Inner Anatolia was the site of the ancient districts of Phrygia, Galatia, Lycaonia, and Cappadocia.

The Mediterranean region is approximately coextensive with the Taurus and Anti-Taurus mountains. The population is more scanty than in the Pontus area, but concentrations appear in the coastal deltas and in the northwest. The largest city is Adana, Turkey's fourth in size. Seaports have developed at Antalya, Mersin, and Iskenderon. In the extreme southeast is Antakya, the ancient Antioch, on the Orontes River. Classical names along this coast include Lycia, Pisidia, Pamphylia, and Cilicia.

Eastern Anatolia is a complex of rugged mountains and canyons along the headwaters of the Euphrates. Great volcanic peaks are interspersed between snow ranges. Here lies Lake Van, Turkey's largest in size. Population densities are nowhere high, though concentrations of 100 per square mile occur around Erzurum, the largest city, and elsewhere. This area was once the homeland of the Armenians, hence the use of their name for the mountain complex which crosses into Iran.

The Southeastern Anatolian Region is a northward extension of the Syrian-Iraq area, drained by the Tigris and the middle Eu-

The Bosporus links the Black Sea and the Mediterranean and has long been one of the key avenues of history. Turkish control dates from the fifteenth century. (Courtesy KLM, Royal Dutch Airlines.)

phrates. The Mesopotamian steppe extends a few tens of miles across the border, followed by desolate volcanic flows and rolling upland plains around Gaziantep and Diyarbekir. Southwestern Anatolia forms the central part of the so-called Fertile Crescent, deriving its scanty rainfall through a gap in the mountains at the corner of the Mediterranean. With minor exceptions, the population is scanty. The region is the smallest of the seven, and also ranks at the bottom in total population. Kurds and Arabs live alongside ethnic Turks. Nomads move up and down the mountainside with the seasons.

TURKEY'S PROSPECTS

The location of a country is one of the prime factors in its history, politics, and economics. This includes both the position of the territory itself, and of the neighbors around it. So long as Turkey lies astride the Straits, it is inescapably one of the key powers of the Eastern Hemisphere. Few other "narrow seas" are so important as the 180-mile link between the Mediterranean and Black seas. Few other nations face two continents, and not many face two seas. Turkey is both a bridgehead and a passageway.

For five millennia the Straits have been significant, and for five hundred years Turkey has been a major force in the eastern Mediterranean. During the sixteenth century her territory spread into three continents to cover as much as 1.7 million square miles, with a population of forty million. Then came a long decline, which led to a collapse at the end of World War I. The rebirth of Turkey as a modern democratic state is nothing short of a miracle. Even as late as 1920, it seemed likely that most of Turkey would be carved up between France, Italy, Greece, and Russia.

Since a proper democracy requires educated and responsible citizens, Turkey still faces problems, but her progress is remarkable. By 1960 there were over 2.5 million children in school, double the number for 1950. Land redistribution during the 1950's brought the number of farmers who were full-owners to over 75 per cent. Under Turkey's constitution, "Every citizen is born free, and free he lives . . . . All citizens are equal before the law," and "The life, property, honor, and home of each and all are inviolate."

While Turkey faced no pressing boundary problems at the midcentury, this has not always been the case. Border disputes along the 367-mile Soviet frontier date from 1878 when Russia annexed the area of Batumi, previously under Turkish control. During World War I, the Russians invaded Turkey, where they were aided by the Armenians who had long sought independence and thought that they had found a savior in the invading Russian army. When the Russians were forced to retreat, Turkish troops massacred many Armenians and proceeded across the border to reacquire the Kars-Ardahan area, seized by Russia in 1878. Following World War II, the Soviet government sought the return of Kars and Ardahan and did not relinquish their demands until 1953.

The boundary next to the U.S.S.R. cuts through the traditional Armenian homeland. Armenians number some 3 million in all, spread from the Soviet Union into Iraq and Iran. Only in the Armenian Soviet Socialist Republic do they have political autonomy. Turkish persecution of Armenians dates from 1894.

Long discussions at the end of World War I centered around the Turkish province of Mosul, already suspected to contain oil. The final agreement was to place it with Iraq.

Relations with Greece and Bulgaria have also presented problems. In 1950, a quarter of a million Turks were expelled from Bulgaria, while in 1923, 350,000 Turks were repatriated from Greece in return for 1.75 million Greeks who were expelled from Turkey. These forced migrations have deprived Turkey of useful citizens but have left her with a relatively homogeneous population.

In 1939, when France, then holding a mandate over Syria, transferred the Alexandretta or Hatay province to Turkey, they restored the largest block of Turkish people living outside the borders. Ethnic Turks living on the island of Cyprus present a continuing problem.

The most debatable boundary of Turkey has been that in Europe. The present frontier is merely the last of a long series of arbitrary lines drawn across an area where there are neither physical nor ethnic limits. Bulgaria has sought an avenue to reach the Aegean, while Greece has wished to reach the Black Sea and thus encircle Istanbul. The present Turkish limit is that drawn up in Sofia in 1915. This boundary cuts through Thrace, leaving part of it in Greece. Just within the frontier is the one-time Turkish capital at Adrianople, now known as Edirne.

The control of the Dardanelles, the Sea of Marmara, and the Bosporus has long been a political prize. Turkish ownership dates from the fifteenth century, and it has en-

The city of Ankara is a product of the new Turkey. This is a glimpse of Ataturk Boulevard, where winter brings occasional snow. (Courtesy Turkish Information Office, New York.)

abled her to "bottle up" the Black Sea. Not until 1859 was neutral shipping allowed to pass through the Straits without restraint. Transit arrangements are now regulated by the Montreaux Convention of 1936 which gives Turkey the right to fortify the Straits and to close them to all warships when Turkey is at war or threatened. Soviet warships are permitted free passage in peace time, but military vessels of non-Black Sea powers are restricted in their access. Russia has repeatedly pressed for joint administration, but so far without success. The Straits are one of the principal maritime passages of the world, and until 1910 the volume of shipping passing through them exceeded that at Suez.

Russia has so many times invaded Turkish territory or brought political pressure that Turkish animosity is deep. Relations with Britain, France, and Greece, at times have not been much better, but Turkey's orientation toward the Western powers seems assured for the present since it is a loyal member of the North Atlantic Treaty Organization. This is a matter of trade as well as of politics.

Any sketch of international relations must include reference to transit routes which cross Turkey. Some of the ancient caravan ways to China passed through Turkey, and in more modern times, Iran has found a convenient outlet to Europe through Trabzon and the Black Sea. Some of the European merchandise sold in Tehran is trucked overland through Trabzon and Tabriz. Iran also seeks an outlet for its interior oil fields via a new pipeline to the Mediterranean which by-passes the Arab countries.

One railway leads into the Soviet Union, three cross the Syrian frontier, and one goes to Greece, but none lead directly to Iran or Iraq. Railway access to the sea is equally limited. Along the Black Sea, the only terminals are Samsun and Zonguldak; Izmir is the only Aegean port with rail connections, while Mersin and Iskenderon are the sole Mediterranean cities with a railway. Istanbul is linked with western Europe by the route of the famous Simplon-Orient Express, and also with Baghdad via Syria. Road connections are equally limited; Turkey's major foreign contacts are by sea or air.

Turkey needs many commodities from overseas. These include a large array of producer goods. Large scale development projects such as dams and other engineering works or urban rebuilding also call for imported materials. Among the various types of imports, machinery and automobiles lead by far, accounting for nearly a third of the total. Other items high on the list are metals, petroleum, and textiles. To hold foreign trade in balance, Turkey must rely on agricultural products such as cereals, fruits and nuts, raw cotton, tobacco, and on her unique metals, chiefly chromium.

Unfortunately, these exports are not valuable enough, or, rather, the appetite for imports is overly large. Since the late 1940's the balance of trade has been generally against Turkey, often by large amounts. It has therefore been necessary to curtail strictly the import of consumer goods. One measure of the resulting privation in foreign exchange came with the elimination of coffee, long famous as the national drink.

Several countries share in this trade. Germany is usually well in the lead, followed by the United States, the United Kingdom, Italy, and France. Istanbul handles two-thirds of the imports. Izmir leads in exports.

The restriction on the import of consumer goods has had some beneficial results. Elsewhere in Swasia one may readily buy imported foods, such as corn flakes from England, canned fruit from California, jam from Australia, or corned beef from the Argentine. None of these imports are available in Turkish stores; instead there are domestic canned vegetables and fruits. This is not only an indication that all these are produced within the country, but that the domestic market is large and rich enough to support local industry. While limitations on the importation of luxury items may be only uncomfortable, the shortage of foreign exchange for books and magazines is more serious.

In an appraisal of domestic problems made by the International Bank for Reconstruction and Development in 1951, the recommendations gave priority to agriculture, followed by health and education, and transport. Farther down the line, but higher in the government's own programs, are public works, power, industry, and mining. The importance of agriculture is obvious, since it is the major source of national wealth. So too are the needs in public health and the expansion of general education. Turkey already has a fair road network, plus 5,000 miles of railway.

Although Turkey enters the 1960's with acute financial problems, the over-all economic prospects are good. Unlike some of its fortunate neighbors the oil reserves are modest, but Turkey does have coal and iron, and the possibilities of modest industrialization. In agriculture, the prospects are the best in Swasia.

Here as elsewhere, the decisive factor in any geographic evaluation is the people. If Turkey wants to work for a bright future, the possibilities are available.

REFERENCES

General References

Banse, Ewald: DIE TURKEI: EINE MODERNE GEOGRAPHIE. Brunswick: Westermann (1919).

Birge, John Kingsley: A GUIDE TO TURKISH AREA STUDY. Washington: Amer. Council of Learned Societies (1949).

Blanchard, Raoul: "L'Asie Mineure," in GEOGRAPHIE UNIVERSALLE, VIII, ASIE OCCIDENTALE. Paris: Armand Colin (1929), 59–108. [Standard French volume]

Ceram, E. W.: NARROW PASS, BLACK MOUNTAINS: THE DISCOVERY OF THE HITTITE EMPIRE. London: Gollancz with Sidgwick and Johnson (1956).

Diehl, Charles: BYZANTIUM, GREATNESS AND DECLINE. New Brunswick: Rutgers (1957).

Frey, Ulrich: "Turkei and Zypern," in KLUTE HANDBUCH DER GEOGRAPHISCHEN WISSENSCHAFT, VORDER UND SUDASIEN. VI, Potsdam: Akademische Verlagsgesellschaft Athenaion (1937), 1–62. [Standard German volume]

Gurney, O. R.: THE HITTITES. Baltimore: Penguin (1952).

* International Bank for Reconstruction and Development: THE ECONOMY OF TURKEY. Washington: Internat. Bank (1951). [Comprehensive evaluation]

Kinross, J. P. D. B.: "Turkey Today," *Jour. Royal Central Asian Soc.,* XLII (1955), 38–50.

Lewis, Geoffrey: TURKEY, New York: Praeger (1955).

Mantran, R.: TURKEY, New York: Hastings (1958).

Nahai, L.: "The Mineral Industry of Turkey," U. S. Bureau of Mines, *Information Circular* 7855 (1958).

Ravndal, G. Bie: TURKEY, A COMMERCIAL AND INDUSTRIAL HANDBOOK, TRADE PROMOTION SERIES NO. 28. Washington: Govt. Printing Office (1926).

* Republique Turque, Office Central de Statistique: ANNUAIRE STATISTIQUE DE LA REPUBLIQUE TURQUE. (Annual), Ankara and Istanbul: Cumhuriyet Matbaasi. [Detailed statistical data]

Review, Istanbul: Geographical Institute, University of Istanbul. [Annual]

Ryan, C. W.: GUIDE TO THE KNOWN MINERALS IN TURKEY. Ankara: Guzelis Matbaasi (1954).

* Thornburg, Max W., Spry, Graham, and Soule, George: TURKEY: AN ECONOMIC APPRAISAL. New York: Twentieth Century Fund (1949).

Tumertekin, E.: "The Iron and Steel Industry of Turkey," *Econ. Geog,* XXXI (1955), 179–184.

Turkish Information Office, New York City. [Various publications]

U. S. Library of Congress: TURKEY: A SELECTED LIST OF REFERENCES. Washington: Library of Congress (1944).

U. S. Board of Geographic Names: TURKEY. Washington: Dept. of Interior (1949). [Gazetteer]

Istanbul and the Straits

Esmer, Ahmed Sukru: "The Straits: Crux of World Politics," *Foreign Affairs,* XXV (1947), 290–302.

* Howard, Harry N.: "The United States and the Problem of the Turkish Straits," *Middle East Journal,* I (1947), 59–72.

Howard, Harry N.: THE PROBLEM OF THE TURKISH STRAITS. Washington: U. S. Dept. of State (1947).

* Hurlimann, Martin: ISTANBUL. London: Thames and Hudson (1958).

Kucherov, Samuel: "The Problem of Constantinople and the Straits," *Russian Rev.,* VIII (1949), 205–220.

Paddleford, Norman J.: "Solutions to the Problem of the Turkish Straits, A Brief Appraisal," *Middle East Jour.,* II (1948), 175–190.

Shor, Franc: "Robert College, Turkish Gateway to the Future," *Nat. Geog. Mag.,* CXII (1957), 399–418.

Smith, W. E.: "Some Observations on Water Levels and other Phenomena Along the

Bosphorus," *Transactions, Amer. Geophysical Union,* XXVII (1946), 61–68.

Stotz, Carl L.: "The Human Geography of the Dardanelles," *Jour. of Geog.* XXXIV (1935), 173–186.

Stotz, Carl L.: "Life in the Communities Along the Bosphorus," *Jour. of Geog.,* XXXI (1932), 181–192.

Stotz, Carl L.: "Coastal Lands of the Sea of Marmara," *Jour. of Geog.,* XXXII (1933), 305–315.

Ullyott, Philip and Ilgaz, Orphan: "The Hydrography of the Bosporus. An Introduction," *Geog. Rev.,* XXXVI (1946), 44–46.

People

Brice, W. C.: "The Population of Turkey in 1950," *Geog. Jour.,* CXX (1954), 347–352.

Dominian, Leon: "The Peoples of Northern and Central Asiatic Turkey," *Bull. Amer. Geog. Soc.,* XLVII (1915), 832–871.

Louis, Herbert: "Die Bevolkerungskarte der Turkei," *Berliner Geog. Arbeiten,* XX (1940), 1–43.

Pallis, A. A.: "The Population of Turkey in 1935," *Geog. Jour.,* XCI (1938), 439–445.

Sarc, Omer C.: "Growth of the Turkish Rural Population," *Middle Eastern Affairs,* III (1952), 71–80.

Spencer, William: "The Turkish Village," *Landscape,* VII (1958), 23–26.

Taeuber, Irene: "Population and Modernization in Turkey," *Population Index,* XXIV (1958), 101–122.

VonGrunebaum, G. E.: "The Muslim Town," *Landscape,* VII (1958), 1–4.

Agriculture

Aktan, Resat: "Mechanization of Agriculture in Turkey," *Land Economics,* XXXIII (1957), 273–285.

* Erinc, Sirri and Tuncdilek, Necdet: "The Agricultural Regions of Turkey," *Geog. Rev.,* XLII (1952), 179–203.

Hazen, N. Wilhain: "Turkish Agriculture—Changing Agro-economic Policy," *Foreign Agriculture,* IV (1940), 221–272.

* Helburn, Nicholas: "A Stereotype of Agriculture in Semiarid Turkey," *Geog. Rev.,* XLV (1955), 375–384.

Oram, P. A. and Jones, D. K.: "The Agricultural Revolution in Turkey," *World Crops,* VII (1955), 137–142, 278–283.

Stratil-Sauer, G.: "Cereal Production in Turkey," *Econ. Geog.,* IX (1933), 325–336.

Tumertekin, Erol: "Some Observations Concerning Dry Farming in Arid Regions of Turkey," *Rev. of the Geog. Inst., Univ. of Istanbul,* No. 3 (1956), 19–30.

Physical Geography

* Erinc, Sirri: "The Climate of Turkey According to Thornthwaite's Classifications," *Annals Assoc. Amer. Geogs.,* XXXIX (1949), 26–46.

* Erinc, Sirri: "Climatic Types and the Variation of Moisture Regions in Turkey," *Geog. Rev.,* XL (1950), 224–235.

Erinc, Sirri: "Glacial Evidences of the Climatic Variations in Turkey," *Geografiska Annaler,* XXXIV (1952), 89–97.

Lahn, E.: "Seismological Investigations in Turkey," *Bull. Seismol. Soc. Amer.,* XXXIX (1949), 67–71.

Lahn, E.: "Seismic Activity in Turkey from 1947 to 1949," *Bull. Seismol. Soc. Amer.*, XLII (1952), 111–114.

Peterson, A. Delbert and Stepanova, Nina A.: BIBLIOGRAPHY ON THE CLIMATE OF TURKEY. Washington: U. S. Weather Bureau (1957).

* Russell, Richard J.: "Alluvial Morphology of Anatolian Rivers," *Annals Assoc. Amer. Geogs., XLIV* (1954), 363–391.

Tromp, S. W.: "A Tentative Classification of the Main Structural Units of the Anatolian Orogenic Belt," *Jour. of Geol.*, LV (1947), 362–377.

Tumertekin, Erol: "Note on the Rainfall Intensity in Turkey," *Rev. of the Geog. Inst., Univ. of Istanbul* (1954), 183–184.

Tumertekin, Erol: "Study of Droughts in Turkey by Statistical Methods," *Rev. of the Geog. Inst., Univ. of Istanbul* (1956), 47–61.

Tumertekin, Erol: "Dry Months and Dry Seasons in Turkey (according to DeMartonne's and Thornthwaite's formula)," *Rev. of the Geog. Inst., Univ. of Istanbul* (1956), 74–75.

Travel and Description

Bean, G. E.: "Smyrna, Ancient and Modern," *Geog. Mag.*, XVII (1944), 357–363.

Bissing, Ronimund: "Turkey's Freak Valley," *Geog. Mag.*, XIV (1941) 26–33.

Chater, Melville: "East of Constantinople," *Nat. Geog. Mag.*, XLIII (1923), 509–534.

Cornwall, J. H. M.: "A Journey in Anatolia," *Geog. Jour.*, LXIV (1924), 213–222.

Davis, P. H.: "Lake Van and Turkish Kurdistan: a botanical journey," *Geog. Jour.*, CXXII (1956), 156–166.

* Douglas, William O.: "Station Wagon Odyssey: Baghdad to Istanbul," *Nat. Geog. Mag.*, CXV (1959), 48–87.

Hodgkin, Robin: "Climbing in the Taurus Mountains," *Geog. Mag.*, XVII (1945), 510–518.

Kinross, Lord: WITHIN THE TAURUS. London: Murray (1954).

Kinross, Lord: EUROPA MINOR, JOURNEYS IN COASTAL TURKEY. London: Murray (1956).

Kuhn, Ferdinand: "Where Turk and Russian Meet," *Nat. Geog. Mag.*, CI (1952), 743–766.

Louis, Herbert: "Anatolien," *Geog. Zeitschrift*, XLV (1939), 354–376.

Marchionini, Alfred: "Peasants of Anatolia," *Nat. Geog. Mag.*, XCIV (1948), 57–72.

Merriam, Gordon P.: "The Regional Geography of Anatolia," *Econ. Geog.*, II (1926), 86–107.

Morrison, John A.: ALISAR: A UNIT OF LAND OCCUPANCE IN THE KANAK SU BASIN OF CENTRAL ANATOLIA. Chicago: Univ. of Chicago (1939).

Norris, H. T.: "Ibn Battuta's Andalusian Journey," *Geog. Jour.*, CXXV (1959), 185–196.

Nowack, E.: "Journeys in Northern Anatolia," *Geog. Rev.*, XXI (1931), 70–92.

Price, M. P.: "Recent Developments in Anatolia and the Caucasus," *Jour. Royal Central Asian Soc.*, XXXIV (1947), 287–298.

Riboud, Marc: "Cappadocia: Turkey's Country of Cones," *Nat. Geog. Mag.*, CXIII (1958), 122–146.

Stotz, Carl Louis: "The Bursa Region of Turkey," *Geog. Rev.*, XXIX (1939), 81–100.

Williams, Maynard Owen: "Seeing 3,000 Years of History in Four Hours," *Nat. Geog. Mag.*, LIV (1928), 718–739.

Williams, Maynard Owen: "The Turkish Republic Comes of Age," *Nat. Geog. Mag.*, LXXXVII (1945), 581–616.

Wright, Iona and Wright, Densi: "The Black Sea Coast of Turkey," *Geog. Mag.*, XVIII (1945), 118–125.

Wright, D. A. H.: "Trebizond and North-Eastern Turkey," *Jour. Royal Central Asian Soc.*, XXXIII (1946), 121–132.

CHAPTER 11

Arabia

Arabian Journeys
Desert Agriculture
The Bedouin
Cities in the Desert
Highland Oases
The Political Framework
References

ARABIAN JOURNEYS

INTERIOR ARABIA is the only area in the entire Southwest Asian realm which has never been conquered by an outside power. Successive tides of invaders have swept over Turkey, Iran, and the periphery of the Arab world, but they were never able to penetrate the heart of the desert.

In order to visualize the physical landscape of the Arabian peninsula, as well as to see something of its life, this section will be devoted to four journeys.[1] The first might be called a pilgrimage to Mecca, following the caravan road south from Baghdad. The second journey is a trip northward over the ancient incense route from the Hadhramaut coast through the Hejaz. Then follows a journey into the highlands of Yemen. The fourth trip will take us along the thousand mile pipeline road from the Persian Gulf to the Mediterranean.

[1] The author has traveled over portions of each route.

(Opposite) The Holy Mosque of the Prophet at Medina in western Arabia contains the tomb of Mohammed and his daughter Fatima. It is one of the great shrines of Islam. (Courtesy Arabian American Oil Co.)

A Pilgrimage to Mecca

For sixteen hundred years, followers of the Prophet have been making the pilgrimage to Mecca. Five pillars of faith are required of all Moslems: (1) the profession that "there is no god but Allah," (2) prayer five times a day, (3) almsgiving, (4) fasting during Ramadan, the ninth month of the Moslem lunar year, and (5) the pilgrimage to Mecca, an act of piety required of all those who can afford it.

The great pilgrimage or *hajj* occurs after Ramadan. Since the Moslem calendar is variable, once in thirteen years the pilgrimage occurs during mid-summer. During the hajj as many as 200,000 people assemble in Mecca. Two historic overland routes lead to the city across Arabia. When the Ommiad capital was at Damascus, this was the gather-

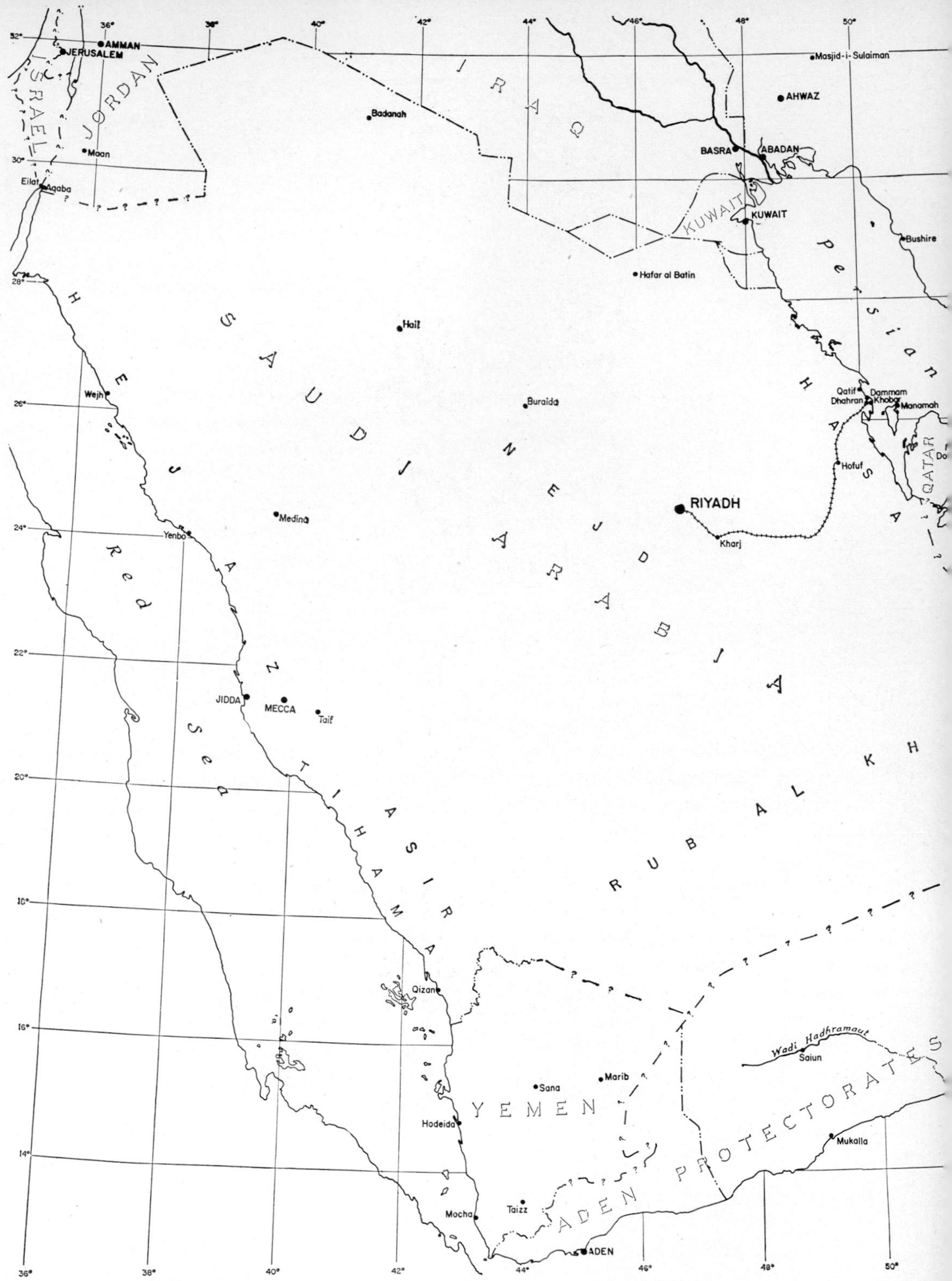

The Arabian Peninsula covers nearly a million square miles and is too large to crowd onto a single page. The scarcity of place names reflects the emptiness of the area. Roads are omitted since most of them are merely desert trails.

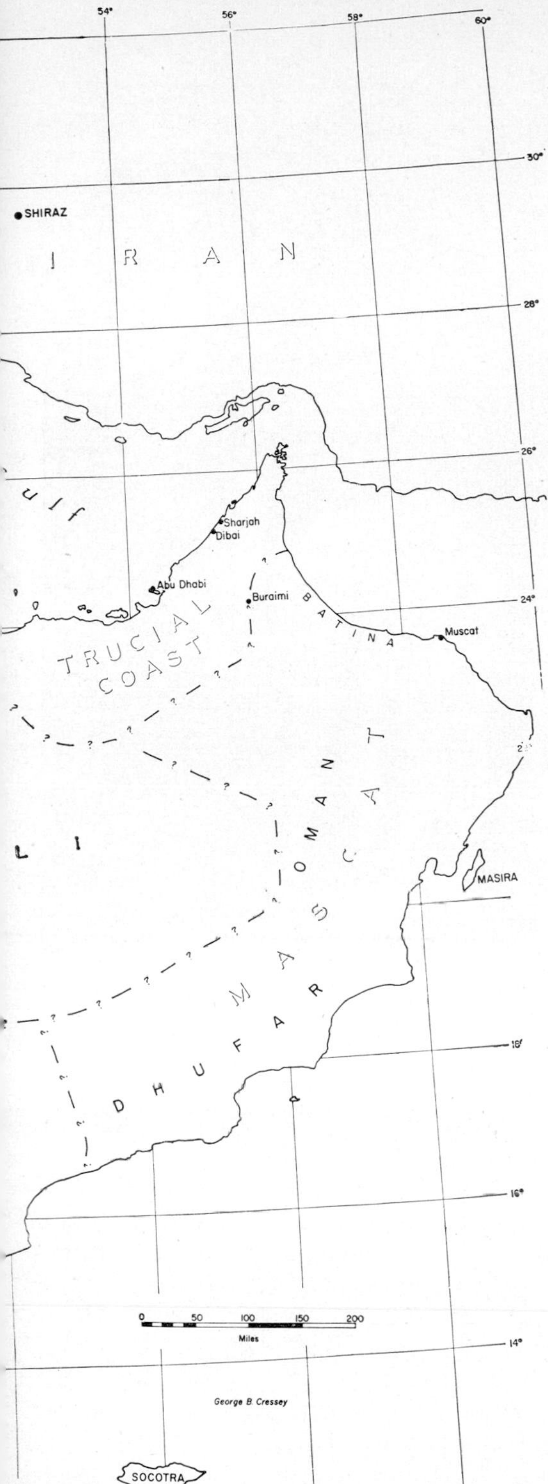

ing place for the western hajj. Later on, when the Abbassides ruled from Baghdad, other caravans started there or, more accurately, from nearby Najaf, one of the sacred cities of Islam since it contains the shrine of Ali, Mohammed's son-in-law; this was the eastern hajj.

In 800 A.D., the favorite wife of Harun-al-Rashid, Queen Zubaydah, improved the Baghdad or eastern road by means of reservoirs and fortified stations at each day's stopping point. This road, known as the Darb Zubaydah served the pilgrims from Iraq, Iran, and as far as Central Asia. Since caravans numbered as many as 5,000 to 10,000 pilgrims, they were veritable moving cities. In 1935, the Darb Zubaydah was opened to motor traffic, and camels fell into disuse. Two decades later the road was nearly abandoned since pilgrims found it cheaper to travel in chartered planes.

Najaf lies a hundred miles south of Baghdad on the edge of the desert just west of the Euphrates. Here travelers leave the last flowing stream, almost the last trees, and the last abundant food supply for the thousand mile journey to Mecca. Now, as earlier, the desert can be treacherous, and one should not venture into it without full preparations and a healthy respect for its hazards.

At first, the road follows the dissected wadi country which slopes toward the Euphrates. Since the rainfall averages but five or six inches, only rarely do the wadis carry any water, but when they do, travel becomes impossible for a day or two. This is rolling countryside, veneered with pebbles that form a desert armor; only here and there have low sand dunes developed. There is no proper road, but rather a wandering set of faint trails that converge toward a favorable wadi crossing or ridge gap but elsewhere

NOTE: Additional material on Arabia is scattered through the pages of the first nine chapters; see especially: Chapter 2, Arab Empires: the Ommiad and Abbasside, page 56, Chapter 3, Sand Dunes, page 83, Chapter 5, The Wadi Hanifa, a Sample from Arabia, page 127, Chapter 8, Oil, page 193. I am indebted to Mr. Don Holm of the Arabian American Oil Company for assistance in the field.

Deep wells supply modern watering troughs which form new focal points for camel herds, enabling them to graze in areas far from natural supplies of water. This mother and baby are in northern Arabia. (Courtesy Trans-Arabian Pipe Line Co.)

fan out in a braided pattern which may be several miles wide.

To say that this is desolate, monotonous country is only part of the story. Desert landscapes tend to be monochromatic and uniform, but there is also charm and variety; the difference between most deserts and some humid lands is that in the former the landscape patterns are cut in larger pieces. But here, a caravan may make its entire day's march across the same featureless countryside: a uniform array of gravel, sand, or bare rock; scattered traces of the same dry grasses; brilliant skies with high clouds; far horizons without landmarks; occasional sheep or camels with their keepers; and a few glimpses of standardized black tents. Not only is there no water, but for tens of miles there may be no gullies or rills to suggest that water has ever flowed over the surface.

Wells are few and deep. The Bedouin knows where he may find moisture by digging into the sand of certain wadi floors, there to tap the "upside down streams," but pilgrim caravans, with their thousands of animals, require larger amounts of water. It was to supply them that Queen Zubaydah provided stone-lined wells and reservoirs. Many wells are 100 and 200 feet deep, as measured by the nearby inclined plane down which the camel or donkey walks while pulling a rope attached to a leather bag. Pebbles dropped down these wells take seven or eight seconds to "touch bottom," and often a dry bottom at that. When brigands fill in one or two wells, travelers are at their mercy.

The reservoirs are known as *birkets* and are commonly a cement- and stone-lined tank, up to a hundred feet across and twenty feet deep, near the center of a playa. They are filled by inflow from the adjacent basin, in places through a special opening, but the water also brings mud, causing many reservoirs to be partly filled with sediment.

Two hundred miles south of Najaf, the Darb Zubaydah enters the sand dunes of the Great Nafud. This irregular sand sea is 300 miles long and in the center measures 150 miles in width. The pilgrim road wisely stays well to the east where the Nafud is divided into three offshoots, none of them more than fifteen miles in width. This is pure and unmitigated desert although even here some extremely xerophytic vegetation manages to find a little moisture beneath the sand.

A traveler of a century ago, William Palgrave, wrote of the Nafud as follows: [1]

> We are now traversing an immense ocean of loose reddish sand, unlimited to the eye, and heaped up in enormous ridges running parallel to each other from north to south, undulation after undulation, each swell one or two hundred feet in average height, with slant sides and rounded crests furrowed in every direction by the capricious gales of the desert. In the depths between, the traveller finds himself as it were imprisoned in a suffocating sandpit, hemmed in by burning walls on every side; while at other times, while labouring up the slope, he overlooks what seems a vast sea of fire, swelling under a heavy monsoon wind and ruffled by a crossblast into little red-hot waves. Neither shelter nor rest for eye or limb amid torrents of light and heat poured from above on an answering glare reflected below.

Roughly halfway from Baghdad to Mecca is the oasis of Hail, one of the half-dozen surprising spots of green within the interior deserts. Hail lies between twin mountain ranges, at an elevation of 2,800 feet. As there are no permanent streams, water must be

[1] William Gifford Palgrave: *Personal Narrative of a Year's Journey Through Central and Eastern Arabia.* London: Macmillan (1873) 62–63.

Sand surfaces with scattered clumps of vegetation are known as *dikaka.* The tents are those of an oil party in the Hasa area. (Courtesy Standard Oil Co. of New Jersey.)

The Rub al Khali is a vast sand waste in which geologists are searching for oil. These four wheel drive trucks are equipped with 16″ x 16″ tires, inflated to ten pounds air pressure. Despite the very low rainfall, few areas are completely without vegetation. (Courtesy Arabian American Oil Co.)

lifted in skin buckets from wells thirty to eighty feet in depth. Several hundred acres are irrigated in this manner. Today this is one of the leading towns of northern Arabia, with a population of some 10,000; like many isolated centers, it has regular air services. The historic importance of Hail is shown by its massive city wall and defending forts. One may well imagine how welcome the oasis proved to be for the hajj pilgrim.

To the south of Hail, the route to Mecca enters the crystalline complex which underlies most of west central Arabia, in which low rugged mountains replace gravel plains and sand dunes. Some areas have lava fields and recent cones. Here and there are small playa basins, wet after the occasional rains. Elevations reach 4,000 feet so that rainfall is slightly higher and evaporation less. The pasture is scanty but adequate for Bedouin shepherds. Hence, when Doughty traveled in this area, he reported the following greeting: "They asked us of the land backward, by which we had passed, 'was the rabia (tender sprigs of herbs) sprung, and which plants for pasture had we seen there?' "

This central area of the peninsula is known as the Nejd and forms the heart of Arabia. To the west is a higher and more mountainous area, parallel to the Red Sea and in part a west-facing escarpment, known as the Hejaz.

Two possibilities were next open to the hajj traveler: either to proceed along the inner side of the Hejaz directly to Mecca or

The holy Kaba in Mecca is the central shrine toward which all Moslems turn in prayer and around which pilgrims must walk seven times starting from the famous black stone set in one corner. (Courtesy Arabian American Oil Co.)

to turn westward by way of Medina and thence along the Red Sea.

Medina, or Al Madinat al Munawwarah, "the city of the enlightened," is the burial place of Mohammed and the scene of his temporal power after the flight from Mecca in 622. Medina receives water from the highlands, and is noted for its excellent dates and vegetables. At one time it had a considerable Jewish population which had fled from Palestine at the time of its conquest by Rome.

In order to accommodate pilgrims on the western hajj, a narrow gauge railway was completed from Damascus to Medina in 1908, but it was torn up during World War I. The city is connected with Jidda, to the south, by a paved road 280 miles long, from whence it is forty-six miles inland to the holy city of Mecca.

The pilgrimage to Mecca, or Mecca al Mukarina, "the blessed," is one of the great unifying factors in Islam, of social as well as spiritual value for it brings together Moslems from all over the world. As Mohammed once said, "The Believers in their love and affection and sympathy for each other are like the body: if one member complains the whole body remains awake and feverish."

The sacred center of Mecca is a cubical building known as the Kaba, forty-five feet high, which stands in the courtyard of the central mosque. It is shrouded in black silk which is embroidered with ornate quotations from the Koran. Set in a lower corner

Bedouin shepherds live in black tents whose locations shift with the availability of pasture. The size of one's tent is measured by the number of supporting poles. (Courtesy Arabian American Oil Co.)

is a sacred black stone, possibly a meteorite, about a foot in diameter.

During the intense heat from April to October, many people in Mecca move eastward into the mountains at Taif. When the lunar calendar brings Ramadan and the ensuing hajj to the mid-summer months, pilgrims find the weather very uncomfortable.

Both Hebrews and Arabs trace their ancestry to Abraham, the former through Isaac, born to Abraham's wife Sarah late in her life, the latter through Ishmael, born earlier by Hagar, the Egyptian handmaiden of Sarah. When Abraham sent Hagar and Ishmael into the wilderness, they nearly perished of thirst until the angel Gabriel directed them to water. According to the Arab version, this occurred at the well of Zamzam within the present site of Mecca. Pilgrims now drink from this well and often take back some of the water to their friends. Queen Zubaydah made several pilgrimages to Mecca, and the city now receives most of its water supply from a spring named after her, the Ain Zubaydah, nine miles away, developed by her engineers.

The Incense Road

The ancient world placed high value on incense, and the Arabs became the great distributors of this and other products from the Indian Ocean. Along with incense, the trade included items such as pearls, gold,

Rice and lamb are standard foods for the desert Arab, often supplemented by dates. Guests are served far more than they can eat, but the surplus is turned over to the women and servants. (Courtesy Trans-Arabian Pipe Line Co.)

ivory from India, tortoise shell, spices from the East Indies, and silk from China.

Frank (or real) incense and myrrh are fragrant gum resins, containing volatile oils secreted from various low trees in southernmost Arabia, chiefly in Dhufar (longitude 55°E) where they grow at elevations of around 2,000 feet in an area unique for its summer rain. The trees are tapped for their sap in a manner similar to tapping of the rubber tree. Some frankincense is still produced in Dhufar, where it sells at $50 to $300 a ton. A few tens of tons reach the United States each year for use as a fixative in perfumes, face powder, and for fumigating preparations. Five to ten tons of myrrh are also used by pharmaceutical and cosmetic companies in the United States.

Incense was employed by the ancients for embalming, on funeral pyres, as a medicine, at weddings, and for religious purposes. The temple at Jerusalem had a holy chamber for storing incense. It is reported that the Temple of Bel at Babylon used thirty tons a year, and that Darius received a similar amount as an annual tribute from the Arabs. Egyptian records tell of trips for incense as early as 2800 B.C.

Three routes were available for transporting these commodities northward. One was by way of the Red Sea, but treacherous coral reefs and the absence of harbors discouraged shipping. Another followed the Persian Gulf and the Euphrates. Most trade moved overland through Arabia by caravans which started near the Hadhramaut coast, continued between the highlands of Yemen and the sand wastes of the Rub al Khali, moved northward through the Hejaz, passed Petra, and ended at Damascus or some Mediterranean port, such as Gaza or Sidon where Phoenicians were distributors as early as 370 B.C. For 500 years, this Incense Route was one of the main highways of the world. Along this inland route arose a series of merchant cities, each an oasis stepping stone, each taking its tribute from passing caravans.

A glimpse of this caravan trade is provided in Genesis XXXVII : 25 where we read of Joseph and his brothers: "Then they sat down to eat; and looking up they saw a caravan of Ishmaelites coming from Gilead, with their camels bearing gum, balm, and myrrh, on their way to carry it down to Egypt." This was the group of Arabs to whom Joseph was sold by his brethren.

Legend even describes the Magi who brought their gold, frankincense, and myrrh to the Christ child, as having come from the Hadhramaut. On their return they were said to have been buried there. Later, the Empress Helena is supposed to have removed their bones to Constantinople, whence they were taken to Milan, and in 1164 to Cologne.

Pliny describes the incense trade nineteen centuries ago as follows:

> The incense, after being collected, is carried on camels backs to Sabota (Shabwa), of which place a single gate is left open for its admission. To deviate from the high road while carrying it, the laws have made a capital offense. At this place the priests take, by measure and not by weight, a tenth part in honor of their god, whom they call Sabis . . . out of this tenth the public expenses are defrayed, for the divinity generously entertains all those strangers who have made a certain number of days journey in coming thither. The incense can only be exported through the country of the Gebanitae, and for this reason it is that a certain tax is paid to the king as well . . . . The whole trade is an immense machine, delicately adjusted. There are certain portions also of frankincense which are given to the priests and king's secretaries and in addition to these, the keepers of it, as well as the soldiers who guard it, the gatekeepers and various other employees have their share as well. And then besides, all along the route there is at one place water to pay for, at another fodder, lodging of the stations, and various taxes and imposts besides; the consequence of which is that the expense for each camel before it arrives at the shore of our sea (the Mediterranean) is 688 denarii; after all this, too, there are certain payments still to be made to the farmers of the revenue of our empire.

Whereas the southern and western shorelines of the Arabian peninsula are desolate, conditions farther inland are more attractive. One such area is the Hadhramaut, northeast of Aden. This is an area of rolling uplands into which have been cut some remarkable canyons, flat-floored and a thousand and more feet in depth. A series of springs at the base of the cliffs supply water for date and coconut groves, wheat, indigo, cotton, and tobacco for water pipes. Some of the tobacco is watered by qanats. Honey is also important.

These oases have given rise to a group of remarkable skyscraper cities. Ancient but modernistic buildings rise to six and eight stories, appearing even higher because of the high ceilings and double windows. This area appears to be as rich in history and romance as any in Arabia, but it is still imperfectly known. According to one Arab legend, Yoktan, "the father of the Arabs," was born here about 2246 B.C. and later moved to Yemen. In the days of the incense trade, the Hadhramaut dominated the southern end of the caravan route. Trade connections in other directions now lead many Hadhramauti to Bombay and Zanzibar and even to Indonesia.

Due west of the Hadhramaut, near the

edge of highland Yemen, is Marib, the next major point on the Incense Road. Marib was the capital of the ancient Sabaean kingdom of Sheba, which flourished from the eighth century B.C. to the sixth century A.D. Whether Sheba ever had a queen who visited Solomon, or whether she came from Ethiopia instead, has not been demonstrated from the limited archaeological evidence, but Marib was once the center of a rich agricultural area. Other city states grew up in nearby parts of Yemen, some of them Jewish and Christian as at Najran, where the palm oases are said to excel all others in beauty.

The high price of incense and other items which passed along the same route led the Romans to launch a campaign to conquer its source in 24 B.C. Ten thousand troops crossed the Red Sea from Egypt and moved south along the Incense Road almost to Marib. The obstacles of hostile tribes, inadequate water, and harsh terrain finally broke Roman courage so that they retreated to Egypt without having reached the frankincense country. Sixteen centuries elapsed before another power, this time the Turks, attempted a major military campaign in Arabia.

Northward and parallel to the Red Sea, the incense caravans usually kept well inland. The coastal plain is waterless and very hot, and although the inland area of the Hejaz is dissected, travel through it is easier. From Najran, most caravans aimed for Mecca or for Taif in the highlands to the east, and on to Medina, Tabuk, and eventually to the vicinity of Petra in what is now southern Jordan.

The Hejaz and its southern continuation in Asir and Yemen is a dissected escarpment, a part of the fault system which accounts for the Red Sea. Great fields of basaltic lava have been poured out along some of these fracture lines. Elevations decrease northward, dropping from about 8,000 feet at Sanaa in Yemen to 7,215 feet at Abha in Asir, 5,785 feet at Taif, and 2,095 feet at Medina; higher elevations occur near each city. Precipitation and vegetation increase with altitude, so that scanty pasture is available for caravans along the inland routes.

The great structures at Petra are carved from the living rock. This is known as the Treasury and was possibly a royal tomb. (Courtesy Jordan Tourist Dept., New York.)

Around Mecca, the rainfall may reach twelve inches; temperatures range from an extreme of 115°F. down to freezing. In contrast, coastal Jidda averages only two and one half inches, but as an illustration of the unusual, Jidda once received four inches in two and a half hours. Plots of cultivated land are present in a few valleys.

Petra has a history as fabulous as that of the Hadhramaut. This was the center of the Nabataeans who emerged in the sixth century B.C. and developed a spectacular city with temples carved in brilliant red sandstones, hidden away in the arid canyons of the broken plateaus south of the Dead Sea. Beginning with the fourth century B.C., Petra was one of the key cities along the Incense Road. This area became known to classical writers, such as Ptolemy, as Arabia Petra; whereas the attractive areas of Yemen and the Hadhramaut were called Arabia Felix, leaving the dry core as Arabia Deserta. The northern extension of the desert, by then under Roman influence, was called Syria.

Arabia Petra is an arid waste, with few agricultural possibilities; the city flourished only through commerce. Not only did Petra command the overland trade from the Hadhramaut, but through its control of Aqaba it also had access to Red Sea shipments.

The Incense Road is no more, but as one travels it today in imagination, it reveals a mixed picture of romance and desolation. Southern and western Arabia have more variety and history than that of the center and north.

A Journey into Yemen

Highland Yemen is unique, for it is the only humid part of the peninsula. As a result, Yemen has almost as many people as all the rest of Arabia together. Few of them are nomads, for this is a land of the farmer. The country has always been difficult to penetrate; even today Yemen remains one of the most inaccessible nations in the world.

The easiest way to enter Yemen is via the Ethiopian Airlines from Africa, or by way of the Saudi Arabian Airlines from Jidda. If one comes overland, there is a rough road from Aden, but border difficulties often make such travel hazardous. The present seaport is Hodeida, but of more historic interest is the ancient port of Mocha, famous in earlier centuries for its coffee trade.

When he visited in 1709, La Roque described the area as follows: [1]

> . . . the city of Moka is not so large as that of Aden, but is of late becoming far more considerable for its commerce, having much lessened the trade of the other. It contains about ten thousand inhabitants . . . . The town is surrounded with walls, after the ancient manner, half stone, half earth: there are four gates, but no ditch, and several towers with guns mounted on some of them . . . Having given an account of the country of Moka and its inhabitants, I must acquaint you, that the country in general is dry, as is almost all the coast of the Red Sea, but the territory of Moka is worse than any of the rest; the water here is very bad, being mixed with saltpeter, and a vast deal of salt: the heat is excessive, and there seldom falls any rain; neither had it rained for two years together before our coming thither. . . . There are several palm trees without Moka, planted among the sands, which they take care to water from wells dug for that purpose: the dates they bear are a very common sort. There is likewise millet, in some places white, and three times as big as ours.

A cross section eastward for 175 miles from the Red Sea coast over the mountains and on to the edge of the desert reveals some of the physical characteristics of Yemen. Such a trip may be made, with difficulty, from Hodeida through Sanaa to Marib.

The coastal plain of western Arabia is known as the Tihama, and the description by LaRoque, just cited, is still true. The Tihama is a sandy waste which measures from thirty to fifty miles in width; in part it

[1] La Roque: *A Voyage to Arabia the Happy*. London. (1726), 84, 192–3.

is an uplifted coastal plain and elsewhere it is a compound alluvial fan. Some runoff from the interior reaches the inner margins of the plain but only three wadis which cross the Tihama occasionally carry water to the sea. Nowhere is there any year-round flow; in fact, nowhere in the entire Arabian peninsula does a single perennial river enter the sea.

Due to the aridity and intense heat, the plain is generally uninhabited. A few sections are cultivated, generally related to a local high water table as in the floor of a broad wadi or to the accumulation of the scanty runoff by means of low check dams. Such diversion structures are swept away by the occasional floods, but on the other hand are valueless in the years without rain. Millet, or dhurra, is the chief crop, with some dates and cotton.

Inland from the Tihama is a dissected foothill zone; then comes the margin of the faulted escarpment, now deeply dissected. Within fifteen miles by road, elevations increase from 1,600 feet to 6,500 feet. Elevation brings a striking change in vegetation. Whereas Hodeida receives some three inches of rain a year, these windward slopes apparently have as much as thirty inches. On these slopes, deserts give way to green forests. This is the principal area for Mocha coffee, still prized around the world.

Yemen is noteworthy for its remarkable terracing, with hundreds of levels on steep mountain sides. The management of soil and water dates back for many centuries and represents a conservationist's dream. Although there are few large canals, small aqueducts distribute water from tiny streams or cisterns known as *birkets.*

The city of Sanaa lies in a basin at 8,000 feet, partly in the rain shadow of higher peaks so that its precipitation is about fifteen inches. Like most highlands in the tropics, Sanaa enjoys a delightful climate. The range from the coolest to the warmest months is from 59°F. to 68°F., with the extremes of 17°F. and 82°F. As a result, the Sanaa basin is an immense garden, with dhurra millet, wheat, barley, and deciduous fruit trees. The city, formerly the capital, is noteworthy for its impressive architecture. The Imman now rules from Taizz.

Farther east, with decreasing rainfall and gradually decreasing elevations, cultivation fades out as one approaches the interior deserts. The city of Marib, already mentioned in connection with the Incense Road, was once the site of one of the great dams of antiquity, which was a mile long and fifty feet high. The dam, built between 1000 and 700 B.C., was destroyed through unknown causes in 542 B.C. In the absence of stored water, cultivation is now limited to scattered attempts at dry farming. According to the Koran, "The people of Saba had beautiful gardens with good fruits. Then the people turned away from God, and to punish them, He burst the dam, turning the good gardens into gardens bearing bitter fruit."

Southern Arabia is the only highland area in Swasia without the third landscape color, the white of winter snow. One reason is that the climatic regime results in summer monsoon rain in the highlands, in contrast to the winter maximum in the surrounding lowlands. But Sanaa does have rare frosts, and snow is occasionally reported in the mountains.

Although Yemen's landscape is very different from that of Saudi Arabia, it has close cultural ties with the rest of the peninsula. This is Arabia Felix, the happy land. Yemen probably represents one of the fountains of Arabic culture.

Across the Desert along Tapline

Our fourth trip starts along the Persian Gulf, in the province of Hasa. Lacking the rich history of southern and western Arabia, the east was until recently relatively empty. Prior to the discovery of oil, settlement centered around the harbors of Kuwait and Bahrein, with their dhow traffic and pearling, and the palm and rice oases of Hofuf and Qatif. The discovery of oil has brought a dramatic social and economic revolution with the emergence of the exotic cities of Dhahran, Dammam, and Khobar and the nearby American air base.

Hasa is the principal section of Arabia which has natural artesian supplies of water. The sedimentary formations of the central peninsula dip gently eastward, so that some of the scanty intake along the Tuwaiq Escarpment emerges near the Persian Gulf. Both Hofuf and Qatif have flowing springs, in places with such an abundant supply that the area has become a swamp. Offshore Bahrein also receives artesian water. As a result of good water and high temperatures, eastern Arabia is noted for its excellent dates.

The Trans-Arabian Pipe Line, known as Tapline, was completed in 1950 in order to connect the oil fields of Ghawar and Abqaiq with the Mediterranean port of Sidon, 1,068 miles to the northwest. Along most of the distance there is a modern gravel highway. Just as the Incense Road brought legendary treasures to the Mediterranean, in some cases to the ancient port of Sidon, so Tapline now carries "liquid gold" to the Western world. Since there are no water holes on this route, no camel caravans ever followed it; neither is there any present-day bus service, but by courtesy of Tapline and its associate company Aramco, one may drive across the heart of Arabian aridity. The oil requires eleven days from well to terminal tank farm, but the trip by car can be made in half that time.

Five pump stations constitute modern oases: Nariyah, Qaisumah, Rafha, Badanah, and Turaif. There is no surface water, so that to supply the stations, dozens of deep wells have been dug. In many cases, however, the hardness reaches 1,500 parts per million so that water for drinking must be distilled. Thanks to modern transport, each station is supplied with chilled beef from Australia, canned food and frozen vegetables from America, and fresh fruit flown in from Beirut; each station also makes its own ice cream.

Tapline crosses empty country with no indigenous population, but one stipulation in the contract provided that the company should supply water to any passing Bedouin and his camels. The scanty vegetation is marginally adequate for grazing but, in the absence of water, flocks could not take advantage of it. Word travels rapidly in the desert, and in the course of a year, one station was called on to supply water to 12,000 Bedouin, 20,000 camels, and 40,000 sheep. Some tribes came from Syria and Iraq, as far as 500 miles away. In one June, Turaif had 2,000 tents with about six people each, 25,000 camels, and several thousand sheep and goats; this occurs only in summer for during the winter camels may even go entirely without water.

New government wells in northern Arabia have increased the grazing area. While camels in summer require water once a week, or at least once in ten days, sheep must be watered every day or two so that the radius of their grazing ground is limited. In a few cases, the owners of sheep own trucks which carry water to areas without wells, a case of bringing the mountain to Mohammed. Camels greatly outnumber sheep and goats; the reverse of conditions in the slightly more humid Syrian desert. But as trucks replace camels for transport, sheep become more profitable.

Each pump station employs 100 to 300 Arabs and some two dozen Americans or Europeans. Around each station, a new town with a *suq* or market place to supply the district has developed; thus Badanah grew from nothing to 3,000 in five years.

With the introduction of cash economy,

The city of Qatif lies in one of several date palm oases in eastern Saudi Arabia, watered by artesian springs. (Courtesy Arabian American Oil Co.)

life has been revolutionized for the Bedouin who have "come to town." The variety of merchandise available in the tiny mud-walled shops is amazing. In one store were products from fourteen countries: corned beef from the Argentine; tomato paste from Italy; dried milk from Holland; sardines from Norway; tuna and enameled ware from Japan; soap and pineapple from Singapore; canned okra and other vegetables from Syria; jam, butter, and cheese from Australia; mosquito spray, orange juice, flour, and vegetables from the United States; cocoa, biscuits, detergents, and steel wool from the United Kingdom; matches made in Kuwait; primus stoves from Sweden; dishes from Czechoslovakia; and fresh bananas from Lebanon. Elsewhere, one may find cloth from India, "sugar loaf" cones of sugar from Belgium, merchandise from Germany, and goods from half the world. It is obvious that countries which export oil have plenty of foreign exchange.

For the most part, this is a monochromatic gravel desert, remarkably smooth and generally free from shifting sand dunes except along the wadis. Large areas show no trace of running water, and even the larger valleys carry water only once or twice a year. Many areas have a relief of only twenty-five feet in a square mile, so that slopes are gentle. In a car equipped with super-balloon tires, one may drive across country almost everywhere. Many surfaces are blanketed by a veneer of angular but shiny pebbles of chert or lava, from one to four inches in size. In the absence of running water or the effective work of the wind, these plains may be of considerable geological antiquity.

Toward the Persian Gulf there are flat areas with no effective runoff. Some have developed a salt-crusted playa kuown as a *sabkha,* across which travel is easy during the dry season but impossible when wet. Elsewhere lava flows or limestone lie near

Cultivated land in the Qatif oasis of eastern Arabia is supplied by a counterbalanced water lift known as the *shadoof*. (Courtesy Arabian American Oil Co.)

the surface, both capable of absorbing the light rainfall without yielding any surface runoff. In some places the limestone bedrock has a very hard caliche-type veneer known as a *duri* crust.

The rainfall is scanty and erratic. In 1955, Turaif recorded 1.77 inches scattered through sixteen days, but only five days had as much as a tenth of an inch. During the same year, Rafha had 1.83 inches, but only on a few occasions did the periods of rainfall coincide with those at Turaif. At Quaisumah the rainfall amounted to eleven inches in one winter season but dropped to less than one inch the next. Snow is rare although it has been known to occur.

The natural cover of vegetation is obviously sparse. Seen from the air, there is rarely a suggestion of greenness, but after the rains, one may look along the surface and find a greenish caste to the scattered grass and brush. A suggestion to the government that a helicopter service might locate fresh grazing areas was met with the reply that the Bedouin spread the word faster. So scanty is the pasturage that Bedouin seldom keep their tents in the same position for more than a few weeks. Although this is truly a desert, it is well to add that no part of Arabia is totally without life.

In the midst of this empty land and in the Rub al Khali as well, it is astonishing to find in many areas paleolithic spear points, scrapers, and other artifacts in abundance. All across Arabia are signs of ancient cultures, in some cases accompanied by little-known inscriptions.

The trip from the Persian Gulf to the Mediterranean may be divided into three sections. In the east the route stays near the coast as far as Nariyah, crossing a succession of low-shifting dunes, silt and salt sabkhahs, and soft Tertiary formations. The central section is largely made up of the rolling

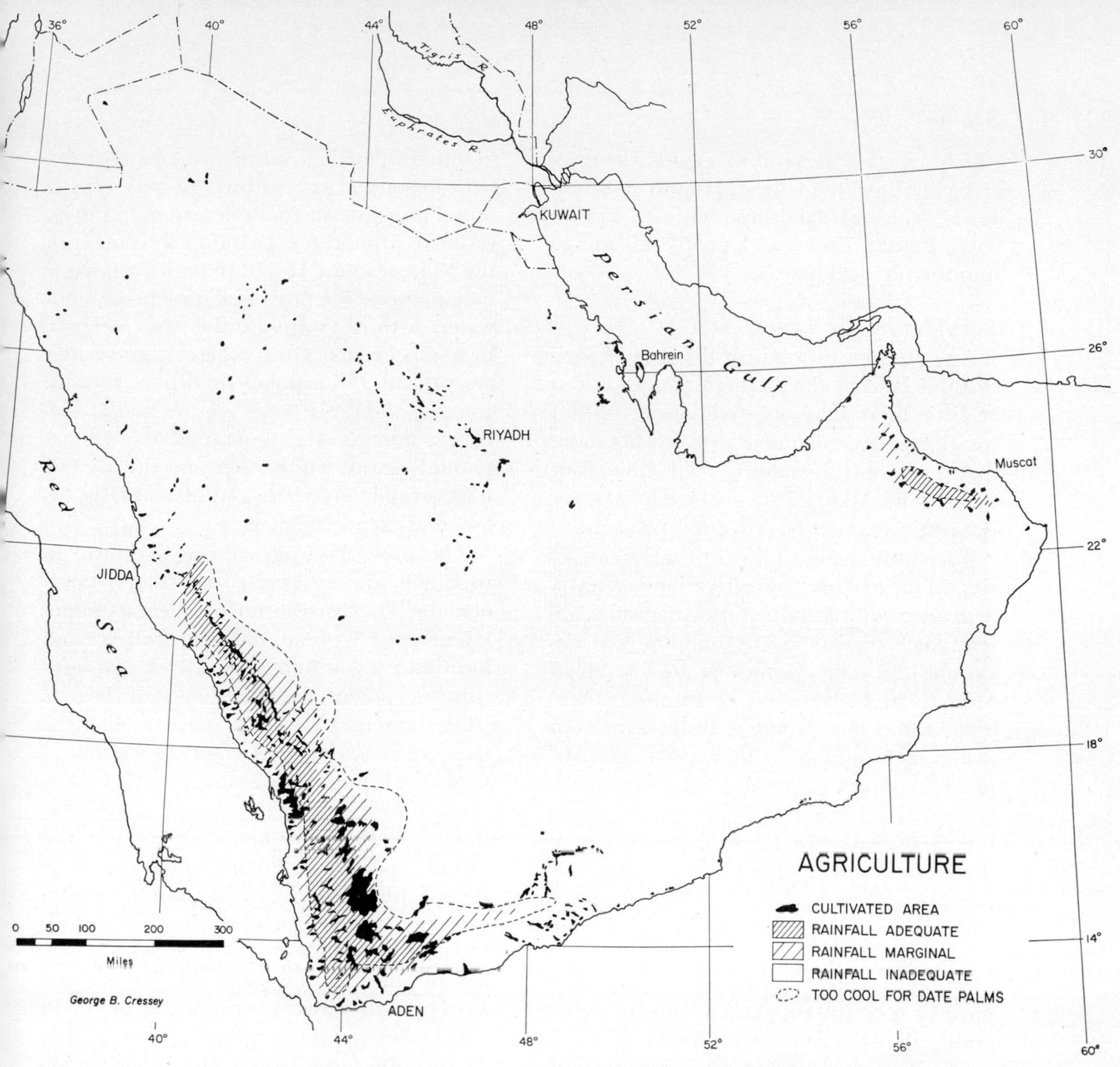

Only a small fraction of Arabia is cultivated; either tiny oases supplied by springs and wells or highland areas with adequate rainfall. This original map is based largely on U. S. Geological Survey–Saudi Arabian Government topographic maps, in turn derived from aerial photography.

gravel areas previously described. After the pipeline leaves Saudi Arabia, it crosses the hilly lands of Jordan, Syria, and Lebanon, in part underlain by rough lava flows.

DESERT AGRICULTURE

THE INTERCONTINENTAL planes which fly from Cairo to India make a transect across central Arabia. From heights of 20,000 feet, the traveler looks down for hour after hour on land apparently devoid of life. The panorama unfolds so rapidly that one cannot visualize the monotony experienced by the camel caravan traveling across gravel surfaces, dunes, or lava fields.

Only large features, such as an oasis, stand out in the desert; the few settlements appear so small that one may easily overlook them. If there are towns, and there are some which serve as radio control points, the traveler is not aware of them. Almost nowhere is the cultural landscape visible. Trails, tents, houses, flocks, and people all merge into the physical base.

Farmers in the Desert

Any attempt to total up the area of agricultural land of the Arabian peninsula can be little more than approximation. Within Saudi Arabia the figure is probably not more than 1 per cent. By adding the highlands of Yemen and Masqat, the average for the entire peninsula may be raised to 2 per cent.

Agricultural land falls into three categories. In the first, settled cultivation is directly dependent on rainfall, and nomadism is absent. Such conditions are found only at elevations of a mile or more in the interior of Masqat, in Yemen, and in adjoining Asir. The second type is one with moderate but insufficient rainfall so that cultivation depends in part on diverted runoff from nearby mountains. These conditions surround the highlands just listed, for nowhere else is there sufficient rainfall for dependable streams.

Oases make up the third category. In them, rainfall is so limited and evapotranspiration so high that all of the water deficit must be specially supplied. Cultivation generally depends on wells where there is ground water within fifty feet of the surface, or where there are springs. Surface runoff is so undependable that few oases can safely count on transitory streams. The introduction of modern pumps enables deep-seated water to be tapped, but too often this involves drawing on supplies which have required millennia to accumulate. Furthermore, when underground water remains stagnant for long periods, it is often too high in dissolved minerals to be safe for irrigation purposes.

The distribution of oases follows three patterns. One type lies near the base of the mountains, farther out than the partly rainfed category of agriculture. Another type is found near intermediate elevations in the interior, as around the Tuwaiq Escarpment in the Nejd or in the Hejaz. In both areas a few qanats, or karez, are used to tap groundwater. A third group are the oases of Hasa, near the Persian Gulf, where large springs are present and artesian conditions prevail. In most of Arabia, oases are few and far between. Some cover thousands of acres, as around Hofuf, while others are tiny. A lost pilot would surely run out of fuel long before finding a settlement.

The pattern of agriculture is shown on page 309, and is reflected on several kinds of maps. The distribution of sedentary population, page 37, is an obvious parallel. Land form and vegetation maps also reveal agricultural potentials. The map of brown, white, green, and black, page 8, likewise shows the scattered pattern of cultivation.

Arabia is hot. All lowland areas have daytime summer air temperatures which may reach 120°F. while sand temperatures rise to 170° and 180°F. Thanks to the dryness of the air, nights are often 40° cooler, with an extreme recorded range during twenty-four hours from a high of 113°F. down to 57°F. Several stations along both the Red Sea and Persian Gulf coasts experience day and night average temperatures of 95°F. from June to August. In these latter situations, the humidity is also high so that wet and dry bulb temperatures are only a few degrees apart. As a result, the discomfort index reaches figures scarcely duplicated anywhere in the world. During August, the temperature of the water in the Persian Gulf is seldom below 90°F. Winters are short and cool rather than cold.

Arabia is dry. For much of the year the winds are northerly and bring little moisture. In winter, a few cyclonic depressions cross the area but they seldom produce much rain. Summer convection fails to yield rain

Dates are gathered by men who climb the palm tree and lower the dates in woven baskets. This view is at Kharj near Riyadh. (Courtesy Standard Oil Co. of New Jersey.)

because the cloud base is too high. The highlands of the southwest and southeast are an exception, for they intercept a little summer monsoon rain. Except in the mountains, few areas receive more than five inches a year.

The resulting handicaps of agriculture are revealed in the map of potential evapotranspiration, page 108, and precipitation, page 105. Potential evapotranspiration is primarily an index of solar energy; it thus indicates the amount of evaporation plus transpiration which would occur if there were always an adequate water supply. Megathermal conditions, with amounts in excess of forty-five inches, prevail over all of lowland Arabia. Along the southern coasts of the Red Sea and in the eastern Rub al Khali, the figure exceeds sixty-five inches. Mesothermal conditions, with thirty-inch evaporation figures, are found only with elevation or in the Syrian extension of the desert; these are the only areas where dry farming is to be considered.

Water deficit is a measure of drought; and in Arabia, it is both intense and persistent. The map pattern resembles that for evapotranspiration. Deficits reach a maximum of seventy-five inches along the Tihama coast of Yemen and exceed fifty inches in all of eastern Arabia. Even in highland Yemen, the deficiency is twenty inches.

In a very rough sense, these figures suggest the large amounts of water which must be added by irrigation in order to raise a crop.

In other words, allowing for seasonal conditions, irrigation must supply the difference between five inches of rainfall and evaporation requirements ten times as great.

Arabian agriculture suffers under these climatic restrictions. Irrigated cultivation is centered on tree crops (such as dates, deciduous and citrus fruits, or coffee) and on grains, notably millet, wheat, and rice.

Dates are the mainstay of the oasis dweller, both for food and for commerce. Dates are to him what the camel is to the Bedouin. Mohammed is reported to have said "Honor your paternal aunt, the date palm. I call it your paternal aunt because it was created out of the earth left over after the creation of Adam." Dates supply more food per acre than any other Arabian crop, and palms occupy nine-tenths of the irrigated area. Date trees are a main source of landed wealth, and a small cluster of trees commonly provides the chief income of a villager. More than seventy varieties are grown, most of them ripening in August or September.

New groves are established by planting the suckers or shoots which grow out from the trunk of the female tree; they then bear fruit by the eighth year and may live for a century. Only female trees bear dates, and the blossoms must be fertilized by hand. Since dates contain more than 50 per cent sugar, they are self-preserving.

Date palms grow only below elevations of 4,500 feet and are tolerant of brackish water. In addition to their value as food, the palm tree provides firewood; construction materials for bridges, houses, and furniture; and fibers for cordage and matting. Not the least of its advantages is the provision of shade in the blazing desert.

The oasis of Hasa is especially famous, chiefly for the dates known as *khulas,* a term which may be translated as "quintessence." More than 2 million trees grow here, and the harvest weighs 125 million pounds. The average tree yields sixty pounds, with some trees bearing as much as 400 pounds in a season.

When its oil is gone, Arabia may have to return to agriculture. It is doubtful whether the nomad has much future, and there seems to be only a limited resource base for industry. The problem during the remainder of the twentieth century is to use the country's exhaustible wealth in order to develop a permanent one capable of yielding a steady income. This involves long-range plans for the development of water. Deep wells may prove only a palliative, for their aquifers recharge very slowly. Reservoirs are feasible in several valleys in the Hejaz and Asir province of Saudi Arabia, and also in Yemen and Oman. To reduce evaporation losses, these should have as limited a surface area in proportion to volume as possible. Small check and diversion dams may divert flood waters in numerous wadis, but they depend on transitory rains. Better management will enable present supplies to be used more widely. In only a few places, however, are there significant areas of good, unused soil where "the desert may blossom as the rose."

Three Oases

Three oases deserve attention; the area around Kharj near Riyadh, Hofuf in the Hasa area of the east, and the Hadhramaut in the Aden Protectorate. All of them are old, and each is distinctive.

The Kharj area lies near the Wadi Hanifa, already described on page 127. Kharj depends for most of its water on four remarkable karst sink holes, about 300 feet in diameter and 400 feet deep, from which as much as 23,000 gallons per minute are lifted sixty to eighty feet by modern pumps. Earlier, donkey or camel lift was employed.

Some of the land has been cultivated for four centuries, and there are thousands of graves from still earlier settlements, some of them thought to be Christian. Modern developments date from 1942, with the com-

Each Arabian village has its market place, the focal point for tribesmen and city merchants. This is the central square at Hofuf, near the Persian Gulf. (Courtesy Arabian American Oil Co.)

bined assistance of the United States, Aramco, and the Saudi government. Three thousand acres are irrigated from the karst pits, with a network of canals which measures a hundred miles. In addition, other areas are supplied by 100 wells, 50 to 150 feet deep. Wheat makes up the largest acreage, followed by vegetables, melons, alfalfa, and dates. The alfalfa is given four inches of water twice a month and yields ten cuttings a year. In addition, there are dairy herds which supply 200 gallons of milk a day to Riyadh.

Salt accumulation is a serious problem in the Kharj area, and considerable areas once irrigated have been abandoned. One difficulty is that the irrigation water is initially high in soluble materials. Deep drainage is called for to lower the water table.

Hofuf is the center for the largest oasis in Arabia, and its 30,000 acres place it among the largest in the world. The area is also known as Hasa, but that term is more commonly applied to the entire Eastern Province.[1]

The city of Hofuf lies fifty miles from the Persian Gulf and seventy-five miles south of Dhahran. The oasis area measures some fifteen by ten miles over-all, and includes sev-

[1] I am indebted to Mr. F. S. Vidal for guidance in the field. Some of the following material is based on his volume entitled *The Oasis of Al-Hasa*. Dhahran: Arabian American Oil Co. (1955).

eral separate areas of cultivation. Climatic conditions are similar to the rest of eastern Arabia: four inches of rain, high summer temperatures, and generally high humidity. Hofuf experiences dense fog and 100 per cent humidity several times a year.

Beneath the area are artesian aquifers, from which water rises to the surface in more than fifty springs, or *ain*. The total discharge amounts to 150,000 gallons per minute, and four springs each yield at least 20,000 gallons per minute. In addition there are a few drilled artesian wells, commonly under 600 feet in depth.

Life in the oasis is tied to the springs and canals much as the nomad is tied to his camel. Two kinds of gardens are distinguished, those with gravity, or *saih* flow and those where water must be lifted, known as the *mugharraf* type. The former are commonly devoted to palms and rice, while the latter fields, generally smaller in size, raise vegetables and alfalfa.

Gardens supplied by gravity canals are entitled to "drink" water at certain carefully regulated times as specified in the deed. Any surplus water drains off into a secondary canal to supply fields downslope. Gardens toward the end of the line are spoken of disdainfully as drinking twice-used water; due to the increasing saline content dissolved from the fields above.

Chemical analyses show that water from one spring, with an initial content of 1,247 parts per million, increases in salinity as it passes through field after field until it reaches 4,120 parts per million fifteen miles away and is then almost useless for irrigation. For this reason, where possible, fresh water is not mixed with drainage water. These canals eventually lead to a sabkhah or variable salt lake whose only outlet is via evaporation.

Much water is lost by seepage from unlined canals, and custom has led to miles of unnecessary ditches. Farmers also tend to overirrigate. Some areas near the springs become waterlogged due to the high water table. With proper management, it might be possible to increase the irrigated area by 50 per cent.

In the pump supplied or mugharraf type, water is used as needed, so that less is wasted. Two devices are used to lift the water; one operated by hand, the other by donkey power. The former is used for short lifts, as along a canal, and involves a horizontal beam, weighted at one end and with a pole or rope and having a scoop at the other. The device is known as the *shadoof*.

Donkey lifts are widely used. From four to six pulleys are fastened above the well, with a rope over each wheel. At one end is a skin bucket, or one made from the inner tube of a truck tire, with a donkey at the other. To ease the animal's task, there is commonly an inclined plane down which he walks during the lifting cycle. The water to be lifted may equal a quarter of the animal's weight. In the absence of lubrication, each wheel emits a screeching sound, and it has been humorously suggested that the owner of a donkey lift can tell from a distance whether or not each animal is working.

Dates are the main product of the Hofuf oasis and are reported to be the best around the Persian Gulf. In addition to their economic return, the date gardens provide welcome shade. People who have no palm trees lack social prestige; some desert Bedouin groups own small groves primarily so that they may gather for social purposes.

Crops of a wide variety are raised. Among fruits, these include figs, pomegranates, peaches, apricots, citrons, lemons, and limes. A variety of vegetables are grown between the palm trees. Cotton is not important, but some is grown. Cereals, none of which are significant, include sorghum, wheat, rice, millet, barley, and a little corn.

On the basis of local estimates, Vidal considers that the oasis has a total population of

The deep canyons of the Hadhramaut contain numerous skyscraper cities. This is Yashbum in the Western Aden Protectorate. (Courtesy Public Relation Department, Aden.)

160,000, or a density of 2,300 people per square mile, counting both village and country people. The people are about equally divided between Sunnites and Shiites, although they do not commonly live in the same village.

The Wadi Hadhramaut is one of the most remarkable canyon oases in the world. In cross section, conditions are the reverse of normal. Near its source in south central Arabia, the valley is forty miles wide. Downstream, it narrows to a vertical walled canyon four miles wide, while at the point where it enters the Arabian Sea, under the name of the Wadi Maseila, it is some 200 yards in width. Through most of its 300-mile course, the sheer valley walls rise a thousand feet and more above the flat floor. On either side is a barren, windswept plateau known as the *jol,* a mile above sea level. Only at times does the wadi carry a continuous stream, and the oases depend on wells or on springs at the base of the cliffs.

The term Hadhramaut is variously used. In a strict sense, it refers only to the upper half of the valley floor, dotted with oases. In broader terms, the word refers to much of the Eastern Aden Protectorate in the hinterland of Mukalla. This was once within the Himyaritic kingdom of antiquity, whose undeciphered inscriptions are carved on many ruins.

Hidden away in these ramifying canyons

This is a member of the Arab police force known as the Hadhramaut Legion, with his daughter. (Courtesy Public Relation Department, Aden.)

are a series of remarkable oasis cities. Harold Ingrams describes his initial approach as follows: [1]

On a ledge we got our first view of the valley. Nine hundred feet below the perpendicular cliffs ran a river of green date palms mingled with the lighter green of the 'elb trees and the cultivation. At first we saw no houses; then out of the pale brown, sandy cliffs appeared great castles, so harmonizing with their background as to be invisible at first, huddling at the foot of the opposite cliff as though they wanted to climb the wall. Several towns lay below us, . . . their high buildings like fantastic fairy-book palaces raised pile on pile.

[1] Harold Ingrams: *Arabia and the Isles*. London: Murray (1942). 159. Quoted by permission.

The leading towns are Shibam, Tarim, and Saiun; each a collection of hundreds of skyscrapers, modern enough at a distance to be of tomorrow, yet centuries old. Six stories is an average height, but they appear twice that height because each floor has a double set of windows. Even more dramatic is the presence of automobiles, electricity, and, in some homes, luxurious appointments which would be acceptable in the best Western circles. This is a reflection of the extent to which many people of the Hadhramaut have traveled abroad.

The Hadhramaut is traditionally rich. Its wealth began in the days of the incense trade, and it has always cultivated relations with the outside world. Emigration is characteristic, and each settlement has its overseas

SAUDI ARABIAN POPULATION [1]

Province	*Nomads*	*Towns*	*Total*
Hejaz	700,000	400,000	1,100,000
Tihama Asir	200,000	100,000	300,000
Sirah Asir	350,000	650,000	1,000,000
Nejd	1,200,000	800,000	2,000,000
Hasa	200,000	100,000	300,000
Others	350,000	150,000	500,000
	3,000,000	2,200,000	5,200,000

[1] Unsubstantiated magazine data published in Riyadh, 1958.

colony. The largest group lives in Java, where 70,000 people send back large remittances or bring back their wealth when they return to retire. Other Hadhrumi live in Singapore, Zanzibar, and East Africa. When these remittances fail and local rainfall drops off at the same time, or when overseas nationalism causes doors to be closed, local distress may be acute since the area depends on imported food. The people say of themselves that their only industries are tea drinking, marrying, and making poetry; unfortunately these pursuits require money and three-quarters of the population seem to have a dislike of manual labor.

Around each settlement are irrigated areas of palm trees and small plots of grain and vegetables, but there is seldom enough water to make these areas large or dependable. Five hundred engine-powered wells now draw on water in the wadi gravels. As elsewhere, rainfall is low and capricious, and even though the surrounding plateau

These Bedouin herdsmen look after the King's camels which graze in the vicinity of Jauf in central Arabia. (Courtesy Standard Oil Co. of New Jersey.)

Bedouin hospitality is proverbial; coffee is served in small cups to every passerby. Tents have a curtain to separate the men's area from that of the women. This scene is at Abqaiq in the Hasa district. (Courtesy Standard Oil Co. of New Jersey.)

reaches elevations of several thousand feet, it receives little precipitation.

Crops in the Hadhramaut include wheat, corn, millet, indigo, tobacco for water pipes, sesame, dates, coconuts, cotton, and honey.

THE BEDOUIN

THE REPORTED POPULATION of the Arabian peninsula exceeds 12 million. About half live in Saudi Arabia with most of the others in Yemen. There is no way of knowing how many are farmers, how many live in cities, and how many are nomads. It is doubtful whether more than 2 million Saudi are urban dwellers, even including towns, and the number of nomads may not be much larger, perhaps around 3 million. Since the area over which the Bedouin may roam takes in most of the country, there is a tendency to exaggerate their importance. There is no question, however, that they constitute a dramatic and significant element in the cultural landscape, one whose importance was doubtless greater in the past. The importance of the Bedouin, even today, is shown by the fact that Arabian livestock surpasses date palms as a source of wealth.

The Arabs divide themselves into two main categories. Those who dwell in permanent houses, that is to say the townsfolk, are

The camel is the ship of the desert; no other domestic animal is so well adapted to life in arid lands. Arabian camels are all of the one-humped dromedary variety. (Courtesy Arabian American Oil Co.)

the *hadhar*. Those who dwell in black, haircloth tents and live a nomadic existence are the *badia;* from this comes our word Bedouin. In the latter group are numerous seminomads who either have houses in a town or camp near its borders in summer, and during winter move a hundred miles or less into the desert. There is a further distinction between the proper Bedouin, who have their own camels and range widely, and tribes which care for sheep which may belong to wealthy town dwellers or even to other Bedouin tribes. Camels can survive longer periods without water than sheep and thus have a longer grazing radius.

The proper Bedouin breed only camels and regard themselves as the salt of the earth. This is particularly true of the *Sharif* tribes who claim descent from the Patriarchs Qahtan and Ishmael. The Anaiza tribes of central Arabia consider themselves to be the aristocrats of the desert, and in their numbers are included the rulers of Saudi Arabia, Kuwait, Bahrein, and Qatar. Other Sharif tribes are the Ruwala, Shammar, Harb, and Mutair.

Formerly, there were established areas for each tribe and its subdivisions; today, many groups are found hundreds of miles away from their traditional area. These are clearly decades of major sociological as well as economic change, but tribal animosities still run deep and change slowly.

Bedouin have a remarkable ability to find their way across the desert. There is an Arab saying that a Murra tribesman can be taken on a three-day journey across trackless country, blindfolded, and then told to bury a coin in the sand at night. A decade later he will be able to return and locate his coin.

Bedouin hospitality is proverbial. A stranger will always find a welcome, and may even remain for three days before revealing his objective. When important guests are to be received, the women, who are behind a curtain at the other end of the tent, roast some coffee beans on a long-handled pan held over a fire of desert brush or camel dung. The beans are then pounded to powder in an iron mortar. The coffee is mixed with cardamom seeds and freshly brewed in a small pot. Any coffee left over after the guests have been served is put in a larger pot for use later in the day, and coffee which remains after that is poured into a still larger pot for the women's use the following day. The coffee is drunk from small cups, a thimble-full at a time. After several rounds of coffee, heavily sweetened tea is served in small glasses and then more coffee. If this is a formal affair, the termination of the visit will be politely signalized by passing around a small charcoal brazier on which incense is burning, or drops of perfume may be placed on one's hands.

Some of the changes of the midtwentieth century are described by H. St. John Philby, one of the most widely traveled Europeans in Arabia. He writes as follows: [1]

> It is a remarkable fact that, while the Arab undoubtably owes his traditional fame and pride of race to his Bedouin ancestors, the contemporary descendants of the latter are disliked and despised by their kinsmen of the towns and the borderlands, who boast inordinantly of their hybrid "civilization" largely derived from alien sources. The Bedouin themselves are by no means without blame in the matter: in the old days they made themselves hated and feared as potential enemies of unlimited rapacity, while today they tend to fawn on the idle rich, serving as drawers of water and hewers of wood. Yet, to my mind, one of the saddest aspects of modern Arabia is the short shrift it allows to desert virtues, and the acquiescence of the desert men in a fate which will place them some day in the same category as the Red Indians, the Maoris, and other once distinctive elements of humanity which have been submerged in the struggle for existence by European penetration.

The camels of Arabia are all of the one-

These graphs present monthly average temperature and rainfall, plus the daily temperature range, shaded, and the extreme recorded temperatures, in dots; as well as the monthly potential evapotranspiration, in thin bars.

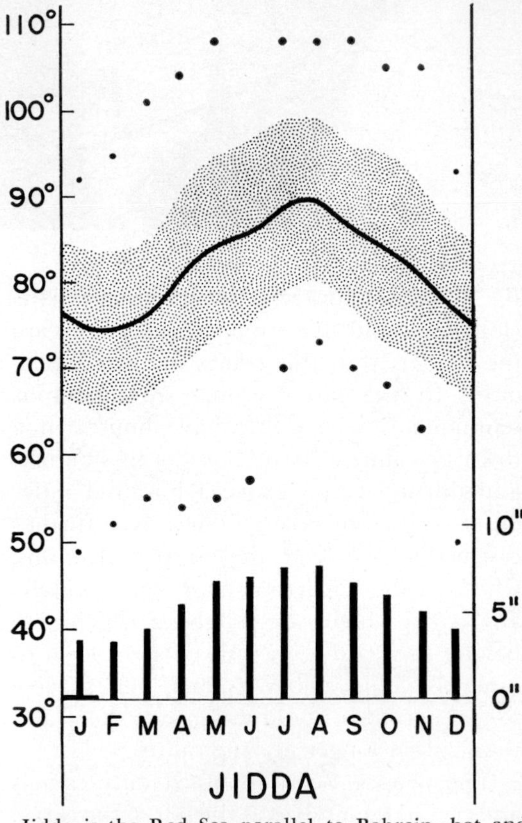

Jidda is the Red Sea parallel to Bahrein, hot and arid. Elevation 20 feet, annual rainfall 2.5 inches.

[1] H. St. John Philby; *Forty Years in the Wilderness.* London: Robert Hale (1957). 58–59. Quoted by permission.

humped dromedary variety, in contrast to the two-humped Bactrian type of Central Asia. In general, those of the north are larger than the camels of the southern peninsula. Some tribes, such as the Ruwala, breed white camels, others prefer brown, red, or black. Racing camels from Oman will travel fourteen miles per hour, and camels have been known to cover 800 miles in eight days. Bedouin camel herds are kept primarily for their milk, secondarily for meat. With the availability of modern transport, camel caravans are rapidly disappearing, but camels remain the best "converter" of desert vegetation into products useful to man.

CITIES IN THE DESERT

THE URBAN revolution of the twentieth century is nowhere more striking than in the transformation of Arabian mud villages into modern metropolitan cities. Westerners who think of the desert only in terms of Bedouin tents and sleepy market towns should revise their prejudices. Certainly, Jidda is not a Beirut, but parts of it are thoroughly Westernized.

These paragraphs deal with five cities: Jidda, Riyadh, the triple centers around Dhahran, Kuwait City, and Aden. In each

Riyadh has a climate which is representative of interior Arabia. Elevation 1,938 feet, annual rainfall 3.2 inches.

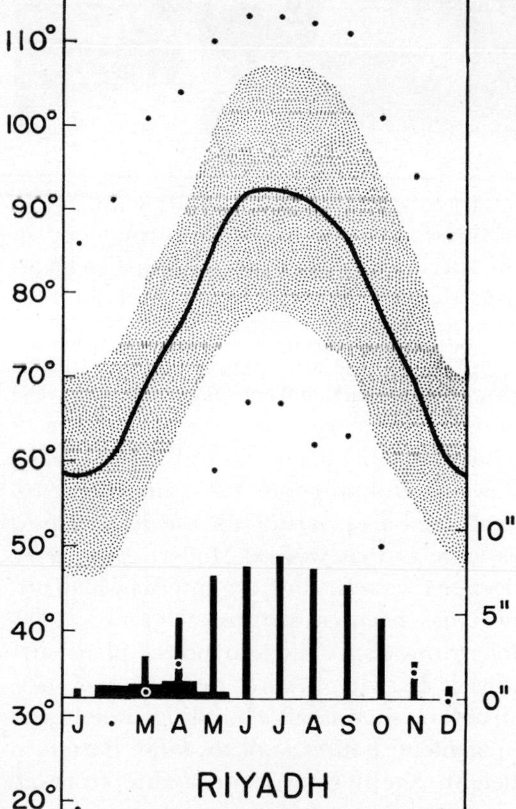

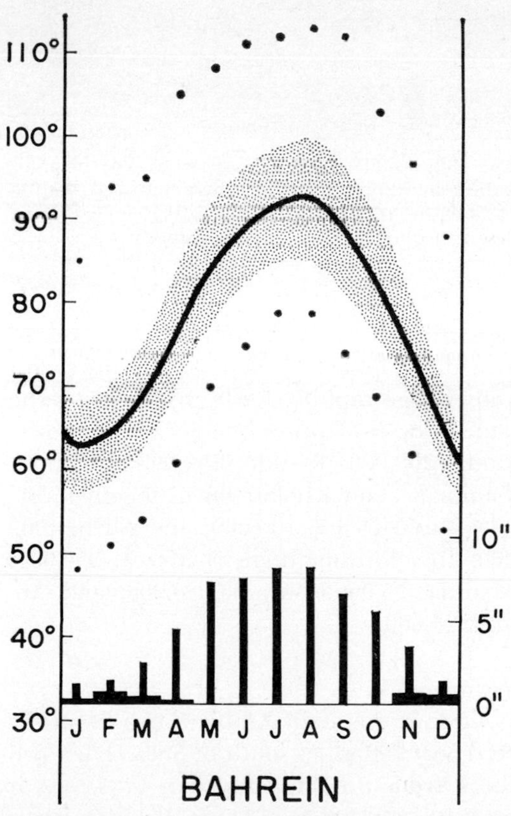

Bahrein has a Persian Gulf climate, low in rainfall but often with high humidity. Elevation 18 feet, annual rainfall 3.2 inches.

The old capital city of Riyadh was a city of mud-walled buildings, many of them crowned with a parapet; all very much in tune with the enveloping desert. (Courtesy Arabian American Oil Co.)

case, oil is directly or indirectly the key to growth. Population figures are uncertain and change rapidly. Early in the 1960's the figures were approximately as follows: Jidda, 200,000; Riyadh, 150,000; Dhahran, Dammam, and Khobar taken together, 50,000; Kuwait City, 100,000; and Aden, 100,000. In addition, there is Mecca, 250,000; Medina, 75,000; Buraida, 30,000; and Anaiza, 25,000.

Jidda

Jidda is the main Arabian seaport on the Red Sea, 700 miles south of Suez. The town dates from pre-Mohammedan days, but it owes its importance to being the sea gateway to Mecca. Like all modern cities of Arabia, it shares in the prosperity brought by the oil business. The site has little to commend it, for the dust of the coastal plain lies heavy over the city. Water must be brought by a pipe line from fifty miles inland.

Parts of Jidda are obviously old, with narrow lanes and harem balconies on the houses; elsewhere it has the appearance of a boom town. The former walls were pushed down by bulldozers in 1947, and the newly developed area outside the old walls is now as large as that within. Modern piers serve deep-sea vessels, and an international airport has been constructed with two 6,000-foot runways. A modern power plant supplies electricity. There are dozens of new structures such as office buildings, hotels, and apartment houses, up to nine stories in height. Shops carry merchandise from all over the world. Women rarely appear unveiled or on the streets at all, but store windows display the usual Western array of

Modern Riyadh is being transformed into an up to date metropolis. These buildings house the Ministries of Agriculture, Education, Health, and Finance. (Courtesy Arabian American Oil Co.)

feminine clothing. Moslem restrictions discourage public movies and the use of tobacco, but radios are common.

Commerce and construction enterprises have given Saudi Arabia a new class of people, many of whom have been abroad or who are in touch with the modern world around them. Thousands of these live in Jidda, although they are clearly a minority.

No railway enters Jidda, but paved roads extend east to Mecca, two hours away, and on to Taif in the mountains, as well as north to Medina and its seaport of Yenbo. The port thus serves as the gateway to all of western Saudi Arabia.

Riyadh

Riyadh's chief advantages as a capital lie in its central position and in its tradition as the home of the royal family. The province of Nejd is the heart of Bedouin history and power, and no other center could equally command the loyalty, or at least the acceptance, of both east and west coasts.

The city lies in the broad valley of the Wadi Hanifa, already discussed in Chapter 5. The rainfall is no more than three or four inches, and 80 per cent is of such low intensity that there is no runoff. Nearby are several palm oases, and fifty miles to the east is the large agricultural area around Kharj with its great springs.

Riyadh formerly suffered from a shortage of municipal water, but there are now several 3,500-foot wells, and a twenty-four inch pipe brings water from wadi gravels twenty miles away. A railway, with stainless steel air-conditioned Budd Cars, leads to the port of Dammam on the Persian Gulf, 370 miles to the east. Only poor truck roads connect Riyadh with Jidda, 600 airline miles to the west. Air services link the capitol with two dozen Arabian towns.

Old Riyadh was a mud-walled town; new Riyadh is becoming dramatically modern. The boulevard which leads to the airport is lined with splendid buildings for the Ministries of Defense, Interior, Communications, Agriculture, Education, Health, and Finance. The Ministry of Foreign Affairs and the Diplomatic Corps remain in Jidda. Elsewhere are several hotels, a printing plant, brightly lit shops with merchandise from all the world, a zoo, six public gardens with flowers, a hospital, and a university which graduates its first class in 1961. The Nasriyah Palace has a 5 million dollar air conditioning plant designed by the Carrier Corporation.

In order to appreciate the importance of Riyadh, it is necessary to understand something of Wahabiism, the puritanical sect of Islam which favors a return to the strict teachings of Mohammed, with the Koran as an adequate guide for all legal procedures. As an example of their strictness, Wahabiis frown on tall minarets. Sheikh Mohammed Wahab was born near Riyadh about 1703, and developed his ideas under the protection of the lord of a nearby town, Mohammed ibn Saud. The Saud family grew in importance, as did Wahabiism, and King Abdul Aziz ibn Saud, who began his creation of modern Saudi Arabia by the capture of Riyadh in 1902, was in the fifth generation of the protectors of Wahabiism. While Westerners speak of the group as Wahabiis, they call themselves Unitarians. The Nejd has always been their center of power.

All Arabs are proud, but the Wahabiis are even more so. While conceding the holy character of the Hejaz as the cradle of Islam, the people of the Nejd give to their area a co-equal status with the homeland of the Prophet.

The Dhahran Group

Oil has brought money to the Persian Gulf. Previously, the two centers of population were the agricultural areas around Hofuf and Qatif, with present populations in the oases of 160,000 and 60,000 respectively. The Arabian American Oil Company has built a company town near its first oil field at Dhahran, while on the coast nearby is the administrative center, seaport, and rail terminus of Dammam, and the commercial town of Khobar. Completing the modern complex is the great airfield which serves as an American base, the refinery and loading facilities at Ras Tanura, and other oil centers such as Abqaiq.

Each of these centers has a Western touch, and Dhahran is a bit of America dropped down in the desert, with a supermarket, golf course, and the only cinema in Saudi Arabia, but, owing to official restrictions, it has neither liquor nor churches. Fortunately, all buildings are air conditioned since, except during the two "winter" months, temperatures and humidity are uncomfortably high. The normal rainfall is 2.6 inches, but has ranged from 1.5 to 7 inches. Walking down the tree-lined residential streets past green lawns and a profusion of flowers around thoroughly American homes, one may forget the vast, arid desert surrounding the city.

Just as the successive hurricanes of the West Indies are given names following the letters of the alphabet, so Dhahran residents name the strong north storms known as the *shamal.* The March 9, 1959, issue of the Aramco publication known as *Sun and Flair* reports as follows:

> Shamal "Abdullah" whipped out of the west-northwest at 6:57 p.m. last Saturady night to assume hurricane proportions, with a rise to a maximum of 80-miles-per-hour velocity within a five-minute period. The wind storm, reported as the worst in the area in 35 years, left in its wake damage roughly estimated at $150,000 in

The new city of Khobar has become the commercial center for the Persian Gulf coast of Saudi Arabia. Nearby lies the oil town of Dhahran. (Courtesy Arabian American Oil Co.)

the three Aramco districts. . . . The storm started gathering with 35-mile-per-hour winds reported at Nariyah at 5.30 p.m. An hour later, Safaniya reported an increase in velocity and then the storm hit the Dhahran area with its greatest fury between 7:00 and 7:15 p.m. The Dhahran Airfield weather station reported an increase of from 5 to 47 knots between 7 and 7:05 p.m. Abqaiq's maximum winds were 60 miles per hour and at Ras Tanura the storm reached 61 miles-per-hour velocity between 7:15 and 7:30 p.m. In Dhahran, roof damage in the general storeyard and in al-Salamah Camp was severe. Over a hundred trees were uprooted . . . . The communications antenna on the roof of the Administration Building was twisted and damage to sand fences and backfill over pipelines was considerable.

Kuwait

Kuwait harbor lies in the largest bay along the Persian Gulf and has long been a center of shipbuilding, dhow traffic, and pearl fishing. As early as 1760, a German traveler noted that Kuwait had a fleet of 800 ships, operating as far as India and Africa. Exports of dates, wool, hides, skins, and horses enabled Kuwait to bring in cloth, rice, sugar, tea, and teak from the Malabar Coast. Fresh water is unavailable, so that, until recently, drinking water was brought by barges from the mouth of the Shatt-al-Arab, sixty miles distant. Although Kuwait is a port of local importance, the town's hinterland is poor.

Now that the tiny sheikhdom has become a major oil producer, all this has changed. The world's largest distillation plant supplies 2 million gallons of water daily and replaces the water barges from Iraq. Pearling has virtually ended for there is easier money

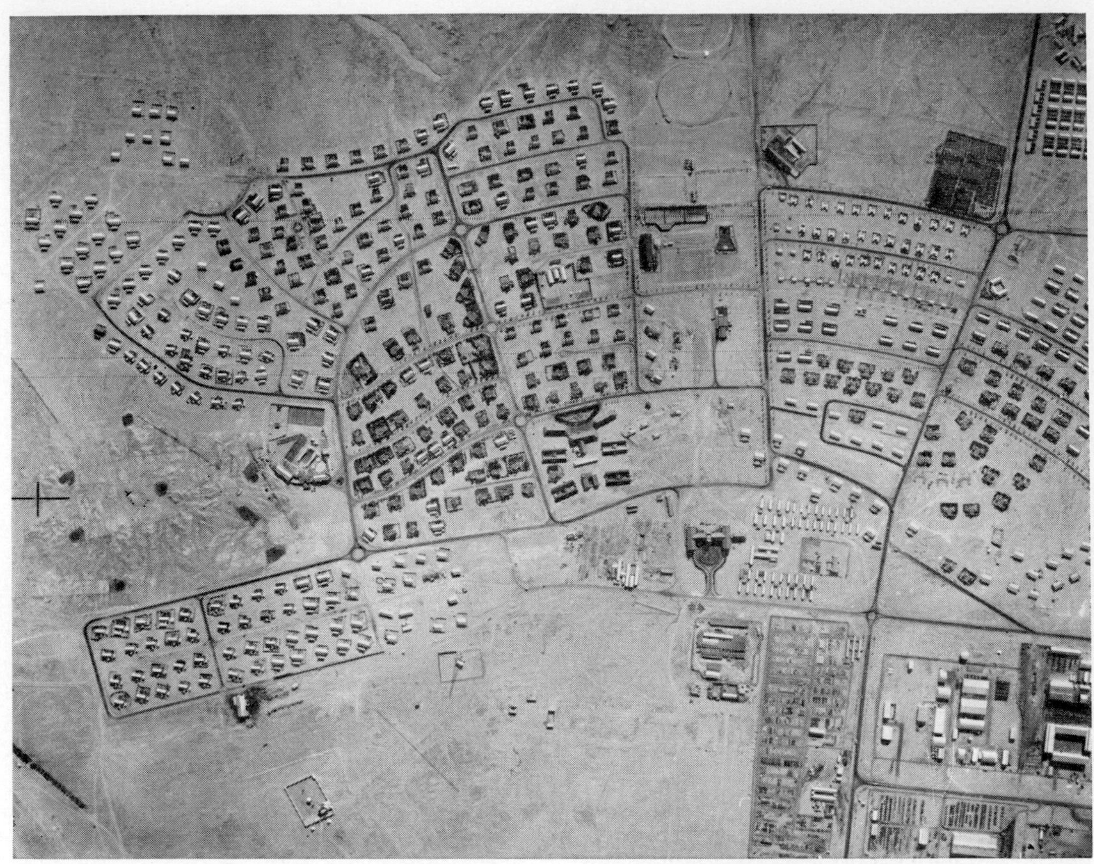

This aerial view, taken at 8,000 feet, shows the company town of Ahmadi, headquarters for the Kuwait Oil Company. Scarcely a trace of vegetation is to be seen. (Courtesy Kuwait Oil Co.)

in the oil field. Royalties are coming in faster than anyone can spend them, even though there has been a reconstruction program costing a third of a billion dollars.

Richard P. Hunt describes life under the new welfare state as follows: [1]

Twenty years ago a Kuwait man bought a bit of land for 30 rupees ($6.33) and a donkey. Last year he sold the property to the state for 100,000 rupees ($23,370).

He pays no direct taxes. His son goes to a foreign university at government expense, and his niece will receive a free sewing machine when she completes her free course in dressmaking.

His electricity and water service are partly subsidized. His government job is guaranteed. His new American-made car glides over the boulevards that replaced the donkey tracks, to the air-conditioned villa that replaced his mud-walled house.

In short, he lives in a welfare state financed by Kuwait's $400,000,000 a year in oil revenues, generously shared by his paternal Government.

But is everybody happy? No.

A visitor to this city, which appears to sprout almost miraculously from the searing desert, readily finds that most complaints are laid at the door of the sheikhs, who are members of the ruling el-Sabbah family.

By most accounts the Ruler, Emir Abdullah el-Salem el-Sabbah, is a devout and fatherly man who feels the oil money is a duty placed upon him by God. He believes he must administer it himself, but wisely, in the interest of his people. . . .

[1] *The New York Times,* May 5, 1959.

In accord with his views, Kuwait has built eighty splendid new schools in the last ten years, furnished welfare services for all the poor and spent heavily for roads, waterworks and public gardens to improve life for everybody . . . .

That is one side of life in Kuwait. The other is that many Kuwaitis, no matter how prosperous because of the system, believe that their Government is extravagant and old-fashioned . . . .

Aden

Aden shares in the prosperity of the oil business. Since Aden can draw crude oil from various fields, wherever the price is advantageous, the British have built a major refinery. Aden is now one of the world's largest petroleum bunkerage ports. Every ship passing through the Red Sea pauses for a few hours at Aden, for it is on the main street of the world. The port has the only good harbor between Egypt and Pakistan.

The old city lies on a peninsula and within the breached walls of a volcano and is known as Crater. Aden derives its traditional water supply from hillside reservoirs or tanks, built in the sixth century, but now draws on mainland wells. Crescent, on the outside of the crater, is the seaport and new commercial area. The airport lies on the sandy spit which ties the volcano to the mainland. Across the bay is the refinery at Little Aden.

Several industries have become important in addition to oil refining. The solar production of salt is one of the chief enterprises. The evaporation pans occupy 4,000 acres with a capacity of 400,000 tons of salt a year. Other products are soap, aluminum dishes, cigarettes, oil seeds, hides, and textiles.

Aden is a free port and serves as a great entrepot for the western Indian Ocean, with transit goods to and from all the world. Every year, 5,000 ships and 500,000 passengers enter the port, a tribute to its commanding position and to British energy. It may be sufficient comment on Aden's climate to mention that the common name for the strong, dry northerly wind, which carries dust, is the *kawi* or hot iron.

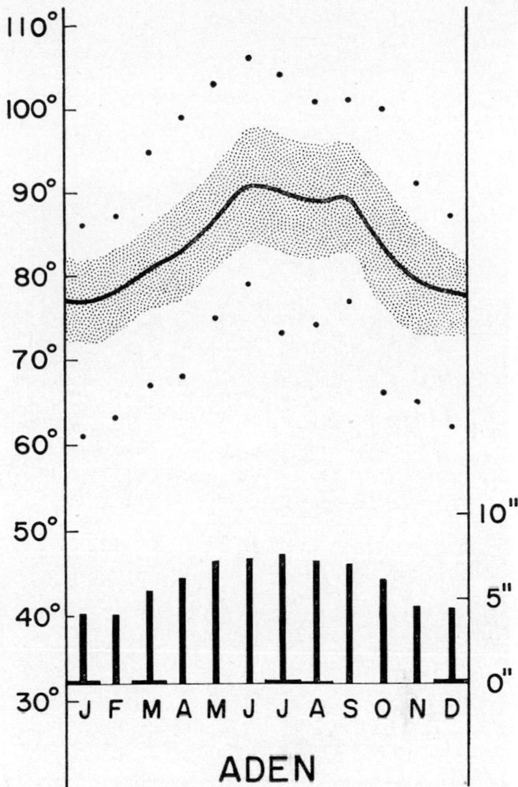

Aden is the driest of all Arabian stations. Elevation 22 feet, annual rainfall 0.9 inches.

Despite more than a century of British rule, Aden remains among the least attractive large cities in all of Southwest Asia. Until 1937, it was administered by the Government of India, and there is still a large Indian population. The buildings are drab and the shops shabby. Only the parade of great ships gives it a sense of interest or importance. But there is business in the city, with new houses being built in great numbers. A little physical beauty might help.

The international character of Aden is revealed in its mixed population. Yemenese Arabs lead, followed by Protectorate Arabs, Indians, Somalis and other Africans, Persians, and several thousand Europeans.

Several separate settlements make up the city of Aden, all of them around or within an ancient volcanic crater. The port area, here shown, is known as the Crescent. (Courtesy Public Relations Department, Aden.)

HIGHLAND OASES

WITH A NORMAL LAPSE RATE of some three degrees fahrenheit per thousand feet, and lowland summer temperatures of around 100°F., it would require an increase in elevation of roughly a mile to experience 80°F. Such elevations occur in four parts of the peninsula, which are accompanied fortunately by higher rainfall and less evaporation. These are the Hejaz Escarpment, with maximum elevations of 8,462 feet opposite the Gulf of Aqaba and 8,027 feet near Taif; its southern continuation in Asir with 8,226 feet; Yemen in the southern corner of the peninsula where the highest peak is 12,336 feet; and the interior of Masqat in the east where elevations reach 8,669 feet. The Tuwaiq Escarpment of central Arabia does not exceed 3,600 feet and is not properly one of the humid oases.

In total, the Arabian highlands over a mile in elevation cover about 75,000 square miles. Only the southwest is included in the traditional Arabia Felix, but all of the mountains are "happy" lands. The area is narrow and discontinuous in the northwest. South of the latitude of Mecca the Hejaz highlands are a few tens of miles wide, while in Yemen they extend more than a hundred miles inland.

These highland oases have a rich history, still imperfectly known, and may well prove to have been the fountain source of Arab cul-

Many mountain slopes in Yemen are terraced from base to summit, as on Jebel Sabir near Taiz. These fields lie between 6,000 and 9,000 feet, and are used for growing barley. (Courtesy Bruce Conde.)

ture. Their recorded history dates back at least a thousand years before Christ, and taken together, their population equals that of all the rest of the peninsula.

Few of these areas experience winter snow, and then only but rarely, so that they scarcely fall into the "white" category of Swasia's landscape colors. However, insofar as they are underlain by porous lava flows or cavernous limestones, there is a storage factor for the seasonal precipitation. Winter is the rainy period throughout the mountains, with the exception of the south where a touch of the southwest monsoon also brings light summer rain. The cold fronts which advance from the north become progressively thinner so that they tend to pass around rather than over the top of the higher peaks. Satisfactory climatic records are lacking, but in general the rainfall is under fifteen inches.

Land forms can best be understood in terms of structure. Great normal faults, with displacements measured in thousands of feet, bound the Red Sea, and the Gulf of Oman. Each of the highlands is asymmetrical, with deep erosion and precipitous slopes on the seaward side and moderate gradients toward the interior. Vast lava flows have poured out along some of the fracture lines, but currently there are no active volcanoes. Earthquakes are recurrent.

Agriculture has been developed in the various high basins and on terraced slopes.

The latter are remarkable in Yemen where they cover steep valley sides which have a relief of 2,000 feet. Most terraces are faced with stone walls, three to twenty feet in height which protect narrow strips of agricultural land. On the steepest slopes, walls twenty-five feet high may border a ribbon of cropland only fifteen feet wide, thus representing a slope of more than forty-five degrees. Terrace construction has become a fine art, and it is uncommon to find the walls in disrepair.

The mountain of Jebel Sabir, 9,863 feet in height, lies near the city of Taizz, the capital of Yemen, which is at 4,500 feet. Standing near the base of the mountain, one sees only bare rocks, tinged with the dull green of euphorbia and scattered trees; but from the summit, one sees a myriad array of terraces, so closely spaced that in many areas the actual cultivated land approaches 80 per cent. What seemed to be only stone and rubble when seen from the base of the mountain now appears from above as the walls of the terraces. Wherever there is soil, the land is in use.

If one were adept at scaling the nearly vertical rock face of the terrace fronts on Jabel Sabir, one might start from Taizz and climb continuously from one terrace to another all the way to the summit. In most places, there are no more than a few dozen or a hundred terraces in sequence, but from the uppermost level of one series, a climber might follow along the contour to the base of the next. In this manner, there are doubtless a succession of 1,000 terraces on this one mountain. Many of these are known to date from the Rasulid Dynasty in the thirteenth century; some walls may be a thousand years old for such are known to be the ages of buildings along them. In the perfection of terracing and water management, the Yemenese farmer ranks with the Ifugao in Luzon, the Chinese in Szechwan, or the Incas of Peru, even though Yemen is much drier.

In the case of cold highlands in Turkey, Iran, or Afghanistan, agriculture is concentrated around their base where snow-melt streams are diverted by irrigation canals. The Arabian highlands seldom experience below-freezing temperatures, nor do they have the available moisture, so that water is used within the mountains, where and as it falls. Most fields depend only on rain water. Only small and short canals are involved, but to conserve moisture from seepage or evaporation, these aqueducts may be cement-lined and covered with large stones. Since the rainfall is seldom more than marginal, careful conservation of the moisture is necessary. Fields are nearly level and are plowed along the contour to encourage the raindrop to sink in rather than run off.

In place of large-scale irrigation works, many devices add water to the fields. These include flood-water spreading in wadis by means of temporary check and diversion dams. Where rainfall is inadequate, bare hillsides above cultivated fields may be bordered by dikes which concentrate the runoff and lead it to the cultivated area. Thus in the drier areas of Yemen, from four to forty acres of slopeland may be required for each acre of cropland, and ownership or control of barren hills is essential for cultivation. Qanats and karez are used around the base of some mountains but are not widespread. They are numerous in Oman due to Persian influence and are called *feledj*.

If there is a long succession of terraces and the possibility of considerable runoff, the flow of water is controlled to check erosion. Escape-ways or stone chutes are provided, or there may be a stone screen at the lowest point of a terrace rim.

There are a variety of crops. Millets, such as dhurra, are raised from sea level to 8,000 feet. Wheat begins at intermediate elevations and is grown up to 8,000 feet; the same is true for barley, except that it grows to 9,000 feet. Corn is found locally. A wide assortment of fruits are raised between 6,500 and 8,000 feet, including apricots, peaches, plums, pears, pomegranates, figs, and grapes. Bananas, mango, and citrus grow between 400 and 6,500 feet. Date palms and cotton are found only below 2,500 feet. These height limits refer to Yemen; farther north they are presumably lower.

The two major cash crops in Yemen and adjoining Asir are coffee and qat. *Coffee arabica* was probably introduced from Ethiopia. It is grown under shade trees on humid slopes facing the Red Sea between 4,500 and 7,000 feet. The latter is probably the highest elevation for coffee in the world. The most famous area is around Manakha, southwest of Sanaa, but the producing areas extend from the latter city southward to Taizz. The coffee trees, grown on terraces, attain maturity in five years and reach a height of eight to fifteen feet; they then bear for about twenty years. Some coffee fields are irrigated. The top grades command prices equal to the best Colombian coffees. Most of the coffee is shipped from Hodeida to Aden, where it is often downgraded by admixture with African coffees. The government of Yemen hopes to revive direct export through the ancient port of Mocha.

In competition with coffee is qat, *catha edulis,* a tree whose leaves contain an alkaloid with a mildly sedative effect. When the fresh leaves are chewed, they produce a feeling of alertness; while not habit forming, the excessive use of qat has unfortunate physiologic and economic results. There is a proverb in Yemen which reads "God has afflicted the Jews with wine and the Moslem with qat." Although qat will mature into a full grown tree, the best leaves are obtained from young plants about the size of tea bushes. The climatic requirements of coffee and qat are about the same, except that the maximum elevation for qat reaches 8,500 feet, 1,500 feet higher than for coffee, and that coffee grows best under shade trees while qat prefers sunshine.

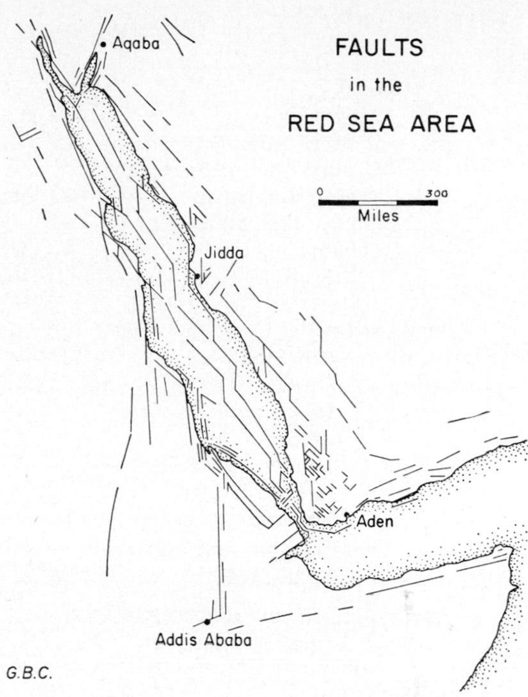

Fault lines mark the borders of the Red and Arabian seas. Earth movements and vulcanism continue. (Based on British Naval Intelligence Division, Geographical Handbook.)

There are no statistics on any aspect of agriculture in any of these highland areas. In the case of Yemen, field observations suggest an average of an acre of cropland per capita and a total of some 6,000 square miles under cultivation. Some fields yield two harvests a year, but this is not common. As a first esimate, cropland may amount to 5 per cent of the total area.

Yemen is by far the most developed of the Arabian highlands. Next comes Asir which adjoins it on the north and was once a part of Yemen. Its capital city of Abha is particularly praised. Neither the Hejaz nor Masqat have large areas at sufficient heights to support many people. Unlike conditions in other countries of Southwest Asia, there is only a limited amount of seasonal up-and-down slope nomadism or transhumance.

Arabia

THE ARABIAN PENINSULA[1]

Country	Capital City	Capital Population	Area in square miles	Population
Aden Colony	Aden	100,000	75,000	139,600
Western Aden Protectorate	(Lahej)		112,000 (Western and Eastern Aden Protectorates together)	400,000
Eastern Aden Protectorate	(Mukalla)			350,000
Masqat and Oman	Masqat	5,000	82,000	550,000
Persian Gulf States				
Bahrein	Manama	45,000	213	125,000
Kuwait	Kuwait	125,000	5,800	206,177
Qatar	Doha	8,000		40,000
Trucial Coast			32,300	70,000
Abu Dhabi				5,000
Dibai	Dibai	25,000		40,000
Sharjah and Kalba				3,000
Ajman				2,000
Umm al Qaiwain				3,000
Ras al Khaima				15,000
Fujairah				3,000
Saudi Arabia	Riyadh	150,000	870,000 to 930,000	5,200,000 to 6,500,000
Yemen	Taizz	20,000	74,000	4,300,000
Total			1,250,000	12,000,000

[1] Data from United Nations *Statistical Yearbook, Stateman's Year-Book, World Almanac,* and other sources.

A glimpse of interior Masqat is given by James Morris, writing at Nizwa, the capital of Oman.[1]

Directly above the plain, rising grandly above a ripple of palm trees, stood the mountain mass of Jebel Akhdar—the Green Mountain. It did not seem very green. On the contrary it was bare and tawny, and looked watchful and implacable. It reaches a height of nearly 10,000 feet, making it one of the highest mountains in Arabia. Some of the Arabs say they have seen it "covered with salt" presumably meaning that for a few weeks of a savagely severe winter the mountain is snow capped.

THE POLITICAL FRAMEWORK

It is difficult to tabulate the political situation in the Arabian Peninsula for there are several categories of sovereignty. Saudi Arabia is a monarchy with an appointed Council of Ministers but without an elected Parliament. Yemen has a similar absolute government but has special treaty agreements with the United Arab Republic. Kuwait, Bahrein, Qatar, and the states of the Trucial Coast are independent sheikhdoms under the protection of the British government. The Sultanate of Masqat is also independent but is in a treaty relationship with Great Britain. Aden is a British crown colony, and adjoining it are the Eastern and Western Aden Protectorates. In addition there are two Neutral Zones; one Saudi-Iraq, the other Saudi-Kuwait.

Few boundaries have been properly surveyed, and serious disagreements exist along 1,500 miles of the frontiers. Where only Bedouin are involved, little matters; where oil may be present, millions of dollars and worldwide politics are at stake.

Saudi Arabia

Saudi Arabia, or al Mamlaka al' Arabiya as-Saudiya, is a sovereign unitary kingdom. It was founded in 1932 by the Wahabis, un-

[1] James Morris: *Sultan in Oman.* London: Faber (1957). 99. Quoted by permission.

Stainless steel, air conditioned Budd cars operate over the government railway from Dammam on the Persian Gulf to the capital at Riyadh. This is the Al Kharj station. (Courtesy Arabian American Oil Co.)

der Ibn Saud, following the consolidation of Nejd and the Kingdom of Hejaz and their dependencies such as Hasa and Asir. The entire southern border is undefined except for part of the area between Asir and Yemen, and there is also uncertainty as to the border in the northwest next to Jordan.

The exports are predominantly oil, supplemented by small amounts of dates, livestock, hides, and wool. Since much of the oil moves to Europe, royalties are paid in local currencies; and this tends to control the countries which supply imports.

Although Saudi Arabia lacks a modern government and an adequate core of educated people, it enjoys great political strength through its oil royalties and particularly through its guardianship of the holy places of Islam: Mecca and Medina. It is thus one of the major contenders for leadership in the Arab world. Arabia's oil is vital in the economy of Europe, and the Dhahran air base is one of America's strategic overseas installations.

Change is coming rapidly to Saudi Arabia. Although a portion of the oil royalties are spent on the large royal family, the bulk is devoted to public works, cultural enterprises, and the army. Hundreds of village schools, scores of hospitals, and improved communications have resulted from the new wealth. Arabia's only railway is the line which links Dammam with Riyadh. There are proposals to extend this to Jidda and also to reconstruct the old narrow gauge Hejaz railway to Damascus.

Persian Gulf States

The Persian Gulf States include Bahrein, Kuwait, Qatar, and the seven sheikhdoms of the Trucial Coast. While independent in their internal affairs, all are under the protection of the British government. Were it not for these treaty relations, developed during the nineteenth century for bygone reasons, all of the area might now be part of Saudi Arabia.

Bahrein occupies a small group of islands opposite Dhahran. It first appears in history through an Assyrian inscription of 2782 B.C. Strabo also describes the city in 63 B.C. Archaeological discoveries confirm the town's early existence and make it clear that a pre-Akkadian civilization flourished here as early as 3000 B.C. This early city-state traded with Mesopotamia and the Indus Valley. Nearby are 100,000 mounds or tumuli, perhaps the largest known prehistoric cemetery. Stone-age implements indicate that Bahrein was already inhabited 50,000 years ago.

From the days of the Romans until the sixteenth century, Bahrein was a contested area between Arabs and Persians. Then came a century of Portugese control from 1507 until 1622, after which the Persian flag flew over Bahrein from 1622 until 1783. It then returned to Arab control, and the present ruling family dates from that time. Because of Iran's earlier ownership, and a British note of 1869 which recognized Persian sovereignty, Iran is making strong efforts to regain Bahrein, and the Iranian Parliament has voted that Bahrein is rightfully theirs. For an alien to enter Iran with a Bahrein visa in his passport, to be obtained only through British Consulates, is somewhat comparable to entering Arab countries with a passport containing an Israeli visa.

Owing to the prevalence of piracy and the slave trade around the Persian Gulf in the early nineteenth century, Britain intruded in 1820 and entered into a treaty with the local ruler of Bahrein "for the cessation of plunder and piracy by land and sea." The official British position today is that the Sheikh is independent but under special treaty relations whereby foreign affairs and defense are in British hands.

Although the Bahrein Oil Company is jointly owned by two American corporations, California Standard and Texaco, it is registered as a Canadian concern to bring it under British requirements. While oil production and refining provide the major sources of income, Bahrein does a considerable merchandise business in the Persian Gulf and India.

The capital city of Manama has long been a center for pearl fishing. In the mid-nineteenth century, it had 300 pearling boats, but the importance of the industry has declined greatly. At one time pearls were said to have given Bahrein the highest per capita income in the world. As a reflection of the industry, the importation of cultured pearls is forbidden by law.

The island has fresh-water springs and raises dates, citrus crops, alfalfa, and vegetables.

Kuwait is a phenomenon. This tiny sheikhdom, scarcely larger than Connecticut, contains as much oil as the entire United States. Its ruler has an income well in excess of a million dollars a day. On a per capita basis, this places Kuwait on a par with America. Because of the close relations with the United Kingdom, a considerable part of the ruler's income is invested in British securities so that Kuwait has become a significant source of new money on the London stock exchange.

Much coastwise trade in the Persian Gulf and Red Sea is carried in locally made dhows. This Arab is carrying ashore a bag of wheat at Safaniya. (Courtesy Standard Oil Co. of New Jersey.)

Kuwait's agriculture plays a very minor role since the limited well water is brackish. Pearls and the dhow traffic once resembled conditions in Bahrein. Trade extended to both India and East Africa, usually timed to take advantage of the monsoon.

As with the other Persian Gulf states, Kuwait is fully independent with respect to its domestic affairs; but by treaties dating from 1899, Great Britain is responsible for foreign relations, and Kuwait undertakes never to cede or lease any portion of its territory to any foreign government or national without express authorization of the British government. Kuwait had passed under nominal Turkish suzerainty in 1829, and the treaty with Britain was made at the request of the ruling Sheikh who feared that the Ottoman Empire intended to make its nominal authority more effective. As was the case with Bahrein, there was also a period of Persian control.

Kuwait lies between two powerful neighbors, Iraq and Saudi Arabia, each of whom might like to absorb the sheikhdom. While its relationship to Britain does not permit Kuwait to join the Arab League, the people are ardent Arab nationalists. Here as elsewhere in the peninsula, the presence of large numbers of Egyptian business men, contractors, teachers, and technical men creates an influential "fifth column."

When the boundaries between Kuwait and Saudi Arabia were established in 1922, it proved impossible to agree on jurisdiction over two diamond-shaped areas, each covering roughly fifty square miles of poor desert land. Tribes from Kuwait, Iraq, and Saudi Arabia used them on the occasions when there was pasture. The final decision was to set up two neutral zones, one Iraq-Saudi, the other Kuwait-Saudi. In each case, the respective governments hold full sway and own an undivided half.

This dual control has proven awkward with the discovery of oil and with its occurrence offshore. Each country has signed oil concessions, and each shares in the profits of the other company. Two American companies have concession rights in the Kuwait-Saudi Arabian Neutral Zone, each free to drill anywhere and each required to divide its profits equally with both countries. The offshore rights are held by a single Japanese concern, but it had to bid separately, and at a different price, with the two governments.

Qatar is desolate even for Arabia. The peninsula is made up of 8,000 square miles of desert, scarcely fit for grazing. Until modern times, the chief occupation of its small population was pearling and fishing. The rainfall amounts to only four inches a year, and the summer humidity of the Gulf combines with the burning heat of the desert to make the climate almost unbearable. As with the nearby states, Qatar's foreign affairs are under British direction. The capital is Doha, on the east coast. Thanks to the export of oil after 1950, the country is becoming a junior Kuwait. Doha, like Kuwait, has a plant which distills sea water for drinking purposes.

The story of the Trucial Coast is revealed in its former name of the Pirate Coast, and the political confusion is implied by the incorrect title of Trucial Oman. The area extends for nearly 400 miles and includes seven sheikhdoms. The two most important centers are Dibai and Sharjah. In 1820, the rulers signed treaties with the British East India Company, prescribing peace with Britain and perpetual abstention from plunder and piracy, specifically including the slave trade, by land and by sea. In further treaties, dated 1892, the sheikhs on behalf of their heirs and successors, undertook that "they would on no account enter into any agreement or correspondence with any power other than the British government, receive foreign agents, or cede, sell, or give for occupation any part of their territory save to the British government."

One of the problems of the Trucial Coast concerns the inland limits. No boundaries have been surveyed, and the only precedent lies in tribal grazing grounds. Nomads wander widely and pay little attention to political matters or taxes. Certain tribes have given nominal allegiance to the king of Saudi Arabia and his predecessors. Does this extend Saudi jurisdiction to the limits of their farthest grazing grounds? The same condition holds for subjects of the Trucial states. The fact that the Bedouin have occasionally paid taxes to one ruler or another is not a sure sign of sovereignty.

Boundary problems become especially significant when oil concessions are involved. American interests hold rights in Saudi territory; other companies, British-dominated, have purchased similar rights along the coast. One point of conflict is the group of nine tiny villages which make up the Buraimi oasis. Buraimi lies near the boundary between Saudi Arabia, Masqat, and Abu Dhabi and is actually administered by the last two.

Each sheikhdom fronts on the sea and has an anchorage or shallow inlet. Fishing, camels, and dates provide the principal native income. In addition, the several rulers re-

Once-barren land around Abyan in the Western Aden Protectorate has been brought under cultivation through a large irrigation plan. Cotton is a major crop. (Courtesy British Information Services, New York.)

ceive considerable sums as advance payments for oil concessions.

Masqat and Oman

The Sultanate of Masqat and Oman is a fully independent state. There is a treaty of commerce and navigation with Great Britain, and British individuals are employed as officers in the small Masqat army, but there is no official control over foreign policy. It is of some interest to point out that America's oldest treaty relations with an Arab state in Asia are with Masqat, dating from 1833. At that time, the island of Zanzibar was also under the Sultan.

Masqat borders the Gulf of Oman and the Indian Ocean for a thousand miles and extends inland to vague boundaries next to Saudi Arabia. Physically, the country consists of three parts, a narrow coastal plain, a range of hills and mountains, and an interior upland plain. Most of the area is barren, but there are a few oases, especially the date gardens of the Batinah coast in the east. The interior is among the least known parts of the Arabian peninsula.

Along the western coast of Masqat lies the slightly humid and semiautonomous district of Dhufar, once famous for its incense and now an area with cattle grazing and a little sugar cane. The discovery of oil may be expected to bring the changes which have occurred elsewhere. The term Oman is properly limited to the interior highlands, an area administered by an Imam who is theoretically under the Sultan, but who regards himself as independent.

The capital city of Masqat and the adjoining town of Matrah apparently have one of the most uncomfortable climates in the world. They lie in a cliff-surrounded harbor which seems to concentrate the blazing sun and intensify the humidity. Daytime temperatures frequently reach 125°F., and there is little cooling at night. The Portugese built a fort and "factory" here in 1508, but they were expelled by the Arabs in 1650. Persian rule followed, and British relations commenced in 1798 as an attempt to counter the expanding interests of Napoleon. In addition to the Arab population, most of whom belong to the Ibadhi sect of Islam, Masqat has many Baluchi, Indians, and Negros.

Masqat's only exports are dates, camels, fruit, and dried fish.

Aden

Aden's command of the entrance to the Red Sea has long given it political importance. The Romans captured the city about 24 A.D., and Marco Polo visited Aden in 1285. It was unsuccessfully attacked by the Portugese in 1513 and 1516, and captured by the Turks in 1538. Later on, Aden was controlled by Yemen until 1728. The Dutch East India Company once used it as a port for the export of coffee. Aden became a traditional base for pirates, including Americans, Captain Kidd among them, and it was partly for this reason that Britain took possession in 1839 and in 1896 entered into treaty relations with seventeen inland rulers. The city became a colony in 1937; prior to this it had been administered from India.

Salt forms a major export from Aden. Evaporation pans cover some 4,000 acres and are provided with windmills to lift sea water. Much of the shipment goes to India.

The coastal border of southern Arabia is a patchwork of petty states: sultanates, amirates, and sheikhdoms, several dozen in all. These are quasi-independent, but in varying degrees have a British Resident Advisor. The area is poor, with negligible exports, and the economy is partly supported by British subsidies.

Two separate protectorates have arisen. The Western Aden Protectorate is the more developed, with Lahej as the leading area. In 1959, six of the eighteen states were reorganized into a constitutional federation. The Eastern Aden Proctectorate, which includes the Hadhramaut, is more complex in political structure and is partly "unadministered," meaning that there is no effective British control in some areas. Thus, no British official from Aden had visited the Hadhramaut until 1915. The chief units are the Quayti State around Mukalla and the Kathiri State based on Saiun.

Both Protectorates are dry and generally unproductive, with some similarities to Yemen at the higher elevations in the west. Conditions in the Hadhramaut have already been described. Several valleys near Aden provide a variety of fruits, grain, and vegetables, but less than 1 per cent of the area is in agricultural use. A modern development is the introduction of the long-staple Egyptian cotton in the newly irrigated Abyan Delta, fifty miles east of Aden, where 50,000 acres have been brought into production. As a result, the population increased tenfold in a decade. The British have invested several million pounds in various development projects, including roads.

Yemen

The kingdom of Yemen, al Mamlayah al Mutawakilyah Alyamaniah, is among the least known members of the United Nations.

The picturesque port of Mukalla, east of Aden, is the capital of the Quayti State and one of the gateways to southern Arabia. (Courtesy Public Relations Dept., Aden.)

This represents more of a political than an environmental problem because Yemen has 250 miles of frontage on the Red Sea, and the climatic barriers which make other Arabian areas unattractive are missing here. The rugged terrain is an obstacle, but the chief difficulties lie in the character of the government and the desire for independence.

Yemen's history may well be the oldest of any Arabian area, with partially deciphered evidence leading back for thousands of years. Early in the Islamic period, the various Christian chiefs made treaties with Mohammed, but the tribes later were forced to become Moslems. In the tenth century, Yemen became independent under a flag which carries the two-edged sword of Ali. At this time, there arose the Zeidi sect, a variant of Shia Islam. The king of Yemen is equally revered as the Imam, "the one who leads in prayer," and is both temporal and spiritual ruler. In addition to the Zeidi, there are numerous Ismaili and some Shafei Sunni Moslems.

The first Turkish occupation began in 1538 but ended in 1630. Dutch and Portugese were at times interested in the coastal areas. In 1869, the Turks again subjugated Yemen and remained in nominal control until 1918. Italian influence has also been significant.

The story of the twentieth century involves boundary troubles on both the north and south. At times, Yemen has included the province of Asir to the north, but following a brief border war, this was lost to Saudi Arabia in 1934. Uncertainties continue along the frontier with the Aden Protectorate, despite a somewhat ambiguous treaty in 1935. While Yemenese authority once extended south to Aden, effective control over Protectorate areas ended about 1760. Frequent assertions have been made that Yemen should regain these lost territories.

During the late 1950's, Yemen came into a close association with the United Arab Republic, the combination being known as the United Arab States. Substantial aid agreements were also entered into with the Soviet Union and the People's Republic of China for roads, textile plants, a harbor, and military support. The possibilities of a port on the Red Sea available to Soviet shipping presents some interesting military speculation.

Yemen's resources remain uncertain. Oil and mining concessions have proven unproductive. There is a large salt dome close to the port of Salif, where production began in 1953. Coffee is an important export, but the prospects of significant foreign trade remain for the future. While Aden has been the traditional entrepot, political difficulties have shifted trade to Hodeida, and in the future, this commerce may well extend also to Mocha and Salif.

There are no reliable statistics for Yemen. The official population was announced as 4.3 million in 1955, but this generous estimate may be too large. The largest city is Sanaa, which may have 50,000, but the capital at Taizz has only 12,000. No more than 700 Jews remain out of the former 50,000; the others have migrated to Israel.

REFERENCES

General References

Blanchard, Raoul: "L'Arabie," in GEOGRAPHIE UNIVERSALLE, VIII, ASIE OCCIDENTALE. Paris: Armand Colin (1929), 171–185.

Carol, Olaf: WELLS OF POWER. London: Macmillan (1951).

DeGaury, Gerald: "Arabia and the Future," *Jour. Royal Central Asian Soc.,* XXXI (1944), 40–47.

* Hazard, Harry W.: SAUDI ARABIA. New Haven, Conn.: Human Relations Area Files (1956).

Hitti, Philip K.: HISTORY OF THE ARABS. New York: Macmillan (1951).

Hoskins, Halford L.: "Background of British Position in Arabia," *Middle East Jour.,* I (1947), 137–147.

Huzayyin, S. A.: ARABIA AND THE FAR EAST: THEIR COMMERCIAL AND CULTURAL RELATIONS IN GRAECO-ROMAN AND IRANO-ARABIAN TIMES. Cairo: Publications de la Societe Royale de Geographie d'Egypte (1942).

Lebkicher, Roy, Rentz, George, and Steineke, Max: THE ARABIA OF IBN SAUD. New York: Russell F. Moore (1952).

* Lipsky, George A.: SAUDI ARABIA, ITS HISTORY, ITS CULTURE, AND ITS PEOPLE. New Haven: Human Relations Area Files (1959).

Lesch, Walter: "Arabien. Eine Landeskundliche Skizze," *Mag. Geog. Gesselschaft,* XXIV (1931), 1–153.

Liebesny, Herbert J.: "International Relations of Arabia: The Dependent Areas," *Middle East Jour.,* I (1947), 148–168.

Mikesell, Raymond F. and Chenery, Hollis B.: ARABIAN OIL, AMERICA'S STAKE IN THE MIDDLE EAST. Chapel Hill: Univ. of North Carolina Press (1949).

Philby, H. St. J. B.: SAUDI ARABIA. New York: Praeger (1955).

Rutter, Eldon: "The Habitability of the Arabian Desert," *Geog. Jour.*, LXXVI (1930), 512–515.

Rutter, Eldon: "The Hejaz," *Geog. Jour.*, LXXVII (1931), 97–109.

Shaffer, Robert: TENTS AND TOWERS OF ARABIA. New York: Dodd Mead (1952).

* Sanger, Richard H.: THE ARABIAN PENINSULA. Ithaca: Cornell Univ. Press (1954).

* Twitchell, K. S.: SAUDI ARABIA. Princeton: Princeton Univ. Press (1953).

van der Meulen, Daniel: THE WELLS OF IBN SA'UD. New York: Praeger (1957).

Von Wissmann, Hermann: "Arabien," in KLUTE HANDBUCH DER GEOGRAPHISCHEN WISSENSCHAFT, VI, VORDER AND SUDASIEN. Potsdam: Akademische Verlagsgesellschaft Athenaion (1937), 178–211.

Travel and Description

Butter, Grant C.: KINGS AND CAMELS. New York: Devin-Adair (1960).

Carruthers, Douglas: ARABIAN ADVENTURE. London: H. F. & G. Witherby (1935).

Cornwall, P. B.: "Ancient Arabia: Explorations in Hasa 1940–41," *Geog. Jour.*, CVII (1946), 28–50.

Cornwall, P. B.: "In Search of Arabia's Past," *Nat. Geog. Mag.*, XCIII (1948), 493–522.

DeGaury, Gerald: ARABIAN JOURNEY AND OTHER DESERT TRAVELS. London: G. G. Harrap (1950).

Doughty, Charles M.: TRAVELS IN ARABIA DESERTS. 2 vols., New York: Random House (1937).

Field, Henry: "Reconnaissance in Saudi Arabia," *Jour. Royal Central Asian Soc.*, XXXVII (1951), 185–197.

Ghafur, Abdul: "From America to Mecca on an Airborne Pilgrimage," *Nat. Geog. Mag.*, CIV (1953), 1–60.

Musil, Alois: ARABIA DESERTA. New York: Amer. Geog. Soc., (1927).

Musil, Alois: NORTHERN NEGD. New York: Amer. Geog. Soc., (1928).

Musil, Alois: IN THE ARABIAN DESERT. New York: Liveright (1930).

Palgrave, W. G.: CENTRAL AND EASTERN ARABIA. London: Macmillan (1873).

Philby, H. St. J. B.: THE HEART OF ARABIA. 2 vols., London and New York: Putman (1922–1923).

Philby, H. St. J. B.: ARABIA OF THE WAHHABIS. London: Constable (1928).

Philby, H. St. J. B.: ARABIA. London: Ernest Benn (1930).

Philby, H. St. J. B.: A PILGRIM IN ARABIA. London: Robert Hale (1946).

Philby, H. St. J. B.: ARABIAN DAYS: AN AUTOBIOGRAPHY. London: Robert Hale (1948).

Philby, H. St. J. B.: ARABIAN JUBILEE. London: Robert Hale (1951).

Philby, H. St. J. B.: ARABIAN HIGHLANDS. Ithaca: Cornell Univ. Press (1952).

Philby, H. St. J. B.: FORTY YEARS IN THE WILDERNESS. London: Robert Hale, (1957). [Philby is the Dean of Asiatic travellers; this is the latest of many volumes.]

Rutter, Eldon: THE HOLY CITIES OF ARABIA. London and New York: Putman (1928).

Rutter, Eldon: "The Holy Cities of Arabia," *Jour. Central Asian Soc.*, XVI (1929), 196–205.

Stark, Freya: A WINTER IN ARABIA. New York: Dutton (1940).

Thesiger, W.: "A Journey Through the Tihama, the Asir, and the Hijaz Mountains," *Geog. Jour.*, CX (1947), 188–200.

* Thesiger, W.: ARABIAN SANDS. New York: Dutton (1959). [Travel in the Rub al Khali]

Tweedy, Owen: "An Unbeliever Joins the Hadj," *Nat. Geog. Mag.*, LXV (1943), 760–789.

Van Ess, John: "Forty Years Among the Arabs," *Nat. Geog. Mag.*, LXXXII (1942), 382–420.

Williams, Maynard Owen: "Guest in Saudi Arabia," *Nat. Geog. Mag.*, LXXXVIII (1945). 463–487.

Wood, Junius B.: "A Visit to the Three Arab Kingdoms," *Nat. Geog. Mag.*, XLIII (1923), 535–563.

Land Form and Geology

Blanchard, Raoul: "Le Relief de l'Arabie Centrale," *Rev. de Geog. Alpine,* XIV (1926), 765–786.

Blanchard, Raoul: "La Structure de l'Arabie," *Rev. de Geog. Alpine,* XXV (1937), 258–259.

Lamare, Pierre: STRUCTURE GEOLOGIQUE DE L'ARABIE. Paris: Beranger (1936).

Picard, L.: "On the Structure of the Arabian Peninsula," *Bulletin,* Geol. Dept. Hebrew Univ., Jerusalem, Ser. I (1937).

* Twitchell, K. S.: "Water Resources of Saudi Arabia," *Geog. Rev.,* XXXIV (1944), 365–386.

Bedouins

Ashkenazi, Touvia: "The Anazah Tribes," *Southwestern Jour. Anthrop.,* IV (1948), 222–239.

* Dickson, H. R. P.: THE ARAB OF THE DESERT. London: Allen & Unwin (1949).

Glubb, J. B.: "The Salubba," in Coon, Carleton: A READER IN GENERAL ANTHROPOLOGY. New York: Holt (1956).

Musil, Alois: THE MANNERS AND CUSTOMS OF THE RUWALA BEDOUINS. New York: Amer. Geog. Soc. (1928).

Raswan, Carl R.: THE BLACK TENTS OF ARABIA. London: Hutchinson. Boston: Little, Brown (1935).

Van Ess, John: MEET THE ARAB. New York: John Day (1943).

Agriculture and Vegetation

* Crary, Douglas D.: "Recent Agricultural Developments in Saudi Arabia," *Geog. Rev.,* XLI (1951), 366–400.

Dowson, V. H. W.: "To Arabia in Search of Date Palm Offshoots," *Jour. Royal Central Asian Soc.,* XXXIX (1952), 45–56.

Mackie, J. B.: "Hasa: An Arabian Oasis," *Geog. Jour.,* LXIII (1924), 189–207.

Twitchell, K. S., Wathen, A. L., and Hamilton, J. G.: REPORT OF THE U.S. AGRICULTURAL MISSION TO SA'UDI ARABIA. Cairo: Misr. Press (1943).

Vesey-Fitzgerald, D. F.: "Vegetation of Red Sea Coast South of Jedda, Saudi Arabia," *Jour. Ecology,* XLIII (1955), 477–489.

Vesey-Fitzgerald, D. F.: "Vegetation of the Red Sea Coast North of Jedda, Saudi Arabia," *Jour. Ecology,* XLV (1957), 547–562.

Vesey-Fitzgerald, D. F.: "Vegetation of Central and Eastern Arabia," *Jour. Ecology,* XLV (1957), 779–798.

Vidal, F. S.: "Date Culture in the Oasis of al-Hasa," *Middle East Jour.,* VIII (1954), 417–428.

* Vidal, F. S.: THE OASIS OF AL-HASA. Dhahran: Arabian American Oil Co. (1955).

Zohary, M.: "Outline of the Vegetation in Wadi Arabia," *Jour. Ecology,* XXXII (1945), 204–213.

Bibliographies

Amer. Geog. Soc.: BIBLIOGRAPHY OF THE ARABIAN PENINSULA. New Haven, Conn.: Human Relations Area Files (1956).

DeGaury, Gerald: "An Arabian Bibliography," *Jour. Royal Central Asian Soc.,* XXXI (1944), 315–320.

Macro, Eric: BIBLIOGRAPHY OF THE ARABIAN PENINSULA. Miami: University of Miami Press (1958).

U. S. Library of Congress, Reference Dept.: THE ARABIAN PENINSULA, A SELECTED ANNOTATED LIST OF PERIODICALS, BOOKS, AND ARTICLES IN ENGLISH. Washington: Near East Section, Division of Orientalia (1951).

Aden and the Hadhramaut

Caton-Thompson, G. and Gardner, E. W.: "Climate, Irrigation and Early Man in the Hadhramaut," *Geog. Jour.,* XCIII (1939), 18–38.

Caton-Thompson, G.: "The Hadhramaut and its Past," *Jour. Royal Central Asian Soc.,* XXVI (1939), 79–92.

Cochrane, R. A.: "An Air Reconnaissance of the Hadhramaut," *Geog. Jour.,* LXXVII (1931), 209–216.

Daking, C. W. G.: "The Meteorology of Kamaran Island (Red Sea)," *Quart. Jour. Royal Meteorol. Soc.,* LVIII (1932), 441–447.

de Sturler-Raemaekers, M.: "Towns and Architecture of the Hadhramaut," *Jour. Royal Central Asian Soc.,* XL (1953), 241–248.

Eilts, Herman F.: "Along the Storied Incense Roads of Aden," *Nat. Geog. Mag.,* CXI (1957), 230–254.

Hamilton, R. A. B.: "The Social Organization of the Tribes of the Aden Protectorate," *Jour. Royal Central Asian Soc.,* XXX (1943), 142–152, 152–157, 267–274.

Helfritz, Hans: LAND WITHOUT SHADE. New York: Robert McBride (1936).

Huzayyin, S. A.: "Notes on Climatic Conditions in South-West Arabia," *Quart. Jour. Royal Meteorol. Soc.,* LXXI (1945), 129–140.

Ingrams, Doreen: "Excursion into the Hajr Province of Hadhramaut," *Geog. Jour.,* XCVIII (1941), 121–134.

Ingrams, Doreen: A SURVEY OF SOCIAL AND ECONOMIC CONDITIONS IN THE ADEN PROTECTORATE. Eritrea: Govt. Printer (1950).

* Ingrams, Harold: ARABIA AND ISLES. London: J. Murray (1942).

Ingrams, Harold and Ingrams, Doreen: "The Hadhramaut in Time of War," *Geog. Jour.,* CV (1945), 1–29.

Ingrams, Harold: "South-west Arabia: Today and Tomorrow," *Jour. Royal Central Asian Soc.,* XXXII (1945), 135–155.

Ingrams, Harold: "The Outlook in S.W. Arabia," *Jour. Royal Central Asian Soc.,* XLIII (1956), 176–186.

Ingrams, W. H.: "House Building in the Hadhramaut," *Geog. Jour.,* LXXXV (1935), 370–372.

Ingrams, W. H.: "Hadhramaut: A Journey to the Sei'ar Country and through the Wadi Maseila," *Geog. Jour.,* LXXXVIII (1936), 524–551.

Ingrams, W. H.: A REPORT ON THE SOCIAL, ECONOMIC AND POLITICAL CONDITIONS IN THE HADHRAMAUT, ADEN PROTECTORATE. London: H.M. Stationery Office (1936).

Ingrams, W. H.: "The Hadhramaut, Present and Future," *Geog. Jour.,* XCII (1938), 289–312.

Ingrams, W. H.: "The Exploration of the Aden Protectorate," *Geog. Rev.,* XXVIII (1938), 638–651.

Leslie, E. M. D.: "In South-west Arabia," *Canadian Geog. Jour.,* LIII (1956), 64–69.

Little, O. H.: THE GEOGRAPHY AND GEOLOGY OF MAKALLA. Cairo: Govt. Press (1925).

Phillips, Wendell: QATABAN AND SHEBA. New York: Harcourt, Brace (1955).

Arabia

* Pike, Ruthven W.: "Land and Peoples of the Hadhramaut, Aden Protectorate," *Geog. Rev.*, XXX (1940), 627–648.

Reilly, Bernard: "The Aden Protectorate," *Jour. Royal Central Asian Soc.*, XXVIII (1941), 132–145.

Serjeant, R. B.: "The Dhows of Aden," *Geog. Mag.*, XIV (1943), 296–301.

Stark, Freya: "Two Months in the Hadhramaut," *Geog. Jour.*, LXXXVII (1936), 113–126.

Stark, Freya: THE SOUTHERN GATES OF ARABIA: A JOURNEY IN THE HADHRAMAUT. New York: Dutton (1936).

Stark, Freya: "An Exploration in the Hadhramaut and Journey to the Coast," *Geog. Jour.*, XCIII (1939), 1–17.

Stark, Freya: SEEN IN THE HADHRAMAUT. New York: Dutton (1939).

Stark, Freya: "In Southwestern Arabia in Wartime," *Geog. Rev.*, XXXIV (1944), 349–364.

Stark, Freya: THE COAST OF INCENSE. AUTOBIOGRAPHY 1933–1939. London: Murray (1953).

Swayne, H. G. C.: "The Rock of Aden," *Nat. Geog. Mag.*, LXVIII (1935), 723–742.

van der Meulen, Daniel, and von Wissmann, N.: ADEN TO THE HADHRAMAUT. London: Murray (1947).

van der Meulen, Daniel: "Into Burning Hadhramaut," *Nat. Geog. Mag.*, LXII (1932), 387–429.

Bahrein

Belgrave, James H. D.: "A Brief Survey of the History of the Bahrein Islands," *Jour. of the Royal Central Asian Soc.*, XXXIX (1952), 57–68.

Belgrave, James H. D.: WELCOME TO BAHREIN; A COMPLETE ILLUSTRATED GUIDE FOR TOURISTS AND TRAVELLERS. Bahrein: Belgrave (1953).

Cornwall, P. B.: "The Tumuli of Bahrein," *Asia and the Americas*, XLIII (1943), 230–234.

Faroughby, Abbas: THE BAHREIN ISLANDS, 750– 1951. New York: Verry, Fischer (1951).

Williams, Maynard Owen: "Bahrein: Port of Pearls and Petroleum," *Nat. Geog. Mag.*, LXXXIX (1946), 195–210.

Kuwait

Case, Paul E.: "Boom Time in Kuwait," *Nat. Geog. Mag.*, CII (1952), 783–802.

DeCandole, E. A. V.: "Development in Kuwait," *Jour. Royal Central Asian Soc.*, XLVI (1959), 27–38.

* Dickson, H. R. P.: KUWAIT AND HER NEIGHBORS. London: Allen and Unwin (1956).

Epstein, Eliahn: "Kuwait," *Jour. Royal Central Asian Soc.*, XXV (1938) 595–603.

Lockhart, Lawrence: "Outline of the History of Kuwait," *Jour. Royal Central Asian Soc.*, XXXIV (1947), 262–274.

Southwell, C. A. P.: "Kuwait," *Jour. Royal Soc. of Arts*, CII (1953), 24–41.

Van Pelt, Mary C.: "The Sheikdom of Kuwait," *Middle East Jour.*, IV (1950), 12–26.

Muscat and Oman

Codrai, Ronald A.: "Oman, including the Trucial Coast," *Canadian Geog. Jour.*, XL (1950), 185–192.

Eccles, G. J.: "The Sultanate of Mascat and Oman," *Jour. Royal Central Asian Soc.*, XIV (1927), 19–42.

Lees, G. M.: "The Geology and Tectonics of Oman and Parts of South-Eastern Arabia," *Quart. Jour. Geol. Soc.*, LXXXIV (1928), 585–671.

Lees, G. M.: "The Physical Geography of South-Eastern Arabia," *Geog. Jour.,* LXXI (1928), 441–470.

Luke, Harry: "A Visit to Trucial Oman," *Geog. Mag.,* XXVII (1954), 243–247.

Melamid, Alexander: "Political Geography of Trucial Oman and Qatar," *Geog. Rev.,* XLIII (1953), 194–206.

* Morris, James: SULTAN IN OMAN. London: Faber (1957).

O'Shea, Raymond: THE SAND KINGS OF OMAN. London: Methuen & Co. (1947).

Rentz, George: OMAN AND THE SOUTHERN SHORES OF THE PERSIAN GULF. Cairo: Arabian American Oil Co. (1952).

Thesiger, Wilfred: "Travel on the Trucial Coast," *Geog. Mag.,* XXII (1949), 110–118.

Thesiger, Wilfred: "Desert Borderlands of Oman," *Geog. Jour.,* CLVI (1950), 137–171.

Thomas, Bertram: "The Musandam Peninsula and its People," *Jour. Royal Central Asian Soc.,* XVI (1929), 71–86.

Vesey-Fitzgerald, Desmond: "From Hasa to Oman by Car," *Geog. Rev.,* XLI (1951), 544–560.

Persian Gulf

Bowen, Richard LeBaron, Jr.: "Arab Dhows of Eastern Arabia," *Amer. Neptune,* IX (1949), 87–132.

Bowen, Richard LeBaron, Jr.: "The Dhow Sailor," *Amer. Neptune,* XI (1951), 161–202.

Bowen, Richard LeBaron, Jr.: "Marine Industries of Eastern Arabia," *Geog. Rev.,* XLI (1951), 384–400.

Bowen, Richard LeBaron, Jr.: "The Pearl Fisheries of the Persian Gulf," *Middle East Jour.,* V (1951), 161–180.

Codrai, Ronald: "Desert Sheikdoms of Arabia's Pirate Coast," *Nat. Geog. Mag.,* CX (1956), 65–104.

Erdman, Donald S.: "Fishing in Arabia," *Scientific Monthly,* LXX (1950), 58–65.

Hay, Rupert: "The Persian Gulf States and Their Boundary Problems," *Geog. Jour.,* CXX (1954), 433–445.

Hay, Rupert: THE PERSIAN GULF STATES. Washington: Middle East Institute (1959).

Hydrographic Dept., Admiralty: PERSIAN GULF PILOT. London: Hydrographic Dept. Admiralty (1955).

Rihani, Ameen: "AROUND THE COASTS OF ARABIA. London: Constable (1930).

* Owen, Roderick: THE GOLDEN BUBBLE. London: Collins (1957).

Villiers, Alan: "Some Aspects of the Arab Dhow Trade," *Middle East Jour.,* II (1948), 399–416.

Williams, Kenneth: "Britain and the Persian Gulf," *Geog. Mag.,* XIV (1941), 1–11.

* Wilson, Arnold T.: THE PERSIAN GULF. London: Allen and Unwin (1954).

The Rub al Khali

Bagnold, R. A.: "Sand Formations in Southern Arabia," *Geog. Jour.,* CXVII (1951), 78–86.

Bunker, D. G.: "The South-West Borderlands of the Rub al Khali," *Geog. Jour.,* CXIX (1953), 421–430.

Helfritz, Hans: "The First Crossing of Southern Arabia," *Geog. Rev.,* XXV (1935), 395–407.

Philby, H. St. J. B.: THE EMPTY QUARTER. New York: Holt, London: Constable (1933).

Philby, H. St. J. B.: "Rub' al Khali," *Geog. Jour.,* LXXXI (1933), 1–26.

Thesiger, Wilfred: "A New Journey in Southern Arabia," *Geog. Jour.,* CVIII (1946), 129–145.

Arabia

* Thesiger, Wilfred: "Across the Empty Quarter," *Geog. Jour.*, CXI (1948), 1–21.

Thesiger, Wilfred: "A Further Journey Across the Empty Quarter," *Geog. Jour.*, CXIII (1949), 20–46.

Thesiger, W. P.: "The Badu of Southern Arabia," *Jour. Royal Central Asian Soc.*, XXXVII (1950), 66–76.

Thomas, Bertram: "The South-Eastern Borderlands of Rub Al Khali," *Geog. Jour.*, LXXIII (1929), 193–215.

Thomas, Bertram: "A Journey into Rub' Al Khali, The Southern Arabian Desert," *Geog. Jour.*, LXXVII (1931), 1–57.

* Thomas, Bertram: "A Camel Journey Across the Rub' Al Khali," *Geog. Jour.*, LXXVIII (1931), 1–57.

* Thomas, Bertram: ARABIA FELIX: ACROSS THE "EMPTY QUARTER" OF ARABIA. New York: Scribners (1932).

Thomas, Bertram: "Ubar, the Atlantis of the Sands of Rub' al Khali," *Jour. Royal Central Asian Soc.*, XX (1933), 259–265.

Yemen

Clark, Harlan B.: "Yemen—Southern Arabia's Mountain Wonderland," *Nat. Geog. Mag.*, XCII (1947), 631–672.

Crane, Charles R.: "Visit to the Red Sea Littoral and the Yaman," *Jour. Royal Central Asian Soc.*, XV (1928), 48–67.

Cressey, George B.: "Land Use in Yemen," *Annals Assoc. Amer. Geog.*, XLVII (1958), 257–258.

* Fayein, Claudie: A FRENCH DOCTOR IN THE YEMEN. London: Hale (1957).

Field, Henry: ANCIENT AND MODERN MAN IN S.W. ASIA. Miami: Univ. of Miami Press (1956).

Helfritz, Hans: THE YEMEN, A SECRET JOURNEY. London: Allen (1958).

Helfritz, Hans: "To the Queen of Sheba's Legendary Capital," *Nat. Hist.*, XL (1937), 491-504.

Hoogstraal, Harry: "Yemen Opens its Doors to Progress," *Nat. Geog. Mag.*, CI (1952), 213–244.

Ingrams, Harold: "A Journey in the Yemen," *Jour. Royal Central Asian Soc.*, XXXIII (1946), 58–69.

Macro, Eric: "Yemen—a Brief Survey," *Jour. Royal Central Asian Soc.*, XXXVI (1949), 42–53.

Macro, Eric: "The Yemen: Some Recent Literature," *Jour. Royal Central Asian Soc.*, XLV (1958), 43–51.

Macro, Eric: BIBLIOGRAPHY ON YEMEN WITH NOTES ON MOCHA. Miami: Univ. of Miami Press (1959).

Pearn, Norman S. and Barlow, Vernon: QUEST FOR SHEBA. London: Ivor Nicholson & Watson (1937).

Philby, H. St. J. B.: "The Land of Sheba," *Geog. Jour.*, (1938) 1–21, 107–132.

Philby, H. St. J. B.: SHEBA'S DAUGHTERS: BEING A RECORD OF TRAVEL IN SOUTHERN ARABIA. London: Methuen (1939).

Rathjens, C., and vonWissmann, H.: "Sanaa, Eine Sudarabische Stadtlandschaft," *Zeitschrift Gesellschaft Erdkunde* (1929), 329–353.

Robertson, W.: "Yemen Journey, 1942," *Scot. Geog. Mag.*, LIX (1943), 63–70; LXI (1945), 46–51.

Robertson, W.: "Sanaa and the Qat-eaters," *Scot. Geog. Mag.*, LVIII (1942), 49–53.

Ryckmans, G.: "Through Sheba's Kingdom," *Geog. Mag.*, XXVII (1954), 129–137.

* Scott, Hugh: IN THE HIGH YEMEN. London: John Murray (1947).

Scott, Hugh: "The Peoples of South-west Arabia," *Jour. Royal Central Asian Soc.*, XXVIII (1941), 146–151.

Scott, Hugh: "The Yemen in 1937–1938," *Jour. Royal Central Asian Soc.*, XXVII (1940), 21–44.

Scott, Hugh: "A Journey to the Yemen," *Geog. Jour.*, XCIII (1939), 97–125.

Serjeant, R. B.: "The Mountain Tribes of the Yemen," *Geog. Mag.*, XV (1942), 66–72.

CHAPTER 12

Egypt

Egypt and the Arab World
The Nile: Water in the Desert
People and Livelihood
The Suez Canal: Egypt's Second River
References

EGYPT AND THE ARAB WORLD

EGYPT, or Misr, is not a part of Southwest Asia, but for 1,300 years it has been such a significant member of the Arab and Islamic worlds that it cannot be omitted from this volume. The following pages present only a few highlights of its geography, particularly as they relate to Southwest Asia.

The Egyptians are properly Hamitic in race rather than Semitic; in some ways they look westward into Africa rather than east into Asia. However, in historical terms, Egyptian conquests have frequently pressed into the Levant and beyond; while in reverse, Persian commerce and rule followed the Fertile Crescent to the valley of the Nile.

Not until the adoption of its new constitution in 1956, did Egypt formally proclaim itself as an Arab state, but since then it has clearly captured Arab imagination. During the middle of this century, Egypt emerged as a modern state and now strives for leadership throughout the Arab world.

(Opposite) Tall apartment houses in Cairo symbolize the progressive character of modern Egypt. (Courtesy Egyptian State Tourist Administration, New York.)

Whereas the cultures which developed in most of Southwest Asia were exposed to large-scale population movements and extensive cultural contact, Egypt was an isolated pocket where man matured without any major break in the historical continuity. The Egyptian peasant of today is the recognizable descendant of the farmer who paid grain taxes to the pharaohs. This historic continuity and homogeneity are important parts of the present geography. The environment provided by the Nile was both bountiful and demanding; for most people the price of livelihood was a lifetime of unremitting toil. The bordering desert was not a challenge to be conquered but an enemy to be held back; all life turned toward the river.

The Egyptian Revolution of 1953 which overthrew King Farouk and established Gamal Abdul Nasser as President not only brought about social changes within Egypt but also set a beacon for Arab nationalism from Iraq to Morocco. It combined the goal of the French Revolution of 1789 with its desire for a more responsive government and that of the American Revolution of 1776

EGYPT DATA

Area	386,100 square miles
	1,000,000 square kilometers
Arable area	26,100 square kilometers
Population	24,026,000 (1957)
	19,021,840 (1947 census)
	14,213,364 (1927 census)
	11,287,359 (1907 census)
Cities	
Cairo	2,673,800
Alexandria	1,261,100
Port Said	208,100
Tanta	164,800
Mahalla el Kubra	136,800
Suez	134,400
Mansura	132,900

with its goal of eliminating foreign influence.

History may question the extent to which colonialism has retarded the development of the Arab world, but the obvious fact is that the people who live there believe that European and American influence has been a handicap. If there are times when the Arab world still appears anti-Western, it may rather reflect a desire to be themselves, with echos of long pent-up resentment.

In 1958, Egypt joined with Syria to form a new sovereignty, the United Arab Republic. Legislation provided for the abolition of separate Egyptian and Syrian citizenship, and stated that the Arab fatherland comprised the area from the Atlantic Ocean to the Persian Gulf. The proclamation of union announced that the door was open to any other Arab state to join the union "for the purpose of protecting the Arab peoples from harm and evil, strengthening Arab sovereignty, and safeguarding its existence."

Although Egypt has an open boundary on all sides, there is almost no access across the desert, and only two ports face the Mediterranean: Alexandria and Port Said. The Red Sea coast is bordered by coral reefs and lacks good harbors. Few large countries are so limited in accessibility. Cairo serves with Beirut as an aerial gateway to the East.

It may be well to devote a paragraph to the term "Arab." The word is defined in *Webster's New International Dictionary* as follows:

> One of the people which from the earliest known time has occupied the Arabian peninsula. In ancient usage the term was confined to the Bedouin tribes in the north of the peninsula and east of Palestine; in modern times it is applied not only to the pure Semites of Arabia, but also to their descendants, many of whom are mixed with native races, in northern, eastern, and central Africa, in Madagascar, India, and the Malay Archipelago, and in various parts of Syria and Persia. The Arabs are one of the oldest and purest of peoples, and, with the Jews, constitute the best modern representation of the Semitic race.

In view of the racial mixtures which prevail across Southwest Asia and North Africa, it is helpful to think broadly of the term, "Arab" in connection with language and culture, rather than ethnography. In any event, the pure Semites of Swasia regard themselves as superior to the Hamites, Berbers, and others of North Africa.

The League of Arab States was set up at Cairo in 1945 for the purpose of maintaining Arab solidarity. It includes the United Arab Republic, Iraq, Jordan, Lebanon, Saudi Arabia, Yemen, the Sudan, and Libya. A considerable part of its early motivation was anti-Israel. The League has had only limited political effectiveness, in part because of rivalries within its membership, but it serves as a psychological rallying point. For the most part, it has been dominated by Egypt.

Political coherence, if voluntary, requires a community of economic and cultural interests. There should be some common history or motives, a willingness to cooperate, and compatible legislative needs. Continuity of

NOTE: I am indebted to Professor Hassan Awad of Cairo for some of my understanding of the geography of Egypt.

The three pyramids of Giza lie near the edge of the desert next to the floodplain of the Nile, and opposite the city of Cairo. The farthest was built by Khufu, the second by Khephren, and the third by Menkaure. (Courtesy Arab Information Center, New York.)

territory may not be essential, witness Alaska and the continental United States, or the two parts of Pakistan, but its absence raises serious difficulties. Unfortunately for the Arab world, any overland access is blocked by the position of Israel.

Three countries contest for Arab leadership: Egypt, Saudi Arabia, and Iraq. All face geographic limitations in the weakness of their base, and none seems to have the requisite strength. Between each of the centers of gravity are isolating deserts. No railroad or road links the three capitals, few regular ship services connect their seaports, and even air travel is limited. None have had much commerce with the others, nor are there important goods which the others might supply. Unity must center around ideology rather than economics. Radio broadcasts are one of the major links and the means of propaganda.

A glance at the population map of Swasia, page 37, shows how few people live in these three states. Saudi Arabia's inhabited area, dispersed and in oases, is even more difficult to organize than an island archipelago. Egypt does have a compact concentration in the delta, but in the Upper Nile settlement is a mere shoestring through the desert. Inhabited Iraq also occupies only a part of

Egypt's major center of heavy industry is the blast furnace at Helwan near Cairo. While the country has its own iron ore, coking coal must be imported. (Courtesy Egyptian State Tourist Administration, Cairo.)

its whole. Not only do these countries lack a coherent internal settlement pattern, they also lack regional continuity across the intervening Levant states. It is difficult to see how Cairo could hold together and dominate Southwest Asia; the same is true for both Baghdad and Riyadh.

Some sort of Arab union or federation is desired by many of the people themselves and presumably by the United States; perhaps it will ultimately be in two parts, one for North Africa, dominated by Cairo, the other for Asia, possibly centered on Damascus.

The accompanying table represents an attempt to weigh some of the various geopolitical factors. In terms of people, Egypt counts nearly as large a population as all of Arab Asia combined. In education, modernization, and administrative ability it is far in the lead. Egyptian teachers, contractors, and technicians supply essential needs throughout the Arabian Peninsula; thousands of students from other Arab lands come to Cairo for their education. Egypt is a major producer of films and a publisher of books in Arabic. Large numbers of Egyptians have studied abroad, especially in France, so that

THREE ARAB STATES

	Saudi Arabia	*Egypt*	*Iraq*
PEOPLE			
Race	Semites	Hamites	Semites, Kurds, others
Population	6,000,000	25,000,000	6,500,000
Annual Increase	?	2.5%	high
Capital City	Riyadh; 150,000	Cairo; 3,000,000	Baghdad; 1,300,000
Illiteracy	high but declining	75%, rapidly declining	90%, declining
University students	—	75,000	4,000
Trained Civil Servants	dozens	thousands	hundreds
Wealth and culture	very rich to poor	very rich to very poor	rich to poor
Modern Westernization	beginning	advanced	moderate
AGRICULTURE			
Soil	desert types	fertile alluvium	salinity problems
Water	very limited	the Nile	Tigris and Euphrates
Irrigation	100% irrigation	100% irrigation	irrigation in south, rain in Fertile Crescent
Food Supply	adequate	large wheat import	exports barley
Area of Cultivation	5,000,000 acres	6,500,000 acres	6,000,000 acres
Possibilities of expansion	small	limited	extensive
ECONOMICS			
Major export	oil	cotton, teachers	oil
Extra revenue	$300,000,000; oil	$25,000,000; Suez	$200,000,000; oil
Capital	superabundant	limited	abundant
Industry	negligible	own and operate factories	limited
Technicians	outside help essential	surplus skill for export	limited
Major needs	skill	capital	skill
Development potential	low	moderate	high
OTHER ASSETS			
Religion	the Holy Places	Al Azhar University	Shia shrines
Politics	immaturity	relative maturity	uncertain

by now the country can supply its own engineers, doctors, and civil servants with a surplus for export. The country is trying to travel at the rate of a century in a decade, but like Alice in *Through The Looking Glass,* Egypt must run hard simply not to stand still.

Egypt faces serious problems in its rapidily increasing population and the limited possibilities of feeding them. Rural land redistribution has helped, but there still persists a very wide gulf between the very rich and the desperately poor. Egypt and Iraq have about the same cultivated area, but the population in the former is four times as great. Whereas the former has only limited possibilities of expansion, Iraq might considerably enlarge her agricultural acreage.

It is in the field of financial resources that Egypt is most limited. Saudi Arabia and Iraq both enjoy a tremendous asset in their oil royalties. Egypt's chief outside earning power lies in the Suez Canal tolls, many of them from oil tankers in transit and from the export of cotton. Part of the receipts from cotton must be used for buying fertilizer and wheat, so that there is little net gain. Egypt needs outside capital, but the problem of repayment is as yet unsolved.

As a manufacturer, Egypt is beginning to export a variety of goods; in fact, the value of the products of her factories approximates those of her fields. Textiles come first, along with other items of light industry; and she has the only iron and steel plant in the Arab world. Egypt is also the only country which is able to operate its own oil industry by itself, from geology to refining.

Arabia has enjoyed great prestige as the homeland of the Holy Places of Islam. Every faithful Moslem should make the pilgrimage to Mecca, if his means permit, and this has given Saudi Arabia a political as well as spiritual hold on Islam. However, the assets of fabulous royalties and spiritual centrality apparently do not outweigh the lack of administrative skill and sound geographic advantages.

Iraq can scarcely hope to be the leading Arab state, but it resists being swallowed up in a federation with Egypt. Iraq alone has large undeveloped agricultural potentials.

Egypt's great popularity in Swasia dates from the revolution of 1953. Mr. Nasser became the symbol of what most Arabs wanted: a government which cared for the welfare of the people and which was prepared to demonstrate its independence from foreign control.

THE NILE: WATER IN THE DESERT

THE NILE, or Bahr en Nil, receives most of its water from two countries near the Equator. Its eastern branch, the Blue Nile or Bahr el Azraq, heads near Lake Tana in Ethiopia. The western and longer branch, the White Nile or Bahr el Abyad, begins at the outlet of Lake Victoria in Uganda and is thus sometimes known as the Victoria Nile. These tributaries join at Khartoum, 1,300 miles south of the Mediterranean. While the highlands receive more than fifty inches of rain, the plain north of Khartoum has less than five inches. Once the various branches of the Nile leave the humid southern Sudan near latitude 10°N., which roughly corresponds to the twenty-inch rainfall line, the runoff is less than evaporation so that they receive no tributary streams. The volume of the river at Khartoum is larger than at its mouth.

Hydroelectric power is generated near both lakes. The Owen Falls installation at the outlet of Lake Victoria was originally planned merely for power, but the Egyptian Government contributed a million pounds in order to raise the dam three feet above lake level and to compensate property owners along the shore. The dam was completed in 1954, but, since Lake Victoria covers 26,-828 square miles, it will require twenty-five years to raise the water level to the crest of the dam. This will then become the world's largest reservoir.

When Winston Churchill visited Owen Falls in 1908, he wrote in his *My African Journey:*[1]

> So much power running to waste, such a coign of vantage unoccupied, such a lever to control the natural forces of Africa ungripped, cannot

[1] Churchill, Winston: *My African Journey*. London: Hodder and Stoughton (1908), 132–133, 120.

but vex and stimulate the imagination. And what fun to make the immemorial Nile begin its journey by diving through a turbine . . . . It is possible that nowhere else in the world could so enormous a mass of water be held up by so little masonry.

Lake Victoria lies at 3,720 feet and is 3,473 miles from the mouth of the river. After dropping down through 500 miles of canyons, waterfalls, and lakes, the Nile enters the Sudan and spreads out in a vast swamp, known as the Sud, covering 10 million acres. Evapotranspiration is high and out of the 27 billion cubic meters which enter the area, only 14 billion leaves the Sud. Ambitious plans call for a 186-mile canal to speed the flow of the White Nile, thus draining the swamps and turning them into cropland, as well as greatly increasing the water available for irrigation down river. Other reservoir schemes involve a dam at the exit of Lake Albert, as well as hydroelectric plants at Murchison Falls and elsewhere. To bring all of the upper Nile into integrated control will require decades

Swamps in the desert are an anachronism. In addition to these marshlands along the middle Nile, there are similar areas of inundation in Afghanistan and Iran along the lower Helmund, in southern Iraq on the Tigris and Euphrates, and in the Ghab of the Orontes River in Syria.

The two main tributaries of the Nile have very different regimes. The White, or Victoria, Nile leaves most of its silt in the swamps of the Sud, which also serves as a reservoir for its peak flow, so that floods are uncommon and the flow is evened out. From February to August, the White Nile represents 80 per cent of the volume at Khartoum. The Blue Nile from Ethiopia, with no natural storage en route, pours its full flood of monsoon water and silt into the main stream; this seasonal variability is the uncertain factor in down-river floods.

The Blue and the White Nile unite at

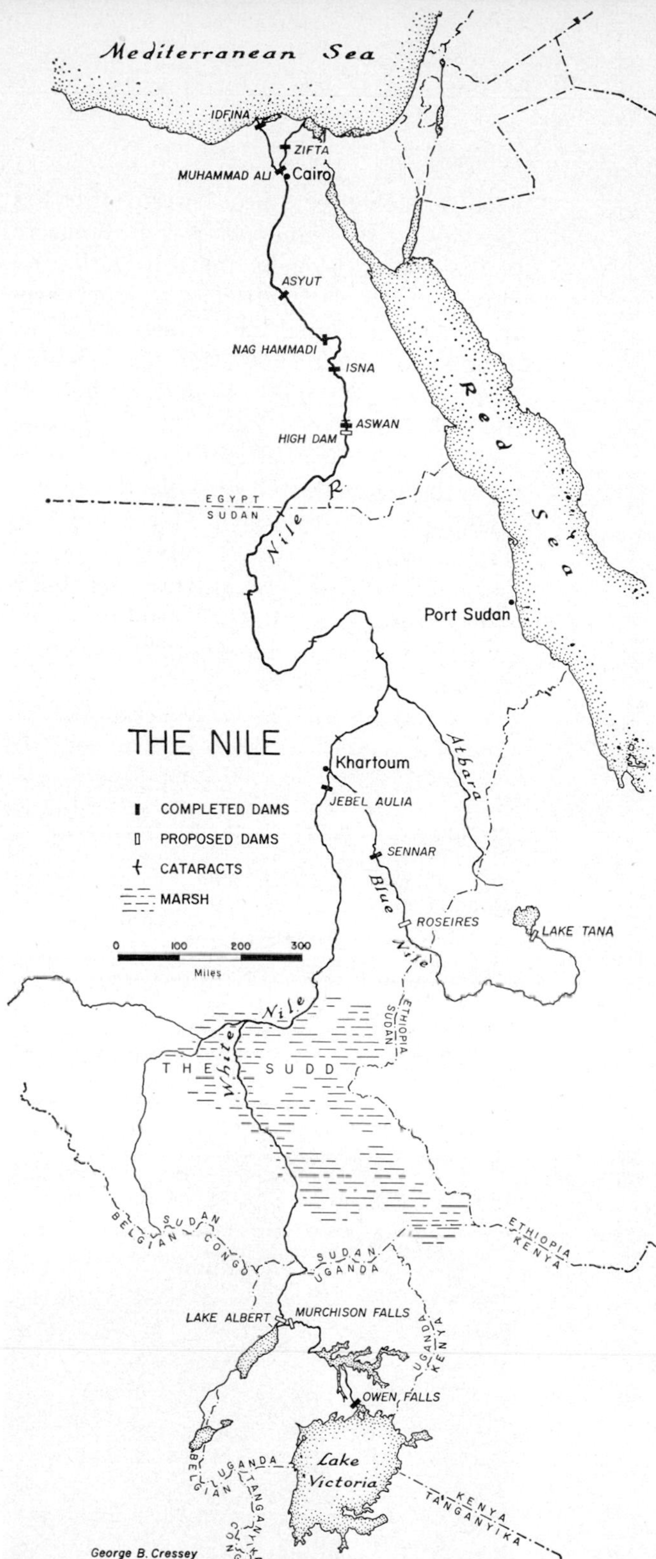

Egypt is the gift of the Nile, for the river brings life-giving water to the desert from the Ethiopian highlands.

Khartoum; between their lower courses lies the Gezira, or island. This 5 million-acre plain is being brought under irrigation by gravity canals, with cotton as the chief crop. In areas where canal water is not available, pumps and flood inundation are bringing large areas into production. Elsewhere in the Sudan, hundreds of ponds have been dug by heavy machinery as rain water reservoirs for watering cattle and for village use, thus opening up thousands of square miles to settlement.

In cultural and physical terms, the Sudan has two distinct parts. The humid south, including the Sud swamps, is inhabited by 3 million Nilotic people, negroid in race, pagan in religion, and socially backward. The dry north, with 7 million people, is Arab and Moslem. Since the latter once raided the south for slaves, animosity still prevails and governmental problems result. The area was an Anglo–Egyptian Condominium until 1956 when the Republic of the Sudan became independent, with the capital at Khartoum.

The old Aswan Dam raises the Nile water 123 feet. The new High Dam, upstream, is three times as high. (Courtesy Egyptian State Tourist Administration, Cairo.)

During the period of joint British and Egyptian control, an agreement recognized Egypt's historic rights to the Nile and restricted the use of water by the Sudan. With independence and the possibilities of a great expansion in her irrigated area, the Sudan is anxious to revise this allocation. Even more than the international rivers in Southwest Asia, the Nile presents serious political problems. Egypt urgently needs more water, but the Sudan has large areas which might become productive if it had access to the river. With half Egypt's population, the Sudan is allocated only one-twelfth of the water.

Under the Agreement of 1929, the Sudan was restricted in its withdrawal of water from the Nile, with all the rest reserved for Egypt. During the low-water period from January 1 to July 15, no water may be taken by the Sudan except as a charge against that which she has stored behind the Sennar Dam on the Blue Nile. No restriction operates for the rest of the year when the Nile is high. The flood period starts in May but does not become conspicuous until mid-July. The river is so silty that storage is impractical until October 31. The Sudan thus depends on water which it can accumulate behind the Sennar Dam during November and December. Water from another reservoir in the Sudan behind the Jebel Aulia Dam (1937) is entirely reserved for Egyptian use.

The Nile enters Egypt north of Wadi Halfa, 400 miles from the Mediterranean. Downstream lies the Aswan Dam, built in 1902 and enlarged in 1912 and 1933. This raises the water by a height of 123 feet. Nearby is the first of the six cataracts and the famous quarries of granite and syenite from which monumental blocks were once exported as far as interior Syria. The reservoir has eliminated much of the seasonal flooding that once characterized lower Egypt. Since the area is exceedingly hot and dry, evaporation losses are excessive; thus the Aswan Reservoir loses nearly ten feet of water per year.

Egypt now irrigates some 7 million acres and has a further 2 million acres more which it might be possible to irrigate with additional storage. In order to provide this extra water, a new High Dam is under construction about four miles south of Aswan.

The High Dam, or Sudd el Aali, represents a major engineering project, technically feasible but of imposing economic uncertainty. It involves a structure three miles long and 365 feet high, at a cost of well over a billion dollars. The water to be stored will have a volume four times that of Lake Mead on the Colorado River and will conserve the surplus flow for years of low discharge. The water will irrigate 1.3 million acres of new land, convert 670,000 acres now under basin irrigation to the perennial type, generate 720,000 kilowatts of hydroelectricity, and permit a major expansion of the food supply. These advantages must be balanced against the high costs, excessive evaporation, and silt accumulation behind the dam.

The reservoir will extend southward for 344 miles, penetrating 125 miles into the Sudan where it will flood Wadi Halfa and cover the present homes of 50,000 Sudanese. The Sudan is to receive financial compensation plus permission to withdraw an additional allotment of water. Without an agreement with the Sudan as to Egypt's share of the Nile water, the High Dam project would have been impossible.

Six dams or barrages have already been built in Egypt, plus two in the Sudan. Others are proposed.

The Nile of the desert begins south of Khartoum. From here to Cairo only a thin ribbon of green vegetation separates the muddy river from the dusty desert. The area is virtually rainless and so desolate that there are few nomads. The settled farmers who live there have generally been safe from desert raids. In places the flood plain widens to a mile or more; elsewhere it is only a few hundred yards in width.

NILE WATER BUDGET[1]

Minimum annual flow	42
Average annual flow	84
Maximum annual flow	180
Agreement of 1929	
To Egypt	48
To Sudan	4
To Mediterranean	32
High dam capacity	130
Sudan's claim	22 to 35

[1] In billion cubic meters.

The following vivid picture of the lower Nile was written in the seventh century by the Arab general, Amr ibn el As, who conquered the country for the Caliph Omar.[1]

> There, an arid waste, lies a desert: on either hand it rises and between the heights lies wonderland. To the west, the range forms a chain of sand hills; to the east, it looks like the belly of a lean horse or a camel's back. This, O Ruler of the Faithful, is Egypt. But all its wealth comes from the blessed river that moves through it with dignity of a caliph. Regular as sun and moon, it rises and falls again. The hour comes when all the springs of the world must pay their tribute to the king of rivers, which Providence has lifted high above all others; then the waters rise and quit their bed, and flood the plains, depositing upon them their fertile mud. Then all the villages are cut off one from the other; only boats can pass between them, and they are countless as the leaves on the palm tree.
>
> But then, in its wisdom the river re-enters the bounds appointed by fate, so that those who live their way may collect the treasure it has confided

[1] Quoted in Emil Ludwig: *The Nile*. New York: Viking Press (1937). 313.

The Nile creates a ribbon-like oasis which extends for hundreds of miles south of Cairo, in most places less than a mile wide. This view is at Khartoum. (Courtesy British Overseas Airways Corp.)

to Mother Earth. And thus, O Ruler of the Faithful, Egypt presents in turn the picture of a dry, sandy waste, of a stretch of silver water, of a swamp covered with thick mud, of a lush green meadow, of a garden rich with many flowers, and again of spreading fields covered with resplendent crops.

Small wonder that the ancient Egyptians prayed for floods and watched the measured rise of the river, recorded in *ells*. Thus Pliny wrote, "Twelve ells means hunger, thirteen sufficiency, fourteen joy, fifteen security, sixteen abundance." Later on, Strabo wrote that "nothing in Egypt is so useful as these Nileometers, both to the farmers, whom they show how much water they can count on and what they must save for their embankments, and to the government which bases its taxes on them, since every increase in the volume of the river and the quantity of water means an increase of taxation."

These measurements are now known for over a thousand years. In Anthony and Cleopatra, Act II, Scene 5, Shakespeare wrote, "The higher the Nilus swells, The more it promises: as it ebbs, the seedsman upon the slime and ooze scatters his grain and shortly comes the harvest."

Such abundance in the midst of aridity, with its surplus of grain for export, naturally gave rise to legends. One exuberant writer of the eighteenth century wrote that sand had to be mixed with the soil, otherwise it would be too rich; even the animals and the women were so fertile that the sheep

Long-staple cotton is Egypt's major export. This scene is in the delta below Cairo. (Courtesy Arab Information Center, New York.)

lambed twice a year and the women generally bore twins.

Lower Egypt begins at Cairo and includes the delta-shaped delta with its network of distributary channels and canals. Here live most Egyptians, occupying one of the world's largest oases. Nowhere in the world is the transition from fertile land to the desert more abrupt. The desert takes command a foot beyond the outermost irrigation canal. When Herodotus observed that Egypt was the gift of the Nile, he was profoundly correct.

The delta is 135 miles wide and extends 155 miles north from Cairo. In contrast to the thin strip of land under cultivation farther south, here is a vast garden, "silvery in September, emerald in November, and golden in August." Cotton is king; whereas the delta once shipped wheat to ancient Rome, it now imports wheat from Australia.

Sixteen miles north of Cairo, a barrage controls the separation of the Nile into its two main branches, the Damietta and Rosetta mouths. These, in turn, divide and redivide to water the delta. When the Nile is low and much of the water is withdrawn for irrigation, the flow of these branches is so low that downstream barrages must be closed to prevent the inflow of the sea. One of the waterways which takes off to the east is the Ismailia Canal which leads to the Suez Canal; a canal farther upstream leads to the Faiyum Depression.

So great is the pressure for food that parts of the swampy delta near the coast have been diked and pumped out as in Holland; as a

Tall apartment houses in Cairo look down on old Nile felluccas with their picturesque sails. Houseboats line the banks. (Courtesy Arab Information Center, New York.)

result, cultivated fields lie below sea level.

Rainfall and runoff are seasonal in the East African highlands. Flood flows take two months to reach the delta, arriving toward the end of July and continuing until September. Prior to the construction of the upstream dams, the water rose some twenty-five feet, thus inundating wide areas. This created Egypt's famous basin-type irrigation. When the river subsided, the moist fields could be cultivated. Seasonal flooding washed out the salts, contributed silt from the Ethiopian highlands, and established a seasonal pattern of crops, known as *nili.*

With the partial regulation of the Nile, summer levels rise but ten feet. In place of basin flooding, water is now conveyed to the fields by gravity canals or in some cases is supplied by pumps. Cultivation can be continued throughout the year, with two or more crops in place of one. Crops grown from October till January belong to the *shitwi* season, while *seifi* crops are grown from February till September. As the water table now remains high, salts tend to accumulate, so that deep drainage ditches have been dug, from which it is generally necessary to pump the outflow. Some flood irrigation still takes place south of Cairo, but not intentionally in the delta. Water for individual fields is often lifted by a hinged pole and bucket, known as a *shadoof,* or by an Archimedes screw. These are still in use but mechanical pumps are now widely used. The exhaust of their engines can be heard around every village.

PEOPLE AND LIVELIHOOD

EGYPT APPEARS large on the map for it covers nearly 400,000 square miles, an area equal to Texas and Arizona combined. However, in terms of cultivated area it measures only 13,500 square miles, approximately the size of Massachusetts plus Connecticut. Over 96 per cent of the country is desert, and not all of the rest is actually productive for agriculture. From this limited area along the Nile, most of its 25 million people must find their livelihood. Egypt's present story is summed up as too many people on too little land.

One of the most impressive problems of Egypt concerns the rate of population increase, now among the highest in the world. When the French occupied the country at the beginning of the nineteenth century, Egypt contained 10 million people. By the middle of the twentieth century the total was 25 million. Egypt appears to be a nation smothered by itself. In 1952 the birth rate was 45 per 1,000 and the death rate stood at 17, with an infant mortality rate of 127 per 1,000.

Three-fifths of the people are farmers, many of them desperately poor, and it is on the basis of these *fellahin,* or plowmen, that Egypt supports its economy. Land redistribution has brought improvement, but it is still true that 50 per cent of the national income goes to 2 per cent of the people.

Population concentrations along the Nile are among the densest in the world, not exceeded in eastern or southern Asia. Many rural areas support 3,000 people per square mile, and more. Only by the most painstaking labor is life possible. Millions of families live in one or two room mud huts; their few possessions limited to some reed floor mats, simple utensils, and one or two garments per person. Food is cooked on a primus cooker or over dung fires whose acrid smoke keeps out some of the mosquitos but irritates the eyes, already inflamed by trachoma. The liver fluke, *bilharzia,* is parasitic in most peasants and enervates great numbers.

The traditional method of cultivation called for one crop a year, following the Nile floods which submerged the land for several weeks. With the regulation of the river, flooding is controlled, and perennial canal irrigation has largely replaced flood agriculture. There are three main crop seasons. From February till May, planting takes place for cotton, rice, sugar cane, millet, peanuts, sesame, and vegetables; these are the *seifi* crops. Old style flood-watered crops, known as *nili,* are sown around July; they include rice as well as some millet. The winter, or *shitwi* crops, are planted in November and comprise wheat, barley, flax, and vegetables.

Cotton rules supreme as the great cash crop. It occupies one-fifth of the cultivated acreage, and in many years cotton pays for half to three-quarters of the nation's imports. The fiber is long, and the quality is among the best in the world. Cotton is now grown so widely that wheat production has not kept pace with the increase in population. Whereas Egypt was once an exporter of wheat, she must now import half a million tons a year.

With year-round cultivation, the soil becomes depleted so that heavy applications of fertilizers are necessary. Egypt has its own phosphates, but nitrogen and potash must be bought from abroad.

Egypt's agricultural potential appears limited. Along most of the Nile valley the river flows between bluffs several hundred feet high. Even if the bordering desert soils were not sterile, it would be impractical to lift water from the river to these upper levels. Around the delta, fertile alluvium gives way to sands devoid of organic material, whose productive capacity is limited. Within the delta there are still marsh lands which might be reclaimed, but only at a high cost.

On the assumption that Egypt may continue to command the lion's share of the Nile water, its full use will bring into cultivation all the remaining good land, an increase of one-fifth. While the extent of agricultural land has been raised by only 5 per cent during the first half of the twentieth century, harvested acreage has increased by 20 per cent due to perennial irrigation and double cropping.

Although agriculture supplies the greatest source of wealth, there are mineral assets as well. While none appear to be of major importance, the variety is considerable. Almost all occur between the Nile and the Red Sea. Oil is Egypt's most valuable fuel, with production on both sides of the Gulf of Suez, refineries at Suez, and a pipeline to Cairo. Production does not fully meet the country's needs.

Phosphate rock of sedimentary origin ranks second to oil in value, with a production in excess of 500,000 tons a year so that Egypt is among the world's major producers. Production takes place in the eastern hills near the Red Sea and also west of the Nile. Some is converted to superphosphate for local use as a fertilizer; some is exported.

Iron ore deposits of high grade near Aswan total 150 million tons, with other occurrences in Sinai and the Eastern Desert. There is a small production.

Manganese from Sinai, gold from the Eastern Desert, gypsum, copper, chromium, lead and zinc, tin, sulphur, talc, salt and other evaporation products are all exported in small amounts. Coal is completely absent. Several cement plants utilize local limestone and clay.

Although manufacturing has recently made rapid strides, it contributes only 10 per cent to the national income. For the most part it is concentrated in Cairo and Alexandria. Textiles and food processing are in the lead, followed by cement, glass, chemicals, and petroleum. A small steel plant had an output of 80,000 tons in 1956.

Cairo, or El Kahira, is the largest city in the Arab world, with a population which passed the 2.5 million mark before 1960. It extends five miles along the eastern bank of the Nile, mostly on the flood plain, but it also extends onto the bluffs where the Citadel was built about 1177. To the west lie the Pyramids and the Western Desert. In winter, the climate is comfortable and even chilly at times. Rainfall averages only two inches a year. Summer months often bring hot, stifling sandstorms, known as the *kamsin.*

Cairo exhibits the widest cultural contrasts. The newer commercial and residential areas are as modern as any city anywhere, in striking contrast to the poverty of the slums. In several ways it is the intellectual capital for the Arab and Moslem worlds. Along with modern universities, including the American University at Cairo, is the venerable Al Azhar University, founded in the tenth century.

Alexandria dates from 332 B.C. when it was founded by the Greeks as a naval base. It occupies the only feasible site along the Nile Delta for elsewhere the river pours out too much mud. For a thousand years after its founding, Alexandria was the capital of Egypt. Today Alexandria and Cairo share the distinction of being the largest cities in Africa. Geographers have a special interest in Alexandria because of its association with Herodotus who described the silt of the Nile, Eratosthenes who measured the circumference of the earth, Hipparchus who designed the first projections, Strabo who spent five years here, and other scholars such as Ptolomy and Cosmas.

Cairo is the largest city in Africa, a crowded metropolis with hundreds of modern buildings alongside areas of poverty stricken slums. (Courtesy KLM, Royal Dutch Airlines.)

THE SUEZ CANAL: EGYPT'S SECOND RIVER

THE ISTHMUS OF SUEZ separates the long narrow seas which the Atlantic and Indian oceans have thrust far into the World Island. Here Africa almost becomes separate from Asia, and through this land bridge now runs the world's most significant artificial waterway. The Suez Canal might well be called Egypt's second river.

In a list of a country's assets one too often overlooks the value of location. Thus Syria capitalizes on its position by securing an income from oil in transit, and Iraq gains revenue from Iranian commerce in the Shatt-al-Arab. So too, one of Egypt's major advantages is that she owns the territory across which the canal was dug.

The Sinai Peninsula and the Isthmus of Suez have long been areas of potential power. They once served as a bridgehead between Africa and Asia, alternately the avenue for Egyptian advance into Palestine or for Mesopotamian and Persian conquests of the Nile. With the digging of the Suez Canal, Sinai has become a north-south gateway from Europe to India and beyond. Here is Egypt's most significant border. As she strives for influence in Asia, she cuts across Europe's lifeline to the East.

Canals have connected the Mediterranean and Red seas recurrently for centuries. The first canal seems to have been constructed during the nineteenth century B.C.

Alexandria is Egypt's second city and a major Mediterranean seaport. This is a glimpse of Stanley Bay Beach. (Courtesy Arab Information Center, New York.)

It joined an eastern branch of the Nile with the Gulf of Suez by way of the Wadi Tumilat and the Bitter Lakes. The canal still operated around 1300 B.C. but later fell into disuse. Six hundred years later the project was partially revived by Darius the Persian, and the link was finished about 285 B.C. Later canals operated until the eighth century A.D. Most of these early waterways were probably seasonal, usable only when the Nile was in flood; silting was a recurrent problem.

The present canal was completed in 1869 on a 99-year concession given to the Compagnie Universelle du Canal Maritime de Suez. This was an Egyptian corporation, with its head office in Paris, and with Great Britain as the major stockholder after Disraeli's purchase of the shares held by the Khedive of Egypt. In 1956, the Republic of Egypt nationalized the company and bought out the former share holders.

Many treaties surround canal operations, among them the Constantinople Convention of 1888, signed by the Ottoman Empire and eight European powers. Article One provides:

> The Suez Maritime Canal shall always be free and open, in time of war as in time of peace,

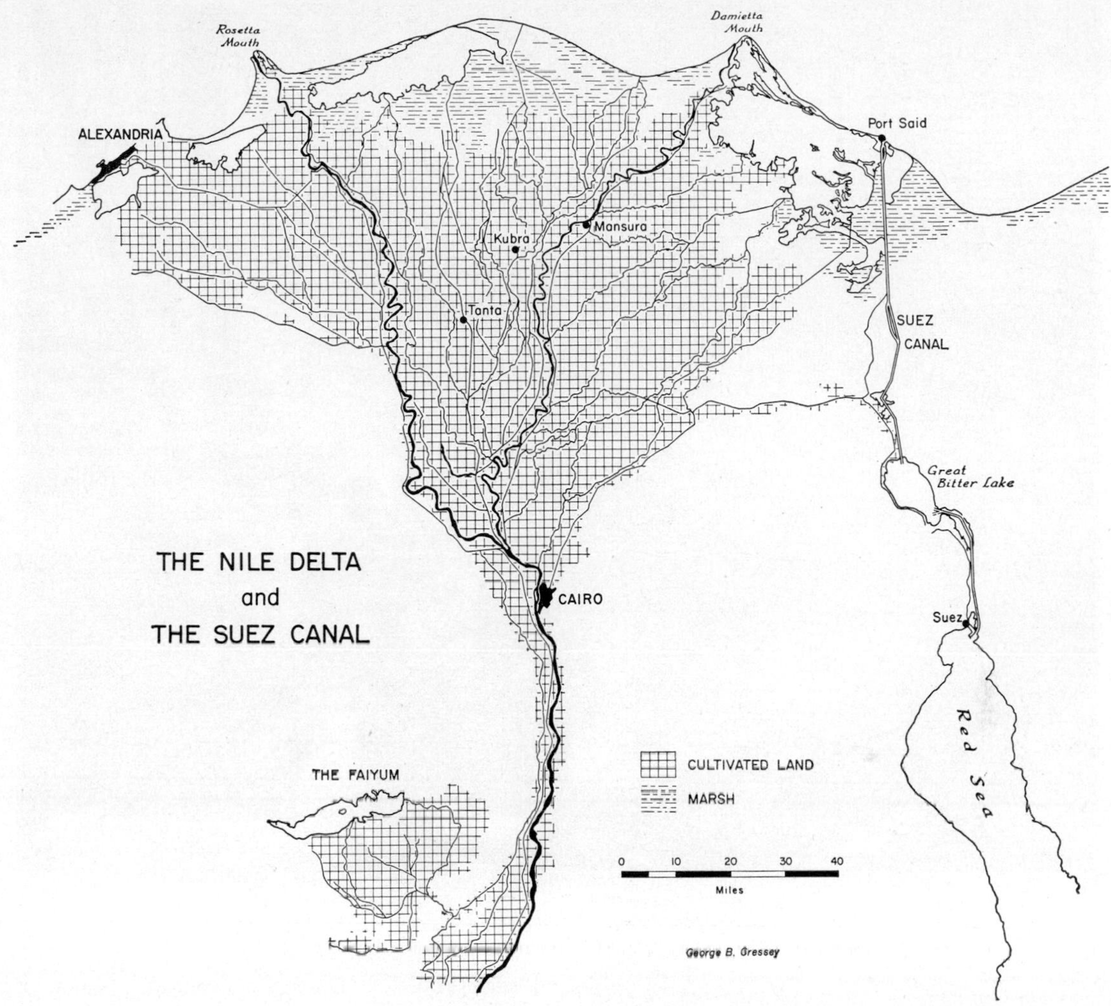

Few parts of the world are more intensively used or so crowded with a rural population as the Nile Delta. The desert begins a few feet from the outermost irrigation ditch, so that the Suez Canal crosses a completely arid landscape.

to every vessel of commerce or of war, without distinction of flag. Consequently, the High Contracting Parties agree not in any way to interfere with the free use of the Canal, in time of war as well as in time of peace. The Canal shall never be subjected to the exercise of the right of blockage.

The Convention also provided in Article Fourteen that, "The High Contracting Parties agree that the engagements resulting from the present Treaty shall not be limited by the duration of the Acts of Concession of the Universal Suez Canal Company."

The above agreements have not always prevailed, as during the Russo-Japanese War of 1904–05 when the Russian fleet was denied transit and had to sail around Africa, and again during both World Wars when German vessels were not free to use Suez.

Further complications arose following the Arab–Israeli War over the partition of Pal-

The Suez Canal is "Egypt's Second River," a crowded sea link between the Mediterranean and Red seas, here seen south of Port Said. Parts of the canal now have a bypass or duplicate channel so that traffic may move in both directions simultaneously. (Ewing Galloway.)

estine when Egypt refused to allow either Israeli ships or foreign vessels carrying Israeli cargo to pass through the Canal. These restrictions are based on the escape clause provided by Article Ten of the 1888 Convention, which states that the above provisions "shall not interfere with the measures which His Majesty the Sultan . . . might find it necessary to take for securing by their own forces the defense of Egypt and the maintenance of public order."

The savings in distance and time which the canal provides between Europe and India have often been stressed and are clear. Some distances are shown in the table on page 377. Too often the expense factor for transiting the canal is overlooked. Tolls are based on ship tonnage and on whether the vessel is laden or in ballast. In general, the tolls approximate the cost of operating a vessel for a week, during which time several thousand miles could be covered.

In an analysis of Suez problems, particularly as they relate to Britain, Halford Hoskins pointed out in 1940: [1]

> In recent times not more than 11 per cent of the total imports of Great Britain have come by

[1] Halford L. Hoskins, "Suez Canal Problems," *Geog. Rev.*, XXX (1940), 668.

The three million people of metropolitan Cairo represent wide contrasts, from the inhabitants of the bazaar streets in the old Mouski to residents in modern structures in the new urban core. (Courtesy British Overseas Airways Corp.)

way of the Canal. In view of the high tolls that had to be paid on this fraction of the British trade, perhaps as much might have been accomplished in the end by relying exclusively on the Cape route, had the Suez Canal not existed to facilitate the competition of other countries.

At no time has the use of Suez put an end to travel by way of the Cape of Good Hope.

Not only has the mid-twentieth century witnessed a great increase in the use of the canal, but there have also been changes in the nationality of shipping and in the character of commodities. Ships using the canal increased from an annual average of 5,800

MARITIME DISTANCES[1]

	Via Suez	*Via the Cape*	*Via Panama*
London to			
Bombay	6,250	10,700	—
Persian Gulf	6,400	11,200	—
Singapore	8,270	11,840	15,200
Hong Kong	9,690	13,160	14,100
Yokohama	11,250	14,570	12,520
New York to			
Bombay	8,200	11,450	—
Persian Gulf	8,400	11,900	—
Singapore	10,170	12,430	—
Hong Kong	11,600	13,750	11,300

[1] In sea miles.

prior to World War II to 11,751 in 1950 and 14,666 in 1955. Passenger traffic, however, declined from 664,000 in 1950 to 521,000 in 1955 due to competition with air travel. Whereas Britain accounted for three-quarters of the ships before 1900, but her share of the tonnage dropped to 60 per cent in 1913, then to 50 per cent in 1938, and to 28 per cent in 1955. Northbound freight has always been greater than southbound, due to Europe's import of raw materials. Traffic is now dominated by oil shipments consigned to Europe, which in a sense replace the former southward movement of British coal when steamships burned coal.

The most striking results from building the Suez Canal have probably been political rather than economic; few works of man have so altered sea routes. It brought closer together the two most densely populated parts of the world, and the power potentials were so great that the prospects influenced international politics even half a century before the canal was started. In the current struggle for world leadership, it is clear that Suez is one of the most coveted prizes. One might chart the political trends of the world by plotting the extent of the literature on Suez decade by decade.

British control over Suez ended shortly after the end of British rule in Asia. The Anglo-French attack of 1956 was the final gasp. Since then, Egypt has operated the canal efficiently and has continued to enlarge it, but the political consequences remain uncertain. As Hoskins wrote two decades ago in other circumstances, "The present situation is full of imponderables." Suez lies entirely within Egyptian sovereignty, but all the world has a stake in its operation.

The canal is 101 miles long, including seven miles of approach channels. The original canal was seventeen feet deep, but repeated enlargements now provide for a thirty-five-foot draft. Several duplicate channels permit convoys to operate simultaneously in both directions, and plans look forward to having two-thirds of the canal so enlarged. Such an enlargement involves moving five times the earth involved in the original cut. The average transit time is eleven hours.

REFERENCES

General References

Badeau, John S., and Nolte, Richard H.: "The Emergence of Modern Egypt and the Problem of the Sudan," *For. Pol. Assoc. Headline Series,* No. 98 (1953).

Ball, J.: CONTRIBUTIONS TO THE GEOGRAPHY OF EGYPT. Cairo. (1939).

Bulletin de la Societe de Geographie d'Egypt (annual).

Cumberbatch, A. N.: EGYPT. London: H. M. Stationery Office (1952).

* Harris, George L., Ed.: EGYPT. New Haven: Human Relations Area Files (1957).

Horbison, Frederick: "Two Centers of Arab Power," *Foreign Affairs,* XXVII (1959), 672–683.

Issawi, Charles: EGYPT, AN ECONOMIC AND SOCIAL ANALYSIS. New York: Oxford (1947).

Joy, Charles R.: ISLAND IN THE DESERT: CHALLENGE OF THE NILE. New York: Coward-McCann (1959).

Little, Tom: EGYPT. New York: Praeger (1958).

* Platt, Raye R., and Hefny, Mohammed Bahy: EGYPT: A COMPENDIUM. New York: Amer. Geog. Soc. (1958).

Roberts, Frank H., Jr.: EGYPT AND THE SUEZ CANAL. Washington: Smithsonian Inst. (1943).

Stamp, L. Dudley: AFRICA. New York: Wiley (1953).

Agriculture

Crary, Douglas B.: "Irrigation and Land Use in Zeiniya Bahari, Upper Egypt," *Geog. Rev.,* XXXIX (1949), 568–583.

Money-Kyrle, A. F.: AGRICULTURAL DEVELOPMENT AND RESEARCH IN EGYPT. Beirut: American University (1957).

Murray, G. W.: "Water from the Desert: Some Ancient Egyptian Achievements," *Geog. Jour.,* CXXI (1955), 171–181.

Parsons, Kenneth H.: "Land Reform in the United Arab Republic," *Land Economics,* XXXV (1959), 319–326.

The Nile

Barbour, K. M.: "New Approach to Nile Waters Problem," *Int. Affairs* XXXIII (1957), 319–330.

Butzer, K. W.: "Contributions to the Pleistocene Geology of the Nile Valley," *Erdkunde* XIII (1959), 46–67.

El Mallakh, Ragael: "Some Economic Aspects of the Aswan High Dam Project in Egypt," *Land Economics,* XXXV (1959), 15–23.

Hurst, H. E.: THE NILE. London: Constable (1952).

Lane, Frederick C.: EARTH'S GRANDEST RIVERS. New York: Doubleday (1949). [Chapter on the Nile]

* Ludwig, Emil; THE NILE. New York: Viking Press (1937).

Sanford, K. S.: "Problems of the Nile Valley," *Geog. Rev.,* XXVI (1936), 67–76. [Geomorphology]

Smith, Anthony: "Waters of the Nile," *Geog. Mag.,* XXIX (1956), 289–298, 337–348.

The Suez Canal

Edgerton, Glen E.: "An Engineers View of the Suez Canal," *Nat. Geog. Mag.,* CXI (1957), 123–140.

Hoskins, Halford L.: "Suez Canal Problems," *Geog. Rev.,* XXX (1940), 665–671.

Mountjoy, Alan B.: "The Suez Canal at Mid-Century," *Econ. Geog.,* XXXIV (1958), 155–167.

CHAPTER 13

Iraq

Changing Landscapes
Land and Soil
Agriculture
Baghdad and Other Cities
Highways, West and East
References

CHANGING LANDSCAPES

GEOGRAPHY has depth as well as horizontal dimensions. In an old land such as Iraq, the landscape portrays both time and space. The geography of the present is not only a matter of people and topography but is also a part of an unfolding panorama of the past. Upwards of a hundred million people may have lived in Mesopotamia, and they have left their indelible impress on both the culture and the physical features of today.

This section considers the historical geography of four periods: 1) the days of Babylon and Assyria, about 1500 B.C.; 2) the Abbasside Caliphate, 750–1258 A.D.; 3) the Ottoman Turks, 1534–1918; and 4) tomorrow.

IRAQ DATA

Area	171,566 square miles
	444,442 square kilometers
Arable area	54,570 square kilometers
Population	6,538,109

(Opposite) Iraq leads the world in the production of dates. These bunches are being cut in a grove near Basra. (Courtesy Iraq Petroleum Co.)

Babylon and Assyria

Two great empires of antiquity arose in Mesopotamia, Babylon in the south and Assyria to the north. The two nations cover a thousand years of history. Three millennia ago, each arose in very different areas. It may be helpful to reconstruct their environments as a key to modern Iraq. See the Historical Chart on pages 44-45.

The twin rivers of the Tigris and Euphrates are to Iraq what the Nile is to Egypt, or what the Indus is to West Pakistan. Without them there would be no Mesopotamia. For 700 miles south of the Turkish highlands, these rivers flow across the lowlands of Iraq. The northern half, ancient Assyria, is a rolling erosional plain; Babylonia to the south is a flat delta.

Unlike the ancient Nile with its general inundation, agriculture in Iraq depended on canal irrigation; and unlike the Indus with a late summer maximum, Iraq's floods come in spring. Ingenuity and labor are necessary for canal maintenance, along with effective government. The oldest canal in the world

Ancient Babylon was once regarded as the center of the world. This avenue, dating from the seventh century B.C., was the royal way which led to the Ishtar Gate. The walls were faced with glazed bricks and ornamented with heraldic symbols in the form of animals. (Courtesy Iraq Petroleum Co.)

may be the Gharraf, dug in the third millennium B.C., which takes off from the Tigris at Kut.

Any attempt to reconstruct the landscape of 3,000 years ago presents uncertainties. Each river has several times shifted its course, often by tens of miles. The climate on the average was probably about the same as now, with minor cyclic fluctuations. Perhaps the major difference was in the cover of natural vegetation, even then no longer "natural" since man had undoubtably begun to cut the few forests and graze the grasslands. The population was much more scanty and perhaps more concentrated. Tides of invasion had altered the earlier Sumerian culture.

When Babylon was in its power, it ruled most of southern Iraq, a dead flat delta 300 miles long by 100 miles in width. Throughout the area, the numerous groups of people held to their own customs, lived on land which varied to a marked degree from region

NOTE: Further material on Iraq may be found in: Chapter 2, Mesopotamian Empires: Babylon and Assyria, page 50 and Chapter 5, The Shatt-al-Arab, page 140. I am deeply indebted to Mr. Vahe J. Sevian, formerly Inspector General of Irrigation in Iraq, for travel assistance and valuable advice, and also to the geographers of Baghdad including Dr. Jassim Khalif and Dr. Ibrahim Shawkit.

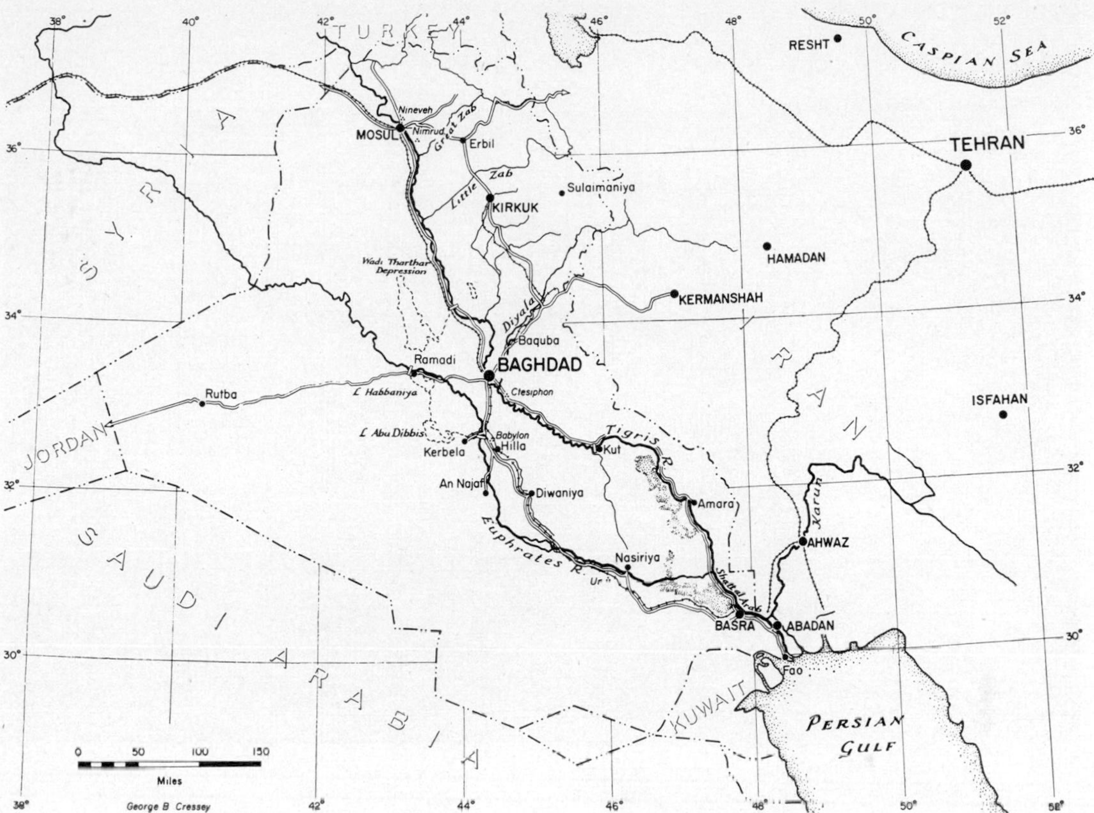

Habitable Iraq is closely tied to the Tigris and Euphrates. The three centers of Mosul, Baghdad, and Basra dominate the cultural and economic life.

to region, and had little systematic irrigation. Then, as now, floods would sweep across the land at recurrent times. Moslem legend places the resting place of the Ark at Kufa at the edge of the delta, a much more likely site than the slope of Mount Ararat.

Both rivers have so built up their beds after entering the delta that many sections lie above the surrounding flood plain; the Euphrates is also generally higher than the Tigris. This facilitates the diversion of irrigation water but results in linear swamps where the water cannot readily drain back into the channel. Such marshlands cover thousands of square miles in the lower delta.

Salt accumulation has always been a problem in southern Iraq, and in many areas the land had to be abandoned when the soil became too saline. The rise and fall of Mesopotamian empires can be read in the story of their ability to manage water and salt.

Away from the green marshlands and the vicinity of rivers or canals, and except for brief periods after the winter rains, this is a brown dusty landscape. Under the blazing summer sun, conditions are almost intolerable.

In such a situation, without building stone, the Babylonians created a mud civilization. Sun-dried bricks, sometimes poorly burned, were their building material. For mortar they used bitumen from the various natural seeps. Roof beams presented a prob-

Careless irrigation has ruined large areas of southern Iraq. These fields near Kut glisten with salt, brought to the surface by capillary action from a high water table. (G. B. C.)

lem, for palm trunks have little strength. In an archaeological sense, the mud buildings had an advantage for as structures collapsed or were abandoned, the mud slumped down to preserve the foundations. Other buildings were built on top of the debris so that modern excavations reveal layer after layer, civilization after civilization. In Assyria, where stone was used, successive construction dismantled the buildings of earlier epochs.

Our knowledge of Babylonian times is remarkably complete. Thanks to tens of thousands of clay tablets from royal archives, palaces, and homes, we have a better picture of ancient Iraq than of parts of Europe four centuries ago. Here are samples of Hammurabi's correspondence. A traveler has visited a town and his account of events in the neighboring countries is reported on a tablet. In one district, locusts have appeared; some are sent to the King who appreciates this delicacy. A certain governor has captured a lion; it has been put in a wooden cage and is being sent to the King. The King has ordered a canal to be dug, but it is a big job; the laborers are not well in hand; the work is progressing slowly; would the King have patience? There is an old-standing dispute about a field and some barley; would the King please settle it? A certain tribe is on the verge of revolt; would the King send more soldiers?

Excavations near the great ziggurat at Ur reveal life in a small town. Narrow streets wound between plastered mud buildings which formed a continuous wall. The streets must have been muddy in winter and dusty in summer. Rubbish, thrown out from the houses, filled the streets. Here and there were little shops, not unlike those of present day *suqs,* with a showroom opening directly on the street and back rooms for storage. Here one might buy rugs, clothes, pots, perfumes, and spices. Restaurants, blacksmith shops, and small chapels are found at intervals along the streets of ancient Ur. Many of these homes were built around a paved central court. At the entrance from the street was a jar of water for washing one's feet. Many houses had two stories. The whole picture was remarkably like that of today, except that burials took place beneath a rear court.

Assyria was different. Level land was limited so that flood problems were only local. Since the rainfall is higher, some cultivation was possible without irrigation. In place of desert, this is a steppe. Mountains lie to the east and north and provide an alternate environment. Grasslands to the west offered a natural avenue for caravans bound for the Mediterranean. This area of northern Iraq and the adjoining parts of Syria form the center of the Fertile Crescent.

The core land of Assyria was small, merely a hundred-mile section along the upper Tigris. Various cities served as capitals, among them Nineveh and Nimrud, both near modern Mosul. In Assyria, as in Babylon, many towns had great terraced pyramids known as ziggurats.

Whereas Babylon was largely a local state, the Assyrian Empire was involved in continuous wars of conquest which at times extended as far as Egypt and into Turkey. Assyrian military power was based on the use of iron for weapons and on superior organization. Some of the conquests were marked by extreme barbarity against the conquered peoples, many of whom were transplanted elsewhere. This fate overtook Israel in 725 B.C. and again in 596–587 B.C. The palaces of the kings were overflowing with wealth, but nothing was done to maintain the economy of the new provinces so that the Empire became impoverished.

In their military expansion, the Assyrians have been likened to the Romans, while the Babylonians, with their interest in culture, resemble the Greeks.

The Abbasside Caliphate

The Abbasside Caliphate, from 750 until 1258, marked the golden era of ancient Iraq, one to which the present generation looks back in an effort to recapture its grandeur and leadership. Previously, the center of Arab and Islamic culture had been in Damascus under the Ommiads. The first Abbasside capital was at Anbar, on the middle Euphrates and along the route to Syria, but under Mansur a new center was created in 762 on the west bank of the Tigris opposite the present city of Baghdad. Mansur chose the site, naming the city Dar es Salaam, the "abode of peace," because:

> it is excellent as a military camp. Besides, here is the Tigris to put us in touch with lands as far as China and bring us all that the seas yield as well as the food products of Mesopotamia, Armenia, and their environs. Then there is the Euphrates to carry for us all that Syria, al-Raqqah and adjacent lands have to offer.[1]

Baghdad soon became a great emporium of trade and a political center of international importance, unrivaled except by Constantinople. Although Islam remained the religion and Arabic the language, many items of culture were borrowed from Persia. Unfortunately nothing remains of Mansur's round city wall or great palaces, and even their precise location is uncertain.

The Abbasside Dynasty reached its peak under the Caliph Harun al Rashid, 786–809; a contemporary of Charlemagne. In intellectual activity and prosperity, Baghdad was then without a peer. A glimpse of the foreign trade is suggested in the tales of Sinbad the

[1] Quoted in Philip K. Hitti: *History Of The Arabs.* London: Macmillan (1956), 292.

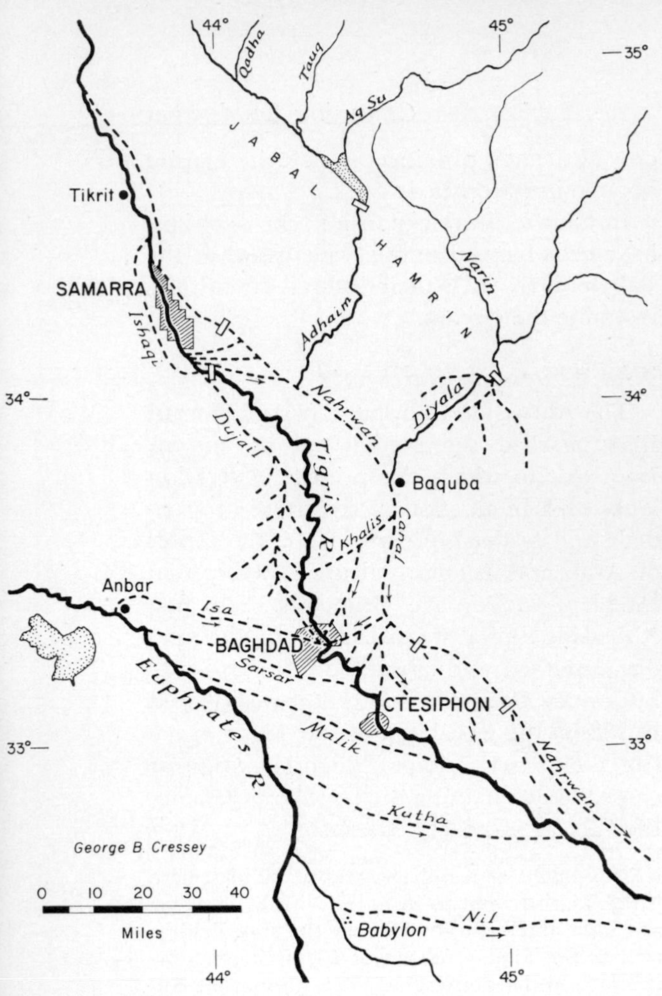

ABBASSIDE IRRIGATION SYSTEM

During the Abbasside period, an extensive system of canals drew water from the Tigris. Since the Euphrates is slightly higher, other canals led from it to the Tigris.

Sailor, while *The Thousand and One Nights* reveals something of the gaiety of Iraq at this time.

Life in Baghdad is described by Philip K. Hitti as follows: [1]

> . . . the Abbaside capital could not be easily surpassed. Its advantageous position as a shipping center made all parts of the then chartered world accessible to it. Along its miles of wharves lay hundreds of vessels, including ships of war and pleasure craft varying from Chinese junks to native rafts of inflated sheepskins, not unlike those of our present day, which were floated down from al-Mawsil (Mosul). Into the bazaars of the city came porcelain, silk, and musk from China; spices, minerals, and dyes from India and the Malay Archipelago; rubies, lapis lazuli, fabrics, and slaves from the lands of the Turks in Central Asia; honey, wax, furs, and white slaves from Scandanavia and Russia; ivory, gold dust, and black slaves from eastern Africa. Chinese wares had a special bazaar devoted to their sale. The provinces of the empire itself sent by caravan or sea their domestic products: rice, grain, and linen from Egypt; glass, metal ware, and fruits from Syria; brocades, pearls, and weapons from Arabia; silks, perfumes, and vegetables from Persia. Communication between the east and west sides of the city was assured by three main pontoon bridges.

Outside of Baghdad, the other great Abbasside city was Samarra, upstream on the Tigris and near the head of its delta. Its ruins still spread over a large area. Outside the wall of the great mosque stands a circular tower, somewhat analogous to the ancient ziggurats, which served as a minaret.

Agriculture flourished, both surrounding Baghdad in the fertile alluvial plain known as *al-Sawad,* and in the lower Tigris and Euphrates valley as well. Old canals, dating from before the Christian era and previously silted, were cleaned out and new canals dug. The extent of irrigation may have reached its all-time maximum limit during these centuries. The first great canal connected the Euphrates at Anbar with the Tigris at Baghdad. Three others farther south linked the two rivers, each with distributary canals. Arab geographers speak of the caliphs as "opening" rivers, probably referring in many cases to the clearing out of former channels. It is difficult to reconstruct the actual canal pattern since both main streams now follow somewhat different courses.

One of the major canal projects was the development of new head works for the high-level Nahrwan Canal which started from

[1] Philip K. Hitti: *History of the Arabs.* London: Macmillan (1956), 305.

The circular minaret of Samarra lies outside the walls of the ancient mosque, built when the city was the capital of the Abbaside Caliphate.

the Tigris above Samarra and continued south for 100 miles to irrigate a large area east of the river. Weirs were installed on the canal and on streams which crossed it, in order to regulate spring floods. The effect of the Nahrwan system and of the five major canals supplied from the left bank of the Euphrates was to create drainage from both sides toward the Tigris, using it as a drain to collect surplus water from the land and thus check the accumulation of salt.

In addition to irrigated agriculture in central Iraq, large areas were cultivated in the marshlands of the south, *al Bataih,* then larger than today. Here the problem was too much water, rather than too little. Dry farming was the mainstay in the far north.

It is sometimes assumed today that all of Iraq was under cultivation during the Abbasside period and that the population was much larger than today. Completely unsubstantiated statements refer to a population many times that of the present. While the irrigated areas presumably had continuous cultivation, at least around the towns, other areas were inhabited by pastoral tribes. Soil salinization undoubtably caused the abandonment of some cultivated areas so that the pattern of irrigated land shifted with each century. Aerial photographs reveal traces of cultivation over thousands of square miles,

The great arch of Ctesiphon, south of Baghdad, is all that remains from the old Persian winter capital. When captured by the Arabs in A.D. 637, the Great Hall had a carpet 105 by 90 feet, woven to represent a garden with pearls for the streams, emeralds for the fields, silver thread for the paths, and gold for the ground. (Courtesy Iraq Petroleum Co.)

but this should not imply simultaneous use.

The staple crops of Abbasside Iraq included barley, wheat, rice, dates, sesame, cotton, and flax. Fruit and vegetables were raised extensively, along with sugar cane. Roses and violets appear to have grown in profusion.

Most of the cultivation was in the hands of the pre-Arab and thus non-Moslem inhabitants, then subject people. Many Arabs considered it beneath their dignity to engage in agriculture. These non-Moslems were known as *dhimmi,* or Scriptuaries, namely Christians, Jews, Sabaeans, Zoroastrians, and Manichaeans. Those of the earlier inhabitants who embraced Islam usually moved to the cities.

The Ottoman Turks

The Ottoman Turks ruled Iraq from 1514 until 1918. Between the Abbasside period and the arrival of the Turks, Iraq was overrun by the Mongols, whom the present day Iraqi blame for the collapse of irrigation and the destruction of Iraq's great culture. Invaders such as Hulugu and Tamerlane created widespread devastation, in part because they wished to eliminate the agricultural population and thus create grazing grounds for their own nomadic flocks and herds. Later on, various Bedouin groups such as the Shammar and Muntafiq arrived from Arabia and set up the tribal pattern which still prevails.

Iraq passed under Turkish rule as part of the contest between two strong neighbors,

Many houses along the canals of Basra still show Turkish influences. This view is on the Ashar Creek. (Courtesy Iraq Petroleum Co.)

Turkey and Persia. In religion, southern Iraq was Shiite like Persia, but Sunni in the north and west as in Turkey. This contest in religion and political orientation remains today, for the great Shia shrines of Kerbela and Najaf and such holy places as Samarra and Kadhimain near Baghdad are in Iraq rather than in Iran.

Although there were periods of minority persecutions, Turkey made peace with the various groups through the millet system of communal autonomy; each people being governed under its own religious leaders. The principle remained however that subject people were regarded as cattle to be exploited. Within Iraq are numerous minority people, some of them refugees and often with compatriots in neighboring countries. The Kurds form the largest group, followed by Armenians, Yezidi, Turkmen, Sabaeans or Mandaeans, Jews, and Christian groups such as the Armenian, Assyrian or Nestorian, Chaldeans, and others of the Eastern Churches.

During the eighteenth and nineteenth centuries, Ottoman Iraq was more of a dependency than an integral part of the empire. The area was divided into four *vilayets* or provinces: Basra, Baghdad, Mosul, and Diyarbekir, each with several *sanjuks* or subregions. Their area extended well into what is now eastern Syria and southern Turkey.

Turkish rule brought Turkish culture. Many of the older buildings today are of Turkish architecture, and for several decades following the end of Ottoman rule Turkish remained the fashionable language. Corruption was widespread so that modern Iraq finds it difficult to develop an honest government.

Turkish troubles with the Arab tribes of the desert finally led to settling them on irrigated lands, sold to their sheikhs who then became landlords over the tribesmen who were now tenants. Here is the basis for current problems of land tenure.

Although never very successful, the British East India Company developed an overland route to India via Aleppo and the Euphrates, with regular navigation on the river for a number of years.

There is often a tendency in recreating history to describe developments in the larger cities and overlook the countryside. It may thus be appropriate to examine the rural picture during the Ottoman period. Tribal names, groupings, and areas changed rapidly and were not always the same as today. In the south were the Bani Lam, who were Shiite in religion and thus pro-Persian, and the Muntafiq; in the northwest were the Shammar and Anizah, both Sunni in religion. Kurds occupied the northern mountains, and Lurs frequently crossed the border from Persia. Fanatical Wahabi tribes also stormed in from Arabia. Here and there lived dozens of other tribes, for the most part Arab in origin, on both sides of the twin rivers.

The Samarra Barage across the Tigris is designed to divert surplus flood water into the Wadi Tharthar depression. The flow here shown measures 2,250 cubic meters per second. (Courtesy Iraq Development Board.)

Repeated campaigns failed to subjugate or pacify many tribes or to eliminate their raids which several times reached to the gates of Baghdad, Basra, and Mosul. Some of the disputes concerned cultivation rights, permits to graze on fallow fields, taxation, subsidies claimed by the tribes, or robbery and excess tolls levied on merchant caravans.

Turkey completely failed to understand or to solve the tribal problem. One Pasha, however, did propose, "Settle your tribes on the land: help them to irrigate by canals: give them security of hold: tax lightly and justly: allow no trespass against those you have settled: reward generously, punish constructively." Instead, the government attempted to crush the life from the tribes by weight of arms.

Instead of studying the tribesmen from the viewpoint of the government or the city dweller, it is important to see them as they pictured themselves. While some were desert herdsmen, others were stock breeders and raised rice, as the Chaab near the Persian Gulf. Still others who lived in the marshlands were "people of the buffalo." Some tribes were wealthy, apparently far more so than today, for one traveler speaks of "scarlet cloth fringed with silk," "great numbers of lovely horses richly harnessed," "tents of a very fine scarlet cloth, and a rich galloon-lace."

Modern Iraq is clearly the heir of the Ottoman period. While cities have grown rapidly in recent decades, their street patterns and division into racial "quarters" are

New Bank Street in Baghdad is lined with many fine structures; this is a view of the Rafidian Bank. (Courtesy U. S. Operations Mission, Baghdad.)

inherited from the past century. Shortly prior to the World War I, several old canal systems were cleaned out, and the Hindiyah Barrage on the Euphrates was completed. The first railway was a short line from Baghdad to Samarra.

Iraq Tomorrow

The Iraq of tomorrow will be different. Thanks to oil royalties and the better management of water, a new era is possible. Great Britain also deserves some credit for its guidance during the mandate period. Iraq has the beginnings of skill and organization to take advantage of her assets. Given peace and good planning, the material life of Iraq can be revolutionized in a few decades.

The development program inaugurated in 1950 had five facets: water management including flood control and irrigation, roads and communications, industrialization and electrification, housing and public buildings, and agriculture and land reclamation. Two five-year programs were completed by 1959, at a cost of nearly a billion dollars, derived from 70 per cent of the income from oil.

The problems of the Tigris and Euphrates have been discussed in Chapter 5. Each river now has low dams in order to supply canals with a dependable flow, and each has a flood storage reservoir with its control works. Two high dams have been completed on Tigris tributaries, and studies look forward to a dozen additional dams elsewhere. Scores of regulators have been constructed on smaller canals.

While no amount of engineering can fully protect against unusual floods, the major hazards are under control. Canal operations and drainage works are gradually increasing and improving the irrigated area. If the bulk of the water which crosses Iraq en route to the sea can be properly managed, the total food supply might be more than doubled. However, several decades and much education will be needed before this can be achieved.

Communications have always been a serious problem. During the rainy season most wheeled traffic has had to stop because of mud and flooded roads. At other times, the roads have been deep in dust. In many cases, so-called roads were merely unimproved desert trails. Modern highway construction across the alluvial plains has been handicapped by the absence of stone for foundations or of crushed rock for concrete. The transport of these raw materials from distant quarries proves to be a major expense. Bridges present other problems, but several large structures have been completed. Whereas automobile trips from Baghdad to Basra or Mosul formerly required two full days each, the 300 or 200 airlines miles, respectively, can now be covered in a few hours. Subsidiary roads remain a problem.

Older railway mileage is narrow guage, and in the absence of proper ballast trains must operate slowly. The new standard gauge line from the capital to the Gulf will greatly relieve the present overloaded railroad.

Agriculture will always provide the income for the bulk of the population. In addition to improvements in irrigation, development programs include crop research, land redistribution, and the settlement of people on the newly reclaimed areas. Some of the new settlers are nomadic tridesmen. Only the beginning of the program was possible during the early five-year plans.

Iraq's great natural resource is oil, already considered in Chapter 8. Some of the production is processed in a government refinery opposite Baghdad and in a government bitumen plant farther north. New textile factories, cement plants, and sugar mills help to make the country self-sufficient in these commodities. These all require electricity, supplied from several large oil-operated generating stations. Those at Baghdad, Basra, and Kirkuk each had initial capacities of 120,000 kilowatts. Facilities built into several dams will make possible the generation of hydroelectric power when needed.

One of the most widespread evidences of change is to be found in the hundreds of new schools and in the many public buildings such as hospitals. Baghdad now has a splendid parliament building and a new museum. Low-cost housing is helping to relieve the growing pains of the larger centers. Baghdad and several other cities are being transformed by the opening of new wide streets and by scores of stores, office buildings, and homes.

All of these accomplishments are impressive; so too are the remaining problems. Cultural evolution takes longer than the physical, and the transformation of a desert community into a modern nation, even with oil and water, requires much thought. Iraq is fortunate; if prosperity fails to arrive, the people will be to blame. As Iraq plans, it is important to have a full inventory of her assets and to evaluate the different potentials, region by region. This is the function of geography.

LAND AND SOIL

Man has always lived very close to the earth in Mesopotamia, for he has had to adjust

Northern Iraq is a land of dry hills and subhumid mountains, cut by numerous canyons. This is the Ruwanduz Gorge east of Erbil. (Courtesy Iraq Petroleum Co.)

his activities to a rather harsh environment. Previous chapters have dealt with climate and with the regime of the great rivers; this section considers land forms and soil.

Geomorphic Regions

Four geomorphic areas lie within the country: the North, the Western Desert, the Jazira, and the Delta. Northern Iraq includes the folded mountains which continue into Turkey and Iran as the Taurus and Zagros ranges. Parallel anticlinal ridges and synclinal valleys follow a strike which curves from west-east around to northwest-southeast. The mountains show powerful thrust movements from the north, and culminate in peaks of 10,000 feet. The sedimentary formations range from late Paleozoic to Quaternary, locally with intense metamorphic and igneous activity.

The scenery is magnificent near the border, with considerable vegetation. Cultivation is possible in a few linear basins now filled with alluvial outwash, but not elsewhere. The Tigris and several of its tributaries cross the structures at right angles in profound canyons. It is in the long narrow folded forelands and outliers of these mountains that oil is present around Kirkuk. These folded mountains are collectively known as the Jebel.

The western desert section is underlain by

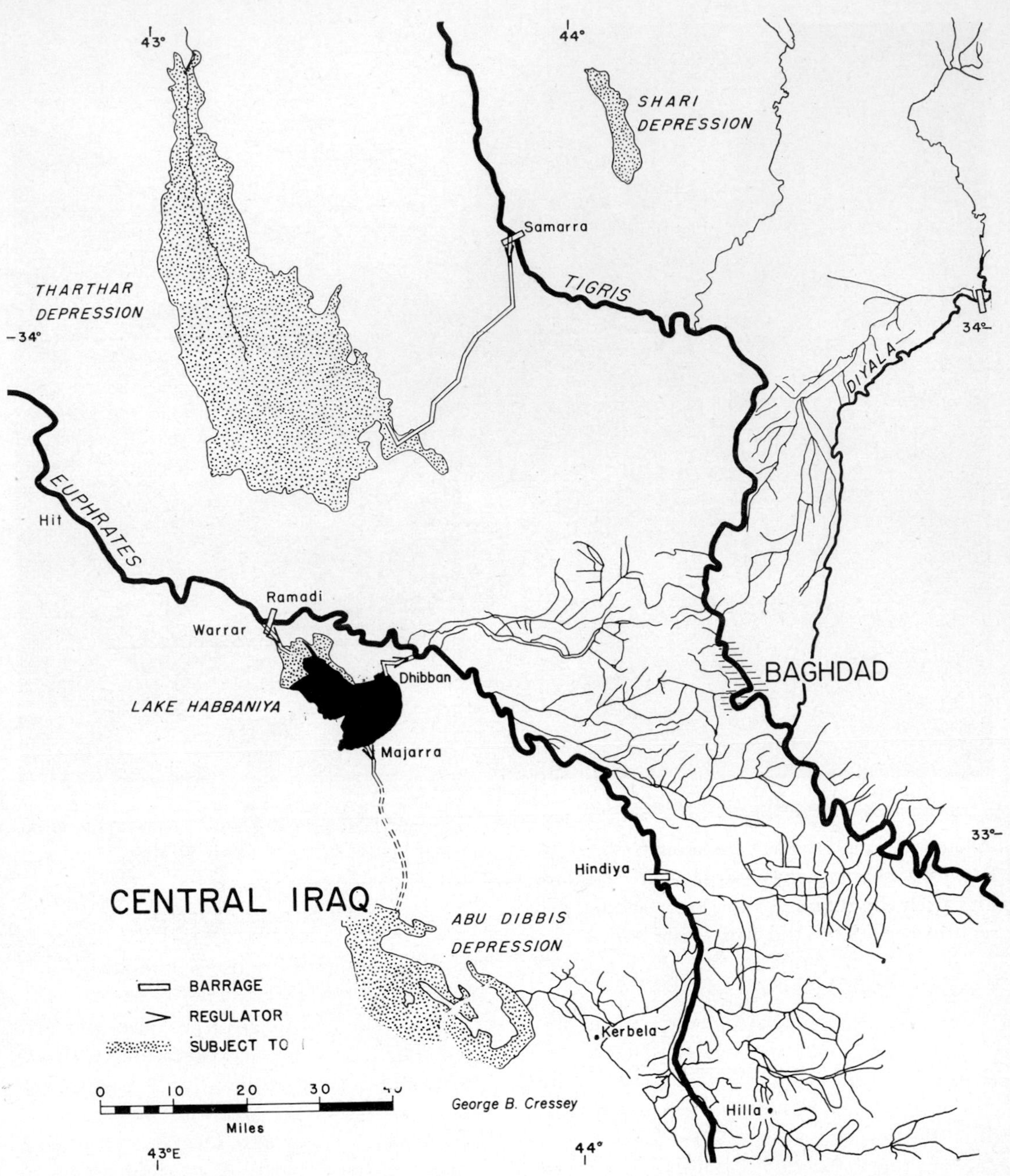

The common delta of the Tigris and Euphrates begins near Samarra and Hit. The Tharthar and the Habbaniya-Abu Dibbis depressions provide storage for surplus flood waters.

a part of the ancient Arabian massif, an area where complex Archaean basement rocks are overlain by almost undisturbed Mesozoic and Tertiary limestones and sandstones. The

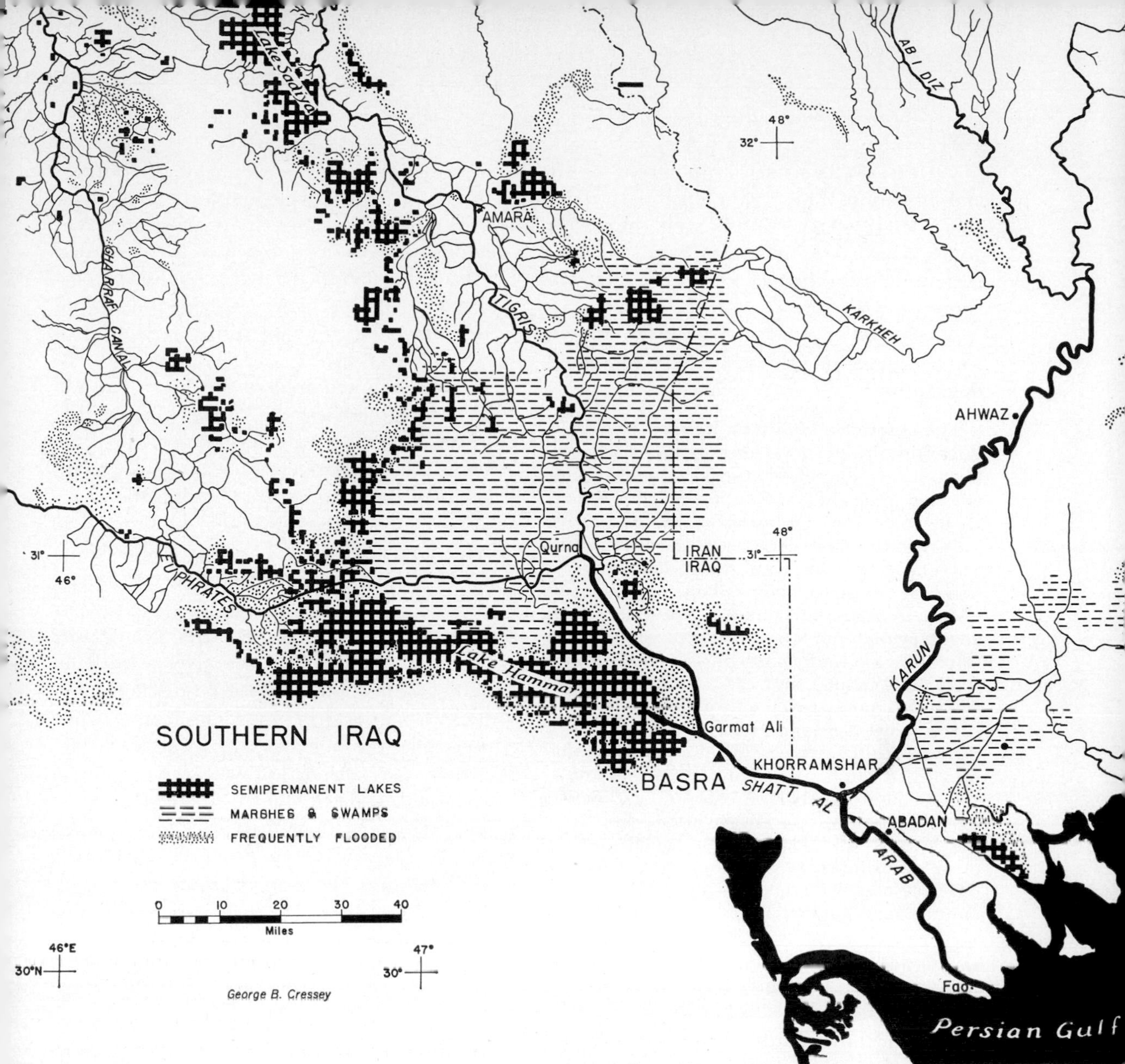

Lower Iraq includes a great area of marsh land and intermittent lakes, supplied by the Tigris and its former course, now the Gharraf Canal, and by the two lower branches of the Euphrates, those ending at Qurna and at Garmat Ali.

Arabs know this as *es-Shamiya*. For the most part, this is a monotonous stony plain strewn with chert and patches of windblown sand. The surface has many peneplain characteristics, cut here and there by wadis tributary to the Euphrates. In contour, stream deposits, and soils, the area reveals long-continued aridity. In several places are broad shallow depressions, related to gentle folding, wind scour, and solution.

At least five subdivisions may be recognized in the west: the el Hamad peneplain in the western sector; the dissected wadi complex in the center; the el Hajara with its many depressions; the Dibdib, a plain next to Kuwait; and the Euphrates sculptured plain with mesas, buttes, and structural features associated with recent uplift and dissection. This region forms part of the great desert which spreads west into Syria and Jordan, and south into Saudi Arabia; even aside from the lack of rainfall, the area is poor for agriculture.

A glimpse of weather conditions in the western desert is provided in the following description:

> The onset of a sandstorm in open country is an awe inspiring sight. The air is unusually calm, hot and even oppressive; the horizon seems shut off by a yellowish cushion which rises unhurriedly as the storm approaches; then an opaque wall rises very high (aviators have met it above 3,000 or even 6,000 feet). Some sharp gusts of scorching air strike the observer, then there is once more a sinister calm; the wall is very near. Suddenly the wind rises in one gust; minute grits from the earth riddle one with a thousand stings; eyes, nose, mouth, and ears are at once filled with sand; one is forced to seek shelter. Without pause, sometimes for an hour, the wind tears in this way at the surface of the ground, wrenching up all that can be raised, until even in the best-closed houses a gritty layer of several millimeters covers everything. At last the wind drops and one breathes once more, but in a yellow fog. In other cases, which are more pleasant, the wind continues but with no descending component, and the air is soon clear.[1]

The two remaining regions comprise Mesopotamia, the land between the rivers. In the north, the area is known as *al Jazira,* the island; the south is sometimes called Iraq proper or *el-Iraq Arabi.* In historic terms, these are Assyria and Babylonia. Both areas are part of an old geosyncline, still subsiding in the south but generally the site of erosion toward the north. These two complementary areas make up the core of modern Iraq and are the site of most of its agriculture.

The Jazira is a rolling upland, in part underlain by gypsum and other evaporites laid down in ancient seas. The area extends westward into Syria and Turkey and merges imperceptibly with es-Shamiya. The major rivers flow in well-incised valleys so that it is difficult to use their water for irrigation outside the floodplain. Large Quaternary basins east of the Tigris are present around Kirkuk and Erbil, not quite flat but with deep alluvial fill.

The combined delta of the Tigris and Euphrates, joined near the Persian Gulf by that of the Karun, presents several geologic problems. The twin rivers each enter the plain north of Baghdad, where low cliffs were once thought to represent an ancient shore line. This larger delta, the entire area of accumulating alluvium, covers some 45,000 square miles.

In Assyria the riverside cities of antiquity are still found along the rivers, while in Babylon the Tigris and Euphrates flow miles away from the sites of ancient centers which were once on their banks. Unlike the northern or Assyrian portion where rivers flow in erosional valleys, the rivers in Babylonia have aggraded their beds and flow between natural levees, surmounted by man-made dikes, so that the rivers lie above the general level of the plain. Drainage from adjoining areas cannot easily reach the master streams and moves slowly toward the Gulf in parallel swamps.

Since this area is one of the cradles of civilization, it has long been of interest to archaeologists. Few monuments of great antiquity lie within the southern part of the delta, and this has sometimes been interpreted to mean that the Persian Gulf formerly extended much farther north, gradually to have been filled in by river sediments. Some maps, quite without substantiation, even show the shore line to have been north of Baghdad in 4000 B.C. This assumption now appears improbable. Changes have certainly occurred in the course of rivers and in the pattern of swamps, but there is little specific evidence as to shifts in the shore line. More

[1] Author unknown, copied from U.S. Weather Bureau manuscript on Syria, Iraq, and Iran, 1942.

Southern Iraq is a delta land, intersected by many distributaries and canals; floods are recurrent. Date palms line many waterways. (Courtesy U.S. Operations Mission, Baghdad.)

likely, slight subsidence has occurred, common to areas of heavy sedimentation and due in part to the weight of accumulating sediments.

The accumulation of sediments has been computed by Raul C. Mitchell as follows: [1]

> From fluviatile and aeolian sources, we may estimate an annual increment in the delta plains of 47.5 million metric tons or 24 million cubic meters. This volume, if spread evenly over the 115,000 square kilometers of the delta plains (which in reality, of course, is not so) would add a thickness to the plains of about 0.21 millimeter per year or 2.1 centimeter per century.

[1] Raul C. Mitchell: "Instability of the Mesopotamian Plains," *Bulletin de la Societe de Geographie d' Egypte,* XXXI (1958), 129.

This overlooks the large contribution during flood times, as during the 1954 flood around Baghdad when "a lake 70 square kilometers and up to 24 meters deep formed east of the Bund outside Baghdad, which took seven months to drain away and left mud deposits 30 centimeters thick." By combining both normal alluviation and flood additions, Mitchell concludes, "It is more likely that the rate of build-up of the delta plains is in the order of 20 centimeters per century."

Slight but important differences exist between the four regions. All have a hot climate, but the precipitation differs in that the north is wetter. The western desert is slightly higher than the center, while the delta is the lowest and flattest. More significant is the character of the soil and ground water. In the desert, particularly in the areas of limestone, the water table lies at depths of 100 feet or more, if it is present at all. In the north, the soils are sandy or otherwise porous, and most of the ground has appreciable slopes so that there is a normal movement of ground water toward drainage ways.

In the flat delta, the alluvial deposits tend to be very fine and tight. Ground water commonly lies near the surface, but it is nearly stagnant. Excess irrigation water, river floods, or heavy rain tend to raise the water table to the surface level, and in the absence of adequate seepage or drainage, these waterlogged conditions persist for months. To a casual observer, the delta appears monotonously uniform; actually there are significant differences in moisture and drainage.

Soils

It has frequently been emphasized that the future of Iraq depends on the management of its water and of its oil. It is equally important to stress the problem of soil.[1] If this holds a key to the future, it is also true that soils furnish part of the explanation for the rise and fall of past empires.

The soils of Iraq may be divided into at least five broad associations, each with distinct environmental and use characteristics. First, there are the Reddish Chestnut, Brown Forest, Red Mediterranean, and associated lithosols. These soils are found in the humid northern mountains above 1,200 feet which have a rainfall of eighteen to fifty-five inches. Limestone forms the chief parent material. Erosion has generally kept ahead of soil formation. This area once carried an oak forest, but this has largely been removed and replaced by wild grasses and legumes. Winter wheat is the principal crop, with some deciduous fruits, almonds, and pistachios.

The second soil association includes Reddish Brown, Brown, and related types. Precipitation ranges from ten to eighteen inches, and elevations are between 600 and 1,200 feet. Limestone is again the chief bedrock. Some translocation of lime is the only observable evidence of the profile forming process. This is the most important winter wheat area in Iraq, and most crops are rain-fed. Irrigated crops include wheat, barley, cotton, melons, and grapes.

Third among soil types are the Red Desert, Seirozems, and Regosols. The area receives less than ten inches of rain and elevations are commonly low. Natural vegetation is limited to a few deep-rooted perennials along watercourses or lower areas and to quick growing grasses. The only use is for grazing, although there is sufficient fertility for agriculture if water were available.

The fourth type are the alluvial and solonchak soils, present within the delta lands of the Shatt-al-Arab and along flood plains upstream. These soils have accumulated through periodic floods and from irrigation silts; few if any profiles have had time to develop. A high percentage of the soils has been salinized through centuries of irrigation without adequate drainage, so that they are artificial solonchaks. The present native vegetation, no doubt different from that before man arrived, includes *shok agul* (camel thorn) and other salt tolerant plants. The chief crops are winter wheat and barley, along with a wide variety of lesser crops. Large areas are out of production due to the increasing percentage of salt or to waterlogging. These problems may increase with the expansion of irrigation.

The fifth soil association includes the wet

[1] I am indebted to J. C. Russell of the Iraq College of Agriculture, and to Burnell G. West of the United Nations Food and Agricultural Organization for some of the following ideas.

Fuel for domestic use is limited, so that it is necessary to burn straw, corn stalks, and brush. Most cooking is done in outdoor ovens. (Courtesy Arab Information Office, New York.)

alluvial and half-bog soils, known as gleys, found in the southern marshlands. Elevations are so low that it is generally impractical to drain these soils. Rice is grown around the swamp margins.

Surveys are far from complete, but all of these soils, except for a few in the mountains, appear to have a high lime content. Chestnut soils carry from 2 to 15 per cent of lime near the surface and 29 to 35 per cent in the subsoil. The brown forest soils have 20 to 28 per cent and 30 to 35 per cent respectively. Desert soils carry 20 to 25 per cent lime throughout the profile. The organic content is generally low. Porosity is also low with permeability tests on heavy clays of .01 inch per hour. Due to erosion in the north and alluviation in the south, there is almost nowhere a true "A" horizon.

Soluble salts range from negligible amounts to as high as 17 per cent in some irrigated areas. Saline soils are usually defined as those in which there is over 0.1 per cent of soluble material other than calcium carbonate in the upper three feet. On this basis, there is probably not a single acre in all of the delta which could be classified as nonsaline. The salinity increases southward from Baghdad, so that south of Amara most lands are too salty to produce satisfactory yields.

There is no indication that any of the original soils of Iraq were saline prior to the arrival of man, even in the driest areas. Inscriptions on ancient monuments make no mention of a salt problem, and it is clear that cities such as Ur could never have flourished if the salt waste which now surrounds them had been present then. Salt accumulation is a product of long-continued and careless irrigation. Vast amounts have accumulated, perhaps as much as a billion tons in lower Iraq. All of this must be removed before soil fertility can be restored.

The rocks beneath the basins of the Tigris and Euphrates above the delta contain considerable quantities of the chlorides and sulphates of calcium, magnesium, and sodium. Some formations accumulated as evaporites in ancient seas. These salts are gradually dissolved and added to the river water. When this water is spread on the fields and evaporates, the salts remain behind. The water of the Tigris and Euphrates averages about 300 parts per million of material in solution, accounting for an addition of 0.4 tons per acre for each foot of irrigation water. Sodium and magnesium salts are generally more toxic than calcium salts. Fortunately, in most Iraq soils calcium predominates, and this reduces the danger of formation of "black alkali."

The critical problem in using irrigation water is to keep the root zone moist but not saturated. This requires a low water table; otherwise capillary action lifts moisture to the surface and concentrates the chemical load there. With low permeability and poor subsurface drainage, there is a tendency to over-irrigate. Ancient Iraq used no drainage ditches so that salt accumulated in most flat areas. It seems probable that ancient land abandonment occurred more often through salinization than because of poor government or invasion.

In common practice, fields are left fallow in alternate years. This allows the perched water table, developed through irrigation, to sink downward gradually and also to be dried out by transpiration from deep-rooted weeds. Whereas irrigation may have brought the ground water to within one or two feet of the surface, a fallow season lowers it to six feet. This carries the accumulating salt down to depths where it does no harm. In time, the subsoil becomes increasingly salty and the surface level of the trapped salt continues to pile up until the land must be abandoned. Few areas in Mesopotamia have been continuously cultivated for more than a few centuries, or a thousand years at most. After a long period of abandonment, natural processes of leaching may again make an area usable.

Since most salts were brought to the fields in solution, most can again be dissolved and flushed away. This may call for deep drains, spaced every few hundred feet. Since the land is so nearly flat, the drainage water may then need to be pumped into the rivers, which is an expensive operation. It has been estimated that to provide a proper drainage system for lands now being irrigated would require the excavation of a billion cubic yards of earth at a cost of some 50 dollars per acre, plus maintenance costs.

On the other hand, salinization is less of a problem in the slope-lands of the north where more permeable soils permit subsurface drainage. Iraq may be well advised to use its available water in these safer areas.

AGRICULTURE

When Herodotus visited Iraq in the fifth century B.C., he wrote: [1]

> Of all the countries that we know there is none which is so fruitful in grain. It makes no pretension indeed of growing the fig, the olive, the vine, or any other tree of the kind; but in grain it is so fruitful as to yield commonly two-hundred fold, and when the production is the greatest,

[1] Herodotus, Book 193 (translation by Rawlinson).

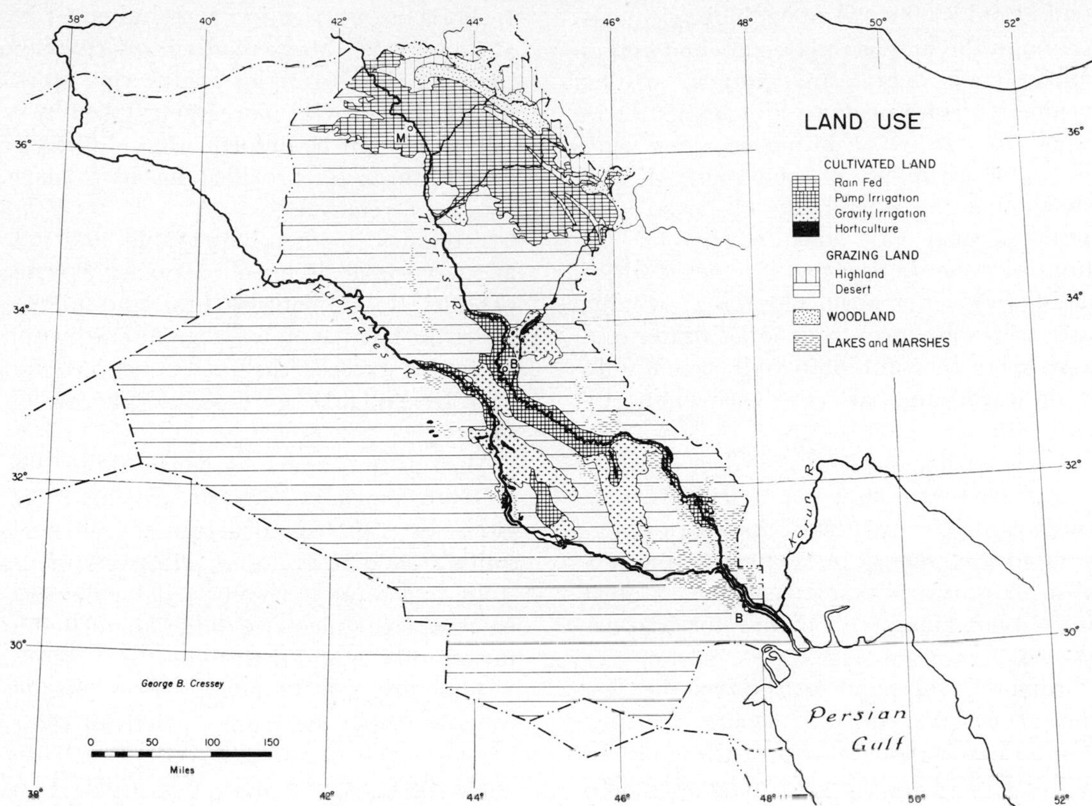

Iraq's agriculture depends on rain-fed cultivation in the north and on river-supplied irrigation in the south. (Based on H. Davies, Provisional Land Use Map of Iraq.)

even three-hundred fold. The blade of the wheat-plant and barley-plant is often four fingers in breadth. As for the millet and the sesame, I shall not say to what height they grow, though within my own knowledge; for I am not ignorant that what I have already written concerning the fruitfulness of Babylon must seem incredible to those who have never visited the country. The only oil they use is made from the sesame plant. Palm trees grow in great numbers over the whole of the flat country.

Alexander the Great was so impressed with the fertility of Mesopotamia that he proposed to make Babylon the capital of the world. Along with these glowing accounts of agriculture go unsubstantiated references to much larger populations in past centuries, even reports of thirty or forty million, several times the current figure. In popular imagination, it is usually added that this golden age ended with the invasion of the Mongols and that the country's present state is the result of neglect during Turkish rule.

As has been already indicated, the total area of land under cultivation at one time or another may have been much larger than today, but there is clear evidence that it was never all in simultaneous use. Likewise, crop yields were doubtless higher before the excess accumulation of salt.

Agriculture has apparently been carried on in Iraq as long as in any other part of the world, perhaps longer. A well-developed agricultural community has been unearthed at Jarmo, in the hills east of Kirkuk, which dates from 5000 B.C. Among the implements found in the successive layers of mud houses and village debris are mortars, pestles, grinders, sickles made of flint blades set in wood by means of bitumen, along with bones of cattle, sheep, and pigs. All this shows that the inhabitants of Jarmo were peasants who had advanced beyond the hunting stage. At least two varieties of wheat and barley were known. This was a favorable area with some twenty inches of winter rain and good chestnut brown silt loam soils. Wild wheats and barleys still grow in northeast Iraq.

Even earlier agricultural developments must have taken place, but their site is as yet unknown. The earliest archaeological records go back tens of millennia. During subsequent centuries man has learned a great deal about living with nature, for Iraq has provided a varied stage.

About a thousand years after the first Jarmo culture, upland people ventured southward, eventually to found the city of Eridu west of Ur, reputed to be the oldest city in the South. No written records are available for this early agricultural period, so that all evidence must come from archaeology. Somewhat later, plows are shown in the earliest pictorial writing, about 3500 B.C. Then, as now, tillage involved loosening rather than turning the soil.

Iraq covers an area of over 170,000 square miles, about equally divided between fourteen *liwas,* or provinces, and three desert areas. On the basis of the 1952–53 agricultural census, only one-seventh is in farms or "holdings," and of this less than half is cultivated in any given year. The planted area of 6 million acres may be compared with the population of 6.5 million; cropland is thus about an acre per capita.

As population increases, more food will be needed. This may come from an expansion of the total cultivated area, or through more intensive use of the present cropland. In both cases, irrigation and drainage play a large role. Most modern efforts have been directed to major engineering works designed to provide more water; taken by itself, this might be unfortunate unless equal expenditures are provided for its management and removal.

Estimates of potentially arable land vary and are closely related to available water supplies. It is probable that the land suitable for crops but not now either in cultivation or fallow exceeds the present agricultural area. Dependable figures should wait on soil surveys.

Most of Iraq has no agricultural use. The cultivated area is found in two major regions, the rain-fed north and the irrigated south. These areas do not effectively merge since irrigation is largely a delta development whereas adequate rainfall is related to the mountains and their foothills.

The line of 12-inch average rainfall roughly marks the southern limit of settlement dependent on rain. As with all dry lands, precipitation fluctuates widely from year to year so that the desert expands and contracts. The 12-inch rainfall line also lies close to the boundary where precipitation seldom drops below eight inches. These figures are clearly low, but the limited precipitation is fortunately concentrated during the cool winter. This area of rain-fed agriculture extends from the mountains to a few miles south of Mosul and west of Kirkuk.

It has already been emphasized that cultivation in the delta is far from continuous. Vast areas are out of reach of water, others are too swampy, still others are excessively saline. Agriculture follows the rivers and canals in ribbon patterns.

Cultivation may be further divided into summer or *seifi* crops and winter grown or *shitwi* crops. The former are sown in the autumn and are fed by the winter rains, supplemented by light irrigation in the south. Summer crops are sown during the spring

LAND USE IN IRAQ [1]

	Mesharas	*Number*	*Acres*	*Sq.miles*
Planted Area	10,108,118		6,186,168	
Barley	4,842,130		2,963,384	
Wheat	4,182,585			
Rice	514,722			
Maize and Sorghum	216,266			
Vegetables	180,870			
Cotton	96,942			
Tobacco	40,731			
Fallow Land	11,178,594			
Uncultivable	2,577,077			
Fruit and Vines	512,651			
Date trees		18,380,709		
Pasture	923,465			
Sheep		4,484,156		
Goats		1,618,145		
Cattle		711,918		
Donkeys		398,798		
Buffalo		47,395		
Woodlands	207,230			
Farms	25,536,039	125,045		
Fourteen Liwa	94,449,200			91,143
Three Desert Areas	83,340,400			80,423
Total Area	177,789,600			171,566

[1] Iraq Ministry of Economics: *Report on Agricultural and Livestock Census (1952–53)*, Baghdad (1954). The above data refer only to the area of "agricultural holdings." Including the nomadic areas and marsh lands, the estimated totals are: sheep—10,000,000, goats—2,900,000, cattle—1,510,000, donkeys—1,000,000, buffalo—718,000, mules—500,000, and camels—362,000. One meshara equals one donum or 0.62 acres or 4 hectares.

and require extensive irrigation for success.

Land ownership presents a complex problem, for few farmers own the land which they till. Large areas of what was once tribal land are held by former sheikhs, now wealthy city dwellers. Elsewhere, government or *miri* land is in the process of redistribution. Attempts to regularize the title to land date back to Turkish rule in the mid-nineteenth century, prior to which there was no registration of ownership. Other attempts were made between World Wars I and II. Property fully owned is known as *mulk* land, but there is little of it outside the cities. Most agricultural land still belongs ultimately to the government, namely miri land, but is used under various terms of lease based on tenancy. There are also large areas belonging to Moslem endowments, known as *waqf* land.

Practical problems arise with new irrigation schemes; some questions posed are whether the water shall be supplied to empty government lands where new farmers can be settled, or whether it shall go to already occupied lands to the profit of powerful but absentee landlords.

One agricultural area stands out as unique, the unique marshlands of southern Iraq. The only comparable areas in desert Swasia are along the lower Helmand in Afghanistan and the Orontes in Syria. No other part of Iraq is so little known, for communications scarcely exist. The narrow, pointed skiffs and the reed houses have not changed for centuries.

Swamps in the desert represent superabundance in the midst of poverty. Instead of irrigation problems the difficulty is one

This is an aerial view of a wadi in the desert of western Iraq where the bottom land has been plowed. The hope of a crop depends on normal rainfall, averaging five inches, and a high water table. Too much rain will wash away the crop; with too little rain nothing will grow. (G.B.C.)

of getting rid of the surplus water, but the area is so close to sea level that drainage is difficult. In place of desert brush, the chief resource is the tall marsh grass which grows to heights of ten to twenty-five feet. Reed boats replace the camel, reed houses replace tents, sedentary rice culture takes the place of nomadic pastoralism. People live on fish and buffalo milk more than on dates and barley. The inhabitants are Arabs, but they lead a very different way of life from their countrymen.

In most of Iraq, barley and wheat are the principal cereals. Both are winter crops and are raised throughout the cultivated area outside the swamplands. Barley has a shorter growing season, requires less water than wheat, and is more tolerant of salinity so that it flourishes in the south. In most years, barley is an important export crop, but the price must compete with world market prices. At times, the export of 500,000 tons has made Iraq the world's fourth largest exporter. Wheat is widely grown on the rain-fed Assyrian plains; in the south it usually requires irrigation. Both crops are sown in the fall, and the harvest is during April and May in the south and during May and June in the north.

Rice is chiefly found around the marshlands of the south, along both the Tigris and the Euphrates. It is a summer crop, sown from February to April and harvested from June to September. Yields may reach half a ton to the acre if adequate water is available, twice the yield of barley.

Iraq accounts for most of the world's dates, and they form the country's leading agricultural export. Dates have been grown since

The Marsh Arabs of southern Iraq travel in boats with an upturned prow, designed to penetrate the dense reeds. Such boats are waterproofed with natural bitumen. This is a view of the Shatt-al-Arab near Basra. (Courtesy Iraq Petroleum Co.)

Babylonian times. Thirty million trees produce 400,000 tons a year. Dates are grown in two areas; a concentrated district along the Shatt-al-Arab, which produces half the crop, and scattered sections in central Iraq as far north as the limits of the delta. The southern district extends for 100 miles below Qurna, with a width of one to ten miles along both the Iraq and Iranian banks. The densest groves are along the right bank below Basra, where there are numerous tidal creeks which circulate the water of the Shatt-al-Arab. On the landward side, the date areas abruptly give way to desert.

The date palm requires long, hot, rain-free summers. The roots must be well watered in order to bear heavy crops. Water may be supplied by canals, and along the Shatt-al-Arab these are fed by the rise and fall of the tides. There are more than two hundred varieties of dates, but only a few are commercially important. The *halawi* are the choicest, with yields of forty pounds per tree; other varieties, such as the *zahdi,* grown around Baghdad, yield up to 125 pounds per tree.

The palm flower is bisexual and needs artificial fertilization to insure heavy crops. Along the Shatt-al-Arab, a common arrangement per acre is 122 female palms, 3 male palms, 15 young trees, and 40 other fruit trees. Cultivators must climb the tree in spring to fertilize the flowers individually. The harvest occurs in the fall.

Dates have many uses. Alcohol is obtained from them which is the basis for *arak,* a local drink. Several thousand tons of syrup and date sugar are made each year. The pits make a good cattle feed. Aside from the date

Date groves border the Shatt-al-Arab near Basra. The trees are irrigated by a canal network where water circulates due to the rise and fall of the tidal river. (Courtesy Iraq Petroleum Co.)

itself, the trunks provide a poor timber for buildings and small bridges. Rope is made from the fiber, and the fronds are used for furniture and fences. The cheaper grades of dates are packed in palm leaves, which may also be woven into mats.

Fruits include pomegranates, oranges, apples, apricots, and lemons, all grown in central Iraq. The number of the above trees, in order, ranges from two million down to half a million.

Cotton is a cash crop of increasing importance, raised widely in the Baghdad area. It is grown in summer and requires heavy irrigation which, however, increases soil salinity causing injury to the cotton.

Tobacco production is limited to the northeastern mountains, especially in Kurdish country, where it forms the chief cash crop corresponding to the dates of the south.

Locusts are a major plague in Iraq, as they are throughout Swasia. They breed in Arabia and eastern Africa and advance northward in vast numbers. In years of adequate desert rainfall, the locust may find sufficient food in the drier areas and remain there longer; by the time they reach Iraq, the crops have been harvested so that little damage results. In times of low winter rain, locusts may invade the cultivated areas prior to the harvest and thus do great damage; in some years losses have run to 70 per cent of the crop. Locusts are especially serious in the north. International efforts are necessary for their control.

Livestock form the principal source of income for the nomads, and they are also of importance in the agricultural areas. Sheep are far in the lead and are commonly grazed along with goats. Water buffalo, not commonly thought of in desert lands, are used in the southern marshlands. Almost no fodder crops are grown.

BAGHDAD AND OTHER CITIES

Baghdad

The visitor to Baghdad should not expect to find echoes of The Arabian Nights nor the glamour of Harun al Rashid who ruled the city eleven centuries ago. Aside from the rather chaotic ruins of Babylon fifty miles to the south and the impressive arch at Ctesiphon twenty-five miles away, there is little for the tourist to see. No trace remains of the famous Round City on the east bank. The Iraq Museum presents a fabulous picture of antiquity, but it is all indoors.

The city of Baghdad lies close to the center of the country, about 300 miles from the northern, southern, and western frontiers. More important, it is near the head of the Tigris delta at a point where the Euphrates comes within forty miles of the Tigris. Therefore, two water routes lead north to the Fertile Crescent and Syria, as well as south to the Gulf. Nearby marsh or oft-flooded lands tend to restrict overland access to a few avenues of slightly higher ground, thus facilitating defense.

Few areas in Mesopotamia are better situated. For several thousand years, this general location has had a great city, Babylonian, Arab, Mongol, Persian, or Ottoman. The English traveler, Robert Finch, visited Baghdad in 1583 and wrote, "The town is not very great but populous and of great traffic of strangers, for that is the way to Persia, Turkey, and Arabia."

Baghdad itself dates from 745 A.D., and the outlines of the present inner city on the east side of the Tigris were defined by a wall built in 1095. Since that time, a bridge of boats has connected the two banks. The city was well-located in the days of camel caravans, and is equally central today by rail, highway, and air. Few better areas could be found for Iraq's capital.

The site, however, presents several problems. The Tigris is bordered by natural levees, three to six feet above the adjoining flood plain. The early city took advantage of this partial protection against flood, developing a linear pattern parallel to the river. On top of the natural ridge, the accumulation of debris from abandoned mud dwellings has gradually raised the elevation by an additional twenty-five feet in the older areas.

Sheep are the leading livestock of Iraq, most of them of the fat-tailed varieties. This view is on the Abu Ghraib Experimental Farm near Baghdad. (Courtesy Iraq Petroleum Co.)

THE CITIES OF IRAQ

City	*Census, 1957*
Baghdad and suburbs	735,714
Metropolitan area	1,306,604
Mosul	179,646
Basra	164,623
Kirkuk	120,593
Najaf	88,809
Kerbela	60,804
Amara	53,311
Hilla	50,005
Sulaimaniya	48,450

The commercial center of Baghdad lies on the eastern bank of the Tigris. Rashid Street, the principal shopping avenue, extends across the picture. (Courtesy Iraq Petroleum Co.)

In fact, one may identify the length of settlement merely from an examination of a detailed contour map. Most of the city lies along the left bank, that is, to the east of the Tigris.

To protect against recurrent floods, dikes, known locally as bunds, encircle two halves of the city on either bank of the river. Although several times enlarged, the modern city extends well beyond them onto lowlands where the unprotected suburbs are frequently inundated.

When the river rises to flood heights upstream, dikes above Baghdad are cut, thus relieving the pressure on the main channel by diverting some of the water around the city, usually to the east. Baghdad then becomes a depressed island, in places ten to twenty feet below river level. A flood in 1931 destroyed 7,000 houses, and 40,000 people died in the resulting plague. In 1954 the bunds were nearly overtopped; since then the flood hazard has been lessened through storage facilities in Wadi Tharthar.

Under Turkish rule, from the sixteenth to nineteenth centuries, Baghdad grew but little. Only half the area within the wall was occupied, but the resulting street and functional pattern persists today. Both Jewish and Christian quarters arose, the latter with

Armenian, Chaldean, Nestorian, and Latin churches and schools. The city was compact and the streets were narrow. Wheeled vehicles were uncommon, and a street was wide enough if two loaded animals could pass each other. To the west of the river was the Shiite shrine city of Kadimain.

Houses, of which many remain from the Turkish period, were of two-story design. Only a strong door and one or two barred windows with balconies faced the street. Within was a quadrangular courtyard, large or small, commonly with a colonnade on one side. The flat roof was often used for sleeping in the summer. Many buildings had a sub-basement or *sirdab,* for a mid-day siesta, with a ventilating shaft to catch any breeze.

Of all the large cities in Swasia, Baghdad has some of the poorest *suqs* or covered bazaars. The old arched roofs were never impressive and are now in disrepair. The passageways are dirty. One distinctive item is that many handicrafts remain, more so than elsewhere. Copper vessels are beaten out of flat sheets in many shops, thousands of shoes are made by hand, exotic spices and condiments fill the food suq. The main business street, with architecture dating from Turkish times, is less attractive than any other Swasian city of equal size.

Surrounding and permeating this old core is the new Baghdad, with broad avenues, dozens of modern business houses and miles of attractive residential streets. Countless grocery stores carry food articles from all the world, not merely for foreign consumption but for the growing group of Iraqi who have been abroad or who think in western terms. Since Iraq has an export surplus and hard currency, there are few restrictions on imports.

Five bridges span the Tigris, and rapid developments are taking place along the west bank as well as beyond the former South Gate. In place of inner courtyards, many middle class homes now have a surrounding

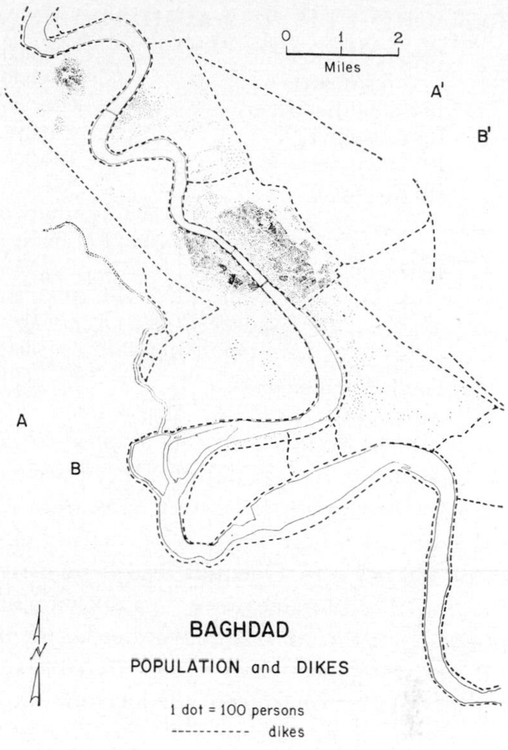

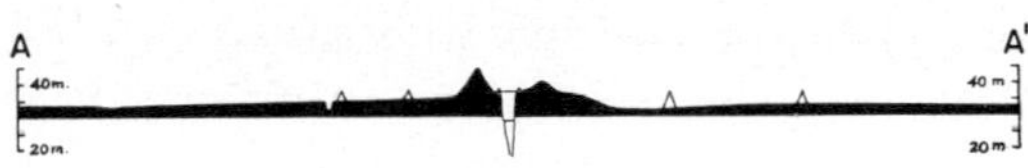

Although Metropolitan Baghdad spreads across most of this map, the extent of the old city wall is clearly shown in the congestion of population. The cross sections reveal the accumulation of debris in the long-settled areas, raising them above most flood levels. (Data after J. H. Lebon.)

THE GROWTH OF BAGHDAD[1]

1816 (Buckingham)	80,000
1831 (estimate)	100,000
1841 (Baillie Fraser)	60,000
1914 (estimate)	180,000
1918 (census)	185,000
1947 (census)	321,225 (plus 145,508 in suburbs, plus 48,676 in Kadimain)
1957 (census)	355,958 (plus 379,756 in suburbs, plus 171,084 in Kadimain; Metropolitan total 1,306,604)

[1] Excluding Kadimain.

garden. The result has been to produce a sharp contrast in population concentration between new open residential areas and the old core city where the average density exceeds 400 per acre. One may readily identify the line of old fortifications on a dot map of population; this marks the frontier between the medieval and twentieth century parts of the city. Three quarters of the metropolitan population now live outside the old city walls. Some of these are prosperous middle-class people, others are Bedouin or impoverished tenants who have sought a better livelihood in the city but who live in squalid huts.

The main functions of Baghdad are political, commercial, and cultural. Industry is still largely of the handicraft or machine repair character. Agricultural products are processed, and there is a new oil refinery, Iraq's largest.

Basra and Mosul

Two other cities deserve attention, Basra and Mosul, centers for the south and north respectively.

There are three Basras. The old town lies along the Ashar Creek, two miles inland from the Shatt-al-Arab. Along the river is the modern commercial city of Ashar, while four miles upstream is the port, railway station, and airport of Margil. All of these lie seventy miles inland from the mouth of the Shatt-al-Arab and are collectively known as Basra. Maritime trade from the head of the Persian Gulf to India is of considerable antiquity, but the town itself was not founded until A.D. 638. As was so common elsewhere, Basra has several times been attacked, destroyed, and rebuilt.

As a port, Basra has excellent arrangements, limited only by the dimensions of the river. Numerous cranes transfer cargo to rail-

Mosul, in northern Iraq, has a greater temperature range and more rainfall than elsewhere. Elevation 730 feet, annual precipitation 15.0 inches.

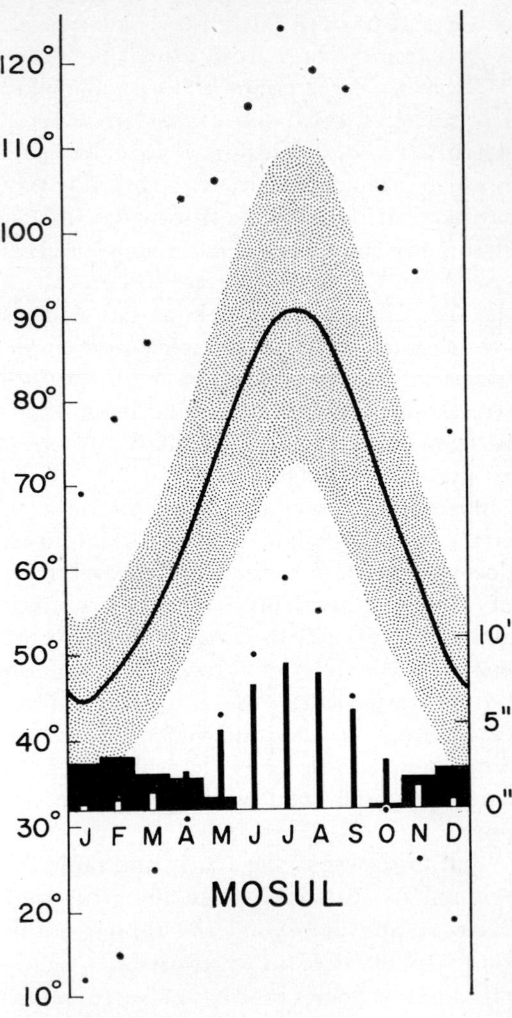

road cars on the wharf, but trade has increased faster than facilities. Standard and narrow guage lines lead north. A dredging program maintains a 25-foot low tide channel across the bar below Fao, the oil terminal near the mouth of the Shatt-al-Arab.

Mosul lies on the Tigris not far from the edge of the mountains. East of the river is ancient Nineveh with people still living on the mound or *tell*. One building holds the tomb of Jonah. In the days of Mosul's greatness it was famed for its craftsmen and for its textiles, hence the word "muslin." New streets are changing the city, but it is less modernized than several other Iraq towns. Mosul is on the standard gauge rail line which leads south to Baghdad, and northwest to Istanbul.

The oil center of Kirkuk, midway between Baghdad and Mosul, is Iraq's fourth city. Since many of the people are newcomers, attracted by the opportunities of petroleum, old family ties tend to be broken, resulting in social problems.

These graphs present monthly average temperature and rainfall, plus the daily temperature range, shaded, and the extreme recorded temperatures, in dots; as well as the monthly potential evapotranspiration, in thin bars.

Baghdad's climate is a fair sample for central Iraq. Elevation 111 feet, annual precipitation 5.5 inches.

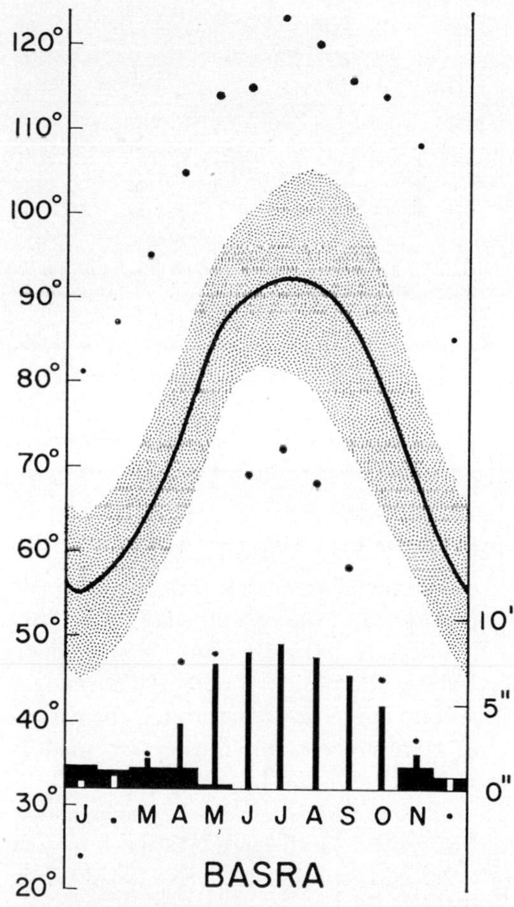

Basra's climate is slightly influenced by the Persian Gulf. Elevation 8 feet, annual rainfall 7.3 inches.

Iraq is using its oil royalties to build a network of modern roads. Construction in the delta area is handicapped by the absence of crushed rock. (Courtesy Iraq Petroleum Co.)

HIGHWAYS, WEST AND EAST

No road, not even a cart trail, leads north from Iraq into Turkey. One may reach Turkey indirectly by rail, or by a very poor road across the plains of northern Syria, but there is no route directly through the mountains. Commerce with Turkey by road is thus nonexistent and by rail negligible.

Southward, there are desert tracks which lead to Kuwait and Saudi Arabia, but with only limited truck traffic. No road leads southeast into Iran, and it is impossible to drive from Basra to Abadan unless one makes special arrangements to hire a barge to get a car across the Karun River. Iraq's only southern gateway is via the Shatt-al-Arab.

To the west, Iraq faces an extension of the Arabian desert, so imposing a barrier that it would be easier to cross if it were an ocean. Wells are almost absent, so that in the pre-automobile age, only the most venturesome caravans traveled directly west from Baghdad. Camel caravans bound for the Levant generally followed a course northwestward along the Euphrates, and then through the grasslands which mark the Fertile Crescent. A somewhat more direct caravan course led across the Syrian desert in the latitude of Palmyra, along a route now paralleled by the oil pipeline from Kirkuk to Tripoli; even this involves more than a hun-

The railway station at Mosul serves the standard gauge line which links Baghdad with Turkey. Elsewhere, most railways are narrow gauge lines. (Courtesy Iraq Petroleum Co.)

dred miles of waterless desert without grass.

Only one paved highway connects Iraq with the Mediterranean. This is the route westward from Baghdad to the Euphrates, then west from Ramadi to the mid-point at Rutba, and on to the far edge of the desert near Mafrak in Jordan. From here, one turns north to Damascus and Beirut. The desert section from Ramadi to Mafrak measures 450 miles, with only one tiny oasis. The entire distance from Baghdad to Beirut requires two days of hard driving. Several dozen trucks use the route daily, with bus service in addition. In part, this road follows the oil pipeline to Haifa, out of use since the formation of Israel.

A second desert road, very poor but passable, follows the Euphrates and then leads west to Aleppo. The only other routes to Jordan or Syria are wandering desert tracks, ill defined, unimproved, seldom used, and not to be recommended. These desert roads are Iraq's side door to Europe, difficult but faster than the round-about sea route through Basra.

One main highway and two secondary roads cross the border eastward to Iran. The first leads from Baghdad to Kermanshah and on to Tehran. In a sense, this is a continuation of the trans-desert road from Beirut, and it normally handles a considerable movement of freight and passengers. Snow in the

Iranian mountain passes may close the road for a few weeks in winter.

Two secondary roads extend east from northern Iraq through the Kurdish country; one through Sulaimaniya to Kermanshah, the other via Ruwandiz to Tabriz.

For all of Iraq's frontier, this gives a total of two main highways and four or five other roads to the outside world. Clearly, Iraq is isolated. One railway connects with northern Syria and goes on to Turkey. No railway leads to Iran, but one may go by launch from Basra and reach the Trans-Iranian line at Khorramshahr; however, few travelers do.

The transport situation by air is quite different. Baghdad is linked directly with each country in Swasia, except Yemen and Israel. Long distance planes fly from Iraq to every continent except South America. Whereas the country is difficult to reach overland and has only minor steamship services, it lies along one of the main air routes of the world.

REFERENCES

General References

Blanchard, Raoul: "La Mesopotamie," in GEOGRAPHIE UNIVERSELLE, VIII, ASIE OCCIDENTALE. Paris: Armand Colin (1929), 215–231.

* Boesch, Hans H.: "El-'Iraq," *Econ. Geog.*, XV (1939), 325–361.

Boesch, Hans H.: WASSER ODER OL. EIN BUCH UBER DEN NAHEN OSTEN. Bern: Kummerly & Frey (1943).

Boxer, Rosemary: A BIBLIOGRAPHY OF MATERIAL ON THE DEVELOPMENT OF MODERN IRAQ. Baghdad: Development Board (1953).

* British Admiralty, Naval Intelligence Division: IRAQ AND THE PERSIAN GULF. London: Naval Intelligence Division (1944).

Douglas, William O.: "Station Wagon Odyssey: Baghdad to Istanbul," *Nat. Geog. Mag.*, CXV (1959), 48–87.

Gowan, C. H.: "Northern Iraq," *Jour. Royal Central Asian Soc.*, XXV (1938), 193–203.

* Grant, Christina Phelps: THE SYRIAN DESERT. London: Black (1937).

* Harris, George L.: IRAQ. New Haven: Human Relations Area Files (1959).

Hogg, E. Gascoigne: "Iraq," *Jour. Royal Central Asian Soc.*, XXVII (1940), 179–190.

* International Bank: THE ECONOMIC DEVELOPMENT OF IRAQ. Baltimore: Johns Hopkins Press (1952).

Iraq Ministry of Economics: STATISTICAL ABSTRACT (annual). Baghdad.

Ireland, Philip W.: "The Baghdad Railway: Its New Role in the Middle East," *Jour. Royal Central Asian Soc.*, XXVIII (1941), 329–339.

Leatherdale, D.: "The Material Background of Life in Northern Iraq," *Jour. Royal Central Asian Soc.*, XXXV (1948), 66–73.

Lebon, J. H. G.: "The Site and Modern Development of Baghdad," *Bull. Soc. Geog. d'Egypte,* XXIX (1956), 7–32.

Longrigg, Stephen H.: "Prospects for Iraq," *Geog. Mag.*, XXV (1953), 276–290.

Longrigg, Stephen H., and Stoakes, Frank: IRAQ. New York: Praeger (1959).

Musil, Alois: THE MIDDLE EUPHRATES. New York: Amer. Geog. Soc. (1927).

Qubain, Fahim I.: THE RECONSTRUCTION OF IRAQ. 1950–1957, New York: Praeger (1958).

* Salter, Lord: THE DEVELOPMENT OF IRAQ. A PLAN OF ACTION. Baghdad: Iraq Development Board (1955).

Shor, Jean, and Shor, Franc: "Iraq—Where Oil and Water Mix," *Nat. Geog. Mag.*, CXIV (1958), 443–489.

Sousa, Ahmed: ADMINISTRATIVE ATLAS OF IRAQ. Baghdad: Survey Press (1952) [34 plates in Arabic].

U. S. Board on Geographic Names: IRAQ. Washington: Dept. of Interior (1957). [Gazetteer]

Weulersse, Jacques: "Problems d'Irak," *Annales de Geog.,* XLIII (1934), 49–75.

Willcocks, William: "Mesopotamia—Past, Present and Future," *Smithsonian Inst. Annual Report* (1910), 401–416, also *Geog. Jour.,* XXXV (1910), 1–18.

Geomorphology

Lane, Ferdinand C.: EARTH'S GRANDEST RIVERS. New York: Doubleday (1949). [Chapter on Tigris and Euphrates]

* Lees, G. M.: "The Geographical History of the Mesopotamian Plains," *Geog. Jour.,* CXVIII (1952), 24–39.

* Mitchell, Raoul C.: "Physiographic Regions of Iraq," *Bull. Soc. Geog. d'Egypte,* XXX (1957), 75–96.

Mitchell, Raoul C.: "Instability of the Mesopotamian Plains," *Bull. Soc. Geog. d'Egypte,* XXXI (1958), 127–140.

History

Awad, M.: "Geographical Aspects of the Mosul Question," *Scot. Geog. Mag.,* XLIII (1927), 1–20, 65–78.

Braidwood, Linda: DIGGING BEYOND THE TIGRIS. New York: H. Schuman (1953).

Burton, H. M.: "The Dawn of History in Iraq," *Geog. Mag.,* XIV (1942), 242–251.

Childe, V. Gordon: "The Structure of the Past. III. Mesopotamia," *Geog. Mag.,* XVI (1943), 268–281.

Contenau, Georges: EVERYDAY LIFE IN BABYLON AND ASSYRIA. New York: St. Martin's Press (1954).

Crawford, O. G. S.: "The Birthplace of Civilization," *Geog. Rev.,* XVI (1926), 73–81.

Gruber, J.: "Irrigation and Land Use in Ancient Mesopotamia," *Agricultural History,* XXII (1948).

Lloyd, H. I.: "The Geography of the Mosul Boundary," *Geog. Jour.,* LXVIII (1926), 104–117.

* Lloyd, Seton: FOUNDATIONS IN THE DUST. New York: Oxford Univ. Press (1947), Baltimore: Penguin (1955).

* Roux, Georges: "The Story of Ancient Iraq," *Iraq Petroleum,* (continuing series started in September 1956).

Semple, Ellen Churchill: "The Ancient Piedmont Route of Northern Mesopotamia," *Geog. Rev.,* VIII (1919), 153–179.

Speiser, E. A.: "Ancient Mesopotamia: A Light That Did Not Fail," *Nat. Geog. Mag.,* XCIX (1951), 41–105.

Wright, H.: "The Geological Setting of Four Pre-Historic Sites in N.E. Iraq," University of Chicago: Amer. School of Oriental Research #128 (1952), 11–24.

Land Use

* Davies, D. Hywel: "Observations on Land Use in Iraq," *Econ. Geog.,* XXXIII (1957), 122–134.

Dowson, V. H. W.: "The Date Cultivation and Date Cultivators of Basrah," *Jour. Royal Central Asian Soc.,* XXVI (1939), 247–260.

Fisk, Brad: "Dujaila: Iraq's Pilot Project for Land Settlement," *Econ. Geog.,* XXVIII (1952), 343–354.

Iraq Ministry of Agriculture Statistics Branch: A GRAPHIC SUMMARY OF AGRICULTURE IN IRAQ. Baghdad (1956).

Kellersohn, Heinrich: "Die Landwirtschaft in Irak," *Erdkunde,* VII (1953), 276–288.

Lennie, A. B.: "Agriculture in Mesopotamia in Ancient and Modern Times," *Scot. Geog. Mag.,* LII (1936), 33–46.

Powers, W. L.: "Soil and Land-Use Capabilities in Iraq; a Preliminary Report," *Geog. Rev.,* XLIV (1954), 373–380.

Yudelman, Montague: "Some Issues in Agricultural Development in Iraq," *Farm Economics,* XL (1958), 78–88.

Climate

* Al-Khashab, Wafiq Hussain: "The Water Budget of the Tigris and Euphrates Basin," Univ. of Chicago: *Dept. of Geog. Research Paper* No. 54 (1958).

Iraq Meteorological Service: CLIMATOLOGICAL ATLAS FOR IRAQ. Baghdad (1945).

Iraq Meteorological Service: CLIMATOLOGICAL MEANS FOR IRAQ. Baghdad (1955).

Peterson, A. D.: BIBLIOGRAPHY OF THE CLIMATE OF IRAQ. Washington: U. S. Weather Bureau (1956).

Water and Irrigation

* Cressey, George B.: "The Shatt al Arab Basin," *Middle East Jour.,* XII (1958), 448–460.

* deVaumas, Etienne: "Etudes Irakiennes. Le controle et l'utilisation des eaux du Tigre et de l'Euphrate," *Bull. Soc. Geog. l'Egypte,* XXVIII (1955), 125–194, also *Rev. Geog. Alpine,* XLVI (1958), 235–332.

Dimmock, Lionel: "The Waterways of 'Iraq," *Jour. Royal Central Asian Soc.,* XXXII (1945), 307–313.

Eaton, Frank M.: "Irrigation Agriculture Along the Nile and the Euphrates," *Scientific Monthly,* LXIX (1949), 34–42.

Ionides, M. G.: "Two Ancient Irrigation Canals in Northern Iraq," *Geog. Jour.,* XCII (1938), 351–354.

* Jacobson, Thorkild, and Adams, Robert M.: "Salt and Silt in Ancient Mesopotamian Agriculture," *Science,* CXXVIII (1958), 1251–1258.

Khalaf, Jassim: "Water Resources of Lower Colorado River Basin—With Applications of Study to Water Resource Problems in Iraq," Univ. of Chicago, *Dept. of Geog. Research Paper* #22 (1951).

* Lebon, J. H. G.: "The New Irrigation Era in Iraq," *Econ. Geog.,* XXXI (1955), 47–59.

Richards, E. V.: "The Flood Problem in Irak," *Jour. Inst. Civil Engineers* (1945), 145–168.

* Sevian, Vahe J.: "Economic Utilization and Development of the Water Resources of the Euphrates and Tigris," *Bull. Soc. Royale Geog. d'Egypte,* XXIV (1951), 177–200.

Sevian, Vahe J.: "Irrigation in Iraq," *Indian Geog. Jour.* (1951), 46–52.

Willcocks, William: THE IRRIGATION OF MESOPOTAMIA. London: Spon (1917).

People

Adams, Doris G.: "Current Population Trends in Iraq," *Middle East Jour.,* X (1956), 151–164.

Adams, Doris G.: IRAQ'S PEOPLE AND RESOURCES. Berkeley: Univ. of Cal. Press (1958).

Baer, Gabriel: "The Agrarian Problem in Iraq," *Middle Eastern Affairs,* III (1952), 381–391.

Field, Henry: "Arabs of Central Iraq: Their History, Ethnology and Physical Characters," *Anthrop. Mem.,* IV (1935).

Field, Henry: THE ANTHROPOLOGY OF IRAQ. 4 vols., Chicago, vols. I & II (1940, 1949) Cambridge, vols. III & IV (1951, 1952).

Field, Henry: "The Anthropology of Iraq," *Field Mus. of Nat. Hist. Anthrop Ser.*, XXX (1940).

Field, Henry, and Glubb, J. B.: "The Yezidis, Salubba, and Other Tribes of Iraq and Adjacent Regions," *General Series in Anthropology*, No. 10, Menasha, Wisconsin (1943).

Glubb, J. B.: "The Bedouins of Northern Iraq," *Jour. Royal Central Asian Soc.*, XXII (1935), 13–32.

* Lebon, J. H. G.: "Population Distribution and the Agricultural Regions of Iraq," *Geog. Rev.*, XLIII (1953), 223–228.

Miller, Valentin: "Types of Mesopotamian Houses," *Jour. Amer. Oriental Soc.*, LX (1940), 151–180.

Stark, Freya: "The Yezidi Devil Worshippers," *Geog. Mag.*, XXX (1958), 527–537.

Kurds in Iraq and Elsewhere

Burton, H. M.: "The Kurds," *Jour. Royal Central Asian Soc.*, XXXI (1944), 64–73.

Chater, Melville: "The Kizilbash Clans of Kurdistan," *Nat. Geog. Mag.*, LIV (1928), 485–504.

Edmunds, C. J.: KURDS, TURKS AND ARABS. London: Oxford (1957).

Edmonds, C. J.: "The Kurds of Iraq," *Middle East Jour.*, XI (1957), 52–62.

Elphinston, W. G.: "Kurds and the Kurdish Question," *Jour. Royal Central Asian Soc.*, XXXV (1948), 38–51.

Field, Henry, "Mountain Peoples of Iraq and Iran," *Amer. Jour. of Phys. Anthrop.*, IX (1951).

Galloway, J. P. N.: "A Kurdish Village of North-East Iraq," *Geog. Jour.*, CXXIV (1958), 361–366.

Hamilton, A. M.: ROAD THROUGH KURDISTAN. London: Faber & Faber (1958).

Johnson, J. C. A.: "The Kurds of Iraq," *Geog. Mag.*, X (1940), 382–393, XI (1940), 50–59.

Mumford, Philip: "Kurds, Assyrians and Iraq," *Jour. Royal Central Asian Soc.*, (1933), 110–119.

Safrastian, Arshak: KURDS AND KURDISTAN. London: Harvill Press (1948).

Wilkinson, John: "Oxford Univ. Expedition to Iraqi Kurdistan, 1956," *Jour. Royal Central Asian Soc.*, XLV (1958), 58–64.

Wilson, W. F.: "Northern Iraq and its People," *Jour. Royal Central Asian Soc.*, XXIV (1937).

Marsh Arabs

Dowes, Lady: "Marsh People of South Iraq," *Jour. Royal Central Asian Soc.*, XXXIV (1947), 83–90.

Drower, Ethel Stevens: THE MANDAEANS OF IRAQ AND IRAN. Oxford: Clarendon Press (1937).

* Maxwell, Gavin: PEOPLE OF THE REEDS. New York: Harpers (1957).

Maxwell, Gavin: "The Ma'dan: Marsh Dwellers of Iraq," *Nat. History*, LXVIII (1959), 266–274.

Philby, H. St. J. B.: "The Eastern Marshes of Mesopotamia," *Geog. Jour.*, CXXV (1959), 65–69.

* Thesiger, Wilfred: "The Marshmen of Southern Iraq," *Geog. Jour.*, CXX (1954), 272–281.

Thesiger, Wilfred: "The Ma'dan or Marsh Dwellers of Southern Iraq," *Jour. Royal Central Asian Soc.*, XLI (1954), 4–25.

Thesiger, Wilfred: "Marsh Dwellers of Southern Iraq," *Nat. Geog. Mag.*, CXIII (1958). 205–239.

CHAPTER 14

The Levant

Sea Coast, Mountains, Valleys, and Desert
Mediterranean Climate
The Tides of History
Syria: Water and Food
Syria: Countryside and City
Syria: Problems and Prospects
Lebanon: Progressive Mountain Land
Lebanon: Gateway to the East
Jordan: Present and Past
Jordan: Land and Minerals
References

SEA COAST, MOUNTAINS, VALLEYS, AND DESERT

"WHERE THE SUN RISES over the Mediterranean, there the East begins." The term Levant, "rising," reflects French usage for the lands east of the Mediterranean, once largely in Greater Syria. Four nations have risen in the Levant: Syria, since 1958 a province of the United Arab Republic; the Republic of Lebanon; the Hashemite Kingdom of Jordan; and the State of Israel.

(Opposite) The cedar is the official symbol of Lebanon. Only a few hundred trees remain, all in protected groves about a mile above sea level. (Courtesy U.S. Operations Missions, Beirut.)

The Levant States, taken together, represent the smallest area considered in any of these regional chapters on Southwest Asia. Even their combined population is only somewhat larger than that of Iraq. Yet in historical and cultural importance, no area outranks them. All the world is their debtor; half of mankind are followers of one of its three great religions. Those of Jewish faith look back to their early homeland in Palestine, Christians turn to Jerusalem, and Moslems from the Atlantic to Indonesia respect much of Biblical lore.

Much history has been made in these

The Levant

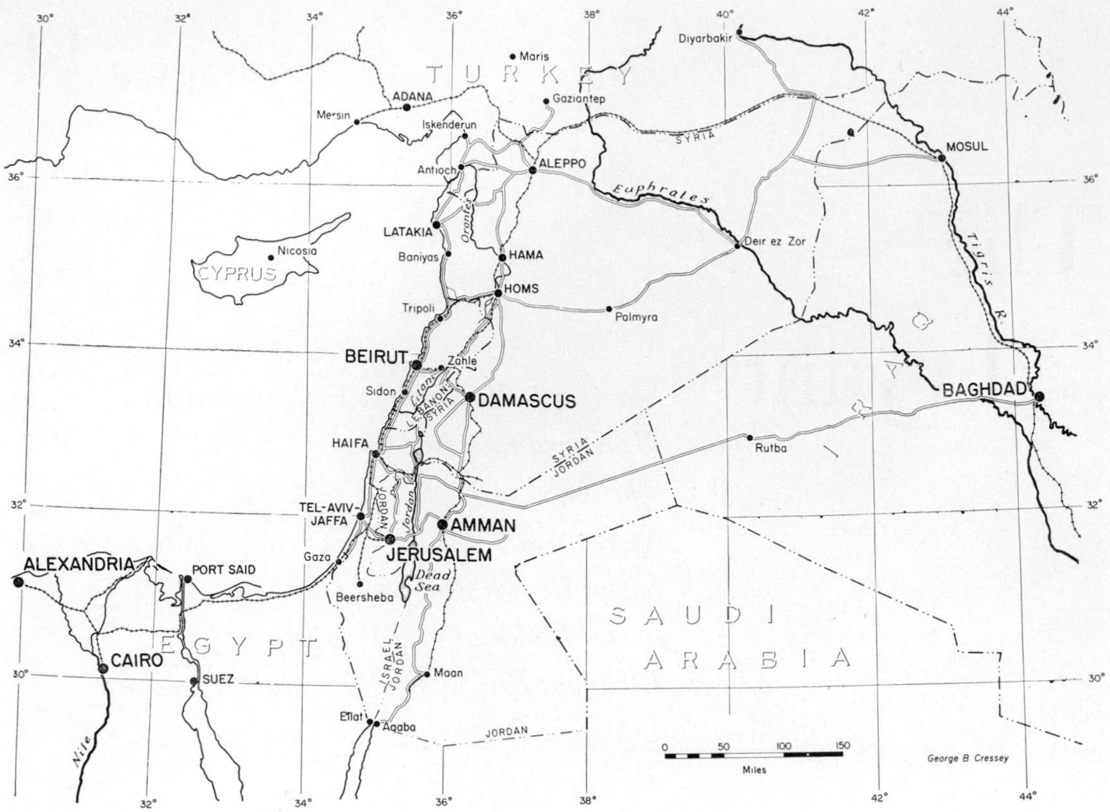

The Levant States are made up of Syria, Lebanon, Jordan, and Israel. Most cities and most agriculture lie close to the Mediterranean.

lands. Although they were repeatedly a target for outside conquerors, this area was never the center of great international power such as was developed in Turkey, Iran, or Iraq. Although Damascus did dominate the Arab world during the Ommiad period, its strength came out of the desert rather than from the coastal fringe. Perhaps the most significant historical factor was the transit or crossroads character of the area. In the early centuries, it was on the caravan routes which linked Egypt with Mesopotamia via the Fertile Crescent; while today, it is a gateway to the east by sea, air, road, and oil pipeline. Just as the Suez is the sea avenue to Asia and the Pacific, so Beirut is the gateway by plane. Every day a million barrels of oil reach the Mediterranean terminals from Iraq and Arabia.

The four Levant States are distinct but have several things in common. They are isolated on the east by desert, and, except in Lebanon, each has a dry area. Each shares a common history, most recently under Ottoman and mandate control. Each country benefits from irrigation water derived from mountain snows, but each has a water short-

NOTE: Additional material on the Levant States is presented in the following sections: Chapter 1, Flight to the East, page 13; Chapter 5, The Jordan River, page 130; Chapter 15, Israel, page 473. Many people have contributed to my understanding of the Levant, including my colleagues at the American University of Beirut and Mr. Maurice Fevret of the L'Institut de Geographie du Proche et Moyen Orient.

The rocky coast of Lebanon has numerous salt evaporating pans. Sea water is lifted by windmills. (G. B. C.)

age. Each country has a Mediterranean frontage except Jordan. All have problems along their present artificial boundaries.

The straight eastern shore of the Mediterranean Sea measures 400 miles from north to south. A hundred miles of this represents areas desired by the Levant states but denied them by Egypt's occupation of the Gaza Strip and Turkey's ownership of the Hatay area surrounding Iskenderon. The remaining 300 miles of frontage are almost matched by the eastward extent of the area. Only the first 100 miles inland are readily productive; farther east lies the nearly empty desert. Every city of importance is within seventy-five miles of the sea.

The coast of the Levant is a succession of bold headlands and shallow bays. Rocky cliffs alternate with sandy beaches backed by strips of dunes. Along the shore are discontinuous fragments of coastal plain or alluvial fans, only in a few places more than three or four miles in width. A road winds along most of the coastline, and a railway along a part, but so precipitous are some of the promontories that the road is either carved out of the cliffs or detours inland.

Nowhere is there an irregularity in the coastline which might make a good harbor. A succession of north-facing, half-moon bays provide shelter against some of the southern storms, but all of the modern ports depend on a breakwater for a safe anchorage. The few islands are generally tied to the land by sand spits. One of the most famous seaports was Tyre, which was once on an island, but is now built on a peninsula. Alexander cap-

The snow-capped Lebanese Mountains rise above terraced hills. Mountain villages occupy many intermediate slopes, as in this scene north of Beirut. (Courtesy Iraq Petroleum Co.)

tured the Phoenician city in 332 B.C., after he had constructed a causeway from the shore. Once a great mart of the Mediterranean world, it now has an insignificant export trade in cotton and tobacco.

Despite the hazards of the coast, the people have long been interested in maritime activities, as in the days of the Phoenicians. To the modern ports of Latakia, Baniyas, Tripoli, Beirut, Sidon, Haifa, and Tel Aviv may be added such ancient names, also reading from north to south, as Tartus, Byblos, Tyre, Acre, and Ashkelon.

Mountains rise inland, in most areas close enough so that one may stand on a coast bordered with palm trees and look up at snow peaks less than an hour away by car. To understand their structure it is necessary to review the geology of the area. To the north is the geosyncline and folded structure of the trans-Asian Tethys system; to the south and east lies the stable Arabian massif. Parallel to the eastern Mediterranean is another sedimentary trough which has accumulated thick layers of Mesozoic and early Cenozoic limestones and other sediments. This linear area is now folded to make a pair of broad anticlinal mountains, bounded by more or less parallel north-south faults. The result is a twin pair of ranges extending from Turkey to the Sinai Peninsula.

The series begins with the Amanus range in the Hatay province east of Iskenderon, in effect a part of the Anti-Taurus system. To

Level land is limited in the western Levant, so that most agricultural land must be laboriously terraced. (Courtesy U. S. Operations Mission, Beirut.)

the south, separated by cross faults along the valley of the lower Orontes, lies the Jebel Ansariya which is east of Latakia. The range is a simple anticline, with a core of Jurassic limestone; elevations reach 5,125 feet. The Jebel Ansariya has a width of twenty miles and a length of over a hundred miles, extending from Antakya (Antioch) almost to the border of Lebanon. Much of the range is a rounded highland, cut by deep valleys which flow to the west. Near the southern end of the range, commanding the lowland from Tripoli to Homs, is one of the greatest Crusader castles, the Krac des Chevaliers, at an elevation of 2,460 feet.

To the east, the Jebel Ansariya is bounded by a fault along which the mountains descend abruptly 3,000 feet to the Ghab, the floodplain valley of the north-flowing Orontes River. The Ghab is the northernmost of the structural depressions which parallel the Mediterranean coast. The lowland has a width of as much as nine miles and a length of forty miles. The area measures about 100,000 acres and was once a lake, impounded by a lava flow which blocked the Orontes.

East of the Orontes is another low-mountain series; the Kurd Dagh in the north, partly in Turkey, and the Jebel Zawiyeh to the south. Elevations rise to 3,940 feet in the former and to 3,068 feet in the latter.

These Syrian mountains are separated from those of Lebanon by a gap which connects coastal Tripoli with Homs in the interior. This includes the alluvial plains of

The Krak des Chevaliers in western Syria is one of the finest of the Crusader castles, never captured by the Arabs. (Courtesy Arab Information Center, New York.)

Akkar, next to the sea, and that of Bukeiah, inland.

Lebanon continues the threefold division, with the snow-crowned Lebanon Mountains, the faulted lowland of the Bekaa drained by the Litani, and the Anti-Lebanon dominated by Mount Herman. The Lebanon Mountains, like the Jebel Ansariya, are a great limestone anticline. Many peaks rise above 9,000 feet, with the highest reaching 10,131 feet. The upper slopes are bleak and without permanent settlement; they are known as the *jurd* in Arabic. The middle slopes, below 5,500 feet, are called the *wusut* and are among the most densely populated parts of Lebanon. They show the traveler painstakingly terraced fields. Cavernous limestones, overlying impervious formations, have resulted in large springs, found even at elevations of several thousand feet. Since these intermediate elevations are bordered by deep canyons and are thus difficult to enter, they have long formed a refuge for minority peoples. The coastal foothills are termed the *sahel*, and were the home of the ancient Phoenicians.

The Bekaa lowland has a length of seventy miles and is up to sixteen miles in width. The valley is drained by the south-flowing Litani, and the depression is in line with that of the Jordan, farther south. Thick accumulations of alluvium cover part of the structural valley.

The Anti-Lebanon is roughly the twin of the Lebanon range; both are limestone anticlines, both have linear faults, but folding and faulting are each less developed in the

Large areas of the Syrian desert are monotonously flat, veneered by residual pebbles which form a desert pavement. This desert track parallels the pipe line from Kirkuk to the Mediterranean. (G. B. C.)

eastern range. In both areas, porous limestone absorbs much of the rainfall so that there is little surface run off; the Anti-Lebanon, however, has few springs. Mount Herman rises to nearly 10,000 feet.

No topographic boundary separates Lebanon from Palestine. The deeply eroded Lebanon range gradually merges with the rounded hills of Galilee where elevations for the most part are under 2,000 feet. The uplands end at the Plain of Esdraelon, which forms a funnel-shaped east-west corridor twenty miles wide north of Haifa, narrowing to a few miles near the Jordan. As was once true in all of the lowlands of the Levant, swampy conditions here led to malaria.

Farther south along the coast is another broad limestone anticline which makes up the hills of Judea. These are deeply dissected in Samaria, plateau-like in central Judea, and lower in the Negeb. Between the uplands and the coast is a faulted foothill zone known as the Sephaleh. One of the most striking ridge summits is that of Mount Carmel which reaches the sea at Haifa. The elevation is only 1,791 feet but the headland provides one of the better harbors of the eastern Mediterranean. Here Elijah called down fire in his contest with the prophets of Baal (I Kings XVIII:17–40).

Whereas the coastal plain is absent or narrow along most of Syria and Lebanon, in Palestine it generally widens to several miles, notably in the plains of Esdraelon and Sharon. Sand dunes border some of the shore, especially near Gaza.

The Jordan River lies in a graben or structural depression which extends 250 miles from the Lebanon border southward through the Dead Sea and continues along the Wadi Araba to the Gulf of Aqaba. Elevations decrease from 260 feet at the source of the Jordan proper to 2,598 below sea level at the bottom of the Dead Sea. That portion of the linear depression between Lake Tiberias and the Dead Sea is known as the Ghor, from two to fourteen miles in width. East of Jerusalem, where the road descends to Jericho, a series of soft clays and marls have been eroded into badland topography, and the area is known as the Wilderness of Judea.

To the east of the Jordan valley lie the uplands of Moab, dominated by Mount Nebo, 2,631 feet, where Moses "saw the promised land." (Deuteronomy XXXIV:1) Elevations west and east of the Dead Sea reach 3,323 feet and 4,281 feet, respectively. Farther south, mountains east of the Wadi Araba reach 5,413 feet.

Although not a part of this structural series, one additional upland must be named, the volcanic dome of Jebel Druze in southwestern Syria. There are no outstanding peaks but the elevation reaches 5,900 feet.

The seashore and mountains of the Levant face westward across the sea, or look north and south in terms of the great highways which linked Egypt with Mesopotamia. Beyond the mountains, the orientation was eastward to the desert. A fringe of oases lies along the eastern slopes of the Jebel Zawiyeh, Anti-Lebanon, and Moab uplands. These include Aleppo (Haleb), Homs, Damascus (Esh Sham), and Amman; each an oasis in the rain shadow of higher elevations to the west. A few miles to the east of each city, cultivation fades out, grazing comes in, and not far away lies the real desert.

The deserts of Arabia grade imperceptably northward into those of Syria. All of the area from the Levantine mountains eastward to the Euphrates may be termed the Syrian Desert, although a part is in Jordan and Iraq. Conditions resemble those described in the chapter on Arabia, except that winters are cooler. Almost nowhere south of latitude 35°N. is there any cultivation.

Each of the four countries, except Israel, have mile-high mountains with snow; all but Jordan have a Mediterranean coastline; all but Lebanon include a desert. Each country has areas with enough rain so that irrigation is optional, but each is in the midst of ambitious schemes to expand irrigation.

Palestine is properly a part of the Levant, but political considerations in Israel point to the option of a separate following chapter.

MEDITERRANEAN CLIMATE

In latitude, area, and climate the Levant states find an analogy in the southwestern United States from San Francisco to San Diego, and inland to Nevada. In the extreme south, the frontage on the Gulf of Aqaba suggests a similarity with the Gulf of California. The coastal mountains in North America are lower than those of Asia, but the valley of California is not unlike the linear lowland of interior Levant. Both areas have sharp physical contrasts, with arid wastelands adjacent to irrigated fields. Both areas have maritime influences; both are backed by desert.

While there is no single situation which may be described as having a typical Mediterranean climate, conditions in the Levant are representative of the variations in Swasia. Thus, coastal Beirut receives thirty-five inches of rain a year whereas interior Damascus, fifty miles to the east and in the rain shadow of high mountains, has only nine inches. Temperatures in the two cities are comparable, with a slightly greater range in the interior. Beirut has recorded an all time high of 107°F. as compared with 113°F. in Damascus; Beirut has experienced 30°F. while in Damascus the thermometer has gone down as low as 21°F. in January.

The coastal Levant enjoys a mild, humid climate which gives rise to a natural forest landscape. Unfortunately, many hillsides have lost their original soil cover, as here in Lebanon. (Courtesy U. S. Operations Mission, Beirut.)

These temperature figures need to be measured against the humidity. Even during the rainless summer, Beirut is damp: the discomfort index in July with a daily average maximum of 87°F. and a humidity of 58 per cent at 3 p.m. may be more unpleasant than Damascus with 96°F. and a humidity of 19 per cent.

The dominant feature of the Levant climate is the contrast between a rainy season from November to March and a dry period during the rest of the year. This pronounced division is a result of the location between two major climatic regimes which migrate with the tilt of the earth's axis. To the south are the deserts of Arabia and Africa, "trade wind" in character. Here the air descends, and as it is steadily drawn into warmer areas by a low pressure circulation farther south, it increases its evaporative and water holding capacity. To the north lies the broad belt of "prevailing westerlies" with their variable cyclonic winds circling around migrating low pressure eddies. These lows originate over the Atlantic and bring precipitation every week or so.

The rainy winter of the Mediterranean occurs as the parade of cyclonic low-pressure areas shift southward following the sun, occasionally bringing European-style weather into the Levant. Summer drought follows the northward retreat of these rain-produc-

Heavy snows blanket the mountains of Lebanon and Syria. This is a glimpse of the famous cedars. (Courtesy Arab Information Center, New York.)

ing variables which have been replaced by steady dry winds that have had little chance to pick up moisture.

Cyclonic storms are fickle rainmakers, for in some years they bring much more rain than in others. An encampment in the desert which has had only a trace of rain for years may be washed out by a flash flood. A field which has produced crops for many years yields no harvest in a season when precipitation drops to one inch. Many rains last for two or three days and are followed by a week or two of sunny spring-like weather. Some rain comes in gentle showers; at other times it occurs in a torrential downpour with three or four inches falling in a day. Haifa has had as much as eleven inches in twenty-four hours.

Since variations in rainfall play such a large role in agriculture, it may be helpful to indicate specific situations in Palestine.[1]

Whereas the rainfall year 1950–51 was one of the driest years on record in Israel, the annual totals for the years 1951–52 were through most of the country above average. The beginning of the rainfall season 1951–52 looked rather unpromising. Pessimistic observers even feared a recurrence of the drought of 1950–51, to repeat the dreaded memory of 1931–32, 1932–33, or to a lesser extent 1875–76, 1876–77. All these fears

[1] *Israel Exploration Journal,* IV (1952), 250–51; V (1955) 268–69.

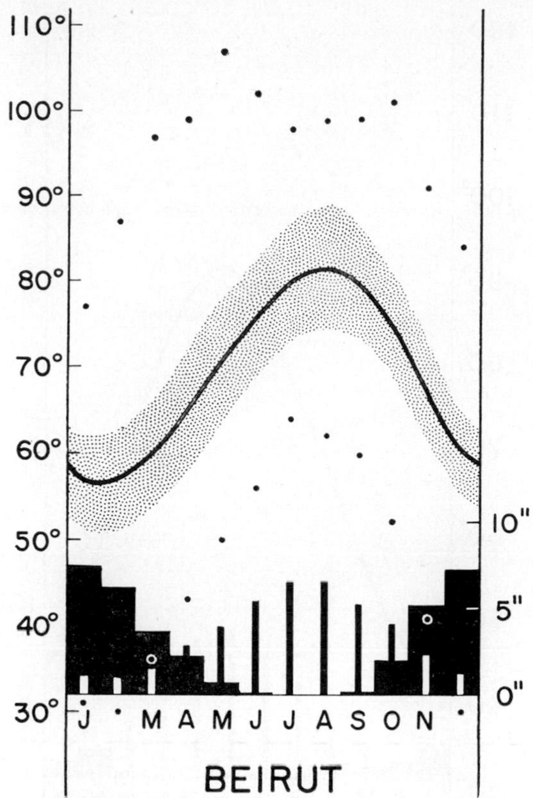

Coastal Beirut enjoys a pleasant Mediterranean climate. Elevation 111 feet, annual precipitation 35.1 inches.

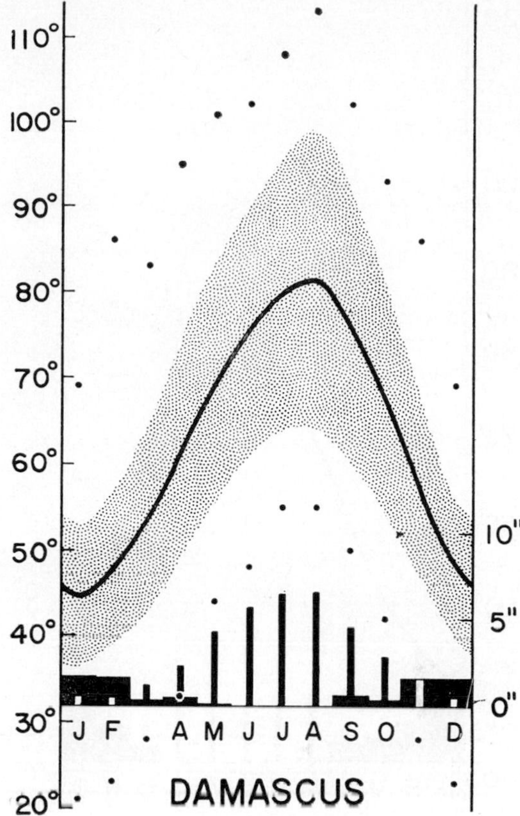

Damascus lies in the rain shadow of the Lebanon Mountains and is rather dry. Elevation 2,362 feet, annual precipitation 8.6 inches.

These graphs present monthly average temperature and rainfall, plus the daily temperature range, shaded, and the extreme recorded temperatures, in dots; as well as the monthly potential evapotranspiration, in thin bars.

were reversed by the excessively heavy rainfall pouring out over the country from 13 to 23 December, 1951, almost without interruption. During these eleven days many stations recorded more than 300 mm. of rain (12 inches). The highest records were in the Coastal Plain south of Tel Aviv with a maximum of 569 mm. (22 inches). . . . This heavy inflow occurred with a prolonged inflow of polar air masses into the eastern Mediterranean arriving on a northerly trajectory from Russia . . .

Some of these stations received within eleven days amounts equal to their total annual averages or more. Although last December's figures were particularly excessive, concentrated high rainfall during short periods is by no means exceptional in Israel . . . .

Intermittent rainfall continued until the middle of January. The second part of that month was rainless, a rather exceptional occurrence. The season came to an early end in March, as very little rain fell in April and almost none in May.

Rainfall amounts in 1954–55 were generally below average and the distribution within the season rather unfavorable. Very fair amounts of rain fell in the second half of November and the first week of December, bringing accumulated totals well ahead of the average . . . . The November rains were locally of great intensity for short spells. Tel Aviv recorded on the twenty-ninth, 28 mm. (1 inch) during fifteen minutes, including 16 mm. in five minutes. After a fortnight's interval rain fell again from 19 December.

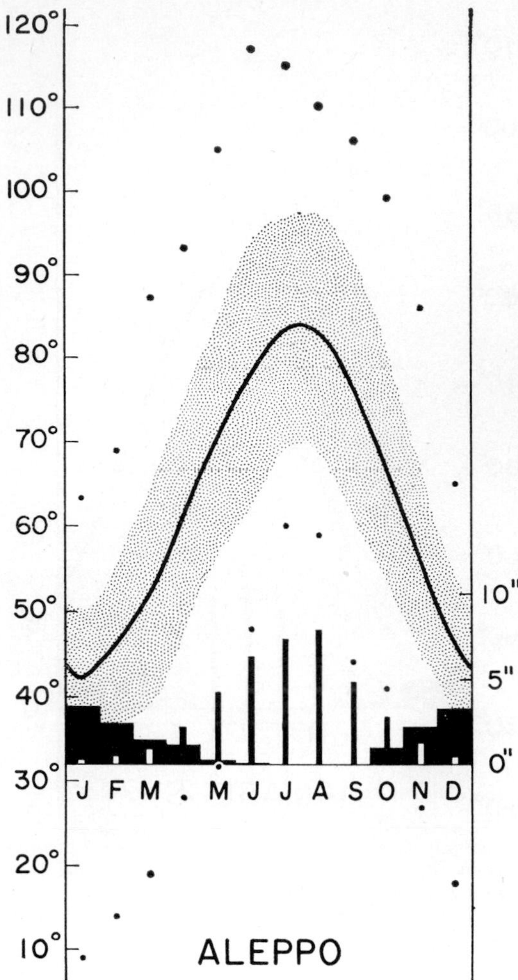

Aleppo receives some moisture directly from the Mediterranean and is thus subhumid. Elevation 1,280 feet, annual precipitation 15.5 inches.

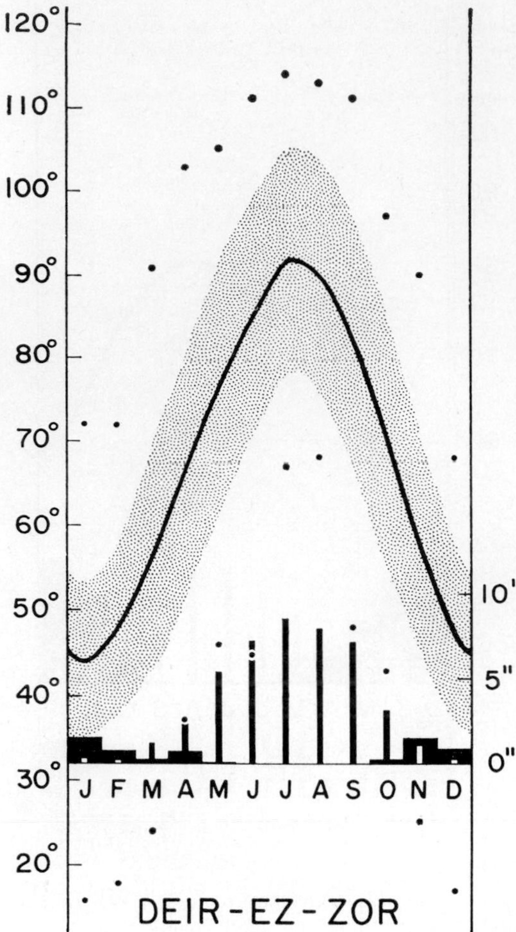

Deir ez Zor, on the Euphrates, has a climate which is representative of eastern Syria. Elevation 699 feet, precipitation 6.2 inches.

At the end of the month a deep upper air trough produced another case of excessive rainfalls over the coastal plain. On 28 and 29 of December very heavy rainfall occurred, no less than eight stations recording more than 100 mm. (4 inches) on each of two successive days, a very rare occurrence . . . .

These downpours caused very considerable damage to crops, roads, and even buildings, and there was much soil erosion.

From early in January until mid-March only insignificant amounts of rain fell. The *sharav* season started as early as the third week in February and the crop situation became desperate . . . . The rains which eventually came on 15 March saved much of the grain crops at the last moment. In most of the country, however, yields were rather poor.

The Bible speaks of the "former and the latter" rains, on either side of the main period. This threefold division is of significance in Palestine as well as elsewhere. The "former" or early rains occur in October and November and yield one to five inches; they are important to agriculture since plowing depends on them. The main rains come

Jerusalem has a rainfall record of more than a century. Elevation 2,485 feet, annual precipitation 20.8 inches.

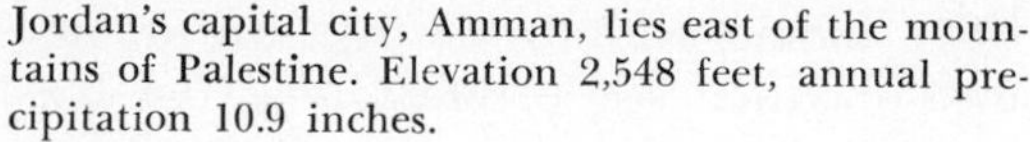

Jordan's capital city, Amman, lies east of the mountains of Palestine. Elevation 2,548 feet, annual precipitation 10.9 inches.

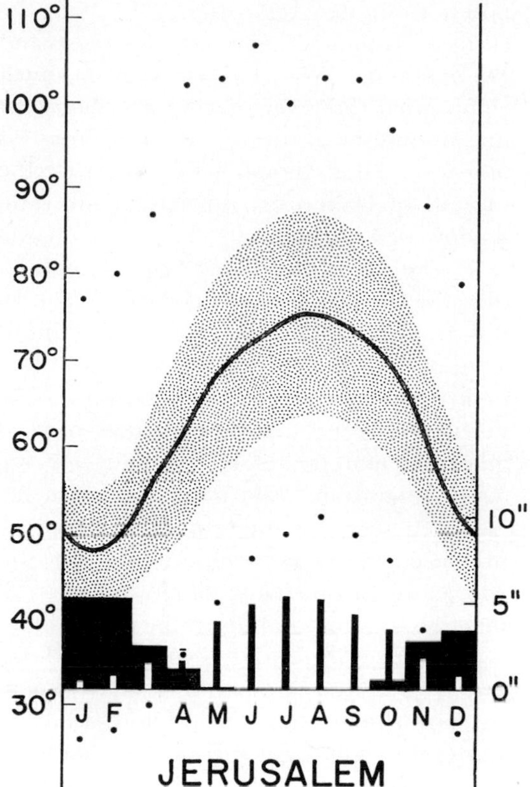

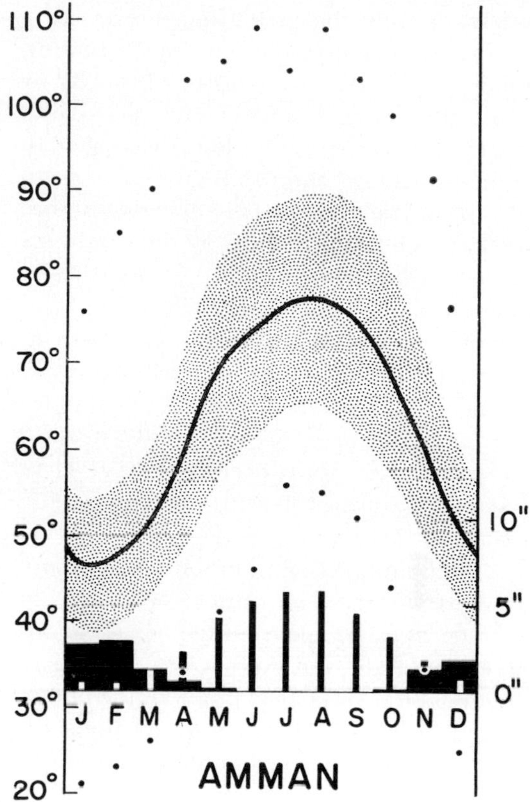

from December through February and yield ten to twenty inches; their value lies in the recharging of wells and springs. The "latter" rains in March and April, with from one to five inches, are important for the harvest.

Evaporation rates reach their maximum over the Dead Sea, where the figure amounts to 157.9 inches per year; Beersheba has measured 105.3 inches.

Pressure patterns vary with the season. In winter, the Levant is a region of relatively low pressure, across which a succession of weak depressions migrate eastward. High-pressure areas cover the continent to the north and also lie over Africa. With the approach of summer, the Levantine low gradually moves to the Persian Gulf, conditions become stable, and cyclonic disturbances are rare.

Winds play an important role and have special names. Southerly winds, which are hot, dry, and oppressive, are known as the *shuluq*, or splitter; these are similar to the sand laden *khamsin* or fifty-day wind. Easterly winds, also dry and hot, are termed *sharqi, sirocco,* or *simoon* meaning poisonous; at times these are violent and dusty, producing severe dust storms, In general, the sharqi is a wind reaching its maximum intensity in the early afternoon. Northwesterly winds dominate in summer and are welcome; peasants plan their winnowing in early summer with these winds. During summer, daytime sea breezes along the coast blow onshore as soon as the land becomes warm; at night the circulation is reversed.

If there were no mountains in the Levant, some of the Atlantic moisture brought by traveling storms would extend far inland, materially reducing the desert character of Iraq. Instead, as the winds from the Mediterranean rise over the Lebanese mountains, heavy precipitation results on the windward slopes, with as much as sixty-four inches at one station. Lee slopes remain dry.

Some of this highland moisture falls as snow, at least half a dozen times a year. Jerusalem, at 2,485 feet, occasionally has snow, but in Lebanon it regularly falls at 1,000 feet. Snow sometimes occurs at sea level in Latakia, is rare in Beirut, and almost unknown in Tel Aviv.

The mountains of Lebanon attract thousands of tourists, in winter for skiing, in summer as an escape from the heated plains of Egypt, Iraq, and Arabia. An Arab poet described the vertical zonation of the mountains as follows: "He bears winter upon his head, spring upon his shoulders, autumn in his bosom, while summer lies slumbering at his feet."

Although the Levant states have only minor amounts of oil, they do typify the other three colors of the landscape: brown, white, and green. Not only do the mountains provide a reservoir of water in the form of snow, but their cavernous limestones also accumulate moisture which gradually feeds inumerable springs. If it had been necessary for man to construct artificial reservoirs to store up the seasonal precipitation, the costs might have been prohibitive.

One gap in the coastal highlands, known as the Syrian Saddle, permits moisture-bearing winds to extend well inland. This lies between the mountains of Lebanon and southern Syria, and those of the Taurus range of Turkey, with the lowland roughly in the latitude of Aleppo. Here the Euphrates approaches within 120 miles of the Mediterranean, and many writers have pointed out that this gateway has long facilitated commerce between the coast and Mesopotamia. What has not been so much emphasized, however, is that this break in the mountains also provides an avenue for moisture. Thus Aleppo has nearly twice the rainfall of Damascus which is in the rain-shadow of Lebanon.

To the east of the Syrian Saddle, and as a direct result of it, lies the Fertile Crescent. In this arc from Aleppo to Mosul, the rainfall amounts to ten or twenty inches, in contrast to five inches due east of Damascus. The Fertile Crescent thus has a good natural grassland and provides an avenue for nomadic migration. A secondary factor in the rainfall pattern of interior Syria lies in the presence of Turkish mountains to the north. As cyclonic winds swing northward, there is some orographic cooling in the foothills.

Differences in rainfall, exposure, and elevation produce corresponding variations in vegetation and crops. Near the coast from sea level to 1,600 feet there is the characteristic Mediterranean flora, with date palms, umbrella pines, sycamore, mulberry, vines, figs, olives, bananas, and oranges. Figs, olives, and vines grow wild and may have been indigenous. Lebanon now has 600,000 olive trees, covering 34,000 acres. Cultivated crops include wheat and barley (both native to the area), millet, corn, and many vegetables.

From 1,600 to 6,500 feet, on exposed slopes with adequate rain, there was once a forest belt, now largely cut; in drier areas steppe vegetation prevails. The vicinity of Aleppo has pines, oak, willow, poplar, walnuts, apples, cypress, and fir. In this zone also grow the famous cedar trees. Only a few groups of the cedars remain out of the forests which supplied the Phoenicians with timber for their ships and for export to Egypt.

The alpine zone, an area of stunted trees

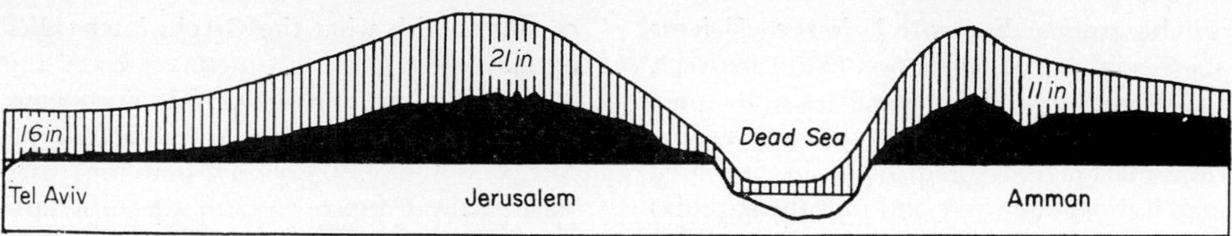

Rainfall matches elevation in this cross section from Israel into Jordan where land above sea level is shown in black and the amount of annual rainfall is shaded. The Dead Sea lies in the rain shadow of the Jerusalem hills.

and shrubs, lies above 6,500 feet. Snow lies on the ground for several months, and there is negligible cultivation or settlement.

The possibility of climatic change has been discussed by many writers, particularly as related to a decrease of rainfall in Palestine since Biblical times. Lands once reported to be "flowing with milk and honey" are clearly desolate today. Some people have suggested that various parts of the interior Levant once supported a much larger population than at present. Such changes are indicated by the ruins of towns, now surrounded by desert, where crops could not possibly be raised today in adequate amounts to feed the probable past population. If the land was then more productive, it is argued, rainfall must have been heavier.

Another reason for assumed dessication is the decrease of woodlands. Certainly most areas are now bare, and the once-forested hillsides are in a sorry state of erosion. It is quite possible, however, that this result is to be blamed on careless cutting and on overgrazing rather than on a decrease in rainfall. When the cover of natural vegetation is altered, the runoff sequence changes and streams acquire a new character.

In place of climatic change, there are other arguments in favor of marked stability. Crops in antiquity were the same as now, as were the seasons of planting and harvest. The ruins of all cities in dry lands contain aqueducts and cisterns, showing that water was a problem then as now. Ancient fields, as revealed in aerial photos, may represent the destruction of complex irrigation works by invaders, or their abandonment through silt accumulation in the canals which was too costly to remove.

In geological terms, the Pleistocene Period certainly brought climatic changes. What was an ice age in Europe may have been a pluvial period here. The Dead Sea overflowed and the desert was wetter. Within the past 5,000 years, however, no basic change in climate has been demonstrated. Minor cycles doubtless exist, but the evidence is yet to be unscrambled.

One clue as to climatic fluctuations is found in the growth rate of trees. Complex factors are involved, but on the whole, a wider spacing of the rings reflects more abundant moisture. Some of the cedars of Lebanon are presumably 1,000 and perhaps even 2,000 years old. The remaining trees are in protected groves, but if it were possible to take core borings, they might throw significant light on past climates.

Similar studies have been made on hundreds of California sequoias, a few of which are 3,000 years old. When their average annual growth rates for the past century are compared with known rainfall for the same years, satisfactory correlation coefficients appear. It is thus demonstrated that sequoia growth mirrors the climate of California for some thirty centuries; there are variations but an over-all uniformity.

California and Palestine both have a Mediterranean climate. Long-range comparisons are hazardous, but correlation coefficients show reasonable correspondence between San Francisco and Jerusalem rainfall for a hundred years. There is thus some suggestion that periods of drought in one area match those elsewhere and that the sequoias provide a clue to the Levant.[1]

Rainfall records in Jerusalem date back to 1846, and in Beirut to 1876. While there have been extremes of twice and of half the average, and even three to one, no clear periodicity is evident.

THE TIDES OF HISTORY

So many conquerors have moved across the Levant that a list of their exploits becomes a lengthy though fascinating record. After a summary sketch, it may be more meaningful to examine the record in terms of three cities: ancient coastal Byblos, Jerusalem with its cultural traditions, and Palmyra, a caravan city of the desert.

The earliest known community along the coast was that of the Canaanites, a Semitic group around 3000 B.C., later known as the Phoenicians. About the same time, a similar people, the Amorites, moved into the Fertile Crescent. The former became oriented to the sea and Egypt, while the latter turned toward Mesopotamia and the Sumerians. From the north came pressures from the Hittites in Turkey; from the south was the threat of invasion from Egypt. Until Roman times, Phoenicia was made up of a string of coastal towns, each set against a thickly wooded and thinly populated mountain background.

In the course of the fourteenth and thirteenth centuries B.C. the interior was overrun by a new Semitic horde, the Aramaeans, who drove the earlier inhabitants into the mountains of Lebanon. The area of the Aramaeans, centered on Damascus, became synonomous with what the Greeks later called Syria.

Shortly after this time, Indo-Europeans, known as the Sea People or Philistines, moved out of Turkey, invaded the coast, pushed the Canaanites into the hills, and gave Palestine its present name.

At the same time that Aramaeans were occupying the interior and Philistines the coast, a third people, the Hebrews, arrived in the south from Egypt. After assimilating the earlier hill people, the Hebrews created a monarchy under David about 1004 B.C. It is interesting to note that the traditional homeland of the Jews was the hill country, whereas present-day Israel is in the lowlands, leaving the hills of Judea in Arab hands.

Successively, influences and conquest came from Egypt, Babylonia and Assyria, Persia, Greece, Rome, the Crusaders, Islamic Arabia, Turkey, and several European powers. A suggestion of these successive invaders may be seen near the mouth of the Dog River north of Beirut. Here on the face of a cliff are nineteen inscriptions in eight languages recording one conqueror after another. The sequence begins with Ramses II and continues through Nebuchadnezzar, Marcus Aurelius, and Napoleon.

Modern French influence in the Levant has already been mentioned. It was in 1521 that the French secured the first "Capitulations" from the Turkish Empire, giving them extraterritorial rights and laying the basis for French trade in the Levant. Later on, France was given exclusive protection over vessels of all foreign states, and in 1740 both French pilgrims to the Holy Land and all other visitors to the Ottoman Empire were placed under the protection of the French flag. These historic concessions still serve as the basis of French claims to be the protector of all Catholics in Syria.

The British were not far behind, for in 1581 Queen Elizabeth chartered the Levant Company, whose commercial operations con-

[1] See data by George B. Cressey in Huntington and Visher, *Climatic Changes*. New Haven: Yale Univ. Press (1922). 76–86.

The modern village at Byblos uses the narrow beach to dry fishing nets. Many houses contain stones which have been re-used over the centuries. (G. B. C.)

tinued into the eighteenth century. The company made Aleppo its main base for trade and in due time outstripped the Venetians and French who were there ahead of them.

Modern Arab ambitions reached high tide following the defeat of Turkey during World War I. With the consent of the United Kingdom, King Feisal proclaimed the independence of Greater Syria on October 13, 1919. A few months later the provisional government was terminated and the mandate situation imposed under the League of Nations. These mandates lasted for nearly three decades.

History remains in flux, for major changes in government and boundaries have occurred during the twentieth century. These current developments will be considered under the separate countries to follow.

Byblos

Byblos is one of the oldest continuously inhabited towns in the world, for the port dates back to the fourth millenium B.C. One of the city's most lasting claims to fame is that our word Bible is derived from the Greek word meaning papyrus, since it was exported from here. Here too was developed one of the earliest alphabets.

The town lies on the coast less than an hour's drive north from Beirut. It is also known by its ancient name of Jubayl. Beneath and within the modern city are the remains of Crusader, Greco-Roman, and Phoenician buildings, many built out of stones used in earlier periods. The foundations of a present-day home may include large stones quarried for a Phoenician temple, re-used and partly reshaped for a Roman building, and later incorporated into a Crusader castle.

Phoenician Byblos covers the period following the Chalcolithic or Neolithic Age, which ended about 2150 B.C. Only traces remain of the palace, royal tombs, temples, and ramparts, but the museum at Beirut has an array of gold ornaments and of delicately carved stone sarcophagi from the eleventh century B.C. The city's early fame came through its export of cedar to Egypt and its production of purple dye from mollusk shells. Freshly opened tombs in Egypt, 4,000 years old, still carry a faint odor of cedar. Egypt needed large amounts of timber for boats, houses, and coffins; in return it sent alabaster, gold, linen, and slaves. One may say that the exported cedar beams were exchanged for granite columns. An old Egyptian text bewails the interruption of the trade: "Men do not sail to Byblos today. What can we do to get cedar for our mummies? Priests are buried with their produce and princes embalmed with their resin as far as the land of Keftin (Crete or Cilicia) and now they come no more."

The most striking buildings in Byblos are connected with the Crusaders, who marched into the land from 1103 until 1299 A.D. They built a castle city with a towering citadel, picturesque ramparts, four gateways, and a church. Incorporated into the walls are massive stone sarcophagi, classic temple columns, and many other twice-used stones.

Following Alexander's capture of the Phoenician coast in 333–332 B.C., Byblos entered a six-century period of Hellenized and Romanized culture. This was the most glorious period in the city's history, and the tiny city-state was resplendent with temples and shrines to Adonis, colonnades and grand avenues, villas, and monuments. An aqueduct brought water from the Adonis River. Only six of the granite columns on the acropolis remain standing, but hundreds are scattered elsewhere. Most of these stones were brought from southern Egypt.

Jerusalem

"Jerusalem is builded as a city that is compact together: whither the tribes go up" (Psalms CXXII : 3); in short, a fortified high place of refuge. Whether one comes from the coast or from the Jordan Valley, the traveler must climb to an elevation of 2,500 feet. Although the Hills of Judea are among the lower of the Levant mountains, they can be penetrated only through narrow valleys which are easy to defend. Here the Israelites were able to preserve their characteristics for a thousand years.

Jerusalem lies at the intersection of trade routes from north to south along the ridge heights and east to west along opposite valleys. Fortunately, water is available. Only if the enormous debris of ancient buildings could be cleared away would the natural site be visible. In places it is necessary to dig down thirty and even sixty feet to strike virgin soil. For the archaeologist, Jerusalem is an inexhaustible source for research; the area was civilized well before Abraham arrived. Egyptian records refer to "Urusalem, city of peace," around 2000 B.C.

The Hebrew history of Jerusalem begins after the arrival of the twelve tribes from Egypt, possibly during the thirteenth century B.C. Their final conquest of Canaan was not completed until Jerusalem was captured by David about 1004 B.C. Under Solomon, the three great architectural contributions were the Temple, the palace, and the city walls. Much of the work was under the direction of the Phoenicians for the Hebrews were still nomads and farmers, unskilled in architecture. The Phoenicians could supply cedar timbers, and shared the hatred of the coastal Philistines. In 701 B.C. Jerusalem was attacked though not captured by the Assyrians; however, it was captured in 587 B.C. Even

The city of Jerusalem crowns a hilltop opposite the Mount of Olives. The Old City with the Dome of the Rock lies in the foreground, in Jordan, while Israeli Jerusalem appears on the skyline. (G. B. C.)

though the Israelites were deported to Babylon, they were one of the few people of antiquity who remained themselves even in defeat. On their return, the Temple was rebuilt between 537 and 515 B.C. The wall was reconstructed under Nehemiah "in fifty and two days," largely from the rubble of earlier buildings. The political history of these days was complex, for only seldom were Jerusalem or Israel fully free.

Roman rule began in 63 B.C. and was marked by another reconstruction of the Temple, whose huge foundation stones form the present "wailing wall." Revolts in 70 and 132 A.D. led to further destruction and to a widespread dispersal of the Jews.

Christian Jerusalem dates from the events of Holy Week, which occurred during a Passover, perhaps in April of 30 A.D. The early Judeo-Christians led a precarious existence in Jerusalem but flourished elsewhere, as in Antioch. Not until the days of the Crusades could Jerusalem be called a Christian city, although with the growth of Christianity in Rome and Constantinople it became a pilgrimage center, with the resulting construction of many churches.

The Crusades had more than a spiritual goal, for they proved of great commercial profit and enabled a large number of young men to acquire wealth. The first Crusade reached Jerusalem in 1099 and resulted in a general massacre of Jews and Moslems. The story of succeeding years is varied, with alternations between conquest and defeat. Numerous churches and monastaries were built and endowed. The Moslem shrine known as the Dome of the Rock was converted to a church, with an altar on the rock and with a cross on top of the dome. In 1187, Jerusalem was captured by Saladin, and the defenders had every reason to fear a general massacre in revenge for that of 1099; but the surrender was peaceful in return for a promise of protection for the Dome of the Rock.

Islam came to Jerusalem in 638, within six years after the death of the Prophet. After having been the spiritual center of the Hebrew religion for six centuries, Jerusalem became one of the holy cities of the Moslems. The Dome of the Rock, also known as the Dome of Omar, adjoining the great mosque on Mount Moriah, stands on the site of Solomon's temple, where still earlier there had been a pagan sanctuary. This monument reflects the common ideas of three faiths, for it is built over the stone sacred to the Jews as the point where Abraham prepared to sacrifice Isaac, to the Christians as one of the possible points of Christ's ascension, and to the Moslems as the place where Mohammed stopped on his way to heaven.

All of these events have meaning to Moslems, for, as indicated, Islam is built on Judeo-Christian traditions. To a reader of the Koran, Abraham, Joseph, Moses, Aaron, Jonas, David, Solomon, Job, and Jesus are all among the great prophets. Mohammed is merely the latest messenger of God.

At least in the earlier centuries, Moslems had considerable regard for Jews and Christians. Mohammed at first prayed toward Jerusalem rather than toward Mecca. Islam claims to represent a return to the purest traditions of Judaism, for the Koran reads: "The Jews and the Christians say: Embrace our faith if you would be saved. Reply to them: We follow the faith of Abraham, who refused to burn incense to idols and worshipped only one God."

The extent to which Old Testament ideas have been taken into Islam is suggested by the fact that Adam is supposed to have been buried near Aden, while Eve's tomb is purported to lie outside Jidda.

Soon after the Islamic occupation, Jerusalem developed distinct residential quarters, one for the Jews with their synagogues and access to the "Wailing Wall," others for various Christian groups, elsewhere for the Moslems. Later on, certain political rights and privileges were granted to the different groups to keep them in a delicate equilibrium.

The Arab–Israeli war of 1948 tragically divided the city into two parts, the old walled city in the east remaining in Arab hands, with the newer city on the west passing to Israel.

Palmyra

Palmyra is old, but it flashed into brilliance during a few centuries at the beginning of the Christian era. When its ruins were discovered by the first British visitors during the seventeenth century, their impressions of its grandeur led them to ask, "Whether any city in the world could have challenged precedence of this in its glory."

The city lies in central Syria, 150 miles from both the Mediterranean and the Euphrates. To the east is desert, to the west is a dry steppe with some cultivation. Sulphur springs supply a small oasis, but the city has always depended on commerce. No easy route crosses the Syrian Desert. The direct line from Baghdad to Damascus is far too dry for ancient caravan travel. The best-watered route with fair pasturage swings far to the north, crossing a narrow desert west of Aleppo; Palmyra is intermediate between the two.

Of Palmyra's early centuries we know little. Under its Arabic name of Tadmor, the oasis is mentioned on Assyrian tablets dating from the twentieth century B.C. During the eleventh century, Tiglath-Pileser I fought near the city, and both then and a

The magnificent ruins of Palmyra are a monument to Queen Zenobia and her empire. This triple pylon is but one of many architectural achievements. (Courtesy Iraq Petroleum Co.)

thousand years later the Aramaic language was in use. The city was said to have been built in the wilderness by Solomon (II Chronicles VIII: 4), who undoubtedly controlled the area to the Euphrates, but his relation to Palmyra is not clear.

One key to Palmyra's fame lies in Pliny's description of the location of Tadmor: "Situated in the midst of an almost impassable desert and on the confines of two powerful and hostile kingdoms." During the first century prior to the Christian era and for two centuries following, the great powers were Rome and Persia. Palmyra profited from the rivalry and for a time defied each; the end came when it could not stand alone.

The earliest known inscriptions at Palmyra date from 32 B.C., when the city was already an important trading center between Rome and Persia. The products of Europe were exchanged for silks and jades of the Han dynasty from China, along with jewels, pearls, and perfumes from India. Trade and religion led to,

> the amazing rapid development of Palmyra into one of the most elegant towns in Syria. One would almost imagine that she had sprung from the desert sands at the wave of a magic wand, so rapidly was the old and apparently small and unpretentious temple of the village of Tadmor transformed. Already at the time of Augustus

Palmyra contained a splendid theatre, built 1,700 years ago, but only recently excavated. (G. B. C.)

and Tiberius it was one of the most important sanctuaries of Syria, and could vie in magnificence with any of the temple groups in that province.[1]

Although Palmyra came to recognize the suzerainty of Rome, the city enjoyed full tax independence. The fall of Petra in 105 A.D. left her with no competition in trade with the east or south. Palmyra's greatest period was under Queen Zenobia who ruled from 267 until 272. Under her direction, Alexandria was captured and a merchant empire spread from the Nile to the Caucasus; a Palmyrene flotilla was stationed on the lower Euphrates to watch the Persian Gulf and Palmyra's merchants spread west to Spain. Small wonder that Zenobia assumed the title of "Queen of the East." Her ambition outweighed her prudence, and when her coinage ceased to carry the image of the Roman Emperor Palmyra was attacked and later sacked by Rome.

Palmyra never fully recovered from this defeat. Later on, during the Byzantine period, it had four churches. Still later, it surrendered to one of the early Moslem generals, and there is a magnificent Arab fort which still overlooks the city. The city remained important during both Ommiad and Abbasside times, but today it is a mere village along the oil pipeline. As recently as 1912, Baedeker advised travelers that the trip from Damascus required nine days and that an armed escort was advisable.

[1] Rostovtzeff, M. I.: *Caravan Cities*. Oxford: Clarendon Press (1932), 103. Quoted by permission.

Few monuments of antiquity are more romantic or magnificent than Palmyra; in the Levant these might include Balbek, Jerash, and Petra; elsewhere in Swasia only Persepolis. The main street was lined with classic columns, fifty-five feet high, beautifully carved in the best Greek style, and supplied with brackets for statues of the leading merchants. One hundred and fifty of these columns still stand, along with triumphal arches, magnificent temples to Baal, palace-like tombs, and one of the finest theatres to be found anywhere. In its day of glory, Palmyra was indeed "Queen of the East."

Minority Peoples

To these highlights of history must be added some reference to minority peoples. It is clear that successive waves of conquest have displaced many cultural groups; what is not so obvious is that religion also has ethnic characteristics. Certainly no pure "races" remain, unless in the interior of Arabia; even the Jews are far from homogeneous.

The modern minority problem in the Levant is particularly acute with Christian groups, all of whom have experienced persecution, massacre, and migration. Most of the present Eastern churches in Swasia descend from the ancient apostolic churches of Jerusalem, Antioch, Thessalonica, and Corinth, which were united under the Byzantine Empire later on. They include two Orthodox groups, first the Greek and the Syrian Churches, both tracing back to Constantinople, and second the separated churches which broke off in the fifth and sixth centuries, such as the Armenian Church, the Assyrian or ancient Nestorian Church, the Syrian Jacobite Church, the Chaldean Church, and the Maronite Church. The last two are members of the Uniat group, in communion with Rome. Other churches have within them both Eastern Catholic and Evangelical or Protestant divisions. All of these are tightly-knit groups, with such a long record of persecution that they are suspicious of outsiders and it is rare for a person to change his religion.

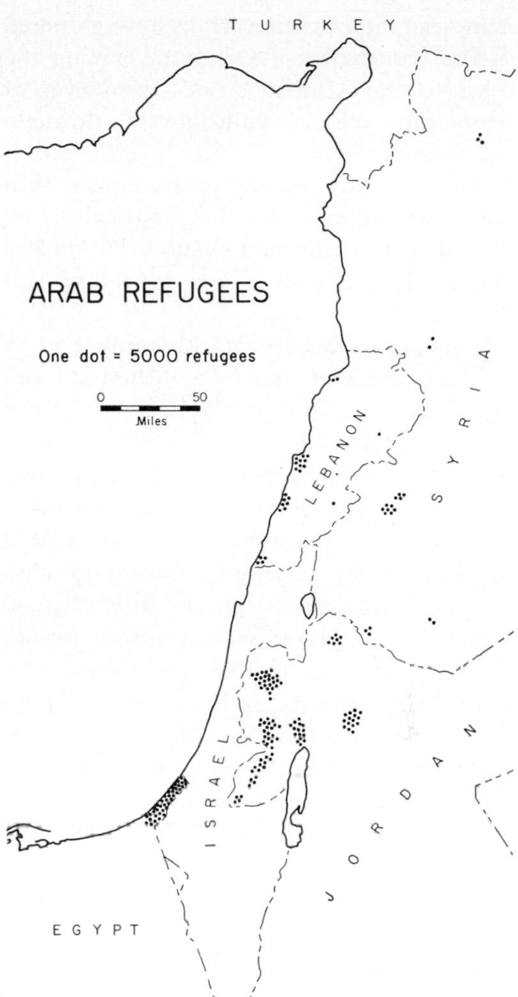

About a million refugees from their former homes in Palestine are gathered around the borders of Israel, especially in the Gaza Strip, now under Egyptian administration, and in Jordan.

Just as Zionist Israel has become a modern rallying place for displaced Jews, so Lebanon is a traditional place of refuge for Christians; and as it was in the hills that the Jews found refuge against the coastal Philistines, so the Christian Arabs have gathered in the mountains of Lebanon, leaving the coast to the Moslem Arabs. Memories of persecution play a significant role throughout Swasia.

There are also minority situations within Islam, as for example the fanatical Druse who live in southern Lebanon. Sunni and Shia divisions have a long record of animosity.

The latest chapter in the refugee story relates to the Arabs, nearly a million in number, who were driven out of Palestine by the Zionists and were not allowed to return to their homeland. Pre-Israel Palestine was one of the most prosperous and advanced areas in all Swasia, so that the resulting destitution of the refugee farmers and merchants, barely subsisting on international charity, has produced serious unrest. Jordan certainly offers no feasible agricultural solution; their settlement in Lebanon would upset the delicate Christian-Moslem balance; any new agricultural land in Iraq can only be reclaimed at great expense; and Syria could only absorb them gradually. The fact that Jews have themselves suffered persecution elsewhere should make them sensitive to the injustice which has been created in the establishment of Israel.

SYRIA: WATER AND FOOD

THE NAME SYRIA is of uncertain origin; some regard it as a corruption of Assyria which of course lay well to the east. Ancient writers used the name loosely for the entire area between the Taurus Mountains and the Sinai Peninsula. Thus Strabo, Pliny, and the Arab geographers all assumed that Syria took in all of what we here call the Levant. In the second century A.D. Syria occurs as the names of three Roman provinces: Syria, Syria Phoenice, and Syria Palestine. From 1516 to 1918, Syria was part of the Ottoman Empire, and, at the beginning of the twentieth century, the name was applied to the province around Damascus, extending to the Gulf of Aqaba but not including the Mediterranean coast.

Following World War I and the breakup of the Ottoman Empire, France assumed a League of Nations mandate over a newly-defined Syria, which was shortly divided into Syria and Lebanon. The Republic of Syria became independent in 1946 and in 1958 joined with Egypt to become a province of the United Arab Republic.

Water Supplies

Water is as significant in most parts of Syria as it is elsewhere in Swasia, with similar problems of high evaporation, careless or over-use of irrigation water, and salinization on flat slopes. Even in the areas of more abundant rainfall, its seasonal distribution and uncertainty makes supplemental water desirable. The variability of rainfall is well shown by the figures for Damascus, where February receives an average of 1.7 inches but has experienced as much as 5.0 inches and as little as zero. All months except January and December have at times been rainless.

SYRIA DATA

Area	71,227 square miles 184,479 square kilometers
Arable area	45,900 square kilometers
Population	4,082,000
Cities	
Damascus	408,774
Aleppo	407,613
Homs	132,637
Hama	178,589

In most areas of Syria, cultivation is completely dependent on irrigation. This was apparently true in Roman times, for the great agricultural production in those days seems to have been related to elaborate irrigation systems which later fell into decay. The use of canals in the Jezira area near the

Water Wheels, known as *noria*, line the Orontes near Hama, lifting water to irrigate the terraces. Some of these structures were built by the Romans. (Courtesy Arab Information Center, New York.)

Euphrates dates back to the second millennium B.C.

The area under irrigation in 1957 amounted to 1 million acres, although not all of it received adequate water. This was about 15 per cent of the cultivated land. Most of this area was supplied by pumps; those which drew on river water were chiefly along the Euphrates and its tributary the Khabur, while around Hama and Aleppo the pumps depended on ground water. The remainder was irrigated by gravity canals, springs, or qanats. Only one-fifth of the irrigated area was supplied by government schemes, chiefly in the newer areas.

The possibilities of expanded irrigation are governed by supplies of water in the Orontes and Euphrates. Since both are international rivers, the share of their water available in Syria is a matter for negotiation. The Euphrates accounts for 83 per cent of the aggregate flow of Syria's rivers, but even if all of the country's presumed share might be employed, the irrigated land

DAMASCUS RAINFALL

	Jan	*Feb*	*Mar*	*Apr*	*May*	*Jun*	*Jul*	*Aug*	*Sep*	*Oct*	*Nov*	*Dec*	*Year*
Maximum	3.0	5.0	2.0	1.2	0.6	0.1	0	0	0.6	1.5	3.7	4.1	
Mean	1.7	1.7	0.3	0.5	0.1	0	0	0	0.7	0.4	1.6	1.6	8.6
Minimum	0.4	0	0	0	0	0	0	0	0	0	0	0.1	

The Ghab project calls for draining the extensive marsh lands along the central Orontes River. (Courtesy Iraq Petroleum Co.)

would only amount to a small part of the national area.

A series of eight engineering schemes for irrigation or drainage, under way and proposed, might double the present irrigated land. Optimistic estimates of additional acreage are shown in the accompanying table.

The Barada River makes possible Damascus and the wonderful Ghuta oasis. Few rivers anywhere have rendered such long and useful service as the Barada; small wonder that it has been known since ancient times as "the river of gold." The river rises almost full-grown in an enormous spring in the Anti-Lebanon Mountains, Ain Fijeh. Where it breaks through the mountains, seven major canals divert the water over the alluvial fan of the Ghuta to irrigate 17,000 acres, each plot receiving fixed amounts of water at specific times. Developments on the Barada involve two storage dams and electric power stations, and the irrigation of the lower slopes of the alluvial fan. Soils in the marginal areas, however, may require leaching and drainage.

The Orontes rises in Lebanon and reaches the sea in Turkey; during its course through Syria three areas of hard basaltic lava interrupt the river's profile and form natural reservoirs upstream. These basins are Lake Homs, a reservoir which dates from 3,000 years ago, the Ghab reed-covered marshes and lake area, and Lake Amuk. Considerable parts of the marsh areas have been reclaimed with a resulting increase in agricultural land and a decrease in malaria. For centuries, gigantic water wheels at Homs, known as *noria,* have been turned by the current to lift water. Unlike the Barada, the Orontes had no elaborate system of canals until the mid-twentieth century.

The Orontes is now Syria's principal source of irrigation water. Below Lake Homs, irrigation schemes completed in 1939 supply 50,000 acres of cotton, wheat, barley, fruit, sugar cane, and sugar beets. Future plans call for canal diversion above Lake Homs, plus a storage dam. Several hydroelectric plants have been installed, with others in prospect.

The Ghab project, along the central Orontes, is Syria's most ambitious reclamation scheme. The program is not entirely new, for both Romans and Turks considered it. The river is ponded by basaltic lava, and in the alluvial basin above it, drainage is further limited by natural levees along the river. Swamps cover an area thirty miles long by six miles wide, an excellent breeding ground for ducks, wild boar, and malarial mosquitos; when drained, the area will provide livelihood for 100,000 people. The plan of the Ghab Foundation calls for cutting down the outlet, moving the Orontes to a new and shorter channel on lower ground, construction of two storage dams, and digging 580 miles of canals. Additional land outside the swamp will also be irrigated.

The Nahr el Kebir is a short river near Latakia. Its flow varies from heavy flood to a mere trickle. If regulated by a dam, the river might supply water for vegetable gardens.

The Rondj project calls for a two-mile tunnel in order to drain a swamp area between Latakia and Aleppo, with subsequent irrigation of the reclaimed land.

The Yarmuk is a tributary of the Jordan and irrigation possibilities exist in its headwaters.

The Euphrates and its tributary the Khabur are major Syrian assets, but their development presents both engineering and political problems. Through most of their courses across Syria, the rivers flow in an inner valley a few hundred feet in depth, so that long and expensive canals would be necessary to bring water to the uplands. Furthermore, any large diversion of water would raise problems downstream in Iraq. To cultivate all of the potentially agricultural land within the Euphrates basin in Syria might require 75 per cent of the usable flow of the river, leaving only 25 per cent for Iraq. No agreement has yet been reached as to how much of the water might be used within Syria.

POTENTIAL SYRIAN IRRIGATION

Barada River	30,000 acres
Orontes River	50,000 acres
Ghab drainage	90,000 acres
El Kebir River	7,500 acres
Rondj drainage	10,000 acres
Yarmuk River	17,500 acres
Euphrates River	750,000 acres
Khabur River	21,000 acres
Future Jezira projects	250,000 acres
Total	1,226,000 acres

Along the 300-mile course of the Euphrates and the 150 miles of the Khabur, there are many small plots of cropland formerly supplied by hand or animal lift but now watered by hundreds of mechanical pumps. For the most part, irrigation is confined to the flood plain, three to six miles wide. Engineering studies look forward to a large dam at Youssef Pasha, three miles long and 230 feet high, for storage and hydroelectric power. Additional diversion barrages downstream are also proposed on both rivers.

The city of Aleppo receives its municipal water by pipeline from the Euphrates, and much larger diversion has been proposed for irrigation and even for navigation.

Agriculture

During the mid-twentieth century, Syria experienced a major change in agriculture, both in techniques and acreage. Within a decade the number of farm tractors increased from 200 to 1,500, while combines grew from 14 to 700. Thousands of pumps were added for irrigation, and the use of commercial fertilizers was greatly expanded. As a result, 4 million acres of new land came under cultivation, most of it in the rain-fed zone.

Figures as to cultivated land do not al-

Wooden plows are still in wide use. This view is in the steppe lands between Homs and Palmyra. (G. B. C.)

ways indicate the portion which lies fallow in some years. The total crop area is nearly 9 million acres. Official estimates of land remaining to be developed amount to 3 million acres more. Since population is expanding rapidly, adequate food supplies in the future must come chiefly from larger yields per acre. These, in turn, will require large expense for irrigation, machinery, and fertilizer.

Animal husbandry is carried on by the Bedouin and is not an integral part of agriculture; fodder is seldom grown for feed and mixed farming is rare.

Wheat is by far the most important crop; both in area and by weight it more than equals all other crops combined. Due to the great increase in acreage and the introduction of machinery, there is normally a surplus of several hundred thousand tons for export. Barley is a good second, followed by millet.

Cotton production has expanded rapidly and it is the leading industrial product. Along with wheat, it is a major export crop. The sale of wheat and cotton have given Syria a prosperous economy, probably superior to that of Egypt at the time of their merger in the United Arab Republic. Cotton is followed closely by sugar beets. Tobacco and hemp are also grown. Grapes lead the fruits in area, followed by figs, olives, and apricots.

Cows, oxen, and asses each number a quarter of a million. Sheep exceed 3.25 million, with half that many goats.

Syrian agriculture may be divided into

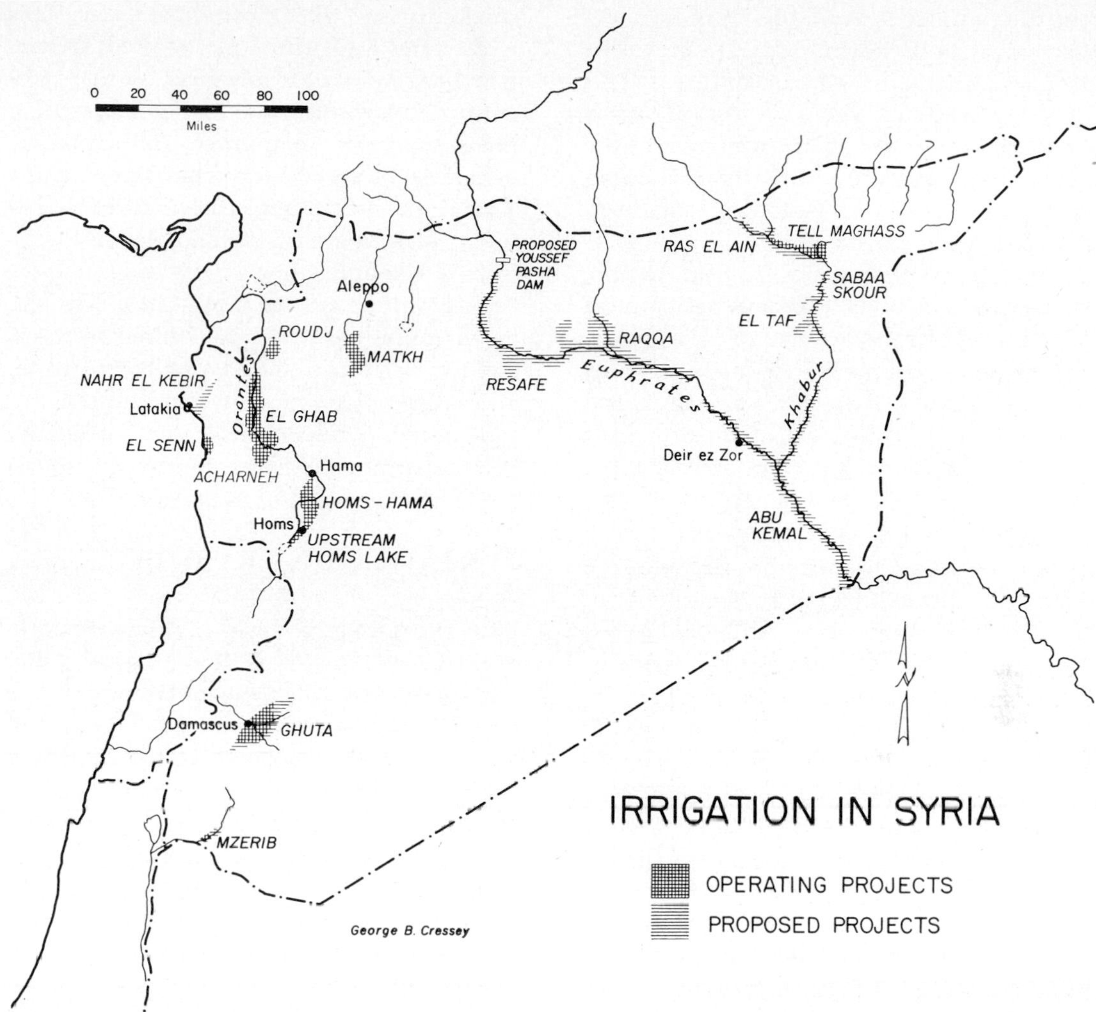

Syria's best agricultural land is irrigated, but water is available for only a small fraction of the good soil. Elsewhere, dry-farming methods are essential. (Based on International Bank for Reconstruction and Development.)

seven regions. The Hauran and Jebel Druze region includes the volcanic areas of the southwest. Rainfall averages from twelve to twenty inches. Soils range from chestnut brown to red desert types, but large areas are covered with lava flows and recent cinders. Wheat and barley are the main winter crops, with vetch and sorghum in summer. Almost none of the area is irrigated.

The Ghuta and the adjoining foothills around Damascus have soils ranging from fertile to saline as one leaves the base of the Anti-Lebanon and moves out into the desert with its terminal basins. Almost all cultivation depends on irrigation from the Barada River and its canals. The Ghuta is a famed garden spot with dairying, vegetables, apricots and other fruit, cereals, hemp, and walnuts. Each small field is surrounded by trees, and there is often interculture of cereals among the fruit trees.

The desert steppe is largely uncultivated,

but where water is available, oases have developed as at Palmyra. Soils are grey, but may support crops of grain and fruit if irrigated. Excellent yields of cotton, sugar beets, and wheat are obtained in some of the newly developed areas. Elsewhere, the natural pastures of the Bedouin, long overgrazed, have been reseeded.

The western plains and hills near Aleppo, Hama, and Homs rank high in agricultural production, although some areas are poor. The region accounts for a third of Syria's wheat and half of its barley. Sugar beets and cotton are new cash crops, along with fruit and nuts. Soils range from desert types through chestnut brown to terra rosa, with a rainfall which varies between fifteen inches in the east to thirty-five inches in the west. This means that crops are rain-fed to the west of the three cities, while to the east, cropland should receive irrigation water or have a fallow period. All of the good land is in cultivation. Where the peasant supplies his own seeds and does all the work, he usually pays the landlord 25 per cent of the crop. Elsewhere, where the landlord provides seed, capital, and water, he receives 75 per cent, but the peasant may be better off.

The coastal zone around Latakia, with its abundant rainfall and deep soils lends itself to a diversified agriculture, with winter wheat, summer legumes, melons, and tobacco, along with citrus, olives, figs, and other tree crops. Manpower is plentiful but land is scarce, so that many farms are too small to be economic. In many instances, they are less than four acres.

The plains of the Jazira lie between the Euphrates and the Turkish border. Much of the land is a steppe, too dry for safe agriculture, but it forms part of the overrated Fertile Crescent. Some areas receive ten inches of rain, or even more in the higher north, but the average in most areas is only half that figure. Fertility increases northward. Where cultivation is possible, the chief crops are wheat, cotton, and rice. This is the area into which mechanized agriculture has made great advances, so that agriculture is strikingly "extensive," matching the shortage in manpower. Individual estates may be several thousand acres in size. The Jezira now raises nearly half of Syria's wheat, with some cotton and rice in the irrigated Khabur valley.

The valleys of the Euphrates, Khabur, and Orontes are somewhat similar in terms of their rich alluvial soils, ease of irrigation, and crops. The crop rotation is often cotton—fallow—wheat. Yields are generally good, but they might be improved through better management of the water.

SYRIA: COUNTRYSIDE AND CITY

The people of Syria have shown remarkable absorptive powers. The original Amorites have been able to assimilate wave after wage of migration, of which the Arab conquest is merely the latest. It has been suggested that some 100,000 Arabs arrived following the conquest, at a time when Greater Syria had a population of 5 or 6 million.

As tribe after tribe of Bedouin reached the agricultural belt, they shed their wandering customs and became farmers. Although the newcomers brought a new religion, the Aramaic tongue has persisted in several mountain villages, particularly with the Maronite Christians. Modern day Armenians represent the latest arrival, but only 100,000 remain out of the million who fled from Turkey. The pattern of population distribution varies widely according to terrain and climate.

Three types of people live in Syria. Nomads amount to fewer than 5 per cent, village and farm people account for 60 per cent, and dwellers in the cities make up 35 per cent. Nomadism is declining but is still important in the total economy since no-

Many Syrian houses are built of stone; every village has its mosque and minaret. This scene is near Homs. (Courtesy Iraq Petroleum Co.)

mads supply the bulk of the meat and wool. Although desert plant life is scanty, fenced experimental plots have shown that if grazing can be controlled for a few years, there is a remarkable increase in the natural vegetation. Reseeding after the rains has also been productive. It appears probable that with controlled grazing, winter shelters, supplemental feeding during bad seasons, modern wells, and some veterinary services, the grazing potential of eastern Syria might be considerably increased.

There are reported to be some 150,000 Bedouin, in various stages of change from pure pastoralism in the desert, through mixed nomadism and farming, to almost permanent agricultural communities. Among the larger tribes, the Tay and some of the Jubar have become partly sedentary, while the Shammar and Shashans are largely nomadic. In Syria, as elsewhere, tribes who keep camels look down upon those who depend on sheep.

As agriculture presses into the steppe, Bedouin are deprived of the better grazing grounds. In the older days this would have produced raids on the settled communities; today it means that the shepherds pasture their sheep on the stubble of fallow fields, turn farmer, or abandon nomadism and move to the cities in search of work. In some

Bee-hive villages made of mud bricks are found in the drier areas of Syria where stone is not readily available. Nomads often camp in the outskirts. (G. B. C.)

cases, tribal lands have been sold by the ruling sheikhs who have then moved to town, so that absentee landlords rule nomads who have become farmers.

Two million village people are spread over 5,500 farm settlements of less than 10,000 inhabitants each. Most of these are subsistence farmers, operating small units. Even when land holdings are large, individual farm plots are small, often too small to yield a good livelihood. Population pressures appear to be most marked in the provinces of Latakia and Jebel Druze where cultivated land per capita is only half that of the national average.

In the vicinity of Aleppo are found the distinctive bee-hive villages where roofs have a high conical dome, entirely built of sun-dried bricks and clay.

Problems of tenancy are suggested by two villages in the Damascus oasis. When examined some years ago, the town of Duma had 1,500 people and occupied some of the best soil in Syria. One-quarter of the land belonged to five owners, most of whom received 25 to 30 per cent of the crop. At Jarba, a poorer village near the edge of the oasis, with a population of 250, all the land belonged to a single owner who received two-thirds of the produce. Elsewhere, as in the Alawi Mountains, tenants are required to perform many special services in addition to paying a share of the harvest; political absolutism is the rule with the landlord's word as law. Where the owner is a Sunnite

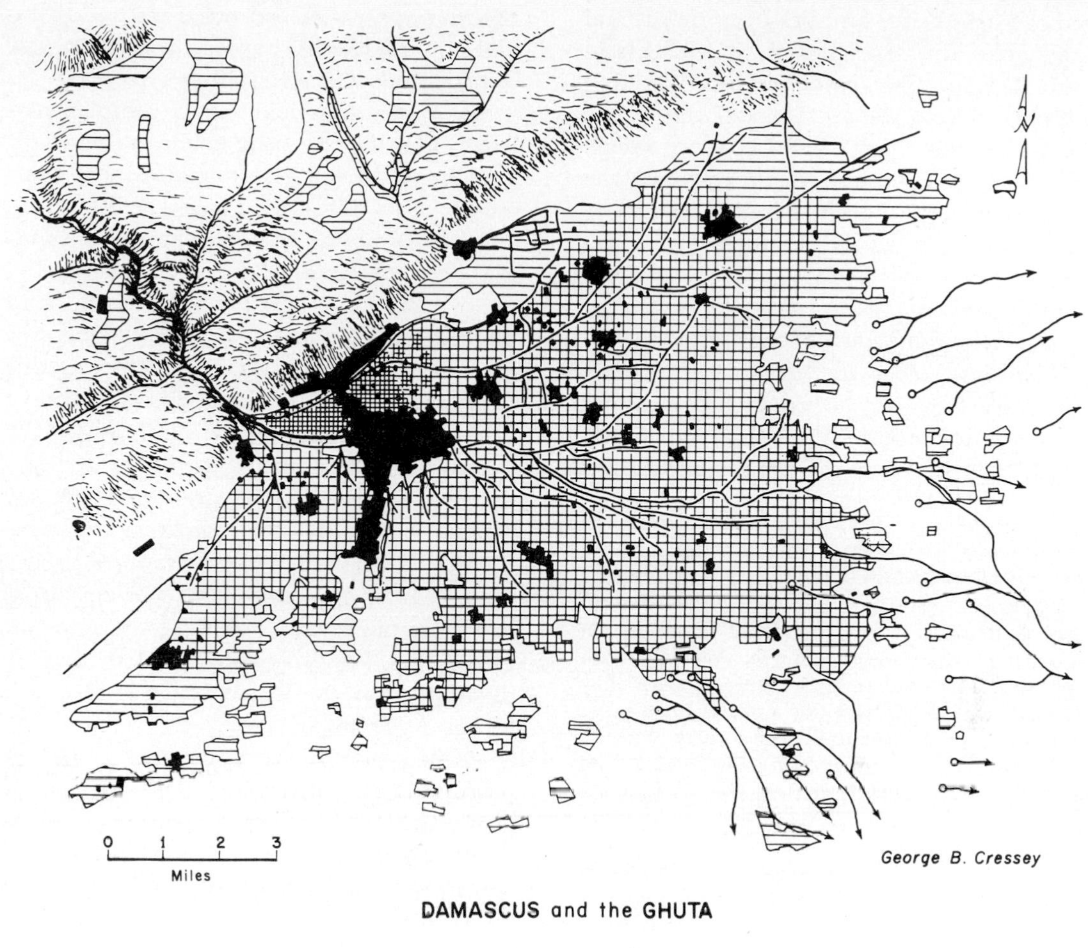

The city of Damascus is surrounded by the fertile oasis known as the Ghuta, watered by the Barada River. Few oases in all Swasia are more important or beautiful.

and the tenant a Shiite, the problem is magnified.

Damascus

Two rival cities have long contested for leadership in Syria: Damascus and Aleppo. Both are very old; yet both are remarkably new. Other urban centers include Homs, Hama, Latakia, and Deir-ez-Zor.

Within a century following the death of Mohammed, Damascus became the capital of an empire larger than that of Rome at its zenith; one which extended from the Bay of Biscay to the borders of China. Long before that, Damascus had been a prosperous oasis and a great center of trade; in fact it claims to be one of the oldest continually inhabited cities on earth. Damascus was important a thousand years before Abraham, and has never lapsed into village status.

The administration of Damascus has changed many times, but its geographic advantages have remained. From Damascus, pilgrims on camels once departed for Mecca;

today trucks bring supplies from Beirut and fan out to Amman, Aleppo, Baghdad, and even Tehran. Few oases are more striking when seen from the air. Immediately to the west rises the high Anti-Lebanon range, snow crowned for half the year, while the desert envelops the city on the remaining three sides. The white buildings of the central city stand like a pearl in an emerald setting of gardens, with the whole enveloped by the yellowish brown of the desert.

The oasis owes its life to the Barada River, fed from the cavernous limestones of the adjoining mountains. Robin Fedden has graphically described this life-giving stream.[1]

> Where the road from Beyrouth to Damascus strays across the desertic eastern slopes of the Anti-Lebanon Mountains, and the landscape is at its barest—a wilderness of stone and shale and sun-baked earth—a slip of water hurrying between the rocks makes its almost miraculous appearance. The road follows it and together they set off downhill. At first the water is little more than a precarious thread urging its way between arid slopes. But as it moves it grows, and fed by subterranean springs it strengthens almost momently. The fringe of green along its banks deepens, and soon the stream is mistress of a narrow gorge-like valley. But the burnt hills still overhang it; it still trespasses in the desert. It is not long, however, before brief orchards and meadows are wedged beside its banks; spare trees multiply into serried ranks of poplar, walnut, and alder; branch touching branch makes a close-packed sea of green. Though the desert rocks still sharply define on either side the limit of its kingdom, the stream has become a small river. As the water races eastward down its twisting course, the stranger is aware of a queer sense of anticipation. This precipitate onrush, this strip of green pouring down between the hills, must have some objective; such energy must find release. It does. With dramatic suddenness the imprisoning desert hills are at an end; river and road cease to twist and hurry. The waters, freed, flow out into the Ghouta, the Oasis of Damascus.

When the Barada suddenly emerges from the mountain wall and starts across its alluvial fan, a series of channels distributes and redistributes the water, first into seven famous canals and then into a complex network. Finally, downslope, the waste water ends in reed-filled desert swamps. The oasis covers about 150 square miles.

Many of the older homes have fountains, and smaller canals water the innumerable courtyards. Small wonder that to the Arab of the desert, Damascus became a symbol of bounty and beauty. So delightful was this garden land that Mohammed is said to have hesitated to enter, not wishing to be deprived of the full joys of the heavenly Paradise by such a splendid preview. The geographer Yaqut of the thirteenth century visited all of the four spots reputed as the most beautiful on earth and found Damascus to be the first among them; he sums up by writing, "nothing attributed by way of description to the heavenly paradise is not found in Damascus."

Within the Ghuta every square inch is painstakingly cultivated. Wheat or barley grow among the olive trees and clover is raised amid the apricots. Small islands of desert, standing on slightly higher ground above the reach of the life-giving Barada, may be dotted about the field. Downslope, as the water becomes more scarce, orchards lose their richness and at last there are only salty pastures and endless desert.

Damascus today is a mixture of old and new. One of the principal avenues is still "The Street called Straight" described in the New Testament, and one may see a reconstruction of the gate where Paul was supposed to have been lowered in a basket. Nearby are the arched bazaars or suqs, wide enough to serve as present-day covered streets, where one may buy gorgeous brocades, intricately inlaid boxes, or ornamented brass ware.

The great architectural souvenir is the Ommiad mosque, with its splendid court-

[1] Robin Fedden, *Syria: An Historical Appreciation.* London: Robert Hale (1955), 13. Quoted by permission.

The new residential districts of Damascus climb the slopes of the Anti-Lebanon Range which borders the city on the west. (Courtesy Iraq Petroleum Co.)

yards, which stands on the site of a Roman temple to Jupiter. In the tenth century, Macdisi described the courtyard as follows: [1]

> The whole area is paved with white marble. The walls of the mosque, for twice the height of a man, are faced with varigated marbles; and above this, even to the ceiling, are mosaics of various colors and in gold, showing figures of trees and towns and beautiful inscriptions, all the most exquisitely and finely worked. And rare are the trees and few the well-known towns that will not be found figured on these walls! The capitals of the columns are covered with gold, and the vaulting above the arcades is everywhere ornamented with mosaic and arabesque designs.

[1] Quoted by Robin Fedden, *Syria: An Historical Appreciation*. London: Robert Hale (1955). 18.

Modern Damascus is as new as anything in Swasia, with fine hotels, wide boulevards, and beautiful residential areas. Nowhere is the contrast between old and new more obvious.

Aleppo

Aleppo, like Damascus, dates back to at least the second millennium B.C., and like Damascus it is a gateway to the desert. As with so many cities in the realm, Aleppo has repeatedly been captured by Egyptian, Turk, Mongol, and Arab conquerors. In

This Roman Arch over "The Street called Straight" is a reminder of Damascus' ancient heritage; one of the oldest continuously inhabited cities on earth. (Courtesy Iraq Petroleum Co.)

other particulars, the cities are different. Whereas Damascus receives only nine inches of rain annually and depends on irrigation, Aleppo has sixteen inches with possibilities of rain-fed agriculture. Aleppo has a good, modern road eastward; Damascus has none. While Damascus as the capital was in itself the goal of travelers, Aleppo has been a halting place on routes leading to other destinations.

The prosperity of Aleppo lies in trade. Seventy miles to the west over low mountains lies the Mediterranean; fifty miles east across grasslands is the Euphrates. Through Aleppo passed the great caravan route of antiquity which linked Mesopotamia with Egypt. Aleppo merchants looked far to the east to tap the trade with Persia and even China, or through the Persian Gulf to India. The city is still famous for its elaborate khans, a combination warehouse and *caravanserai,* and its extensive thirteenth century suks where artisans wove fine silks and cottons.

In the center of the city is the ancient citadel, a fortress-crowned mound which may be in large part an ancient tell, built up by accretion of countless buildings over the centuries. It was used by the Hittites and Assyrians, and before. Here Abraham is supposed to have milked his flocks, hence the city's Arabic name of Haleb, meaning milk.

While most of the present population are Sunni Moslems, there are also large communities of Armenians, Turks, and Jews. The visitor senses that he is near the northern limit of the Arab world.

Modern Aleppo has become an industrial city, but the measure of modernization is suggested by the fact that one may still see blacksmiths pounding out nails individually by hand. Aleppo is Syria's leading industrial center, with textile mills and garment factories, flour mills, vegetable oil mills, tanneries, food processing plants, and cement factories. As a measure of industrialization, the peak electric load in 1960 was about 32,175 kilowatts. The supply will be greatly increased when hydroelectric power is available on the Euphrates. Aleppo's figure may be compared with 30,000 kilowatts in Damascus. The city has always been noted for good buildings of well-shaped stone; to these are now added modern concrete business structures. Trade in cotton, wool, and tobacco reflects the countryside.

One of Syria's economic problems is that her logical seaports are in foreign countries. Lebanese Beirut with its free-trade zone forms the easiest entry to Damascus, only two hours away. Iskenderon would be an appropriate seaport for Aleppo, but it lies in Turkey. The country's only port of significance is thus Latakia, a Crusader town newly equipped with facilities which symbolize Syria's modern progress. There is only a twenty-foot depth of water within the harbor so that larger vessels must be served by lighters. The port has a capacity of a million tons of cargo a year.

SYRIA: PROBLEMS AND PROSPECTS

Two PROBLEMS paramount to Syria are its economic status and its political future. In order to evaluate the first and to establish the place of agriculture, it may be well to review the prospects of mineral wealth. Too little is known of Syria's resources to make valid forecasts, but the evidence to date indicates that prospects are poor.

Placer gold has been reported eighty miles east of Homs, but only in very small amounts. Copper and lead occurrences are known, but appear unimportant. Chromium has been produced in small amounts, but only in scattered years. Iron occurs widely, but production is very small. The Phoenicians exploited deposits of iron ore in central Syria, and Damascus was famous a thousand years ago for its swords. Iron ore occurs forty miles northeast of Latakia, but nowhere of commercial grade or quantity, and there is no current production. Low grade coal and lignite are scattered about Syria, but production is negligible since the quality is too low to warrant commercial development.

If the country is to expand its agriculture, commercial fertilizers will be necessary. Several low-grade deposits of phosphate rock near Damascus may be of value in providing fertilizer.

Salt is the only mineral in significant production, although imports are still necessary. Most of it comes from the salt lake at Jebbul, twenty-two miles southeast of Aleppo. During winter months the lake measures twelve by twenty-two miles, but in summer it becomes completely dry. A salt deposit then forms from one-half to two inches thick. This and other salt lakes might yield as much as 100,000 tons a year.

Petroleum apparently holds one key to Syria's industrial future, particularly in the northeast toward the known fields of Iraq and Turkey. Millions of dollars were invested in prospecting without much success, other than the discovery of gas, salt, and bitumen, until oil in commercial amounts was discovered near Karatchok in 1956. The best estimate, not yet realized, is that Syria might become self-sufficient in oil. There is little prospect of any surplus for export.

The future of Syrian agriculture rests on the wise management of the limited water. This aerial view gives a glimpse of the outer Ghuta oasis around Damascus. (G. B. C.)

Fortunately, oil pipelines from Iraq and Arabia both cross Syrian territory so that the country may draw on them for cheap imported oil.

Another source of power lies in Syria's rivers where hydroelectric plants in connection with irrigation dams will generate several hundred thousand kilowatts.

In the absence of mineral wealth, it would appear that the future of industry rests on agricultural and pastoral products. As has been made obvious already, agriculture in turn rests on the wise management of water. As a nation, Syrian agriculture is more prosperous than that of several other countries, but in individual terms the farmer is still marginally poor.

The discovery of a major oil field would revolutionize the economy but one need not be pessimistic without it. Syria has made remarkable progress, and this should continue.

The economic problem merges into the political. The domestic market is limited since the country is small, so that industry does not find an adequate market at home. Many products now imported might be produced as well within Syria if there were an assured outlet. During the period of the French mandate, Syria and Lebanon had a customs union with the free movement of commodities. Still earlier, the Ottoman Empire was a single trade unit. The economic consequences of union with Egypt remain to be developed.

Here is a basic problem in all the former mandates, with the possible exception of

Iraq. Present-day Syria, Lebanon, Jordan, and Israel are too small in area or resources or population to be easily viable. Those who favor a Greater Syria argue from sound historic and geographic logic.

The creation of the League of Nations mandate system is now many decades in the past and is largely forgotten abroad. Not so in the Levant, where the consequences result in current problems. Beirut and Damascus are complementary, but a boundary separates them. Iskenderon, formerly Alexandretta, and Hatay province were traditionally Syrian but were returned to Turkey by France for political reasons. It is true that Hatay was in part ethnically Turkish, but its transfer deprived Syria of an important seacoast, as well as the mouth of the Orontes. On the purely domestic side, relicts of French rule in the form of internal boundaries and special privileges for minority people such as the Druze and Alawis have made unification difficult.

Out of the frustrations of the mandate period came a general anti-European and ultra-nationalistic feeling. The United States was not originally associated with imperialism, in part because of the findings of the King-Crane Commission which reported to President Wilson in 1919 favoring Arab unity; but American support of Israel in 1947 immediately placed the United States in the category of the colonial powers.

If Syria cannot readily achieve full stature alone, where should it turn? Lebanon's concern for the rights of its Christian citizens makes it hesitant about any political union, but its good business sense provides a basis for economic federation. The problems of Jordan will be considered in a later section, but there are sound reasons for a reunion of Syria and Jordan; if both had comparable governments, the problem would be easier. Iraq's interests are different, and too much desert intervenes for the two to find political coherence or economic unity.

Syria's union with Egypt to form the United Arab Republic in 1957 raises different questions. The move symbolized the passionate desire for Arab unity, and at the moment may have been necessary to check Communism, but in the absence of a common boundary or related economic and historic interests, the union seems artificial. In geographic terms, Syria looks south and even east, rather than to the southwest.

LEBANON: PROGRESSIVE MOUNTAIN LAND

THE PEOPLE OF LEBANON would like to think of their country as the Switzerland of the eastern Mediterranean. In winter scenery there is some similarity, and as a summer resort Lebanon draws tens of thousands of tourists from the heated plains of Egypt, Iraq, and Arabia. Like Switzerland, Lebanon provides financial security for investments from troubled areas and a base of operations for foreign concerns; also, many people come here to retire.

Lebanon is probably the most prosperous of all the countries in Southwest Asia, other than the oil sheikhdoms and perhaps Israel. Data as to standards of living and per capita incomes are incomplete and involve many uncertainties. Based on national incomes as reported to the United Nations and converted to American dollars at the official rates of exchange, the table on the following page presents per capita figures.

Both Turkey and Israel have unrealistic rates of foreign exchange, so that their figures should be reduced, perhaps by half or more. Lebanon has a "hard" currency and may well lead. Of course there is poverty, but the average Lebanese lives comfortably.

Likewise in education, Lebanon is probably near the top. There are three creditable universities in Beirut and general literacy is high. Despite the difficulty of steering an acceptable course between sympathy for America, opposition to French colonialism in North Africa, and support for the various aspects of Arab nationalism, Lebanon has had a good government.

The country owes its independence to the delicate balance between its various minority groups. These racial and religious communities were recognized under Turkish rule, and it was to preserve the rights of the assorted Christians that France established a separate mandate for Lebanon from that assigned to her under Syria. At that time, a census showed that Christians slightly exceeded Moslems, and it was agreed that the President should always be a Maronite Christian and the Prime Minister a Sunni Moslem.

No census has been taken under the Republic, in part because of a suspicion that the division no longer holds. The influx of Palestinian refugees, largely Moslem, coupled with a more rapid increase on the part of the Moslem community stands against a considerable overseas emigration of Christians.

Wide divisions occur within each faith, in some measure due to ethnic backgrounds. Sunni Moslems slightly outnumber Shia

NATIONAL INCOME IN SWASIA [1]

Afghanistan	(1949)	$ 50
Egypt	(1954)	110
Iran	(1949)	85
Iraq	(1949)	85
Israel	(1955)	569
Jordan	—	—50
Lebanon	(1954)	255
Saudi Arabia	(1949)	40
Syria	(1953)	153
Turkey	(1954)	211
Yemen	(1949)	40

[1] Committee for Economic Development: *Economic Development Assistance.* New York (1957).

Moslems, but the latter would prefer to see a Christian government rather than have Sunni domination. The Druse are basically Moslems but refer to Hakim, the sixth of the Fatima caliphs, as the latest prophet. Large numbers of Armenian and Assyrian Christians have found refuge in the Lebanese mountains. All groups normally live in peace, or at least in a continued truce, but political unrest, as in 1958, suddenly revives ancient animosities between adjoining villages.

THE POPULATION OF LEBANON [1]

Christian		698,764 (54%)
Maronite	377,544	
Catholic, Latin	4,127	
Catholic, Greek	81,764	
" Armenian	14,218	
" Syriac	5,911	
Orthodox, Greek	130,858	
" Armenian	67,139	
" Syriac (Jacobite)	4,562	
Protestant	12,641	
Moslem		510,232 (39%)
Sunni	273,125	
Shiite	237,107	
Druse		82,268 (6%)
Jewish		5,993 (0.5%)
Other		6,684 (0.5%)
Total		1,303,941

[1] Royal Institute of International Affairs, "Official Statistics for 1951," *The Middle East* (1954), 466.

The newer residential area of Beirut occupies the peninsula known as Ras Beirut where hundreds of modern apartment houses crowd the limited land. (Courtesy U. S. Operations Mission, Beirut.)

It is interesting to note that many Greek Orthodox churches still look to Moscow as the proper defender of the faith. The present Russian government continues to provide subsidies and gifts to Lebanese Orthodox churches, and the Soviet Ambassador frequently participates in the Easter services.

Lebanon's cultural diversity is paralleled by its physical contrasts; it is surprising that through the centuries there has continued to be a unit by any name. In area, Lebanon is only half the size of New Jersey, in population scarcely a third. In topographic character and variety, it is more like California. As Hitti has suggested: [1]

> It is one of those lands that could be described as microscopic in size but microcosmic in influence. Its history is indeed the history of a considerable part of the history of our civilized world. The mountainous character of the land, its close proximity to the sea, its central location in the cradle of civilization and at the crossroads of the world, astride the great international highway that linked the three historic continents—these are the determining factors in its career.

Hitti goes on to describe the accessible lowlands in terms of "contact, exchange, transfusion, transformation, and transition," whereas in the dissected highlands, out of the way if not inaccessible, the key words are "conservatism, self-containment,

[1] Philip K. Hitti: *Lebanon in History*, London: Macmillan (1957), 4–5. Quoted by permission.

These four cement kilns suggest the industrial progress and international trade of Lebanon. (Courtesy U. S. Operations Mission, Beirut.)

LEBANON DATA

Area	4,015	square miles
	10,400	square kilometers
Arable area	2,780	square kilometers
Population	1,525,000	
Cities		
Beirut	400,000	
Tripoli	80,000	
Sidon	20,000	

independence, isolation, and insulation."

Under various names, the country has had a long record of commerce. Travel in the early eras was difficult, but substantial commerce moved long distances. In the twenty-seventh chapter of Ezekial we read of the widespread trade of Mediterranean Tyre, "at entrance to the sea, merchant of the peoples on many coastlands." Three dozen places are listed, as far distant as Yemen and Persia. The list of commodities is equally long and includes items such as gold, silver, iron, tin, lead, bronze, ivory, ebony, gems, dyes, fine linen, and foods of various kinds. This was about the middle of the first millennium B.C.

Among the many souvenirs from the past, the ruins of Baalbek are among the finest, in fact no structures of Roman days are more glorious anywhere, even in Rome. The city lies in the Bekaa, and was once called Heliopolis, the city of the Sun, but long before it acquired its Greek name it was a center of Phoenician worship. The elaboration of the original temple acropolis dates from Roman construction in the sec-

The ruins of Baalbek are Lebanon's greatest monument from Roman days. The six great columns are all that remain of the vast Temple of Jupiter. The Temple of Baachus appears at the left. (Courtesy Iraq Petroleum Co.)

ond century A.D. Later on, it became a Christian church. After the Moslem conquest it was converted into a citadel which figured in Crusader days. In 1260 it was partly destroyed by the Mongols and later further ruined by earthquakes. Even so, Baalbek remains the most richly sculptured ruins in Southwest Asia.

Of the four dozen great columns which surrounded the Temple of Jupiter, only six now stand. Each column rises sixty-two feet and is made of three blocks, seven and one-half feet in diameter. These porphyry columns were brought from Egypt and must have been rolled over the Lebanese mountains. Some of them were later transported to Constantinople by Justinian and used in building Santa Sophia. The temple of Bacchus has a colossal sculptured doorway, forty-five feet high and twenty-five feet wide, regarded as one of the finest products of Roman architecture. Enormous stones were employed in the temple complex; some of them measure 62 x 14 x 11 feet and weigh 750 tons each. Many have a wealth of ornamentation.

Along with Baalbek, the Lebanese are equally proud of the Cedars, *cedrus libani*, only a few groves of which remain. These trees once provided the chief source of wood for Egypt and for the Phoenician fleets. Lebanese cedar was used in Solomon's temple, and thirty-foot beams were employed in the palace at Persepolis a thousand miles to the east. Most of the remaining trees grow near elevations of about a mile. At this height, growth is very slow due to the severity of the climate. Their maximum age is unknown, probably only a few are as much as a thousand years old. Cedars have a massive trunk, but the height does not exceed eighty feet. The tree is now the Lebanese emblem and appears on the national flag.

Four simple geomorphic areas make up the country. Along the Mediterranean is a coastal strip, nowhere more than four miles wide and in a few places interrupted by sea cliffs. There is hardly a natural harbor, and the ports of Tripoli, Beirut, and Sidon merely occupy open bays or small shelters at one side of a peninsula. Most of the coastal area consists of uplifted marine floor, with chalk overlain by a veneer of alluvium or sand dunes. Fortunately, this plain is very fertile and is intensively used for oranges, bananas, olives, sugar cane, and vegetables.

The Lebanon Mountains parallel the coast and mark the heart of the country, a clearly defined segment of the longer range that extends from Turkey to Sinai. The mountains have a length of 105 miles and are from six to thirty-five miles wide. Elevations reach 10,131 feet in the north and 8,622 feet near Beirut. The name is from the Arabic word for milk, in reference to the snow-crowned summits. Great gorges, many of them over a thousand feet deep, cut through the mountains, so that the rounded appearance of the simple anticline as seen from a distance is misleading. It is this canyon detail with the intervening terrace lands which provides so many isolated havens for minority peoples. Monasteries, convents, and churches are perched on many elevations, in contrast to the mosques and minarets which are more numerous on the plain.

East of the mountain is a rich alluvial plain, 110 miles long and six to ten miles wide, structurally related to the valleys of the Orontes and Jordan on the north and south. It lies at an elevation of 3,000 feet and for the most part is a productive granary. This is the Bekaa, the "valley of Lebanon" described in Joshua XI:17, once known as Hollow Syria. The plain is drained by the Litani River, and here lie the great ruins of Baalbek.

Fourth in the parallel sequence are the Anti-Lebanon Mountains, dominated by 10,000-foot Mount Herman in the south. Since they lie in the rain-shadow of the coastal range, these mountains are drier, less productive, and more thinly populated. The boundary with Syria more or less follows the crest of the mountains.

The list of landscape areas omits, of course, the Mediterranean Sea, visible even from Mount Herman. No sea has a deeper tone of blue, and, in the clear atmosphere which characterizes the region during most of the year, the contrast between the rich indigo of the sea, the green of the orchards and fields, and the snow-crowned mountains gives Lebanon one of the most colorful panoramas in the world.

The Litani is Lebanon's one important river and holds the country's hope for large-scale development of electricity. The program calls for over-all valley development at an eventual cost of a hundred million dollars, with irrigation in both the Bekaa and along the coast, additional domestic water for Beirut, and 88,500 kilowatts of electricity in the first phase to be completed early in the 1960's. Later developments will more than double the power. In summer, so much water is diverted for irrigation from the Litani, 105 miles long, that virtually none reaches the sea. In flood, the recorded flow has reached 140 cubic meters per second, and the forecast maximum reaches 785. Some of this will be conserved behind a dam in the southern Bekaa. In order to generate the maximum power, the water will be conveyed in a nine-mile tunnel and dropped 2,400 feet near the coast.

Lebanon's interior valley, the Bekaa, is its largest area of good agricultural land. (Courtesy U. S. Operations Mission, Beirut.)

Electrical consumption is a measure of industrialization, so that the Litani program will provide much needed power. In 1935, the country consumed 30 million kilowatt hours, in 1952 this rose to 160 million and in 1955 to 200 million. Estimates for 1975 forecast 1,055 million kilowatt hours.

LEBANON: GATEWAY TO THE EAST

NO COUNTRY IN SWASIA is at the same time so closely in tune with the Western world and in such active communication with its hinterland. Israel's dream of being an intermediary is blocked by political problems. Turkey is a land by itself, out of touch with its former empire. Syria is busy with its domestic problems and turns inward rather than to the sea. Only Beirut has the physical port arrangements, established banking facilities, and experienced commercial connections.

In practical terms, much of Lebanon's prosperity depends on transit facilities across Syria by road, air, and pipeline. Should the border be closed, or embargoes imposed, Lebanon might become another Israel, isolated and dependent on outside help for survival. While air corridors across Syria have generally remained open, the planes of some nations have been excluded, as were those of France during part of the Algerian revolt.

Beirut lies in the latitude of Los Angeles, with a harbor about the shape and exposure as Monterey. Although the people are Arabs, many are so fair that they would easily pass for sun-tanned Californians. Beirut's streets are narrower than in Los Angeles, but both cities share in having serious traffic problems; each is also a boom town, for Beirut grew from 120,000 at the turn of the century to 232,000 in 1942 and to over half a million by 1960.

If a resident of Beirut so wishes, he may pattern his life almost identically on the life people lead in California, for the same American groceries, including frozen foods, are readily available; so too are the latest products of Hollywood and Detroit. The American University of Beirut is chartered by the Regents of the State of New York so that its credits are fully transferable; its medical school was the first overseas institution to receive a Class A rating from the American Medical Association. No city in all Asia is more westernized.

One reason for this development is that great numbers of Lebanese have gone overseas, almost as many as remain at home; when these people return they bring new ideas with them. A quarter of a million live in the United States while a third of a million have gone to Brazil, hence the regular flights of Pan Air do Brasil from Beirut to Rio de Janeiro. Tiny mountain villages have people with relatives in Tulsa.

The city of Beirut, once known as Berytus, was one of the less famous Phoenician cities, but its name dates from the fifteenth century B.C. An earthquake in 551 A.D. completely destroyed the city. The modern port depends on a breakwater which was built at the end of the nineteenth century. Despite its unfavorable position, Beirut is still the best and busiest port along the eastern Mediterranean.

The older portion of the city centers around a square which is known to the French as the Place des Canons and to the Lebanese as the Place des Martyrs, according to which end of the artillery one favors. Some of the older section needs rehabilitation badly. The newer residential areas, developed exclusively with apartment houses, lie to the west in the promontory known as Ras Beirut.

Since Beirut contains a third of the Lebanese population, it can hardly survive by itself alone; instead it lives on regional commerce and industry, with warehouse and banking facilities for all of Arab Swasia. The centrality of its airport as a focal point for air travel has already been mentioned. It is not as much in tune with Arab problems as Baghdad, but it is a more comfortable place in which to live.

Good but overcrowded roads lead north from Beirut to Tripoli, eastward over the mountains to Damascus, and south to Sidon. These secondary ports are the terminals for oil pipelines from Iraq and Saudi Arabia, and each have small refineries.

As so many Lebanese have migrated to the two Americas, it is only natural that the country should have a pro-Western foreign policy. And since many of those who have migrated came from the Christian areas in the highlands, it is understandable that such a policy has communal aspects. The Moslem population also has Western interests, but looks with favor on the prospects for Arab nationalism and unity. Most of the Christians are Arabs as well, but have vivid memories of persecution and massacre when tens of thousands were killed. To non-Arab Christians who have been forced to flee from one country after another, the prospect of being submerged in a larger Arab nation holds no attraction.

The question of international orientation has arisen several times during the brief history of the Republic of Lebanon. French culture is still strong, although with strong repercussions at times. Lebanon is a charter member of the Arab League, but does not desire any political federation.

The American University of Beirut brings together 2,000 students from every country in Southwest Asia. (G. B. C.)

The problem of orientation came to a crisis in 1958 and led to American intervention in accordance with the Eisenhower Doctrine. While the government enjoyed only marginal support and there was strong provocation from the United Arab Republic, there is little evidence that the country was about to become a Communist state. Outside intervention from any source runs the danger of upsetting the delicate balance of internal and external relations.

Given reasonable peace, Lebanon should continue to be the main gateway to the East.

JORDAN: PRESENT AND PAST

Jordan's problems can be summarized briefly. When established as the Hashemite Kingdom of Trans-Jordan in 1946, the population amounted to about 375,000, all of them on the east bank of the Jordan River, scattered across 34,500 square miles. With the partition of Palestine, 2,165 square miles and 460,000 west bank residents were added, plus nearly 500,000 refugees who fled from Zionist occupied Palestine.

Since the original mandate territory was mostly empty desert and the newly added west bank area has a quite different potential, the unity and viability of the enlarged state with its tripled population present serious difficulties. Most of the refugees are still without employment. Even with peaceful boundaries and the best of government, the national economy would be marginal; with highly unstable conditions and a large displaced population, the future remains un-

The Place des Martyrs forms the core of Beirut's central business district. The breakwater which encloses the port appears at the top of the picture. (Courtesy U. S. Operations Mission, Beirut.)

certain. It has already been suggested, that, given peace and comparable political regimes, the area of Jordan might be better off to become again part of a Greater Syria.

Sharp contrasts exist between the two parts of the country. West of the river, in former Palestine, there is a high level of the arts and crafts with considerable prosperity; on the east bank, progress has never proceeded as far since poor accessibility and a different history have perpetuated a more simple economy with many Bedouin characteristics. It must immediately be added, however, that some aspects of the former Transjordan area are quite modern. The attractiveness of the newer residential buildings in Amman is not surpassed by anything to the west.

Many of Jordan's problems do not appear on an ordinary political map. The desert comes to within forty miles of the Jordan River in the north, and borders the Dead Sea on the south. Eighty per cent of the country is unpopulated and almost unproductive. In climatic terms, Jordan lies in the rain-shadow of the Judean Hills. The country has a long eastern corridor which leads to Iraq, but Baghdad lies on the other side of a harsh desert. A population map reveals the uneven pattern of occupance.

Jordan's major problem is Israel, to be discussed in the next chapter, but many others remain. Among them are external accessibility, lack of balance in foreign trade, im-

The port of Aqaba provides Jordan's only access to the sea. The Israeli port of Elath lies in the far distance to the left. (Courtesy United Nations.)

proved livelihood, general education, and acceptable government.

Prior to the creation of the mandate, there had never been a political or cultural unit corresponding to Jordan. The present boundaries are thus artificial. The limit next to Saudi Arabia has not been defined. Jordan fortunately includes a few miles of frontage on the Gulf of Aqaba, thus providing her only access to the sea.

Aqaba lies in a semicircular bay, some three miles wide, at the point where the Wadi Araba leads north to the Dead Sea. Under the name of Ezion-Geber, this was the port from which Solomon's fleet sailed to Ophir. It continued to be important under the Romans and Turks. New wharves have increased the capacity of the modern port, but it is still inadequate for the country's needs. Access to the interior is over a road to Ma'an and thence by rail.

The natural port for the area has always been Haifa. Now that access to Israel is closed, most traffic moves through Beirut and Damascus. Good roads enable one to drive from Beirut to Amman in a day, but during times of political difficulties, the Syrian border may be closed. Air traffic across Israel is prohibited and at times calls for considerable detours over Syria.

Amman, the capital city, is situated in a narrow entrenched valley. As the population has increased, new dwellings have been built on the adjoining plateau. The rainfall amounts to eleven inches, in contrast with

This village landscape near Jerusalem suggests the rocky and eroded character of the hills of western Jordan. The outcrops of horizontal sediments form natural terraces. (U. S. Air Force.)

sixteen at Haifa and twenty-one in Jerusalem, so that the vegetation has steppe characteristics. Summer temperatures regularly rise to 100°F., despite the elevation of half a mile, while temperatures fall below freezing in winter.

JORDAN DATA

Area	37,301 square miles	
	96,610 square kilometers	
Arable area	8,930 square kilometers	
Population	1,527,000	
Cities		
Amman	185,032	
Jerusalem (Jordan Sector)	(100,000)	

Jordan's past is filled with rich historical geography, some of which have already been described, as ancient Jericho, the famous incense routes, and the spectacular city of Petra under the Nabataeans. Three culture areas came to be recognized east of the river: Gilead in the north, Amman in the center, and Moab in the south.

During the Roman period, about the time of Christ, ten cities largely Greek in population were grouped for defense against the nomads under the general name of the Decapolis. These lay chiefly in Gilead, and despite their remoteness from Rome or Athens, several developed magnificent public architecture. Among the ten were Phila-

That part of eastern Jordan which drains toward the river is deeply dissected. This is the green valley floor of the Wadi Zarqa north of Amman. (G. B. C.)

delphia, the modern Amman, and Gerasa or Jerash, thirty miles to the north. Both had splendid theaters, and Jerash was especially noted for its avenues of great columns, public fountains, and temples to Artemis, Zeus, and other gods, all delicately carved. Today, there are remains of a synagogue and a dozen churches dating from the fourth to the seventh centuries. Time and earthquakes have destroyed many structures, and in some of those still standing, the great stones are slightly offset as a result of the horizontal component of earthquake shocks.

The people of Jordan have a mixed ethnic background, as elsewhere. In addition to people found in Syria and Lebanon, there are groups of Circassians and Chechens, small Moslem groups who were brought from the Caucasus in the mid-nineteenth century by the Turks. A unique group are the Christian Bedouin living a life apparently similar to their Moslem brothers. Whereas most women in this part of Asia wear somber clothing and may be fully veiled, the women of Palestine wear colorful dresses with distinctive styles for each major town.

JORDAN: LAND AND MINERALS

JORDAN IS PREDOMINATELY an agricultural and pastoral country, with few other economic assets. Crops already occupy every acre of land which it now seems feasible to cultivate. Any considerable expansion of crop area must wait for expensive irrigation projects whose over-all potentials are quite

Jordan's capital city of Amman lies in a narrow valley so that the newer residential area climbs the slopes. (Courtesy Iraq Petroleum Co.)

limited, or on further penetration into the desert. Little increase in the area of rain-fed crops is possible; in fact, some marginal areas now plowed should be taken out of cultivation and be planted to drought-resistant tree crops.

That part of Jordan which lies in the Judean plateau, west of the river, consists of stony moorland, with rough scrub, reinforced by a few dwarf oaks growing among fields of boulders where the underlying limestone, as if impatient of the thin soil, emerges in bare outcrops. Here and there are patches of cultivated grain, springing up from fields which seem more like beds of shingle than of soil. The chief signs of life, other than the wild bee and a few birds, are the flocks of sheep and goats or a few cattle, cropping far apart as an evidence of the scanty vegetation.

Where the plateau has a rolling character, the shadeless slopes are divided between brown scrub and grey rock, and the valleys have dry torrent beds of boulders and cherty clay. Where the plateau is dissected, the ridges are often crowned by a village, whose grey stone walls and mud roofs appear from the distance more like rock outcrops, yet around them are olive-groves, fig trees, and perhaps a few vines.

The prevailing impression of Judea is that of stones everywhere. They are found on the hillsides, in rocky paths, in heaps

The Jordan River meanders within its inner valley, the Zor, which is bordered by the dissected terraces of the Ghor. This aerial view is between Amman and Jerusalem. (G. B. C.)

gathered from the fields, and in the fields themselves. In the more desolate areas, this impression gains force by the remains of ancient settlements with their ruins of stone houses.

Most of Jordan is dry, progressively so toward the east, but the problem lies not so much in the total rainfall as in its conservation. Extensive areas are underlain by soluble limestone or porous lava into which the rain sinks quickly, leaving the soil dry. Large springs emerge downslope. The available moisture will increase crop production if more runoff can be stored in a number of new reservoirs, if the irrigation canals are lined to prevent seepage and if moisture-robbing weeds can be eliminated from fallow fields.

Much of Jordan, both east and west of the river, shows the result of long continued overgrazing and erosion. Although the problem of rehabilitation is difficult, the natural vegetation has a remarkable capacity for recovery, provided that goats can be removed to other areas. Sheep browse on grasses but the goat prefers woody material and can survive in marginal conditions where sheep would die. Proper limitations on sheep and goats would make a large contribution to the future of agriculture and forestry. On the other hand, the goat is valued as the poor man's cow.

The land to the east of the river is generally drier and has a lower population density, but many hillsides have been used only for grazing rather than for cultivation.

Small pumps are used to irrigate fields near the Jordan River. This scene is near the Dead Sea. (G. B. C.)

The total crop area, as shown in the accompanying table, amounts to about 2 million acres, or 3,100 square miles. This represents only 8 per cent of the entire national area of 37,500 square miles. Since the refugees are fed in part by imported food supplies, it may not be fair to include them on a per capita basis, but the crop area averages little more than an acre per person. It must also be recognized that the data on cultivated land include large areas next to the desert with very low yields, as well as large areas which periodically lie fallow.

Wheat is by far the chief crop, but only a third of the wheat-growing area is assured of a good harvest each year. Barley matures more rapidly than wheat and grows with less moisture. Other crops are millet, corn, sesame, beans, tobacco of Virginia grade, fodder, figs, grapes, olives, and vegetables. There is a considerable export of tomatoes from the Jordan valley to Syria, Iraq, and the oil fields of the Persian Gulf. Wool is exported only when the world price is high. Cereal imports are generally required, along with sugar, coffee, and cotton piece goods; their value considerably exceeds that of the exports.

The area of land suitable for irrigation in the Jordan River valley and within Jordan amounts to 125,000 acres, of which half now receives some irrigation. Until effective political solutions are available, when it may be possible, for example, to enlarge Lake Tiberias as a reservoir, increased water supplies must depend on diversion from the Yarmuk. The latter, entirely within Arab lands, might provide for 90,000 acres if expensive dams were built, or 25,000 acres from the unregulated flow. Since all plans involve large investments to be repaid from the sale of crop surpluses and provide for little more than a person per acre, the practicality is marginal.

Much wishful thinking about Jordan River developments, on both sides of the international boundary, has overlooked the limited flow of the river even if water were stored, the high rates of evapotranspiration, the unfavorable terrain, and the saline character of many soils.

Ownership of land is highly prized and carries traditional social values which outweigh economic consideration. Most of the farm land is ultimately owned by the state. It is called *miri* land and is in the hands of small occupant-right holders who have what amounts to a perpetual lease. No data are available on tenancy, but the majority of farmers are in effect owners or part-owners. The tenant's share is usually 30 per cent; when he supplies seed and looks after the plowing and threshing, his share may rise to 70 per cent.

In addition to agricultural resources, Jordan has access to the dissolved minerals of the Dead Sea, three-quarters of whose shoreline lies within the country. The pre-partition evaporating plant near the mouth of the Jordan River, destroyed during the fighting in 1948, has been rebuilt and now produces potash and bromine in the form of potassium chloride and magnesium bromide. The dissolved potash in the sea amounts to 2 billion tons, while magnesium bromide totals 900 million tons, so that the reserves are almost inexhaustible.

The average total salinity of the Dead Sea amounts to 24 per cent, while normal sea water has a salinity of about 3.5 per cent. Since the concentration of salts in the Dead Sea increases with depth, brine for evaporation is pumped from the lower levels.

JORDAN AGRICULTURE[1]

	Acres	*Tons*
Rain-fed crops		
Winter field crops		
Wheat	650,000	150,000
Barley	250,000	80,000
Kersenneh	50,000	14,000
Lentils	48,000	13,000
Total	1,012,000	268,700
Summer field crops		
Sorghum	85,000	19,000
Sesame	35,000	4,000
Chickpeas	20,000	4,000
Tobacco	7,500	700
Vegetables	55,000	114,000
Total	208,000	142,000
Fruit Crops		
Olives	125,000	60,000
Grapes	39,000	50,000
Total	192,000	140,700
Rain-fed Total	1,412,200	551,400
Irrigated Crops		
Field Crops		
Wheat	30,000	10,000
Barley	8,000	3,000
Sorghum	5,500	2,500
Sesame	3,500	800
Vegetables		
Winter	11,000	40,100
Summer	19,000	38,900
Fruit		
Bananas	2,250	9,000
Pomegranates	1,400	5,000
Citrus	500	2,000
Irrigated Total	80,500	112,250
Grand total, all crops	1,992,400	663,650

[1] International Bank: *The Economic Development of Jordan.* Baltimore: Johns Hopkins Press (1957), 79–80. Data for 1952–54.

Due to the low humidity and high temperatures, solar evaporation in the Dead Sea area is rapid, amounting to nearly half an inch a day in summer, and, as a result, production costs are low. The sodium chloride in the evaporating pans is separated in six weeks, while potassium magnesium chloride or carnellite is removed three weeks

The Jordan River is building a delta where it enters the Dead Sea. Evaporating pans for the extraction of chemicals appear to the left of the river. (U. S. Air Force.)

DEAD SEA SALTS

	Surface composition	*175-foot depth*
Sodium chloride	7.0%	9.3%
Potassium chloride	1.0%	1.5%
Magnesium bromide	0.5%	0.7%
Magnesium chloride	11%	17%

later and may be recrystallized as 80 per cent pure potassium chloride. Further evaporation yields a pure magnesium chloride. The residual liquid contains 1.25 per cent magnesium bromide, one of the richest available sources of bromine. Potash is a major fertilizer, while bromine has a wide array of uses in industry. The largest markets for potash are in southern and southeastern Asia and in South Africa. Eventually, many other chemical products may be recovered from the waters.

Rich phosphate deposits, another source of fertilizer, are mined at Ruseifa and at El Hasa near Amman and exported through Aqaba. The deposits occur in limestone beds of Eocene age, four to six feet thick and are mined underground. Proven and inferred reserves at Ruseifa amounted to 32,742,000 tons in 1954, while 1955 estimates place the El Hasa total at 9,345,000 tons. Production amounted to 165,000 tons in 1955, and it was hoped that the annual figure might reach nearly a million tons during the early 1960's. If production plants for making super phosphate fertilizer could be developed within Jordan, and, provided that cheap and unrestricted shipment is available, agriculture would be materially improved throughout Swasia.

Other resources are known to be present, including manganese, copper, iron, and clays; but the amounts are small or uneconomic and there appears no prospect of development. High-grade barite and gypsum are present and may have the potential value to be worth mining. Salt is secured from desert lakes. Cement is already in production.

Petroleum is known to occur in places, but the reserves are uncertain. Asphalt seepages and possible salt dome structures near the Dead Sea suggest oil possibilities. Even though Jordan is without large reserves, it has access to Arabian oil through the Trans-Arabian Pipeline.

REFERENCES

NOTE: Material on Palestine also may be found at the end of the next chapter.

General References

* British Admiralty, Naval Intelligence Division: SYRIA. London: Naval Intelligence Division (1944).

Combier, C. S. J.: "Essai d'une Formule de Classification des Climats du Levant," *Publ. Techn. et Scient. de l'Ecole Fr. d'Ingenieurs de Beyrouth,* No. 14 (1948), 7–27.

Curzon, Robert: VISITS TO THE MONASTERIES OF THE LEVANT. London: Barker (1955).

deVaumas, Etienne: "La Structure de Proche-Orient," *Bull. Soc. Geog. d'Egypte,* XXIII (1950), 265–320.

Dubertret, L.: "Apercu de Geographie Physique sur le Liban, l'Anti-Liban, et la Damascene," in ETUDES GEOLOGIQUES ET GEOGRAPHIQUES SUR LE LIBAN, LA SYRIE, ET LE MOYEN-ORIENT, IV. Beirut (1945–1948), 191–226.

Dubertret, L.: "Problems de la Geologie du Levant," *Bull. Soc. Geol. de Fr.,* XVII (1947) 3–31.

Dubertret, L., and Weulersse, J.: MANUEL DE GEOGRAPHIE. SYRIE, LIBAN ET PROCHE-ORIENT. PREMIER PARTIE. LA PENINSULA ARABIQUE, Beyrouth: Impr. Catholique (1940).

Edde, J.: GEOGRAPHIE LIBAN-SYRIE. Beirut: (1941).

Fedden, Robert, and Thompson, John: CRUSADER CASTLES. London: Murray (1952).

Furon, Raymond: LE PROCHE-ORIENT. Paris; Payot (1957).

Gibert, Andre: "Sur la Structure des Pays du Levant," *Rev. Geog. de Lyon,* XXIV (1949), 279–286.

Gombault, R.: "Apercu sur la Flore de la Syrie, du Liban et de la Region d'Antioche," in ETUDES GEOLOGIQUES ET GEOGRAPHIQUES SUR LE LIBAN, LA SYRIE, ET LE MOYEN ORIENT. Beirut (1945–1948), 123–156.

Hourani, A. H.: SYRIA AND LEBANON: A POLITICAL ESSAY. London: Oxford (1946).

Lamb, Harold: "Crusader Lands Revisited," *Nat. Geog. Mag.,* CVI (1954) 815–852.

Patai, Raphael: ANNOTATED BIBLIOGRAPHY OF JORDAN, LEBANON, AND SYRIA. New Haven: Human Relations Area Files (1957).

Quennell, A. M.: "The Structural & Geomorphic Evolution of the Dead Sea Rift," *Quart. Jour. Geol. Soc. London,* CXIV (1958), 1–24.

Reifenberg, A.: "The Soils of Syria and the Lebanon," *Jour. of Soil Science,* III (1952), 68–88.

Reifenberg, A.: THE STRUGGLE BETWEEN THE DESERT AND THE SOWN: THE RISE AND FALL OF AGRICULTURE IN THE LEVANT. Jerusalem: Govt. Press (1958).

Shalem, N.: "Attributed Climatic Changes in the Levant," *Comptes Rendus, Congres International de Geographie,* II (1950), 593–649.

Sivall, Tage: "Sirocco in the Levant," *Geografiska Annaler,* XXXIX (1957), 114–142.

Williams, Maynard Owen: "Syria and Lebanon Taste Freedom," *Nat. Geog. Mag.,* XC (1946), 729–763.

* Ziadeh, N. A.: SYRIA AND LEBANON. London: Ernest Benn (1957).

Syria: General References

Ashton, Bessie L.: "The Geography of Syria," *Jour. of Geog.,* XXVII (1928), 167–180.

Bell, Gertrude: SYRIA: THE DESERT AND THE SOWN. London: Heinemann (1907).

Blanchard, Raoul: "La Syrie," in GEOGRAPHIE UNIVERSALLE, VIII, ASIE OCCIDENTALE. Paris: Armand Colin (1929), 186–214.

* British Admiralty, Naval Intelligence Division: SYRIA. London: Naval Intelligence Division (1944).

Butler, Howard Crosby: "Desert Syria, the Land of a Lost Civilization," *Geog. Rev.,* IX (1920), 77–108.

Dening, B. H.: "Greater Syria: A Study in Political Geography," *Geog.,* XXXV (1950), 110–123.

* Fedden, Robin: SYRIA: AN HISTORICAL APPRECIATION. London: Hale (1955).

Garrett, Jean: "The Site of Damascus," *Geog.,* XXI (1936), 283–296.

* Grant, Catherine P.: THE SYRIAN DESERT. London: Black (1937).

* Hitti, Philip K.: HISTORY OF SYRIA. New York: Macmillan (1951).

Hitti, Philip K.: SYRIA: A SHORT HISTORY. New York: Macmillan (1959).

Hole, Edwin: SYRIAN HARVEST. London: Hale (1956).

* Hoyningen-Huene, and Robinson, David M.: BAALBEK, PALMYRA. New York: J. J. Augustin (1946).

* International Bank for Reconstruction and Development: THE ECONOMIC DEVELOPMENT OF SYRIA. Baltimore: Johns Hopkins Press (1955).

Lewis, Norman N.: "Malaria, Irrigation and Soil Erosion in Central Syria," *Geog. Rev.,* XXXIX (1949), 291–297.

Merlange, Germaine: "Syrian Landscape," *Geog. Mag.,* XII (1940), 153–167.

Musil, Alois: PALMYRENA. A TOPOGRAPHICAL ITINERARY. New York: Amer. Geog. Soc. (1928).

Poidebard, A.: LA TRACE DE ROME DANS LE DESERT DE SYRIE. Paris: Paul Geuthner (1934).

Rohrbach, Paul: "Syrien mit Palestine und das Zweistromland," in KLUTE HANDBUCH DER GEOGRAPHISCHEN WISSENSCHAFT VI, VORDER UND SUDASIEN. Potsdam: Akademische Verlagsgesellschaft Athenaion (1937), 126–177.

Schaeffer, Claude F. A., and Chenet, Georges: "Secrets from Syrian Hills," *Nat. Geog. Mag.,* LXIV (1933), 97–126.

Syria Ministry of National Economy, Directorate of Statistics: STATISTICAL ABSTRACT OF SYRIA (Annual). Damascus: Directorate of Statistics.

Thomson, Elizabeth: "Roman Syria," *Geog. Mag.,* XXX (1958), 405–418.

Thoumin, R.: GEOGRAPHIE HUMAINE DE LA SYRIE CENTRALE. Paris: Leroux (1936).

Tower, J. A.: "Notes on Recent Studies in Syrian Geography," *Geog. Rev.,* XXVII (1937), 676–678, XXIX (1939), 147–149.

Weulersse, Jacques: PAYSANS DE SYRIE ET DU PROCHE-ORIENT. Tours: Gallinard (1946).

Woolley, Leonard: "North Syria as a Cultural Link in the Ancient World," *Jour. Royal Anthropol. Inst. of Gt. Br. and Ireland,* LXXII (1942), 9–18.

Woolley, Leonard: "Syria as the Gateway Between East and West," *Geog. Jour.,* CVII (1946), 179–190.

Syria: Agriculture and Soil

Mazloum, S.: LE PROBLEM DE L'EAU EN SYRIE ET AU LIBAN. Beirut (1942).

Money-Kyrle, A. F.: AGRICULTURAL DEVELOPMENT AND RESEARCH IN SYRIA. Beirut: American University (1956).

Moussly, Nazim: LE PROBLEME DE L'EAU EN SYRIE. Lyon: Bosc Freres (1951).

Muir, Alex: "Notes on the Soils of Syria," *Jour. of Soil Science,* II (1951), 163–182.

Norman, Lewis N.: "Malaria, Irrigation, and Soil Erosion in Central Syria," *Geog. Rev.,* XXXIX (1949), 278–290.

Parsons, Kenneth H.: "Land Reform in the United Arab Republic," *Land Economics,* XXXV (1959), 319–326.

United States-Syria Agricultural Mission: REPORT OF THE UNITED STATES-SYRIA AGRICULTURAL MISSION. Washington (1947). [Maps]

Syria, Ministry of Agriculture: THE AGRICULTURAL DEVELOPMENT OF SYRIA. Damascus (1955).

Syria: General Geography

Dening, B. H.: "Greater Syria; a Study in Political Geography," *Geog.,* XXXV (1950), 110–123. [Maps]

DeVaumas, Etienne: "Plateaux, Plains et Depressions de la Syrie Interieure Septentrionale," *Bull. Soc. Geog. d'Egypte,* XXX (1957), 97–235.

Garrett, Jean: "The Site of Damascus," *Geog.,* XXI (1936), 283–296.

Gilbert, Andre, and Fevret, Maurice: "La Djezirah Syrienne et Son Reveil Economique," *Rev. Geog. de Lyon,* XXXVIII (1953), 1–15, 83–99.

Merlange, Germaine: "The Syrian Landscape," *Geog. Mag.,* XII (1940–41), 153–167.

Poidebard, A.: "La Haute Djezireh," *La Geog.,* XLVII (1927), 191–206.

Sadek, Dawlat: "Morphology of Damascus," *Bull. Soc. Geog. d'Egypte,* XXVIII (1955), 93–98.

Thoumin, Richard: "Le Ghab," *Rev. Geog. Alpine,* XXIV (1936), 467–538.

Wirth, Eugen: "Morphologische und Bodenkundliche Beobachtungen in der Syrisch-Irakischen Wuste," *Erdkunde,* XII (1958), 26–42.

Jordan: General References

Harris, George L.: JORDAN. New York: Grove (1959).

* International Bank for Reconstruction and Development: THE ECONOMIC DEVELOPMENT OF JORDAN. Baltimore: Johns Hopkins Press (1957).

Jordan, Ministry of Economy, Dept. of Statistics: ANNUAL STATISTICAL YEARBOOK (Annual). Amman: Dept. of Statistics.

* Patai, Raphael, Ed.: JORDAN. New Haven: Human Relations Area Files (1957).

Patai, Raphael: THE KINGDOM OF JORDAN. Princeton: Princeton Univ. Press (1958).

Peake, Frederick G.: A HISTORY OF JORDAN AND ITS TRIBES. Coral Gables: Univ. of Miami Press (1958).

Shwadran, Benjamin: JORDAN: A STATE OF TENSION. New York: Council for Middle Eastern Affairs Press (1959).

U. S. Board on Geographic Names: JORDAN. Washington: Dept. of Interior (1955).

Jordan: Trans-Jordan

Baer, Gabriel: "Land Tenure in the Hashemite Kingdom of Jordan," *Land Economics,* XXXIII (1957), 187–197.

Castro, E. Ray, and Dotson, Oscar W.: "Economic Geography of Trans-Jordan," *Econ. Geog.,* XIV (1938), 121–130.

Epstein, Eliahn: "The Bedouin of Transjordan," *Jour. Royal Central Asian Soc.,* XXV (1938), 228–236.

Erskine, Stuart: THE VANISHED CITIES OF ARABIA. London: Hutchinson (1925). [Petra, Kerak, Philadelphia, and Jerash.]

Feinbrun, N., & Zahary, M.: "Geobotanical Survey of Transjordan," *Israel Res. Council,* B 5D (1955), 5–35.

Glueck, Nelson: THE OTHER SIDE OF THE JORDAN. New Haven: Amer. Schools of Oriental Research (1940).

Kennedy, Alexander: "The Rocks and Monuments of Petra," *Geog. Jour.,* LXIII (1924), 273–301.

Kirk, M. E.: "An Outline of the Ancient Cultural History of Transjordan," *Palestine Exploration Quart.,* LXXVI (1944), 180–198.

Konikoff, A.: TRANSJORDAN: AN ECONOMIC SURVEY. Jerusalem: Jewish Agency for Palestine (1946).

Mackenzie, Marcus: "Transjordan," *Jour. Royal Central Asian Soc.,* XXXIII (1946), 260–270.

Maunsell, F. R.: "The Land of Elam," *Geog. Jour.,* LXV (1925), 432–437.

Phillips, Paul G.: "The Hashemite Kingdom of Jordan: Prolegomena to a Technical Assistance Program," Univ. of Chicago *Dept. of Geog. Research Paper* No. 34 (1954).

Quennell, A. M.: "Geology and Mineral Resources of [former] Trans-Jordan," *Colonial Geol. & Min. Resources,* II (1951), 85–115.

Rhotert, H.: TRANSJORDANIEN. Stuttgart: Strecker & Schroder (1938).

Scofield, John: "Hashemite Jordan, Arab Heartland," *Nat. Geog. Mag.,* CII (1952), 841–856.

Toukan, Baha Uddin: "Transjordan: Past, Present and Future," *Jour. Royal Central Asian Soc.,* XXXI (1944), 253–264.

Toukan, Baha Uddin: A SHORT HISTORY OF TRANS-JORDAN. London: Luzac & Co. (1945).

Van Valkenburg, Samuel: "The Hashemite Kingdom of the Jordan: a Study in Economic Geography," *Econ. Geog.,* XXX (1954), 102–116.

Walpole, G. F.: "Land Problems in Transjordan," *Jour. Royal Central Asian Soc.,* XXXV (1948), 52–65.

Whiting, John D.: "Petra, Ancient Caravan Stronghold," *Nat. Geog. Mag.,* LXVII (1935), 129–167.

Wright, Esmond: "Abdallah's Jordan: 1947–1951," *Middle East Jour.,* V (1951), 439–460.

Jordan: Jordan River and Dead Sea

Ashbel, D.: "The Influence of the Dead Sea on the Climate of its Neighborhood," *Quart. Jour. Royal Meteorol. Soc.,* LXV (1939), 185–194.

Casto, E. Ray: "The Life-Giving Dead Sea," *Jour. of Geog.,* XXXVI (1937), 221–229.

Clapp, Frederick G.: "Geology and Bitumens of the Dead Sea Area, Palestine and Transjordan," *Bull. Amer. Assoc. of Petrol. Geols.,* XX (1936), 881–909.

Davies, H. R. J.: "Irrigation in Jordan," *Econ. Geog.,* XXXIV (1958), 264–271.

Glueck, Nelson: "The Geography of the Jordan," *Nat. Geog. Mag.,* LXXXVI (1944), 719–744.

* Glueck, Nelson: THE RIVER JORDAN. Philadelphia: Westminister (1946).

Ionides, M. G.: REPORT ON THE WATER RESOURCES OF TRANSJORDAN AND THEIR DEVELOPMENT. London: Govt. of Transjordan (1939).

Ionides, M. G.: "The Jordan Valley," *Jour. Royal Central Asian Soc.,* XXXVIII (1951), 217–225.

Ionides, M. G.: "The Disputed Waters of Jordan," *Middle East Jour.,* VII (1953), 153–164.

Irwin, Wilfred: "The Salts of Dead Sea and River Jordan," *Geog. Jour.,* LXI (1923), 428–440.

Irwin, Wilfred: "The Origin of the Salts in the Jordan," *Geog. Jour.,* LXVI (1925), 527–533.

Peretz, Don: "Development of the Jordan Valley Waters," *Middle East Jour.,* IX (1955), 397–412.

Philby, H. St. J. B.: "The Dead Sea to Aqaba," *Geog. Jour.,* LXVI (1925), 134–160.

* Simpich, F., and Whiting, J. D.: "Canoeing Down the River Jordan," *Nat. Geog. Mag.,* LXXVIII (1940), 781–808.

Stevens, Georgiana G.: "Jordan River Valley," *Internat. Conciliation* #506 (1956), 227–283.

Willis, Bailey: "Dead Sea Problem: Rift Valley or Ramp Valley," *Bull. Geol. Soc. Amer.,* XXXIX (1928), 491–542.

Jordan: Jerusalem and Vicinity

Hogg, Quintin: "Discovering Jerusalem," *Geog. Mag.,* XVI (1943), 233–240.

* Join-Lambert, Michel: JERUSALEM. London: Elek, and New York: Putnam's (1958).

Keith-Roach, Edward: "The Pageant of Jerusalem," *Nat. Geog. Mag.,* LII (1927), 635–681.

Kelso, James L.: "The Ghosts of Jericho," *Nat. Geog. Mag.,* C (1951), 825–844.

* Kenyon, Kathleen M.: DIGGING UP JERICHO. London: Benn (1957).

Kenyon, Kathleen M., and Tushingham, A. Douglas: "Jericho Gives up its Secrets," *Nat. Geog. Mag.,* CXIV (1953), 853–870.

Scofield, John, and Brake, Brian: "Jerusalem, the Divided City," *Nat. Geog. Mag.,* CXV (1959), 492–531.

Vester, Bertha Spofford: OUR JERUSALEM. New York: Doubleday (1950).

Whiting, John D.: "Among the Bethlehem Shepherds," *Nat. Geog. Mag.,* (1926), 729–753.

Williams, Maynard Owen: "Color Records from the Changing Life of the Holy City," *Nat. Geog. Mag.*, LII (1927), 682–707.

Lebanon: General References

Abercrombie, Thos. J.: "Young-old Lebanon Lives by Trade," *Nat. Geog. Mag.*, CXIII (1958), 479–523.

Boulanger, Robert: LEBANON: HACHETTE WORLD GUIDE SERIES. Paris: Hachette (1955).

Bouloumy, R. L.: FLORE DU LIBAN ET DE LA SYRIE. 2 vols., Paris: Bigot (1930).

Conde, Bruce: SEE LEBANON. Harissa, Lebanon: Basile Press (1955).

Crist, Raymond E.: "The Mountain Village of Dahr, Lebanon," *Annual Report of the Smithsonian Inst.* (1954), 407–423.

Crowfoot, J. W.: "Syria and Lebanon: the Prospect," *Geog. Jour.*, XCIX (1942), 130–141.

DeVaumas, Etienne: "Les Terraces d'Abrasion Marine de la Cote Limanaise," *Bull. Soc. Royale Geog. d'Egypte*, XXII (1947), 21–85.

DeVaumas, Etienne: "Le Repartition de la Population au Liban," *Bull. Soc. Geog. d'Egypte*, XXVI (1953), 5–76.

* DeVaumas, Etienne: LE LIBAN: ETUDE DE GEOGRAPHIE PHYSIQUE. 2 vols., Paris: Didot (1954).

De Vaumas, Etienne: "La Structure et le modele de la Bekaa," *Bull. Soc. de Geog. d'Egypte*, XXXI (1958), 5–66.

Dowson, V. H. W.: "The Lebanon 1948–1949," *Jour. Royal Central Asian Soc.* XXXVII (1950), 66–76.

Fevret, Maurice: "La Sericulture au Liban," *Rev. Geog. de Lyon*, XXIV (1949), 247–260. 341–362.

Fevret, Maurice: "Un Village du Liban. El Mtaine," *Rev. Geog. de Lyon*, XXV (1950), 267–287.

Fish, W. B.: "The Lebanon," *Geog. Rev.*, XXXIV (1944), 235–258.

Gulick, John: "Conservatism and Change in a Lebanese Village," *Middle East Jour.*, VIII (1954), 295–307.

Highwood, R. W.: "Baalbek," *Geog. Mag.*, XXX (1957), 84–93.

* Hitti, Philip K.: LEBANON IN HISTORY. London: Macmillan (1957).

* Hoyningen Huene, and Robinson, David M.: BAALBEK, PALMYRA. New York: J. J. Augustin (1946).

Laugenie, Jean: "Le Port de Beyrouth," *Rev. Geog. de Lyon*, XXXI (1956), 271–293.

Lewis, Norman N.: "Lebanon—the Mountain and its Terraces," *Geog. Rev.*, XLIII (1953), 1–14.

Renouard, Georges: "Oil Prospects of Lebanon," *Bull. Amer. Assoc. Petrol. Geols.*, XXXIX (1955), 2125–2169.

Rumbold, Constantia: "Baalbek, City of Ruined Temples," *Geog. Mag.*, XIII (1941), 270–279.

Spayen, F. D. N.: "The Landscape of Northern Beqa, Lebanon," *Scot. Geog. Mag.*, LXIII (1947), 108–115.

Tannons, Afif I.: "The Village in the National Life of Lebanon," *Middle East Jour.*, III (1949), 151–163.

Vohes, H. E.: "Geological Observations in the Lebanon Mountains of Western Asia," *Bull. Geol. Soc. Amer.*, LII (1941), 1715–1731.

Wright, H. E., Jr.: "Marine Terraces of the Coast of Lebanon," *Bull. Geol. Soc. Amer.*, LVIII (1947), 12–42.

CHAPTER 15

Israel

Historical Preface
Agriculture, Old and New
Population Patterns
Economic Viability
References

HISTORICAL PREFACE

MANY PEOPLE do not realize the small size of Palestine and particularly of armistice-bound Israel. One may stand in Jordanian Jerusalem and see the Mediterranean Sea; farther north where Israel is limited to the ten-mile coastal plain one may look across and almost see the waves along the shore. It is possible to drive the length of settled Israel, from "Dan to Beersheba," in a few hours. Israel's 7,993 square miles are only slightly larger than New Jersey, and half the area lies in the dry Negeb, often spelled Negev, southwest of the Dead Sea. Here live 2 million people.

Palestine has been more of a geographic expression than a political entity. It includes the area between the Mediterranean and the Jordan Valley, south of the Lebanon Mountains as far as but not always including the Negeb Desert. Today it is divided between Israel and Jordan. As already indicated on page 424, the Semitic Canaanites or Phoenicians were the earliest known coastal residents; later, they were pressed into the hills by invading armies of Philistines or Sea People, who were Indo-Europeans. Then the Jews came from the south.

(Opposite) Modern Tel Aviv is a symbol of the State of Israel. This aerial view shows the Dizengoff Circle. (Courtesy Israel Office of Information, New York.)

Since the area has been frequently a part of Greater Syria under Roman, Byzantine, and Turkish rule, it would be proper to include its discussion under the chapter on the Levant States. On the other hand, significant political considerations require a separate chapter for Israel. Several aspects of the geography of Palestine have been considered in the previous chapter and elsewhere. (See pages 130, 233, and 409.)

The problems of Israel are charged with so much emotion that it may be well to start with some history. In order to understand the events of the twentieth century A.D., it is necessary to go back to the twelfth century B.C. when the Jews were a nomadic Bedouin tribe under a sheikh named Moses.

As the children of Israel stood on the border of the "Promised Land," we read in Numbers XXXIII: 50–55:

> And the Lord said unto Moses in the plains of Moab by the Jordan at Jericho "Say to the people of Israel, when you pass over the Jordan

into the land of Canaan, then you shall drive out all the inhabitants of the land before you, and destroy all their figured stones, and destroy all their molten images, and demolish all their high places, and you shall take possession of the land and settle in it, for I have given the land to you to possess it. You shall inherit the land by lot according to your families; to a large tribe you shall give a large inheritance, and a small tribe a small inheritance; wherever the lot falls to any man, that shall be his inheritance; according to the tribes of your fathers you shall inherit. But if you do not drive out the inhabitants of the land from before you, then those of them whom you let remain shall be as pricks in your eyes and thorns in your sides, and they shall trouble you in the land where you dwell."

Ownership by conquest, with the approval of one's tribal gods, was a common procedure in ancient Swasia. The Canaanites had secured grazing grounds in the same way from their predecessors; the same was true with succeeding peoples.

To many people of Jewish faith the promise to Abraham is still real: "And I will give to you and to your descendants after you, the land of your sojournings, all the land of Canaan, for an everlasting possession" (Genesis XVII: 8). We may question whether God has favorites among the people of the earth or whether he authorizes any one group to take over the rights of another. On the other hand, one must recognize the persecution which Jews have endured in many countries and the belief of some that they can regain self-respect by putting their hands into the soil of Palestine.

ISRAEL DATA

Area	7,993 square miles
	20,700 square kilometers
Arable area	3,920 square kilometers
Population	2,062,000 (1959)
Cities	
Tel Aviv-Jaffa	363,500
Haifa	158,000
Jerusalem (Israel sector)	146,000

Although Jews have lived in Palestine for many centuries, the periods of any effective political kingdom of their own were limited and ended before the time of Christ. At times, Jewish influence extended from the Nile to the Euphrates, at other periods the government controlled only the uplands of Judea. Nevertheless, countless generations have looked forward to the re-enactment of Moses' words as a national and God-given right. An equal desire for return to their homeland permeates the currently displaced Arab Palestinians who have had continuous residence here since 640 A.D.

The Jews who have now returned to Israel are a mixed group. One and two thousand years of separation have introduced ethnic and cultural differences, and even varied theological viewpoints, which have an effect on the fusion of people in a new state. To some Zionists, Israel is merely a materialistic challenge, to others it represents varying degrees of Biblical fulfillment.

Some of the past history has already been sketched in Chapter 9 on International Contacts, page 233, including the 1915 McMahon-Hussein Agreement concerning an Arab national State, the 1917 Balfour Declaration which not only looked forward to a Jewish homeland but equally promised the "civil and religious rights of existing non-Jewish communities in Palestine," and the 1939 White Paper in which "His Majesty's Government therefore now declares unequivocally that it is not part of their policy that Palestine should become a Jewish state. They would indeed regard it as contrary to their obligations to the Arabs under the mandate . . ."

At a time when it appeared that Jewish

NOTE: Additional data on Israel and for Palestine as a whole is contained in the preceding chapter on the Levant States. I am indebted to Professor David H. K. Amiran, Chairman of the Department of Geography at Hebrew University in Jerusalem, for advice and assistance in the field.

The village of Degania lies near the outlet of Lake Tiberius, known to Israel as Lake Kinneret. The hills beyond the lake are in Syria and mark the opposite side of the Jordan Valley graben. (Courtesy Israel Office of Information, New York.)

immigration might displace the established Arab residents, a meeting was arranged between Chaim Weizman as spokesman for the Zionists and King Feisal as ruler of the new Arab state established in Damascus in 1919. The text includes promises that "The Arab State and Palestine in all their relations and undertakings shall be controlled by the most cordial good will and understanding . . . ." and "All necessary measures shall be taken to encourage and stimulate immigration of Jews into Palestine on a large scale . . . ." Feisal's signature and stipulation were in Arabic and have not been widely publicized. It read, in full:

> Provided the Arabs obtain their independence as demanded by my memorandum dated the 4th of January, 1919, to the Foreign Office of the Government of Great Britain, I shall concur in the above articles. But, if the slightest modification or departure were to be made [*sc.* in relation to the demands in the Memorandum] I shall not then be bound by a single word of the present Agreement which shall be deemed void and of no account or validity, and I shall not be answerable in any way whatsoever.[1]

When President Wilson sent out the King-Crane Commission in 1919, preparatory to the Treaty of Versailles, it reported in favor of a unified Arab Syria and recom-

[1] Some of the pertinent documents on Palestine may be consulted in George Antonius: *The Arab Awakening*. Beirut: Khayat's College Book Cooperative (1948), and Carol A. Fisher and Fred Krinsky; *Middle East in Crisis*. Syracuse University Press (1959).

Southern Israel is arid, as shown in this view of the Negeb. The road leads from Beersheba to Sodom on the Dead Sea. (Courtesy Israel Office of Information, New York.)

mended, "serious modification of the extreme Zionist programme for Palestine of unlimited immigration of Jews, looking finally to making Palestine distinctly a Jewish state," and continued, "The Peace Conference should not shut its eyes to the fact that the anti-Zionist feeling in Palestine and Syria is intense and not lightly to be flouted. No British officer, consulted by the Commissioners, believed that the Zionist programme could be carried out except by force of arms."

This is not the place to recount the tragic events which accompanied the mounting Jewish immigration and arms acquisition, the hasty termination of the mandate and the anarchy which preceded British withdrawal, the attempts on the part of the United Nations to establish two Palestines, the creation of the state of Israel in 1948, or the subsequent Arab-Israeli War with the displacement of most of the previous inhabitants.

The opening paragraphs of Israel's Proclamation of Independence, issued on May 14, 1948, in Tel Aviv, read as follows:

> The land of Israel was the birthplace of the Jewish people. Here their spiritual, religious and national identity was formed. Here they achieved independence and created a culture of national and universal significance. Here they wrote and gave the Bible to the world.

The conservation of water has always been a problem in Palestine, but reservoirs also become filled with sediment. This dam in the Negeb near Kurnub dates from Byzantine times. (Courtesy Israel Office of Information, New York.)

Exiled from Palestine, the Jewish people remained faithful to it in all countries of their dispersion, never ceasing to pray and hope for their return and the restoration of their national freedom.

Impelled by this historic association, Jews strove throughout the centuries to go back to the land of their fathers and regain their statehood. In recent decades they returned in their masses. They reclaimed the wilderness, revived their language, built cities and villages, and established a vigorous and ever growing community, with its own economic and cultural life. They sought peace yet were prepared to defend themselves. They brought the blessings of progress to all inhabitants of the country.

The United Nations has repeatedly received reports and passed resolutions. The 1948 "Progress Report" of the United Nations Mediator on Palestine reads as follows: [1]

The following seven basic premises form the basis for my conclusions:

(a) Peace must return to Palestine and every feasible measure should be taken to ensure that hostilities will not be resumed and that harmonious relations between Arab and Jew will ultimately be restored.

(b) A Jewish State called Israel exists in Palestine and there are no sound reasons for assuming that it will not continue to do so.

[1] U. N. General Assembly, *Third Session, Supplement No. 11* (A/648). (1948), 17.

(c) The boundaries of this new State must be finally fixed either by formal agreement between the parties concerned or failing that, by the United Nations.
(d) Adherence to the principal of geographical homogeneity and integration, which should be a major objective of the boundary arrangements, should apply equally to Arab and Jewish territories, whose frontiers should not, therefore, be rigidly controlled by the territorial arrangements envisaged in the resolution of 29 November.
(e) The right of innocent people, uprooted from their homes by the present terror and ravages of war, to return to their homes, should be affirmed and made effective, with assurance of adequate compensation for the property of those who may not choose to return.
(f) The city of Jerusalem, because of its religious and international significance and the complexity of interests involved, should be accorded special and separate treatment.
(g) International responsibility should be expressed where desirable and necessary in the form of international guarantees, as a means of allaying existing fears, and particularly with regard to boundaries and human rights.

These proposals were endorsed by the General Assembly in Resolution 194 (III), December 11, 1948. Unfortunately, few of them have been implemented.

Organized fighting ended with the Armistice of 1949, arranged by the United Nations and signed separately between Israel and Lebanon, Syria, Jordan, and Egypt, but still unsigned by Iraq and Saudi Arabia. The Armistice with Egypt provided for the then current military front to be a demarcation line, "not to be construed in any sense as a political or territorial boundary, and is delimited without prejudice to rights, claims and positions of either Party to the Armistice as regards ultimate settlement of the Palestine question." No peace treaty resulted, so that a technical state of war continued with friction and repeated border raids.

Under the United Nations partition plan, the Zionist state was to cover 5,670 miles, with the remainder of Palestine assigned to the Arabs. As a result of the fighting in 1948–49, Israel came to encompass 7,993 square miles. This gain of 2,314 square miles is matched by Jordan's accession of 2,243 square miles of eastern Palestine. There are also 135 square miles traditionally a part of Palestine but now administered by Egypt in the Gaza area.

The land boundary of Israel follows the Armistice lines which total 595 miles, divided between Lebanon, 50 miles; Syria, 48 miles; Jordan, 332 miles; and Egypt, 165 miles. Water bodies include the Mediterranean coastline of 118 miles, thirty-five miles along the Dead Sea, and a frontage of six miles on the Red Sea.

Israel's population reached 2 million by 1960, and plans look forward to 4 million. While official statements discount further territorial changes, occasional references to unilateral development of Jordan River water, territorial expansion to the river to take in all of Palestine, and the publication of maps showing all the area from the Nile to the Euphrates as properly Zionist, all naturally alarm her Arab neighbors. On the other hand, Arab statements about "driving the Zionists into the sea" obviously call for defensive preparations within Israel. The state of Israel exists and will continue, but time has not yet erased the Arab contention as to its illegality.

During the first decade of its independence, Israel took in 930,000 Zionists. Half the early settlers came from Europe. Later the tide turned to Asia and Africa, as shown by the following national origins: Iraq, 125,-896; Yemen, 45,738; Iran, 27,534; Egypt, 34,140; other Africans, 142,858. What is sometimes overlooked is that in the same period 100,000 Jewish residents left the country, in some years with emigration exceeding immigration. Most of those departing from Israel were originally from North America or Western Europe where economic and social conditions are more favor-

PALESTINE POPULATION [1]

	Jews	*Arabs & others*	*Total*	*Jewish Immigration*	*Jewish Emigration*
Turkish Jerusalem Vilayet [2]					
1900	±30,000	±300,000	330,000		
1910			341,600		
British Palestine [3]					
1922	83,794	673,388	757,182	8,128	
1931	175,006	860,148	1,035,154	5,533	
1940	456,743	1,072,816	1,529,559	5,611	
Israel [4]					
1950	1,202,993	167,101 [5]	1,370,094	169,720	9,966
1955	1,526,016	191,818	1,717,834	36,327	6,400
1959			2,062,000		

[1] *Statesman's Yearbook.*
[2] Area 8,222 square miles.
[3] Area 10,429 square miles.
[4] Area 7,993 square miles.
[5] Moslems, 131,500; Christians, 42,800; Druse, 17,500.

able. In fact, out of the 35,000 who came from the United States and Canada during the two decades preceding and following independence, only 6,000 remain.

The basic problem of Israel's relations with her neighbors is neither racial nor religious, for people of Jewish race and religion still live unmolested in many parts of Swasia. Opposition is directed at the political aspects of Zionism and at the dubious method of Israel's creation. The problem of the refugees is indeed serious, for it is difficult to find a place for them in the adjoining countries and unrealistic to expect Israel to take them back in large numbers; compensation has not been spelled out as a real alternative. It is also fair to point out that Israel has taken in some 200,000 Jews from other Southwest Asian countries. Insofar as Arab opposition is based on fear of territorial expansion and of Israel as a spearhead of European or American imperialism, one of the best hopes for peace may lie in guaranteed boundaries. Conversations of the author with responsible leaders in Beirut, Baghdad, Amman, and Riyadh make this appear hopeful.

Kenneth Cragg has summarized the situation as follows: [1]

> If Israel is not to remain a kind of national ghetto, she must find a means of coexistence with the Arabs; if the Arabs are ever to recover from the Arab tragedy of Israel, they must make terms with it. Otherwise their future will be perpetually mortgaged to their past . . .

Years may elapse before calm judgment is possible; in the meantime, a quiet continuation of the truce is to be hoped for. Some solution is more necessary for Israel than for her neighbors. The Arab world can live without the Zionist state, but Israel can scarcely become viable unless she finds local markets and can serve in a commercial and industrial capacity similar to that of Lebanon.

AGRICULTURE, OLD AND NEW

ISRAEL'S BACKGROUND of rough land, limited rainfall, depleted soil, and meager resources resembles conditions elsewhere in the Le-

[1] Kenneth Cragg: *The Call of the Minaret.* New York: Oxford (1956), 186. Quoted by permission.

LAND CLASSIFICATION

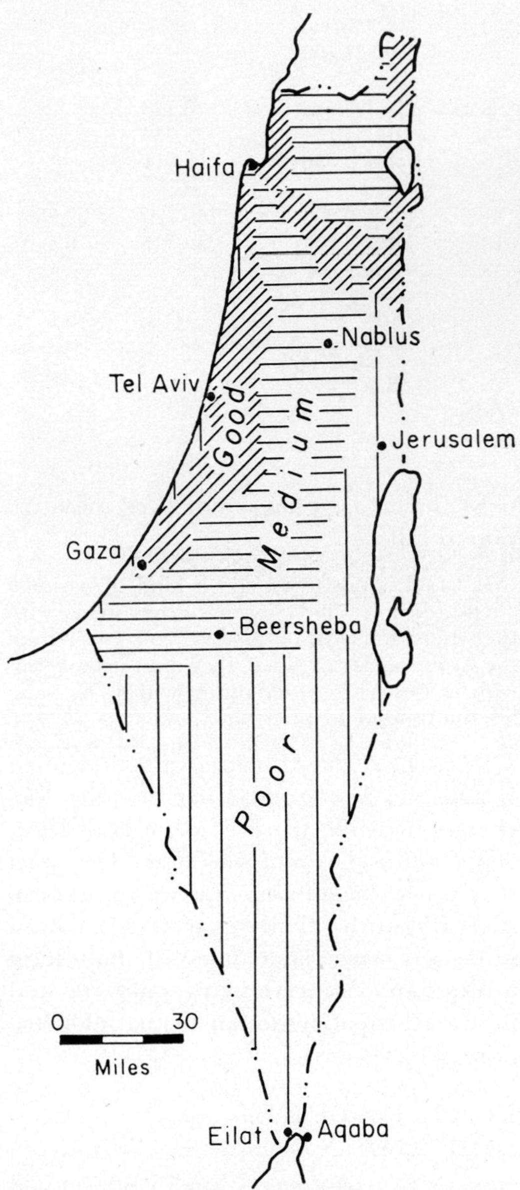

The best land in Palestine lies near the coast and in the Esdraelon valley. (Based on S. Hadawi, "Land Ownership in Palestine.")

vant. It is the dramatic surmounting of these limitations which makes Israel so interesting. The Arab world could indeed learn from Zionist enthusiasm and technology in developing a new pattern of land use.

In order to understand Israel's agricultural potential, it is necessary to look at the regional pattern, for even within this small country there are surprising contrasts in land forms, climate, and soils. Since the conditions are similar in western Jordan, Palestine will be considered here as a unit.

In the north, no topographic break marks the political border next to Lebanon, but elevations become lower and the mountains merge into the Hills of Galilee. Elevations reach 3,962 feet, which is the highest elevation in Israel. Rainfall may be as much as forty inches during the year. Agriculture is quite feasible where topography permits, and many hillsides have been reforested.

The Galilean uplands drop abruptly on three sides, on the east to the Jordan lowland, on the west to a coastal plain, and on the south to the Vale of Esdraelon, or Ernek Jezreel. Galilee measures some twenty-five miles from north to south and the same from east to west. The hill land is the most beautiful part of Israel, with views of Mount Herman to the northeast; Lake Tiberius, known to the Israeli as Lake Kinneret, on the east; and the green fields of the Valley of Jezreel to the south.

The Jezreel lowland is an irregular downfaulted trough which runs entirely across Israel from the Bay of Acre southeast to the Jordan. The lowland has fertile soil and a rainfall of fifteen inches which is enough for rain-fed agriculture, although some irrigation is desirable. The area is intensively cultivated.

To the south of the Vale of Esdraelon or Ernek Jezreel, a broad limestone anticline forms the Hills of Samaria which attain 3,000 feet in height. Due to considerable

Additional agricultural land has been secured by the draining of swamps near Lake Huleh in the upper Jordan Valley. This view looks across the lowland to Syria. (Courtesy Israel Office of Information, New York.)

rainfall, the area has been cut into deep valleys and is more of a hill country than a true plateau. Soil erosion has been severe. Most of Samaria lies in Jordan. Farther south, the upland receives less rainfall and is less dissected; this area is known as the Hills of Judea, again largely in Jordan. Only a narrow Israeli corridor leads to Jerusalem. Nablus is the chief town in Samaria, whereas Jerusalem dominates Judea.

Southern Palestine, entirely within Israel, is a dry steppe and desertland known as the Negeb, which continues to Egypt; it is rolling to rugged in topography, with elevations around 1,000 feet and in places with ridges to three times that height. In the latitude of Beersheba, Israel reaches its maximum width of seventy miles. The rainfall is less than five inches and evaporation is excessive so that dependable cultivation requires irrigation. The area merges with the Sinai Peninsula on the west and just touches the Gulf of Aqaba on the south.

Along with these north to south differences there is also a fourfold division from west to east, extending from the narrow humid coastal plain with its deep soil, known in the center as the Plain of Sharon which is famous for its Jaffa oranges, through the eroded and terraced Shephelah

Groves of the famous Jaffa oranges characterize the coastal plain and provide one of Israel's major exports. (U. S. Air Force.)

foothills with their olive groves, across the central uplands already described, and down to the arid Jordan depression and the Dead Sea, 1,310 feet below sea level. Half the length of the Jordan River and a quarter of the Dead Sea area lie in Israel.

Climate presents a major problem, for conditions resemble those in the area from Los Angeles south into Mexico, without the snow mountains to store winter moisture. Rainfall decreases from twenty-five inches at Haifa and eighteen inches along Lake Tiberias, to twenty-two inches at Tel Aviv, nine inches at Beersheba, and one inch at Elath (Eilat). Dreams of diverting the Jordan overlook the fact that its flow is similar to that of California rivers such as the Salinas or the Jordan River in Utah. The longest streams within Israel are the sixteen-mile Yarkon, which enters the Mediterranean near Tel Aviv, and the eight-mile Kishon at Haifa. Since evapotranspiration rates are high, large amounts of irrigation water are required for crop production. Details of climate have been presented on pages 93 and 416, while the Jordan is described on page 130.

One apparent suggestion of climatic change, which is clearly not the actual case, is found in the greener hillsides at the end of Israel's first decade. Through better conservation techniques for soil and water, and the control of grazing, many previously barren hillsides are now green. Here, as in

This aqueduct carries water from the Yarkon River in the subhumid north to the semiarid Negeb in southern Israel. (Courtesy Israel Office of Information, New York.)

much of the Levant, vegetation will recover the eroded hills if given a chance. Here Israel points the way for much of Swasia.

Israel's food problem centers on the availability of water, especially in the south. Not a single stream reaches the coastal plain the year around. Estimates of the total eventual water supply range from 2 to 3 billion cubic meters a year, but part of this figure is based on access to the Jordan River, partly outside Israel. Much of the balance is based on plans for flood-water storage, ground-water development, the re-use of urban and industrial wastes, and water recovered from irrigation. The amount of water used for irrigation increased from 300 million cubic meters in 1948–49 to 1.2 billion a decade later. In both cases, use of the water averaged 1,000 cubic meters per dunam.

Since average crops need at least 3,120 cubic meters per acre, or 2.5 acre feet, the total water supply, present or theoretical, is far from enough to supply the million and a third acres projected for irrigation. Overpumping of ground water along the coast has already lowered the water table below sea level so that some wells have become brackish. Elsewhere, wells have drawn upon deep supplies which have required centuries to accumulate and which will require equally long to replenish. In other situations, the available water is so charged with dissolved salts that soil salinization becomes a problem.

Spray irrigation is used for raising wheat in the southern plains, where rainfall is under fifteen inches while evapotranspiration exceeds fifty inches. (Courtesy Israel Office of Information, New York.)

Israel is anxious to develop a cheap process for the purification of sea water. This will presumably require power, which Israel lacks, but even if fresh water were free, the cost of lifting it onto the Negeb uplands would remain. In most parts of the world, water cannot economically be pumped more than a few tens of feet for the irrigation of field crops, with 300 feet as an extreme maximum (Grand Coulee). Already, Israel is lifting water 600 feet to irrigate wheat, but the costs probably prevent the venture from being economical.

Great credit must be given to Israel for ambitious water schemes, including hundreds of miles of concrete aqueducts. These bring water from the more humid north to the drier south, irrigating the coastal plain while en route. Elsewhere, as around Lake Huleh and in the coastal marshes, new land has been brought into cultivation through the drainage of swamps.

Large parts of Israel's 5 million acres are of limited agricultural value. At least a million and a half acres are wasteland, largely desert and rough slopes, with no feasible use for food production. Land fit only for pasture amounts to nearly a million acres, all of it a dry steppe too marginal for safe cultivation. Another million acres are suitable for rain-fed crops, some of it only through dry farming methods.

At the close of Israel's first decade, the total cultivated area had increased from 400,-

ISRAEL AGRICULTURE [1]

	1948–49	*1957–58*	*unit*
Cultivated land	1,650,000	3,900,000	dunams [2]
Wheat	302,000	590,000	"
Irrigated land	300,000	1,200,000	"
Field crops	64,000	420,000	"
Cotton	—	65,000	"
Vegetables	54,000	250,000	"
Fruit	150,000	405,000	"
Citrus	125,000	262,000	"
Fish ponds	15,000	40,000	"
Crop yields			
Wheat	105	171	kg. per dunam
Cotton	—	87	"
Sugar beets	—	4,405	"
Citrus exports	16,398,950	47,832,665	U. S. $
Agricultural settlements	230	706	villages
Value agricultural products	44,413	138,138	Israel pounds

[1] Data from Central Bureau of Statistics and Ministry of Agriculture.
[2] One dunam equals about 1,000 square meters or 0.222 acres.

000 acres to nearly a million, while irrigated fields rose from 75,000 acres to 300,000. Details of land use and agriculture are shown in the accompanying table.

The agricultural traditions of the Jewish people extend back for 3,000 years when Palestine was described as ". . . a good land of brooks and water, fountains and depths, springing forth in valleys and hills, a land of wheat and barley, and vines and fig trees, and pomegranates; a land of olive trees and honey. . ." (Deuteronomy VIII:7–9). Parts of Palestine may have flowed with Biblical "milk and honey," but these are only relative phrases and reflect the contrast between the wilderness of Sinai, where the children of Israel had spent two generations, and the subhumid grasslands to the north.

During Israel's first decade, the agricultural area was doubled, production was tripled, irrigation increased fourfold, and forest areas multiplied by five.

Along with the common Mediterranean field crops of wheat and barley, and the olive, fig, and vine, Israel is an important producer of oranges and grapefruit, melons and grapes, bananas, peanuts, tobacco, sugar beets, and cotton. Citrus crops are the major agricultural export, largely consigned to Great Britain. The groves cover 50,000 acres along the coastal plain. Cattle and the dairy business have been greatly expanded. There is also a reduction in the number of goats, which cause soil erosion through eating habits, so that "green pastures" are returning.

Despite remarkable developments in agriculture, Israel has only 18 per cent of its total labor force engaged in all aspects of primary production, including agriculture, grazing, fishing, forestry, and mining. This is one of the lowest percentages for any country in the world and reflects the traditional urban background of the Jewish people. Industry and crafts account for 22 per cent of the labor force, whereas commerce and services represent 30 per cent.

During the first decade, Israel was obliged to import a considerable part of its food supply. By 1960, the country produced three-quarters of its agricultural needs and the value of agricultural exports equaled necessary food purchases. Full autarchy is not the goal, rather that each district specialize in what it can raise best.

Olives are a traditional crop in all lands around the Mediterranean, and many trees produce for several centuries. This grove is near Lydda. (Courtesy Israel Office of Information, New York.)

Continuing problems of agricultural economics are suggested in a dispatch to the New York Times from Jerusalem (Israeli sector) dated September 16, 1959. "Of the 480 agricultural settlements established by the Jewish Agency for Israel since 1948, not one is fully self-sufficient. Only fifty-five are in the final stages of development."

Some of the most interesting agricultural developments have taken place in the Negeb, where rainfall averages under five inches. A part of the area is covered with sand dunes; elsewhere, deep wadis have dissected bare limestone anticlines or areas of igneous rocks. In the midst of what is now a desolate land are traces of what was once an area of considerable agriculture, dating back to the Nabataean period during the first seven centuries A.D. and as early as the ninth century B.C. The climate was then also dry, but hundreds of low dams diverted flood water from the wadis and spread it over adjoining fields. No reservoirs for regular irrigation were possible, but, by delaying the runoff and encouraging it to seep into the soil, enough moisture was stored to permit the growth of crops. Soil is as scanty as rainfall, so there were arrangements for its accumulation near the base of slopes.

The bulk of the Negeb is marginal even

for the pastoralist, but a number of experimental farms have been established in an attempt to recreate ancient agriculture. Optimistic hopes look forward to settling several thousand people in this southern desert; if this ever succeeds, aqueducts from the humid north will indeed be their lifeline.

POPULATION PATTERNS

THE PATTERN of settlement reflects the many-faceted landscape of Palestine. Some areas are attractive for cultivation, others appear preferable as a place of refuge, and still others lead to commerce. The best land for agriculture lies either in plateau remnants, easily defended, or along the exposed coastal plain. Few valley bottoms have much room for cultivation.

Extending irregularly across Palestine is a transition zone between agriculture and grazing, between the village dweller and the nomad. The latter once tended to raid the green pastures of the farmer, so that villages near the border needed defense against the desert Bedouin and thus tended to be larger. In early days, security was also needed against passing caravans which used coastal Palestine as a highway.

Israel's leading geographer, David H. K. Amiran, has pointed out that all the important upland towns of today are centuries old and have had uninterrupted histories, presumably related to their relative security. In contrast, many of the coastal cities of antiquity have disappeared or have diminished as political conditions have changed.[1]

> Whenever a satisfactory state of regional development and public security permitted the organic utilization of the different parts of the country, the coastal plain gained supremacy and the leading city was a city of the plain. Whenever conditions in the country deteriorated and settlement in the coastal plain became marginal, its towns decreased in importance, the upland towns gained in relative importance, and the role of the most important city of the country reverted to Jerusalem, without any increase in its population.
>
> In assessing these fluctuations in importance between mountain towns and those of the coastal plain two factors should be taken into account: First, city populations are much more mobile than villagers . . . . The second factor to be remembered is that times which brought about the development of the largest cities in the coastal plain were times of economic prosperity . . . .

The first detailed map of the country dates from 1875. At that time there were relatively few coastal towns since large parts of the plain were swampy and malarial, and had deteriorated through the passage of the many armies which had followed this *via maris*. These same areas are today the most

Cotton is an expanding crop. Here workers harvest cotton near Lake Huleh. (Courtesy Israel Office of Information, New York.)

[1] D. H. K. Amiran: "The Pattern of Settlement in Palestine," *Israel Exploration Journal,* III (1953), 194–95.

New supplies of water have been discovered in the Negeb, but in a dry land where recharge rates are low there is a temptation to overpump. (Courtesy United Nations.)

prosperous, with hundreds of new villages. The two accompanying maps, prepared by Amiran, show the settlement pattern in 1875 and in 1952 and emphasize the present development of the lowlands.

The nineteenth-century dream of a return to Israel centered around plans for agriculture. Cooperative farm villages, known as *moshavah,* date from 1878. This form of village with individual ownership is still dominant, but a second type, more communal, developed during the twentieth century under the name of the *kibbutz.* Typical settlements have 500 to 1,000 people. A third village form is the *moshav,* a cooperative where each family has an area of its own but operates by mutual aid and has cooperative buying and selling.

In 1914, there were forty-four Jewish agricultural villages, with a population of 12,000; by 1948, the number of settlements had grown to 256 with a population of 105,000. During the first decade of the state, the number increased to 706.

Some of these communal villages reflect a desire for socialist group living, for they represent the expression of five ideas: the moral value of labor, the joint ownership of property, social and economic equality, individual freedom, and the value of group discipline.

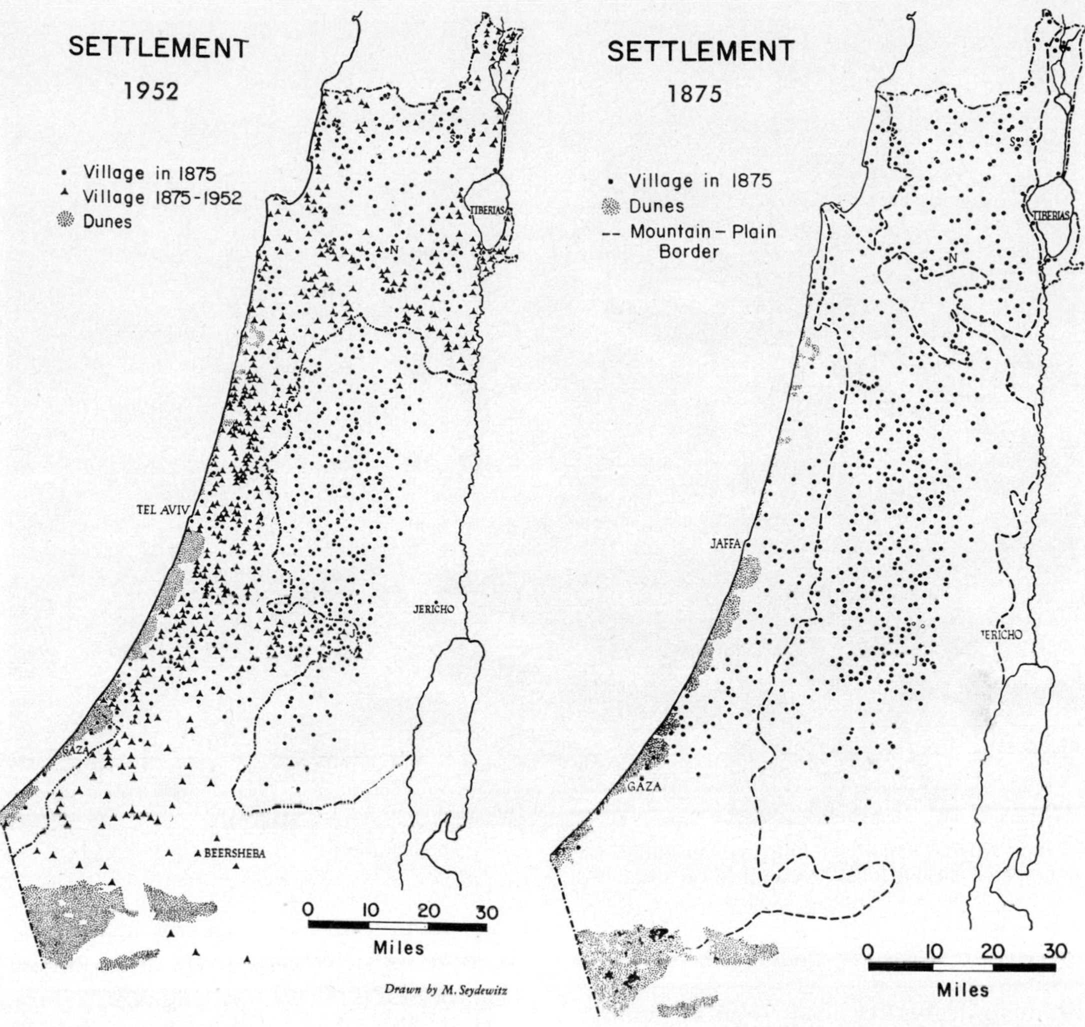

This pair of maps shows the distribution of Palestine settlements in 1875 and 1952. (David H. K. Amiran in Israel Exploration Journal.)

In addition to these agricultural villages, medium to large estates have been developed under public or private ownership, using newly arrived immigrants as hired labor. Most of the large farms lie in the Negeb and are preparatory to village settlement.

Although the Zionist program has emphasized the return to the soil, urban developments are equally striking. In 1941, 65 per cent of the Palestinian Jews lived in cities, as compared with 11 per cent of all Moslems, and 51 per cent of the Christians. By 1960, about 80 per cent of the entire population were urban, with a third of the total living in the three cities of Tel Aviv, Haifa, and Israeli Jerusalem.

The city of Tel Aviv adjoins ancient Jaffa, traditional seaport for Jerusalem. The twin cities lie along an even coastline, with shelter for the port behind a breakwater. Since the along-shore drift, here as

Tel Aviv is Israel's new city, built on sand dunes to the north of ancient Jaffa, here seen in the distance. (Courtesy Israel Government Tourist Office, New York.)

elsewhere in the Levant, is from the south, the breakwaters project northward, but the harbor is shallow so that many vessels discharge into lighters offshore. Cargo capacity for the combined port amounts to 500,000 tons a year. Whereas Jaffa dates back to at least 1492 B.C. when it was captured by Egypt, Tel Aviv is a modern city dating from 1907, when unused sand dunes to the north of Jaffa were purchased by Jewish residents. Today, it is the cultural center of Israel with an excellent philharmonic orchestra. Tel Aviv has grown remarkably, with parts resembling newer developments in the United States. The city owes its early development to refugees from Germany, and many shops signs were in German; but today, Hebrew is the leading language.

Haifa has Israel's best harbor and is its leading industrial center. The city stands on a spur of Mount Carmel overlooking the southern end of the Bay of Acre, with the Plain of Esdraelon providing a lowland avenue to the east. Since the city lies both along the seashore and on the slopes of Mount Carmel, a mile-long inclined subway connects the two parts. Ancient Acre lies across the bay.

Industry has gravitated to the Haifa area. This includes the oil refinery, designed to be served by the pipeline from Iraq but now supplied by pipeline from Elath or from overseas. Other plants fabricate steel, assem-

Much of Haifa represents Arab construction in pre-Israeli days. The city lies on the spurs of Mount Carmel which projects into the Mediterranean to form a sheltered harbor. (Courtesy Israel Government Tourist Office, New York.)

ble automobiles, manufacture tires, and make cement.

Jerusalem has already been considered. Most of the new city outside the old walls is in Israel and includes the official capital of the country. Jerusalem is a cultural and educational center, largely without industry or commerce. Occupying the crest of a ridge half a mile above sea level, the two halves of Jerusalem form "a city which cannot be hid." The only contact between the new Israeli sector and the old Jordanian sector is through the Mandelbaum Gate, open to tourists who wish to pass westward but closed for eastbound travelers.

The two parts of the city have roughly the same population, but the new city covers a much larger area with wide streets and modern buildings in contrast to the narrow and crowded lanes within the old walled town. Western Jerusalem is linked with the rest of Israel by a narrow corridor so that the city is surrounded by Jordan on three sides.

ECONOMIC VIABILITY

ISRAEL HAS MADE spectacular progress in developing a modern economy in a land of limited potential. Her greatest asset is her energy and will to succeed. In few other countries has livelihood been so dramatically changed. This is a tribute to Jewish ingenuity, but would not have been possible without massive aid from abroad, amounting to several billion dollars, in the form of private gifts and bond purchases, extensive loans and grants from the United States, and reparations from Germany in partial payment for Jewish losses under Hitler.

Whether Israel can become a viable state at the desired living standard when outside support terminates is another matter. During its first decade, international trade was highly unbalanced and the Israeli pound, once valued at U.S. $4.00 fell to less than a tenth of its original value on the open market. Large investments have gone into capital items designed to produce income-yielding exports; it remains to be seen how competitive these will prove to be in international terms. The problem of Israel's first decade was a matter of military survival, the problem of the second is economic. Something must be done to close the wide gap between imports and exports.

The country has had dreams of becoming merchant and manufacturer to the Mediterranean and eastern world, but this is impos-

These graphs present monthly average temperature and rainfall, plus the daily temperature range, shaded, and the extreme recorded temperatures, in dots, as well as the monthly potential evapotranspiration, in thin bars.

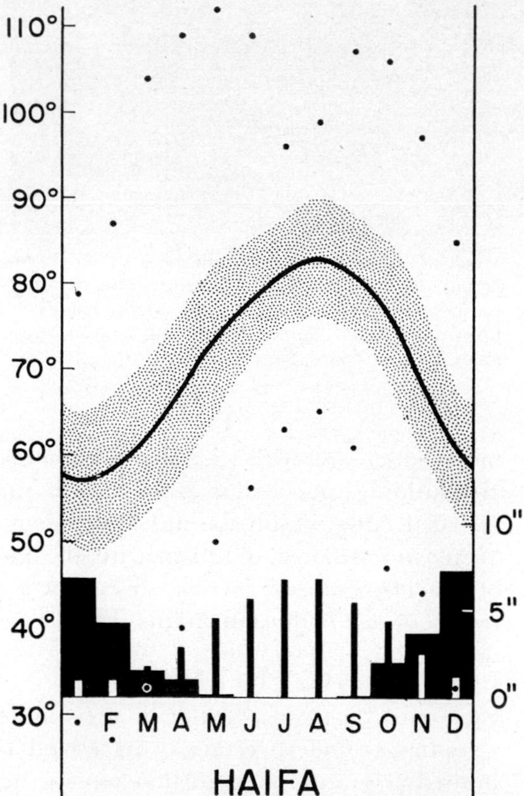

Haifa's climate is representative of coastal Israel. Elevation 33 feet, annual rainfall 26.1 inches.

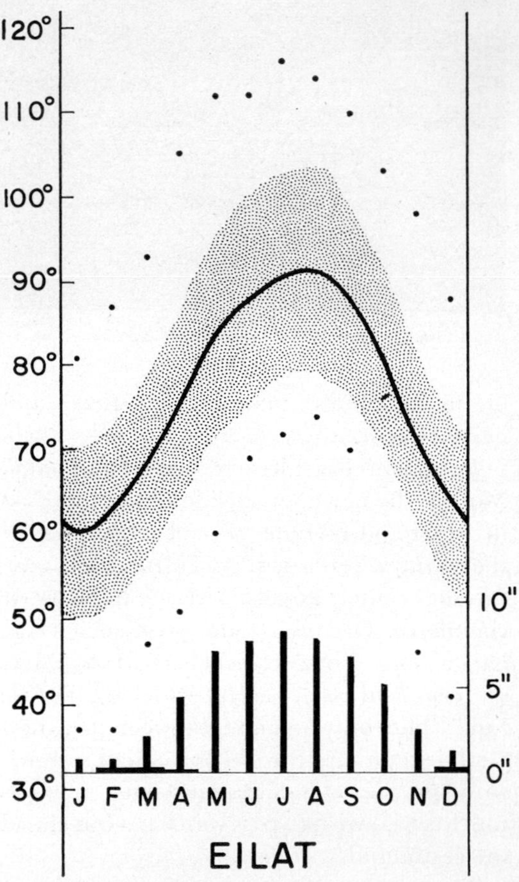

Eilat, or Elath, is Israel's window on the Gulf of Aqaba. Elevation 7 feet, annual rainfall 1.1 inch.

The copper mines at Timna are located in the area near the Dead Sea where King Solomon once produced the metal. (Courtesy Israel Office of Information, New York.)

sible in the Arab countries until good will is achieved. Elsewhere, as in Ghana and Burma, Israeli technology and goods have found a growing outlet. Few countries have such dynamism and determination to achieve, or can show such visible results; these naturally command the respect of African and Asian countries with similar problems.

Some of Palestine's mineral resources have been known since ancient times, with Biblical references to copper, iron, and bitumen. Within modern decades, surveys have shown the presence of phosphates, manganese, feldspar, mica, glass sand, clays, asphalt rock, gypsum, oil, and peat. Peat is found near Lake Huleh in the far north; most of the other minerals are present in the south. Minerals in the ground of unknown quantity are one thing; profitable mining, suitable metallurgy, and fabrication are other matters. As of 1960, there is no evidence that these resources are of major international significance, other than the vast accumulations in the Dead Sea.

The chemicals of the Dead Sea were the only minerals to be exploited commercially in Palestine prior to the establishment of the state of Israel. The plant at the southern end of the sea came back into operation in 1952, and it has an annual capacity of over 100,000 tons of potash and 2,000 tons of bromine, with plans for magnesium salts and other products. Reserves are almost inexhaustible. Mineral products from the Dead Sea accounted for 8 per cent of Israeli exports in 1958.

Phosphate rocks underlie an area of 1,000 acres in the Negeb, southwest of the Dead Sea, where reserves are estimated at 100 million tons. Production amounted to 250,000 tons in 1959, and phosphate rock appears to be one of Israel's most important minerals. Since the P_2O_5 content is only 24 to 26 per cent as compared with a minimum of 30 per cent for the international market, enrichment is necessary before shipment, and much of the product is thus converted into superphosphate at a fertilizer plant in Haifa. The country is now self-sufficient, with a surplus for export. Some of the phosphate ores contain uranium.

Copper ores were dug in the days of Solomon, and a surface mine is now operated at Timna, north of Elath. The ore is of low grade, averaging 1.4 per cent and less of copper but the proved reserves may contain 180,000 tons of copper. The capacity of the plant opened in 1958 amounted to 8,000 tons a year. Nearby deposits of 40 to 45 per cent manganese ore, again low grade, may prove valuable; reserves are estimated at 1 million tons.

Iron ore occurs in several parts of the central Negeb, where reserves of 5 million tons are available by surface mining. Other iron deposits occur in Galilee. The quality of most ores is poor, but plans call for a small steel mill to supply domestic needs; operation will be expensive as coal will need to be imported, but would save the necessity of importing 200,000 tons of iron products annually.

Oil appears to be a valuable resource, with several small wells in the Heletz field just north of Gaza, but they supply only 10 per cent of the country's needs. Asphalt seepages have long been known around the Dead Sea, and structures favorable for oil accumulation are present in the Negeb. Before Palestine was partitioned, there was a large refinery at Haifa, then the terminus of the pipeline from Kirkuk in Iraq. Haifa now receives its oil from overseas, either by tanker from Venezuela or the Soviet Union, or from Iran through the pipeline from the Gulf of Aqaba.

Ceramic clays, glass sands, and gypsum are adequate. The last is among the most abundant of Israel's mineral resources, with much of the production used in the cement factories near Haifa.

Industry is a field where Israel has been surprisingly successful, particularly in view of her limited raw materials and restricted markets. Emphasis has been placed on products where the value added by manufacturing is high. Industrial production contributes a larger share to the national income than in any other country in the area. In Israel the figure is 20 per cent, as compared with 10 per cent for Egypt. Industrial output increased fourfold during the first decade. As a further measure of industrial growth, the electrical generating capacity rose from 48,000 kilowatts in 1948 to 400,000 kilowatts a decade later; some of this represents hydroelectricity.

In the field of light industry, there is a wide array of goods such as food products, razor blades, textiles, pharmaceuticals, electrical appliances, cut diamonds, chocolate, false teeth, and shoes. Heavier types include glass, ceramics, steel fabrication, chemicals, paper, fertilizers, and diesel engines. Unfortunately, most of these are dependent on imported raw materials.

Food processing is Israel's largest industry, both in value of output and in the number of people employed; textiles and clothing rank second and third. The metal

Eilat is Israel's boom town port on the Gulf of Aqaba, linked with the rest of the country by road, oil pipeline, and air. (Courtesy Israel Government Tourist Office, New York.)

industries range from heavy enterprises to household goods. The largest is the steel complex north of Haifa, dependent on local scrap and imported steel, which produces bars, pipes, and structural shapes. Chemical industries include the manufacture of cement, oil refining, fertilizers, and basic chemicals. The diamond industry occupies a unique place, for small, cut stones constitute Israel's second largest export; there are no diamond mines anywhere in Swasia so that this is strictly a "value added" industry.

This industrial growth is indeed phenomenal, with a strikingly Western aspect to the landscape around Haifa and Tel Aviv. The total industrial investment during Israel's first decade amounted to $300 million, 90 per cent of which came from abroad.

One of the country's assets is that it fronts on both the Mediterranean and the Red Sea. The overland road from Haifa to Eilat is Israel's dry-land Suez Canal, and parallel to it is an oil pipeline. This enables materials to be moved by land in case the Suez Canal should be closed. From this side door port on the Gulf of Aqaba, near Solomon's port of Ezion-Geber, the country now has regular sailings to the east coast of Africa and also to Hong Kong and eastern Asia.

One measure of a nation's viability is found in the character of its imports and exports and in the international trade balance. Here again, the state of Israel has shown great energy and ability in expanding the market for its products. On the other hand, imports remain high and the trade deficit has grown. Some of the figures for the first decade are shown in the accompanying table. Unless Israel can close this gap be-

ISRAEL PRODUCTION[1]

Automobiles	2,848
Bromine	200 tons
Canned fruit	2,781 tons
Cement	663,538 tons
Cigarettes	1,986,037 kilograms
Flour	233,800 tons
Glass	1,371,981 sq. meters
Oil coke	57,012 tons
Phosphate rock	71,779 tons
Sulphuric acid	70,855 tons
Superphosphate	101,309 tons
Tires	171,017

[1] 1955.

ISRAEL FOREIGN TRADE[1]

	1949	*1958*
Imports	$253,100,000	$723,462,000
Consumer goods	81,000,000	79,518,000
Raw materials	82,300,000	306,248,000
Fuel and lubricants	15,200,000	66,868,000
Exports	28,495,000	139,200,000
Agricultural	18,021,000	56,600,000
Industrial	5,283,000	45,700,000
Diamonds	5,191,000	34,400,000
Deficit	224,600,000	484,262,000

[1] In U.S. Dollars. Data from Central Bureau of Statistics.

tween imports and exports before the termination of the massive outside aid which characterized its first decade, serious trouble may follow.

Two short words summarize the state's problems: map and gap. The country is small and poor, and there is a natural desire to expand the map. The gap between essential imports and feasible exports is wide, and unless it can be closed national bankruptcy lies around the corner. Peace with its neighbors may settle the first problem; hard work and enthusiasm may resolve the second.

REFERENCES

NOTE: Additional references will be found at the end of Chapter 14, The Levant.

General References

Alexander, Lewis M.: "The Arab-Israeli Boundry Problem," *World Politics*, VI (1954), 322–337.

Amiran, D. H. K., and Gilead, M.: "Early Excessive Rainfall and Soil Erosion in Israel," *Israel Exploration Jour.*, IV (1954), 286–295.

Dayan, Moshe: "Israel's Border and Security Problems," *Foreign Affairs*, XXXIII (1955), 250–267.

Elath, Eliahu: ISRAEL AND HER NEIGHBORS. Cleveland and New York: World (1957).

* Ellis, Harry B.: ISRAEL AND THE MIDDLE EAST. New York: Ronald (1957).

Hutchinson, E. H.: VIOLENT TRUCE. New York: Devin Adair (1956).

Israel, Central Bureau of Statistics: STATISTICAL ABSTRACT OF ISRAEL (Annual). Jerusalem: Central Bureau of Statistics.

Israel Department of Surveys: ATLAS OF ISRAEL. Jerusalem: Ministry of Labor and Bialik Inst. of the Jewish Agency (1956).

Israel, State of: GOVERNMENT YEARBOOK (Annual). Jerusalem: Govt. Printer.

Kallner, D. H.: "Outline of the Geomorphology of Judea," *Bull. Soc. Royale Geog. d'Egypte*, XXI (1943), 35–49.

Lilienthal, Alfred M.: WHAT PRICE ISRAEL? Chicago: Regnery (1953).

* Melamid, Alexander: "The Political Geography of the Gulf of Aqaba," *Annals Assoc. Amer. Geogs.*, XLVII (1957), 231–240.

Nir, Dor: "Etude sur la morphologie littorale d'Israel," *Annales de Geog.*, LXVIII (1959), 424–436.

Picard, L.: GEOMORPHOGENY OF ISRAEL. Jerusalem: Geol. Survey (1951).

Rosenan, Naftali: "One Hundred Years of Rainfall in Jerusalem," *Israel Exploration Jour.*, V (1955), 137–153.

Smith, S. G.: "The Boundaries and Population Problems of Israel," *Geog.*, XXXVII (1952), 152–165.

Williams, Rushbrook L. F.: THE STATE OF ISRAEL. London: Faber & Faber (1958).

Palestine—General References

Abel, le P. F. M.: GEOGRAPHIE DE LA PALESTINE. Paris: J. Gabalda (1933).

* Baly, Denis: THE GEOGRAPHY OF THE BIBLE. New York: Harpers (1957).

Boyer, David S.: "Geographical Twins—A World Apart (Holy Land and Utah)," *Nat. Geog. Mag.*, CXIV (1958), 848–859.

Brewster, Henry C.: "The Wilderness of Judah," *Geog. Mag.*, XVI (1943), 102–107.

* British Admiralty, Naval Intelligence Division: PALESTINE AND TRANSJORDAN. London: Naval Intelligence Division (1943).

Casto, E. Ray: "Economic Geography of Palestine," *Econ. Geog.*, XIII (1937), 253–259.

Chase, Francis, Jr.: "Palestine Today," *Nat. Geog. Mag.*, XC (1946), 501–516.

Du Bruit, M.: GEOGRAPHIE DE LA TERRE SAINTE. Paris: Editions du Cerf (1958).

Epstein, Eliahu: "The Druzes of Palestine," *Jour. Royal Central Asian Soc.*, XXIX (1942), 52–63.

Glueck, Nelson: "An Archaeologist Looks at Palestine," *Nat. Geog. Mag.*, XCII (1947), 739–768.

Goodan, Douglas: "Three Maps of Palestine," *Jour. Geog.*, XLVII (1948), 356–363.

Gottman, Jean: "The Pioneer Fringe in Palestine," *Geog. Rev.*, XXVII (1937), 550–565.

Grollenberg, L. H.: ATLAS OF THE BIBLE. London: Nelson (1956).

Huggins, K. H.: "Problems of Palestine," *Scot. Geog. Mag.*, LV (1939), 85–97.

* Huntington, Ellsworth: PALESTINE AND ITS TRANSFORMATION. Boston: Houghton & Mifflin (1911).

Huntington, Ellsworth: "The Future of Palestine," *Geog. Rev.*, VII (1919), 24–35.

Kallner, D. H., and Rosenau, E.: "The Geographical Regions of Palestine," *Geog. Rev.*, XXIX (1939), 61–80.

* Lowdermilk, Walter C.: PALESTINE, LAND OF PROMISE. New York: Harper & Bros. (1944).

Matthews, Charles D.: "Palestine—Mohammedan Land," *Moslem World*, XXXIII (1943), 239–253.

Reid, T.: "Should a Jewish State be Established in Palestine?," *Jour. Royal Central Asian Soc.*, XXXIII (1946), 161–177.

Runciman, Steven: "The Holy Land: Centre of the World," *Geog. Mag.*, XXIX (1956), 363–373.

Simpich, Frederick: "Change Comes to Bible Lands," *Nat. Geog. Mag.*, LXXIV (1938), 695–750.

* Smith, George Adam: THE HISTORICAL GEOGRAPHY OF THE HOLY LAND. London: Hodder & Stoughton, 25 ed. (1931).

Smith, George Adam: HISTORICAL ATLAS OF THE HOLY LAND. London: Hodder (1936).

* Willatts, E. C.: "Some Geographical Factors in the Palestine Problem," *Geog. Jour.*, CVIII (1946), 146–179.

Williams, Maynard Owen: "Home to the Holy Land," *Nat. Geog. Mag.*, XCVIII (1950), 707–746.

Wright, G. Ernest: "Bringing Old Testament Times to Life," *Nat. Geog. Mag.*, CXII (1957), 833–864.

Wright, G. Ernest, and Filson, Floyd V., Ed.: THE WESTMINSTER HISTORICAL ATLAS TO THE BIBLE. Philadelphia: Westminster Press (1946).

Palestine—Climate and Water

Ashbel, D.: "Frequency and Distribution of Dew in Palestine," *Geog. Rev.*, XXXIX (1949), 291–297.

Gottmann, J.: "L'irrigation en Palestine," *Annales de Geog.*, XLIV (1935), 143–161.

* Gregory, J. W.: "Palestine and the Stability of Climate in Historic Times," *Geog. Jour.*, LXXVI (1930), 487–494.

Ionides, M. G.: "The Perspective of Water Development in Palestine and Transjordan," *Jour. Royal Central Asian Soc.*, XXXIII (1946), 271–280.

Lowdermilk, W. C.: "Floods in Deserts," INTERNATIONAL SYMPOSIUM ON DESERT RESEARCH. Jerusalem (1952). 365–377.

Meissner, Frank: "Prospectives for Artificial Rain Enhancement in the Jordan Valley Development," *Middle East Jour.*, VII (1953), 484–498.

Nuttonson, M. Y.: "Agroclimatology and Crop Ecology in Palestine and Transjordan and Climatic Analogues in the United States," *Geog. Rev.*, XXXVII (1947), 436–456.

Palestine—Geology and Resources

Blake, G. S.: "Old Shore-Lines of Palestine," *Geol. Mag.*, LXXIV (1937), 65–78.

Blake, G. S. and Goldschmidt, M. J.: GEOLOGY AND WATER RESOURCES OF PALESTINE, Jerusalem: Dept. of Land Settlement and Water Commissioner (1947).

Bonne, A.: "Natural Resources of Palestine," *Geog. Jour.*, XCII (1930), 259–266.

Fohs, F. Julius: "Geology and the Petroleum and Natural Gas Possibilities of Palestine and Sinaitic Peninsula," *Bull. Amer. Assoc. of Petrol. Geols.*, XI (1927), 135–149.

Lowenstam, Heinz A.: "Geology of the Eastern Nazareth Mountains, Palestine," *Jour. of Geol.*, L (1942), 813–845.

Picard L.: "Structure and Evolution of Palestine," Jerusalem: Hebrew Univ. (1943).

Willis, Bailey: "Earthquakes in the Holy Land," *Bull. Seismol. Soc. Amer.*, XVIII (1928), 75–103.

Willis, Bailey and Picard, L.: "The Jordan Valley and Judean Highlands," *Geol. Mag.*, LXX (1932), 97–107.

Palestine—Agriculture and Vegetation

Gottmann, J.: "The Pioneer Fringe in Palestine: Settlement Possibilities South and East of the Holy Land," *Geog. Rev.*, XXVII (1937), 550–565.

Hazen, N. W.: "Agriculture in Palestine and the Development of Jewish Colonization," *Foreign Agriculture*, I (1937), 119–148.

Hubbard, George D.: "Agriculture in Palestine," *Amer. Jour. of Economics and Sociology*, X (1951), 247–268.

* Nuttonson, M. J.: "Agroclimatology and Crop Ecology of Palestine and Transjordan and Climate Analogues in the United States," *Geog. Rev.*, XXXVII (1947), 436–456.

Russell, E. John: "Agriculture of Palestine," in Hobman, J. B., Ed., PALESTINE'S ECONOMIC FUTURE. (1946), 116–129.

Strahorn, A. T.: "Agriculture and Soils in Palestine," *Geog. Rev.*, XIX (1929), 581–602.

Whyte, R. O.: "The Phytogeographical Zones of Palestine," *Geog. Rev.* XL (1950), 600–614.

Zohary, M.: "A Vegetation Map of Western Palestine," *Jour. of Ecology,* XXXIV (1947), 1–19.

Palestine—Land Use

Amiran, D. H. Kallner: "The Pattern of Settlement in Palestine," *Israel Exploration Jour.,* III (1953), 65–78, 192–209, 250–260.

Halperin, Haim: CHANGING PATTERNS IN ISRAEL AGRICULTURE. London: Routledge & Kegan Paul (1957).

Kedar, Y.: "Ancient Agriculture at Shivtah in the Negev," *Israel Exploration Jour.,* VII (1957), 178–189.

Lowdermilk, W. C.: "An Inventory of the Land of Israel," *Israel Exploration Jour.,* III (1953), 162–177.

The Negeb

Amiran, D. H. Kallner: "Geomorphology of the Central Negev Highlands," *Israel Exploration Jour.,* I (1950–1951), 107–120.

Bentwich, Norman: "Development in the Negev," *Jour. Royal Central Asian Soc.,* XLII (1955), 176–183.

* DeVaumas, Etienne: "Le Negeb. Etudes Morphologique," *Bull. Soc. Geog. d'Egypte,* XXVI (1953), 119–163.

Elath, Eliahu: "The Bedouin of the Negev," *Jour. Royal Central Asian Soc.,* XLV (1958), 123–140.

Evenari, Michael, and Koller, Dov.: "Ancient Masters of the Desert," *Scientific American,* CXCIV (1956), 39–45.

Evenari, Michael, and Koller, Dov.: "Desert Agriculture: Problems and Results in Israel," *Amer. Assoc. for Adv. of Sci.,* Pub. No. 43 (1956), 390–413.

Evenari, M., Shanon, L., and Tadmor, N. H.: "The Ancient Desert Agriculture of the Negev," Israel: *Ktavin* (1957–1959); *Israel Exploration Jour.* (1958).

* Glueck, Nelson: RIVERS IN THE DESERT: A HISTORY OF THE NEGEV. New York: Farrar, Straus, and Cudahy (1959).

Kedar, Yehuda: "Water and Soil from the Desert: Some Ancient Agricultural Achievements in the Central Negev," *Geog. Jour.,* CXXIII (1957), 179–187.

Lewis, Naphtali: "New Light on the Negev in Ancient Times," *Palestine Exploration Quart.,* LXXX (1948), 102–117.

Tadmor, N. H., and others: THE ANCIENT DESERT AGRICULTURE OF THE NEGEV, REHOVOT. Israel: Ministry of Agriculture (1957–1958) 2 parts.

Economic Developments

Ball, Max W. and Ball, Douglas: "Oil Prospects of Israel," *Bull. Amer. Assoc. Petrol Geols.,* XXXVII (1953), 1–113.

Boxer, Baruch: "Israel Shipping and Foreign Trade," Univ. of Chicago, *Dept. of Geog. Research Paper* No. 48 (1957).

Cohen, Saul B.: "Israel's Fishing Industry," *Geog. Rev.,* XLVII (1957), 66–85.

Cohen, Saul B.: "Israel's Salt Water Fisheries," *Sea Frontiers,* III (1957), 225–237.

Karmon, Yehuda: "The Drainage of the Huleh Swamps," Geog. Rev., 2 (1960), 169–193.

Skrine, Clarmont: "Economic Development in Israel," *Geog. Jour.,* CXVII (1951), 307–329.

Weinryb, B. D.: "The Impact of Urbanization in Israel," *Middle East Jour.,* XI (1957), 23–36.

CHAPTER 16

Iran

Past and Present
Water for Crops
Land Use
Resources for Industry
Geographic Regions
Iranian Cities
Problems and Prospects
References

PAST AND PRESENT

As Iran moves forward into a new epoch of modernization and prosperity, it occasionally looks backward to its own historical greatness. The past is ever present, and many current situations find a parallel somewhere in Iran's long history.

Many people long for a return to the power and glory which were Persia's when it was an international empire extending from the Nile to the Indus, but it is not easy to set this vision of past grandeur in a modern frame. The sense of geopolitical destiny is found in the inscription of Darius I, 522–486 B.C., carved on the cliff at Behistun. "I am Darius, the great king, king of kings, king of the lands peopled by many races, for long king of this great earth, reaching even far away; son of Hystopes, the Achaemenian, a Persian, son of a Persian, an Aryan of Aryan descent."

(Opposite) The golden-domed Shia shrine at Qum suggests the magnificence of Persian architecture. Comparable shrines are found in half a dozen Iranian cities. (Courtesy Iranian Information Office, New York.)

IRAN DATA

Area	636,293	square miles
	1,630,000	square kilometers
Arable area	167,600	square kilometers
Population	19,253,000	

More than two thousand years have elapsed since Persia was at the height of its power during the Achaemenid Dynasty under Cyrus, Darius, and Xerxes. Even the second golden age under the Sassanians ended 1,000 years ago. Persia's modern renaissance came with the Safawid Dynasty after the period of Mongol and Turkish invasions, particularly under Shah Abbas, 1586–1628. Then followed the Qajar Dynasty, 1794–1925; while the Pahlavi Dynasty was inaugurated in 1926.

Qashgai tribesmen occupy the slopes of the Zagros Mountains in southwestern Iran. (Courtesy Iranian Oil Participants.)

While there is considerable ethnic and cultural unity in Iran, it is equally well to stress the diversity. Several language families are represented. The majority of the population speak various dialects of Persian, but several million do not. Many cities are known for their local pronunciation or dialect; some Persians feel that the "purest" speech is found in Shiraz. Persian is an Indo-European language, as are such other tongues spoken in Iran as Kurdish, Baluchi, and Armenian which is spoken by 2 million people. Tribes such as the Lurs and Bakhtiari speak understandable Persian, but "it has the wrong music." Arabic is spoken by 2 million people in the southwestern plains; since it is a Semitic language there is no relation to Persian although the latter has borrowed extensively from Arabic. Variations of Turkish, a division of the Ural-Altaic family, prevail in the northwest, northeast, and in the Zagros; these include Azerbaijani, Turkmen, and Qashqai.

Still other groups include Assyrians, speaking Aramaic; Brahui, related to Dravidian; and Jews who number about 75,000. While French was long the favorite European language, it has now been replaced by English.

Further differences prevail in the religious field, for Persia has been a fertile area for religions over the centuries. Mithraism, some thirty centuries ago, was essentially a fertility cult, with the concept of evolution expressed in the ritual of sacrificing a bull. Its element of mysticism was passed on to Zoroastrianism which dominated Persia until the arrival of Islam and still prevails in some areas. Zoroaster lived about 630 B.C. and introduced the worship of earth, fire, and water as the sacred elements, in a world divided between good and evil.

Islam came to Persia in the seventh century A.D. Nine-tenths of the Moslems in Iran are now followers of the Shia sect which looks to Ali, the cousin and son-in-law of Mohammed, as his true successor. It is believed that Ali's son, Hussein, married the daughter of a Persian Shah and thus established the divine right of the Sassanian kings. Sunni Moslems include the Kurds, Turkmans, the Arabs in Iran, and the Baluchi. Sufi Moslems are another minority.

Present-day Iran represents wide economic contrasts, potentially a dangerous sit-

NOTE: Further material on Iran is contained throughout the Chapters in Part One. See especially Chapter 2, Persian Empires: The Achaeminid, page 54; Chapter 5,Qanats, and Karez, page 149; and Chapter 8, Oil, page 193.

uation. Wealth and poverty have long prevailed and were once accepted with little question. Leadership in government and commerce has resided in a small aristocratic group which considers itself the heir of Persian glory. While the standard of urban living is rising, spectacularly so in Tehran, too little progress is evident among the farmers or nomads.

Some of the political problems arise from the fact that Iran borders the Soviet Union for more than a thousand miles, yet its major trade and cultural contacts relate to distant Europe and America, accessible only via a few inadequate ports or by air. In its quest for security, Russia has built a corridor of satellite or buffer states from Finland to Korea, continuous except next to Turkey, Iran, and Afghanistan. Whether Soviet policy is guided by fear or by aggression, Iran is of obvious concern. Communism might find fertile ground among the underprivileged people of Iran if they remain too long without a better way of life, and the spectacular material success of Communist planning across the frontier is attractive to nations which desire to develop rapidly.

The earliest rights of Russian traders date from 1618, and the first commercial treaty was in 1717. Much of the Caucasus area was once Persian, and Russian troops have occupied parts of Iran three times during the present century.

Iran today is in the midst of transition; it is an area of contest for ideas old and new, domestic and alien. For at least a century, the country has had a role in the pressure politics of outside powers. Iran's problem is whether it can capitalize rapidly enough on its geographic assets and overcome its liabilities in order to keep pace with world developments. These pages cannot solve the problems and can scarcely inventory the potentials; many topics discussed in earlier chapters, such as oil, should be reread to yield an adequate analysis.

If analogies are helpful, it may be pointed out that, on the physical side, the country somewhat resembles a group of states in the southwestern interior of North America. In area, Iran approximates Nevada, Utah, Colorado, Arizona, New Mexico, Sonora, and Chihuahua, but its population is four times as large. Land forms, climate, and land use are comparable, but there is no similarity in history or economic development.

Elsewhere in Southwest Asia, Iran finds its closest parallels with Turkey. Both countries have a dry core with encircling mountains, but Iran is more arid. Both have experienced modernization in the twentieth century, but Turkey is more Europeanized. Iran has oil, whereas Turkey has coal.

Bakhtiari tribeswomen often wear old silver coins as jewelry. (Courtesy Iranian Oil Participants.)

In area and in aridity, Iran ranks second to Saudi Arabia. In population, Iran is second to Turkey. In industrial potential, Iran's oil and other minerals give her a high place in future economy. In history and culture, Iran can hold her own as one of the big three among the other lands of Swasia. No country in Swasia has greater contrasts in topography or climate; few have wider differences between the old and the new.

WATER FOR CROPS

WATER AND SOIL are two of the keys to Iranian agriculture. The lack of balance between precipitation and evaporation is obvious, so that if crop yields are to be dependable, some water must be added. About one-third of the cultivated land is under irrigation; the balance depends on the meager and variable rainfall so that yields are low.

Most Persians are farmers, raising good crops wherever water and soil permit. (Source unknown.)

AGRICULTURAL WATER SUPPLY IN IRAN[1]

Source	*Hectares*
Rivers and springs, including storage behind dams	800,000
Wells	11,000
Qanats	1,200,000
Rain fed	4,000,000
Total crop area	6,011,000

[1] Official estimate, 1950.

Three sources of supplementary water are available: from rivers or springs, either directly or through storage in reservoirs; from wells; and from qanats. Water requirements vary, but it is usually estimated that a flow of one cubic foot per second is required for 100 acres of winter crops or twice that amount for summer crops. Fields which depend on rainfall alone are confined to the more humid areas, especially near the Caspian Sea or on windward slopes. Alluvial fans where ground water lies near the surface may be agriculturally productive even if the rain is inadequate.

Iran lacks large rivers except for the Karun in the southwest and the Helmand in the extreme east; elsewhere streamflow averages only a few hundred cubic feet per second. Most canal systems are small and unintegrated, and each village may have its separate arrangements. Wherever it is necessary to raise stream levels a few feet for diversion into canals, low dams or barrages are in common use. Much additional water would be available if the spring runoff could be conserved in upstream reservoirs. Ruins of ancient dams are present along the Karun at Shushtar and elsewhere in Khuzistan in the area where it is now proposed to develop an Iranian equivalent of the Tennessee Valley Authority.

Canal water is commonly withdrawn

from the rivers without the use of regulators or desilting arrangements, so that canals must be cleaned from time to time. Since canals are unlined, losses from seepage may exceed 50 per cent, and since they are often bordered by thirsty poplars, subtraction by transpiration is high. Areas watered by free-flow canals are known as *fariah* land. Water rights are very complicated and commonly involve permission to use a canal during fixed periods of time rather than for any specified quantity of water.

Well water is used chiefly for vegetables or as a supplement to canal irrigation. A common arrangement, known as a Persian water wheel, involves an endless chain of buckets, made of earthenware or old gasoline tins, which dip down into a stone-lined well some twenty to thirty feet deep. The chain is operated through a gear arrangement by a draft animal which walks round and round. Elsewhere leather buckets are lifted by a rope which passes over a pulley and is pulled by an ox walking down an inclined plane, the length of the plane being equal to the depth of the well. One animal hoist can provide water for half an acre per day. Land watered by such arrangements is known as *dhul*. Diesel pumps are also in wide use, but require a large capital outlay plus maintenance.

Qanats have been described in Chapter 5. Iran is their homeland, par excellence, and they supply more than half of all irrigation water. These horizontal wells tap ground water from the peripheral portions of desert basins, usually starting well up on some alluvial fan near the mountain base, so that their water is fresh. In contrast, wells toward the center of such basins draw upon stagnant water which is apt to be brackish.

The traveler across Persian plains, whether by air or on the ground, is seldom out of sight of qanat holes. The area around Yezd has some 400 qanats, most of them from five to thirty miles long. Both Yezd and Kerman are dependent on qanat water. In Kerman it is said, probably with exaggeration, that one-seventh of the population are qanat diggers. Other areas of importance are around Tehran, Meshed, Isfahan, and Arak. The plain of Nishapur near Meshed is said to have "12,000 springs fed by 12,000 qanats." The city of Tehran is supplied by at least thirty-six qanats which follow the alluvial slopes of the Elburz Mountains eight to sixteen miles distant; one ends in the British Embassy, another supplies a pool in the Gulistan Palace.

This horseman lives near Gach Saran in the southwest. (Courtesy Iranian Oil Participants.)

The Irrigation Department of Iran sets the total number of qanats at 20,000, and has approximate specifications and discharge measurements on 4,073 qanats, scattered through each of the provinces. Other estimates for Iran, often quoted but unsubstantiated, range up to 40,000 qanats. Their aggregate length has been estimated as 100,-

Iran faces both the Caspian Sea and Persian Gulf, but neither water body provides easy access to the outside world. If large parts of this map appear blank it is because so much of Iran is empty.

000 miles, with a discharge of 20,000 cubic meters per second. An examination of the various sheets of the United States Aeronautical Approach Charts for Iran, in part based on air photos, scale 1:250,000, show a total of 1,766 qanats, but omits them entirely in some areas where they are known to be abundant; elsewhere field check shows

Lines of qanat shafts lead down to tunnels which carry water from stream gravels under the Diz River near Dizful. (U. S. Air Force.)

that less than half of the qanats are mapped. Qanats are also shown on many of the quarter-inch maps prepared by the Geographical Section of the British General Staff. By combining the two series, the total number of mapped qanats exceeds two thousand.

The deepest qanat in Iran is thought to be at Gonabad near the Afghan border, constructed some 500 years ago. This qanat is seventeen miles long and is said to be large enough in places so that a horse might be ridden through it. The mother well or *madar chah* is reported to be 1,000 feet deep. Since it would be difficult in cleaning out the accumulated silt to raise the earth this distance in one lift, there are several offset shafts with openings at different levels where the bucket of dirt is transferred from one rope to another. At Birjand a *madar chah* is reported to reach 900 feet. Many long qanats lead into Kerman, some of them twenty miles in length. The longest qanat shown on the U. S. Air Force charts measures 17.4 miles, located near Zarand northwest of Kerman. Unverified reports credit Meshed with two forty-mile qanats, and a qanat near Isfahan is reputed to be fifty-six miles in length.

An engineering survey [1] shows that the average qanat has a length of two and one-half

[1] Overseas Consultants Inc.: *Report on Seven Year Development Plan*. New York (1949).

miles, half of which requires some tile lining due to soft ground. The mother well averages some 100 feet in depth, and the flow at the mouth is 480 gallons per minute. Such a qanat costs $13,500 and requires maintenance averaging $300 a year. In comparison, a six-inch tube well would cost only $7,000, but would involve an annual operating expense of $1,000. The qanat is usually cheaper in the long run, although since the water flows the year round and much of it is not needed during the winter months, there is a large annual waste.

Writing in 1933, Merritt-Hawkes gives the cost of a twenty-one mile qanat, with a 90-foot mother well, as $20,000. This supplied the village of Ahmad-abad with its 7,000 people. The entire value of the village with its houses, shops, mosque, and eighty carpet looms amounted to $9,000 or less than half the cost of the water supply. In another long qanat near Kerman, a storm filled two of the shafts and ruined the system. This impoverished the owners, forced the abandonment of several villages, and resulted in a considerable crop area reverting to desert.

Figures for 1950, assembled by Beckett, place the construction cost at twenty dollars per yard of tunnel, while maintenance costs average at least 0.5 per cent of the capital investment. The qanat at Jupar, which would cost $200,000 to replace, requires the labor of three men at a cost of $1,000 for annual cleaning. In the Yezd area of central Iran, where many of the qanats are fifteen to thirty miles long with mother wells 150 to 350 feet deep, a new qanat of unspecified length was dug in 1956 at a cost of $135,000. Nearby were new eight-inch drilled wells, reaching 180 feet to water, equipped with diesel engines, and costing $20,000 each. These wells produce 750 gallons per minute; if operated twenty hours a day for 275 days per year, that is throughout the growing season, they will supply three acre-feet of water for 250 acres of crops at a cost for fuel and maintenance of $5,000. Few qanats yield as much water.

Large-scale irrigation projects involving dams and a network of canals have been under consideration for a century, in some cases without adequate geographic analysis. Wise programs call for a long record of streamflow, arrangements for the desilting of muddy water, drainage facilities to remove surplus water, and studies of soil composition in the areas to be irrigated. Some of Iran's surface water and much of the ground water is dangerously high in soluble minerals. To use such water for irrigation on soils which already have a salt content and are without adequate subsurface drainage is hazardous.

Until detailed surveys are available, the extent of potentially irrigable new land is uncertain. Modest forecasts for projected schemes total 500,000 acres, with some figures of five times this amount. Much larger areas have acceptable terrain and soils, but are without present prospects of adequate water.

Dryland soils are usually high in their content of unleached minerals but may be deficient in nitrogen and humus. Few parts of Iran have had enough natural cover of vegetation to build up much organic content in the soil. Elsewhere, steep slopes have been denuded of any soil cover which they might have once had.

Extensive areas with gentle slopes, as in the central basins or near the Persian Gulf, lack adequate subsurface drainage. Where the water table is high, and where capillary action has lifted soil moisture to the surface, evaporation salts have accumulated to an excess. It is not uncomomn to find 10 per cent of soluble components in the upper foot of these soils. Thousands of square miles have a salt-encrusted surface; where this whitens the ground, the flat is known as a *kavir*.

The Karkeh Dam in Khuzistan supplies irrigation canals which reclaim large areas near the Persian Gulf. (Courtesy Iranian Oil Participants.)

When irrigation schemes have been introduced without proper drainage facilities, soils may be ruined. On the other hand, many desert soils may be made very productive provided that the excess of soluble salts are flushed out and their organic content built up by proper management.

LAND USE

DUE TO THE shortage of water and to the poverty of the soil, more than half of Iran's agricultural land lies fallow each year; often the figure is two-thirds. Government statistics, as shown in the following table, suggest that about 2 million hectares, or 5 million acres, are irrigated and that the area actually cultivated amounts to some 6 million hectares, or 15 million acres. The total area cultivated in some years and fallow in others exceeds 16 million hectares.

These figures are to be compared with the total national area of over 163,600,000 hectares, so that the food producing cropland is under 4 per cent. This means less than an acre per capita. Fifty per cent of Iran is unproductive desert or mountain land, 20 per cent might optimistically be classed as arable but is currently waste, 11 per cent is called forest but much of this is scrubland of no commercial value, and 6 per cent is listed as grazing land but is mostly too dry for good grasses.

Two-thirds of the people make their livelihood from agriculture or grazing. The percentage is declining because of migration to

LAND USE IN IRAN [1]

	Hectares
Cultivated area (including fallow, which always exceeds 11,000,000 hectare)	16,600,000
Irrigated area	2,016,000
Potential arable land	33,000,000
Farm pasture and woodlands	1,160,000
Grazing land, excluding fallow	10,000,000
Forest land	18,000,000
Desert and waste land without productivity	81,600,000
Villages	1,240,000
Cities	2,000,000
Total area of Iran	163,600,000

[1] Gideon Hodary and Karim Sei: *Handbook of Agricultural Statistics*. Tehran: Bank Melli Press (1949).

the cities, increasing numbers employed in oil and other industries, and the rising importance of transport and commerce. Iran will remain predominantly an agricultural nation for many years.

Tenancy is an old problem. Five factors are taken into consideration in the arrangements: land, water, seeds, animals, and labor. In theory, one-fifth of the crop goes to whoever supplies each item. Locally, there are modifications due to custom, the differences between summer and winter crops, and the cost or availability of irrigation water. Those who supply essential village services, such as the headman, water supervisor, crop watchman, or the barber, may receive a fixed share of the crop.

Few farmers own their own fields, and many landlords supervise their holdings through intermediaries. Tenant farmers seldom have a written agreement or any security. Credit is available from the landlord, the owner of the oxen, or from merchants and middle men, but the interest may amount to 20 to 40 per cent. Government farm banks and the distribution of crown lands is bringing some improvement. Even if tenancy were abolished and the farmer could be given the entire harvest, the income from the area which he now cultivates might be insufficient to provide an adequate standard of living.

The basic problem of livelihood in rural Iran is the shortage of cropland, which in turn is limited by available water. The chief prospects for increased acreage lie along the humid Caspian seacoast and in the potentially irrigable Khuzistan area. Coupled with problems of production is that of transportation to markets.

In general, Iran feeds itself. Sugar and tea must be imported, but in good years there is a surplus of cereals, fruits, and nuts for export.

Winter cultivation, taking advantage of such rain as may fall, is known as *daimi* farming. This is common in northern and western Iran as far south as Ahwaz. Unless the rainfall exceeds twelve inches, daimi crops are speculative, with only one good harvest out of two or three. Fields generally lie fallow in alternate years. While the return is uncertain, less labor is required than with irrigated agriculture. Where rain-fed agriculture involves winter cultivation, it is known as *shitwi* farming, in comparison with summer or *seifi* crops.

Farm life is simple. Most farmers live in villages, and an estimate in 1950 placed the number of such farm units at 42,696. Agricultural tools are primitive; the plow is a simple wooden affair with an iron tip, and it stirs rather than turns the soil. Harvests are usually gathered by hand and threshed by driving the farm animals over the grain. There are many cattle, but manure is seldom adequate since it must be used as a domestic fuel.

The amount of land cultivated by a peasant is traditionally measured by that which can be managed by one pair of oxen. The equipment required by a better class farmer includes a pair of oxen and a donkey, two plows, one thresher, two or three spades, and 2,000 pounds of seed.

IRANIAN CROPS[1]

	Production Thousand metric tons		Area Thousand hectares	
	1948–52	*1957*	*1948–52*	*1957*
Wheat	1,860	2,800	2,080	2,900 (1956)
Barley	767	980	757	1,000 (1956)
Rice (paddy)	424	480	220	250
Total grains	3,074	4,279	2,080	3,666
Sugar beets	349	727	34	46
Tobacco	12	14	16	22
Cotton (lint)	26	65	133	240
Dates	—	—	125	104
Tea	4	—	4	7

[1] Food and Agricultural Organization: PRODUCTION YEARBOOK (1958).

Agriculture centers on four main food crops: wheat, barley, rice, and dates, plus three crops which require processing, namely, cotton, sugar beets, and tobacco. Fruits and vegetables are widespread but limited in acreage.

Wheat is the staple grain and is grown wherever possible. The leading crop area is from Meshed west to Tabriz and south to Shiraz. Wheat is usually planted in the fall, either as an irrigated shitwi or as a dry daimi crop and harvested in the spring. In high altitude areas, wheat is spring-sown and thus requires irrigation as a seifi crop.

Barley is in second place, planted in an area about one-third that of wheat. Its distribution is similar to wheat, but barley tolerates more drought so that its yield per acre may exceed that of wheat.

Rice is a favorite crop, widely grown on the Caspian coastal plain and wherever sufficient water is available. Rice fields are dry-plowed in the early spring and then flooded at the end of April. The seed is sown in May, either directly in the muddy fields or first in seed beds. The harvest takes place four months later.

Dates are a staple food in southern Iran, especially in the coastal areas. Most of the country is too high and thus too cool. It has been estimated that Iran has 10 million date palms, half in the southeast and most of the rest near the northern end of the Persian Gulf.

Many other crops are widespread in Iran, including sorghum and alfalfa. The Ministry of Agriculture places the number of pistachio trees at 2 million, with the same figure for citrus; almond trees number 400,000. Many temperate fruits are raised including exceptionally fine apricots, excellent melons, and grapes for raisins and wine.

Cotton is the chief industrial crop, but requires irrigation. It is grown at levels below 5,000 feet and is widespread in the west. Silk is also an ancient product, especially near the Caspian Sea where mulberry trees grow well.

Tobacco is an old but relatively unimportant product, with the chief output near the Caspian and in the northwest. Both cigarette and pipe varieties are grown.

Opium was once a major export, grown under governmental restrictions, but its production is now negligible.

Livestock provides livelihood for several million people. Details are uncertain since many of the people are nomads who do not welcome any enumeration. Sheep lead, with some 14 million head, followed by goats which number 7 million. Wool is an important raw material for the carpet industry and for export. There are 1.5 million oxen, used as draft animals, and the same number of cows. Donkeys exceed a million, while horses and mules amount to one-third of that figure. Camels are declining in number and probably total only a hundred thousand.

Most of the sheep and goats are the property of nomadic tribes, many of whom migrate across the slopes of the Zagros and Elburz with the change in season. Random counts during such migrations suggest an average of fifty animals per person. Government policies during the twentieth century have favored the compulsory settling of pastoral people, so that the livestock totals are declining.

Very little good grazing land is available outside of mountain pastures; as a result, many animals must feed on the stubble of fallow fields or on the scanty vegetation of semiarid desert margins.

Not all sugar beets grow to this size, but they provide an important crop near Shiraz.

RESOURCES FOR INDUSTRY

IRAN'S GREAT MINERAL RESOURCE is oil, the details of which have been considered in Chapter 8. So large are the known reserves, even though the geological survey is still incomplete, that it is easy to become enthusiastic over the prospects. The major producing area is near the head of the Persian Gulf, but discoveries at Qum, south of Tehran, hold promise for the interior.

The bulk of the oil is exported, either in the form of stabilized crude or as refined products from Abadan. Increasing amounts are used domestically, and there is a growing petrochemical industry for fertilizers and the manufacture of plastics.

In 1901, a sixty-year oil concession was granted to William Knox D'Arcy, covering all of Iran except the north. After many difficulties, oil was discovered at Masjid-i-Sulaiman in 1908, at a depth of 1,180 feet. From then until nationalization in 1951, development was under the British-owned Anglo-Persian Oil Company. During this period, the total oil production reached 333 million metric tons, or some 2.5 billion barrels.

Since 1954, developments in the former concession area have been under the direction of an international consortium. Seven fields have been developed, with phenomenally high yields per well.

Basic rights to all oil in the country are held by the National Iranian Oil Company, which is authorized to negotiate with foreign operators. Agreements have been reached with both Italian and American interests for additional areas, some of them in offshore districts. The large field at Qum, discovered in 1957, could not be developed until the pipeline had been completed.

Much less is known about other natural resources, but Iran appears to hold second place to Turkey in coal and iron reserves. Many mineral occurrences are known, and

The refinery at Abadan was the largest in the world when built, and produces a wide range of petroleum products. (Courtesy Iranian Oil Participants.)

the government reports some 300 "mines" producing thirty minerals, but for the most part these represent small operations.

Building stone, clays, and limestone are widespread. Other nonmetallic products are arsenic, emery, gypsum, salt, sulphur, and turquoise. Commercial production of metallic ores includes antimony, chromite, copper, iron, iron oxide pigment, lead, manganese, magnesite, nickel, sulphur, tungsten, and zinc. Only a few of these are sufficiently important to be listed in the *Statistical Yearbook* of the United Nations.

Coal is widespread in northern Iran and is also present in the south central area; most of it is of Mesozoic age. The largest production is near Tehran, in part a reflection of initiative and market. Eight mines are within fifty miles of the capital, all on the southern slopes of the Elburz Mountains. Ten other mines lie elsewhere in the Elburz. Some of the best coal is produced near Zirab on the northern flanks of the mountains along the railroad northeast of Tehran. The heat value, which is 14,500 B.T.U., is good, but the ash averages 23 per cent and there is 1.5 per cent sulphur. Meshed has two producing occurrences and Tabriz has one. Low-grade powdery coal occurs near Kerman in the south, but production will remain negligible until better transportation is available. Production reached 330,000 tons a year by 1958, and the country will be able to supply its needs for many years to come.

Hydroelectric potentials are present in most of the snow-covered mountains, and

OIL PRODUCTION IN SOUTHWEST IRAN[1]

Oil field	Producing wells	Daily production, barrels
Masjid-i-Sulaiman	23	37,000
Lali	5	18,000
Haft Kel	20	144,000
Naft Safid	17	60,000
Agha Jari	30	503,000
Gach Saran	8	59,000
Ahwaz	—	—
Concession area	103	821,000

[1] *Iranian Oil Consortium*, December 31, 1957.

ambitious plans call for a dozen large installations. Three multi-purpose dams were finished early in the 1960s, two of them in the north. One is near Karaj, the growing industrial center at the base of the Elburz near Tehran. The dam is a double curvature arch, 590 feet high and 1,280 feet in length, and required 915,000 cubic yards of concrete. The power capacity is 120,000 kilowatts. Another is on the north-flowing Sefid Rud or White River where it cuts across the Elburz enroute to the Caspian Sea. The dam has a height of 335 feet and is 1,400 feet long. The power plant has a capacity of 64,000 kilowatts, and the reservoir will store enough water to irrigate 300,000 acres along the Caspian Coast. The third is near Ahwaz on the Diz River, a tributary of the Karun, where it crosses the Zagros Mountains. This dam is 620 feet high, one of the tallest in all

MINERAL PRODUCTION IN IRAN[1]

Commodity	Annual output in metric tons
Antimony	102
Cement	138,900
Chromite	38,600
Coal	330,000
Copper	5,100
Lead	30,400
Manganese	18,100

[1] *United Nations Statistical Yearbook*, 1958.

Swasia, and has an installed capacity of 130,000 kilowatts and an ultimate capacity of 520,000 kilowatts. So precipitous is the Diz canyon site that the four-mile access road involves more than a mile of tunnels.

Iron ore of two varieties is in production. The oldest development historically is the powdery red iron-oxide long exported from Hormuz Island at the entrance to the Persian Gulf, where it is associated with salt plugs. Production amounts to a few tens of thousands of tons a year, exported for use as a pigment. Iron ore of a quality suitable for smelting is reported in several areas, including Samnan, 100 miles east of Tehran; Anarak, 100 miles south of Samnan; Kerman, where there is both 40 and 60 per cent ore; and Isfahan. Proposals for a blast furnace once favored Karaj with its local ore plus nearby coal and hydroelectricity, but now point to the Arak ore deposits, with a plant at Azna on the railway between Tehran and the Gulf as the coming center of heavy industry.

Chromium may be the most valuable of Iran's uncommon minerals; in this respect the situation parallels that of Turkey although production is far lower. Ore with 45 per cent Cr_2O_3 content occurs at ten localities between Meshed and Shahrud, and chromium is known at several places north of Bandar Abbas.

Lead is mined at two dozen localities in the area from Arak southeast past Anarak to Yezd, and also at numerous locations east of Tehran. Small amounts of zinc and antimony are associated with the lead.

Sulphur is obtained as a by-product of oil refining. Ores are mined near Samnan and are present near Bandar Abbas.

Turquoise is Iran's most distinctive gem, long produced from the Madan mines near Meshed. This was once the leading source of good turquoise but is now surpassed by the United States.

Too little is known as to Iran's minerals

or their distribution to make safe forecasts. Production is rising, and new discoveries are frequent. While the present picture appears modest and resources appear considerably below those of Turkey, Iran probably has an adequate mineral base for a considerable industrial development. An important limitation may lie in the amount of suitable metallurgical coke. For the present, most mineral resources are processed abroad.

Two mineralized areas stand out, the Elburz Range and a central district from Arak southeast to Anarak and on to Kerman.

GEOGRAPHIC REGIONS

Five important geographic regions are present in Iran, with numerous subdivisions. Parts of several others have their major development in adjoining countries.

Northwest Persia

This corner of Iran has much in common with eastern Anatolia, already described in Chapter 10 on Turkey, and with the adjacent areas of the Soviet Union. Armenians have traditionally lived in all three areas, but are now absent in Turkey. Azerbaijanians are present in both Iran and the U.S.S.R., as are many other minority peoples. Many residents of northwest Persia are Turks and Kurds. In extent, this geographic region roughly corresponds to the province or *ostan* of Azerbaijan. Within it are four subregions: the Araks Valley, the Urmia Basin, the Qizil Uzun Valley, and the Kurdish Hills.

Much of the region is a mountain and plateau complex, vigorously eroded in places but elsewhere with high undulating surfaces, here and there cut into great blocks by normal faulting. As a whole, the plateau is tilted toward the northeast. Huge volcanic cones rise above the ruined plateau, and a large salt lake occupies the major basin. Large upland areas are a dreary stone waste, bare in summer and snow-clad in winter; in contrast, the lowlands are cultivated wherever irrigation is available. Northwest Iran covers slightly over 60,000 square miles, and it contains one-quarter of Iran's total population.

The Araks River forms the boundary next to the U.S.S.R., both in Iran and in Turkey as well. The area of its basin within the latter countries amounts to 24,770 square miles, with somewhat more than one-third of this in Turkey. The Araks rises near Erzurum, where the divide next to Black Sea and Euphrates drainage is indistinct. The upper river follows an open plain, but cuts through a succession of lava flows so that the valley becomes deeper, even 2,000 feet below the nearby uplands. Numerous volcanos dot the valley; in eastern Turkey lies Ararat, 16,946 feet, while in Iran is Savalan, 14,000 feet. The alluvial

The gusher at Qum blew in at the rate of 85,000 barrels a day. (Courtesy Iranian Information Center, New York.)

plain widens to fifteen miles in a down-faulted block near the Soviet city of Yerevan, narrows to a gorge at Julfa, and spreads out downstream in the semidesert Moghan Steppe. Where the Araks enters the Caspian Sea, both banks are in Soviet territory. Irrigation is usually necessary, and crops include tobacco, cotton, cereals, and fruit. Nomads move up and down the generally treeless slopes with the changing seasons.

The Urmia Basin provides the best agricultural land in northwestern Iran. The drainage area measures 19,900 square miles and centers in the down-faulted basin of Lake Urmia at 4,250 feet. During the rule of Riza Shah, the name was changed to Lake Rizaiyeh, which is still the name of a city near its western shore. The lake measures ninety miles from north to south and thirty miles in width. Since there is no outlet, Lake Urmia is salty. The concentration is less than the Dead Sea, but fish cannot live in it, and the water is sufficiently dense so that swimmers cannot sink. The lake is shallow, and the shoreline changes as the level fluctuates in response to the balance between spring intake and summer evaporation.

Lake Urmia is surrounded by a broad plain, once beneath lake level, which provides excellent agricultural land if irrigated. On the west, this lake plain is twenty miles wide and is watered by streams from snow mountains. The plain is wider on the east, especially around the city of Tabriz. The prosperity of the various villages is a reflection of their available water supply.

The Urmia Basin is the home of the Assyrians, many of whom are Christians of either the original fifth century Nestorian Church or its Uniate branch known as Chaldean.

Since cultivated areas around the lake have elevations of nearly a mile, and the mountains rise to twice that height, winters are bitterly cold and snow remains on the ground for weeks. Summers are hot on the plains. Precipitation is higher than in most parts of Iran. The only forests which re-

These graphs present monthly average temperature and rainfall, plus the daily temperature range, shaded, and the extreme recorded temperatures, in dots, as well as the monthly potential evapotranspiration, in thin bars.

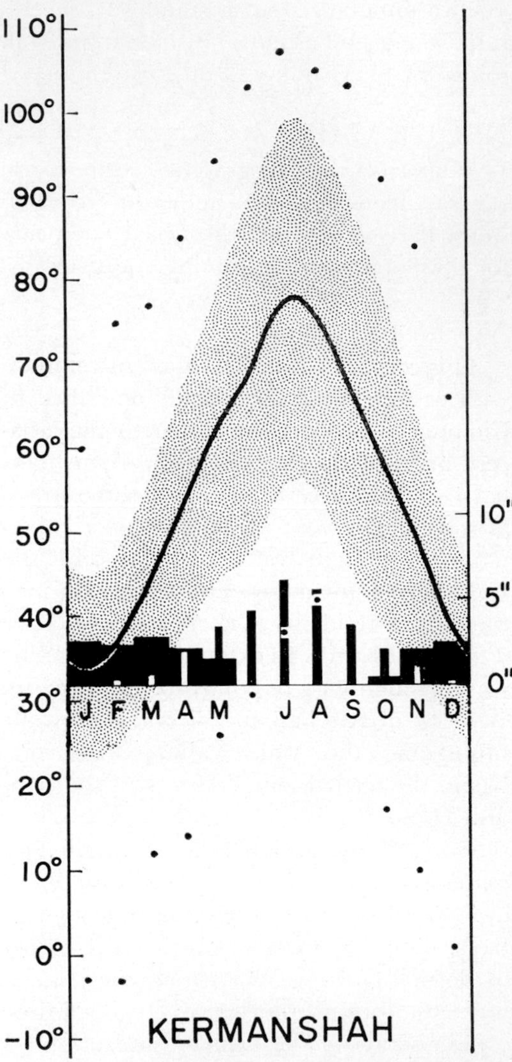

Kermanshah's climate is suggestive of conditions in the Zagros Mountains. Elevation 4,285 feet, annual precipitation 16.3 inches.

main are generally inaccessible, and most trees are of the scrub varieties, fifteen to twenty feet in height.

Agriculture depends on melting snow from the encircling mountains, distributed by miles of irrigation canals, many of which are lined with poplars or willows. Wheat is widely grown. On the plains it is planted in the fall and is raised either with irrigation or as a dry crop. In the highlands, wheat is spring sown and requires irrigation. Vegetables, grapes, flax, cotton, rice, tobacco, melons, and opium poppies grow well in the rich alluvial soil.

The Qizil Uzun Valley drains an area of about 20,000 square miles, south and east of Lake Urmia. Much of the region is a high undulating plateau, essentially monoto-

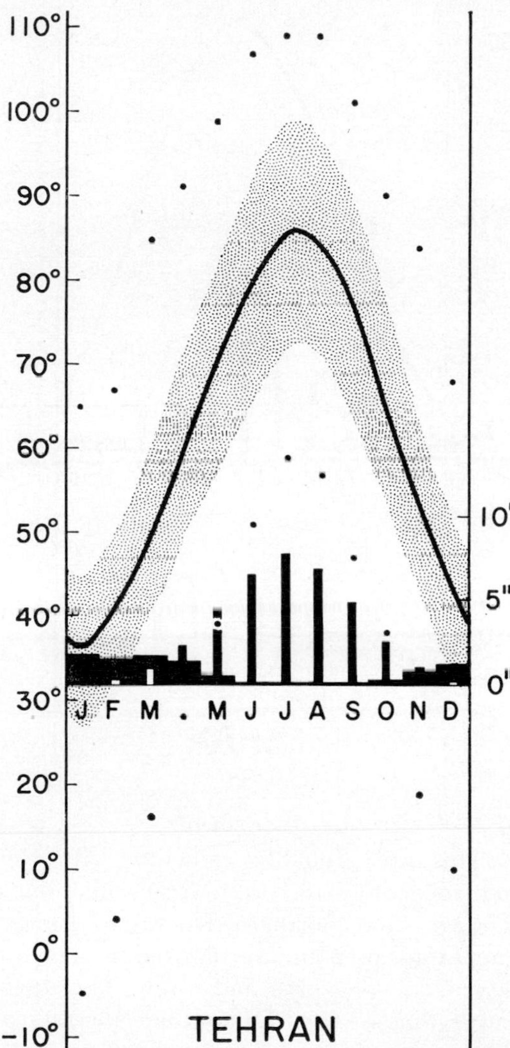

Tehran's continental climate is suggested by the steepness of the temperature curve. Elevation 4,002 feet, annual precipitation 9.7 inches.

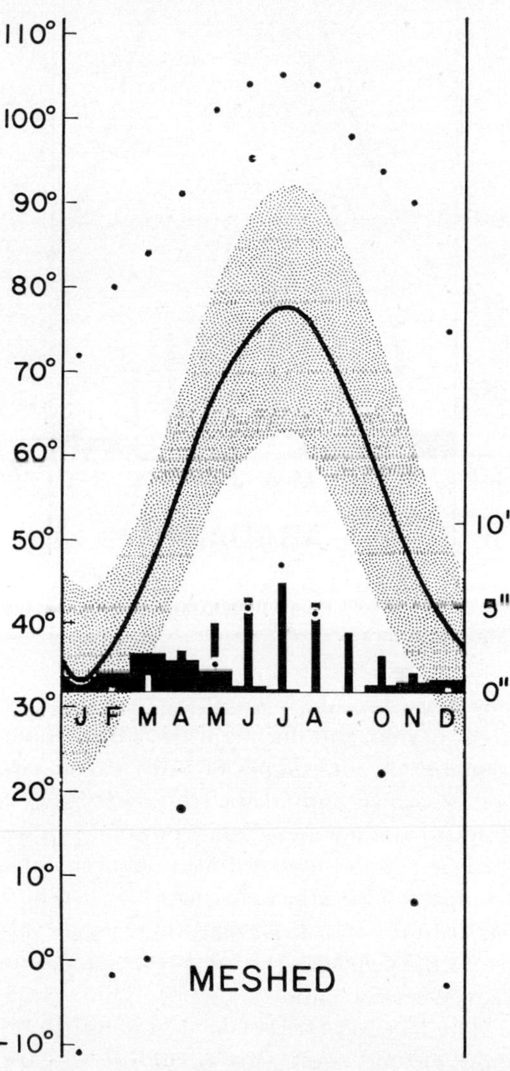

Meshed lies in the northeastern highlands and is both dry and cold. Elevation 3,104 feet, annual precipitation 9.1 inches.

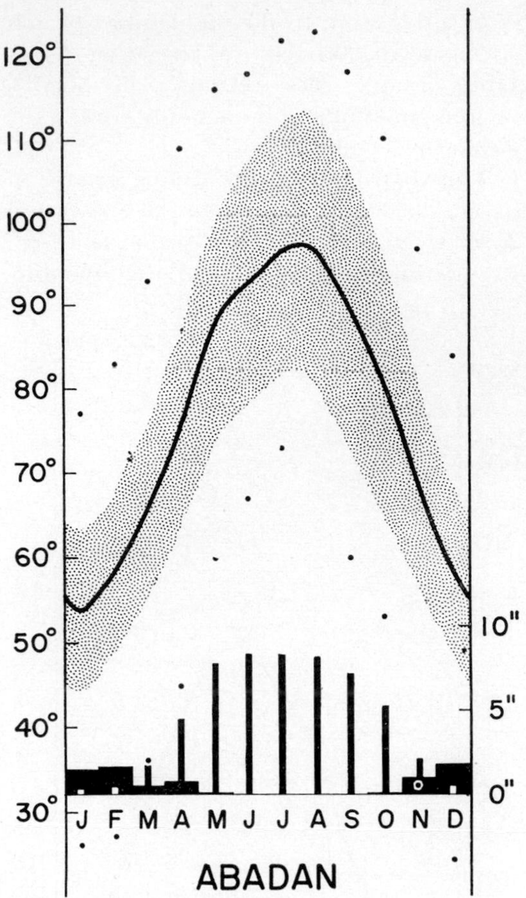

Abadan is hot and dry, with high potential evapotranspiration in summer. Elevation 7 feet, annual rainfall 7.6 inches.

The oasis of Isfahan owes its life to the nearby mountains. Elevation 5,817 feet, annual precipitation 4.3 inches.

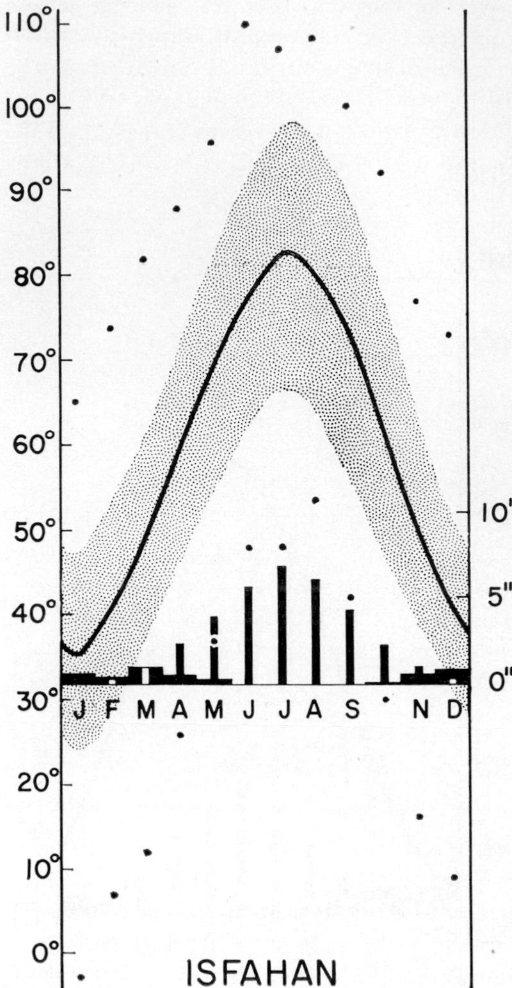

nous, barren, and uninhabited. The climate is semiarid, but patches of unirrigated barley are grown around the scattered villages. Toward the northeast, the country is more dissected and the drainage reflects the northwest to southeast structure. The chief agricultural area lies along the central valley. Kurds and Turks are more numerous than Persian people.

The Kurdish Hills make up the fourth region of northwest Persia, and they have been discussed in Chapter 13 on Iraq since they are more widely developed there.

The Caspian Borderlands

This area roughly coincides with the provinces of Gilan, Mazanderan, the former Gurgan, and northern Khurasan. Linear mountains predominate, flanked by great alluvial fans on north and south. The three subregions are the Caspian coast, the Elburz Mountains, and northern Khurasan.

The Caspian coast has a climate entirely different from any other part of Iran; its

Seistan is probably the driest area of Iran, located in the far southeast. Elevation 2,000 feet, annual precipitation 2.9 inches.

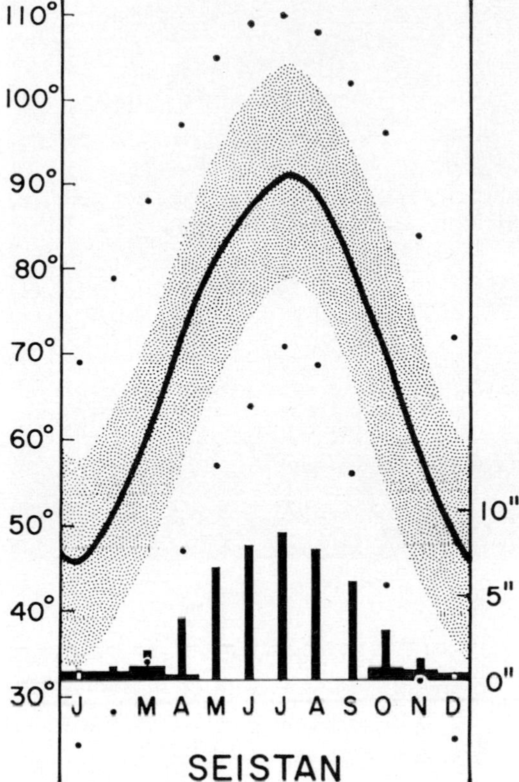

only parallel in Swasia is the eastern Black Sea coast of Turkey. In place of deserts, there is lush vegetation; in place of limited irrigation, there are large areas of malarial swamps. Rain, cloud, and mist are common throughout the year, although summer is the drier season as elsewhere. Moist winds off the Caspian Sea, cooled by orographic lift, cause the humidity.

The Caspian vegetation is so verdant that an unknown writer has described one area as "so abundantly clothed with trees of the forest, that often a pathway can scarcely be forced through the intricate jungle, so riotous in color that the traveler can almost awake with the belief that he has been transformed in sleep to some tropical clime."

Much of the original forest has been cleared for cultivation or for lumber, and virgin timber remains only in the hilly and less accessible areas.

Iran has a crescentic coastline for 400 miles along the Caspian Sea. Since the two extremities turn parallel to the length of the sea and are backed by hills rather than mountains, they receive much less rain; it is only in the south opposite the high Elburz that humid conditions prevail. The Persian poet, Firdausi, has spoken of this area as enjoying perpetual spring. This delightful land, now available by good roads from Tehran, has made the Caspian shore a growing resort area.

The water level of the Caspian Sea is balanced between its supply, 80 per cent of which comes from the Volga River, and evaporation which amounts to over eight feet a year. In recent centuries, the level has been declining irregularly, and the coastal plain represents former sea floor plus subaerial delta alluvium. Since the sea has a salinity of only three-eighths that of the ocean, the water is almost potable, though too saline for irrigation use.

Along-shore currents shift beach material and river mouths eastward. In general, the coast is smooth, harborless, and shallow near shore, but lagoons make possible the ports of Pahlevi and Bandar Shah; in both instances, repeated dredging is necessary due to the continued fall in the sea level.

While there are notable differences along the coast from west to east, the most significant zonation is inland at right angles to the shore. The beach is commonly sandy and wide, often with spits, bars, and small lagoons. Lines of sand dunes rise twenty to sixty feet along the inner margin of the beach, with old dunes and isolated lagoons or swamps farther inland to mark former shorelines. Behind these, the coastal plain extends from one to more than twenty miles to the foothill zone, with evidence of former

Tea is grown near the Caspian Sea where abundant moisture and below sea level elevations create a subtropical climate.

shores in places. Loess, an unstratified deposit of yellowish-brown silt, is found in some foothill locations.

Each of these zones has its characteristic natural vegetation, ranging from the reeds and meadows of the lagoons to splendid deciduous forests of the hills. Each zone has its specialized utilization. Rice is a major crop, along with cotton, flax, sugar cane, tobacco, tea, mulberry trees, oranges, and vegetables. Fishing is handicapped by the lack of harbors, but sturgeon and caviar are important.

In the extreme southeast, the Iranian coast borders the great Turanian Lowland of Soviet Middle Asia. The plain near the Caspian is a steppe, and it formed part of classical Parthia. Grazing is now the chief occupation, but the area was once agriculturally productive for Strabo reported that "Each vine produces seven gallons of wine and each fig tree ninety bushels of fruit." The Gurgan River reaches the Caspian Sea near Bandar Shah; six miles farther north are the ruins of an ancient wall known as "Alexander's Barrier" which extends inland for eighty miles.

The Caspian coast has one of the densest concentrations of people in Iran, with at least one-sixth of the total population. Most are farmers, but some nomads migrate between the foothills and upper slopes of the Elburz. The major city is Resht, in the delta of the Shari Rud.

The Elburz Mountains reach an elevation of 18,934 feet in the volcanic peak of Mount Demavend, the highest point in Swasia west of the Hindu Kush. Elsewhere, crest heights generally exceed 10,000 feet for 200 miles. The length of the Elburz proper is 400 miles, with an extension of 100 miles to the northwest in the Talish Mountains; widths vary from forty to eighty miles. On the west the Talish start from the Soviet frontier, while the Elburz extend from the canyon of the Safid Rud, the only river to cut entirely across the range, to an eastern limit near 56° E.

The core of the Elburz Mountains is made of Jurassic and Cretaceous sediments, with both Paleozoic and Eocene formations along the flanks. Great alluvial aprons blanket the lower slopes. Compression occurred in the late Jurassic, the Upper Cretaceous, and again in the Pliocene, with folding, faulting, and igneous intrusions. Heavy rainfall on the north side and the absence of protective vegetation on the drier south have each led to the cutting of magnificent gorges. In several places there are two or three main ridges, with a resulting trellis drainage pattern. The mountains rise boldly on both sides, but since Tehran to the south lies at 3,639 feet while the Caspian Sea is eighty-five feet below sea level, the northern face is more sharply defined. Earthquakes are recurrent and severe.

The Elburz Mountains form a great climatic divide, certainly the most significant break in Iran and probably in all of Southwest Asia. To the north, there is year-round warmth with abundant moisture; to the south there is a desert with frigid winters and hot summers. The northern slopes receive rain during every month, with a maximum in September and October, each of which receives an average of eight inches. The total is over forty inches and rain falls on 100 days so that the cloud cover is from 0.5 to 0.8. On the southern slopes, the annual total is around fifteen inches, spread over twenty-five days, so that the cloud cover is 0.2 to 0.5; winter is the rainy season, with December and March each accounting for two inches. Snow covers the slopes above 5,000 feet during four or five months and remains throughout the year in the crater of Demavend.

Vegetation matches the climate. Forests once covered wide areas, but centuries of unrestricted cutting for timber and charcoal, plus overgrazing by goats, have eliminated them in all but the more inaccessible areas. Forty varieties of timber trees are found on the north slopes up to 7,000 or 8,000 feet, including beech, oak, maple, plane (sycamore), ash, poplar, walnut, juniper, hornbeam, and alder. Conifers are uncommon. Each altitude zone on the two sides has its distinctive flora. On the north, steppe conditions may prevail up to 10,000 feet.

Amid such an environment, the population is restricted to farmers who cultivate the few open intermontane valleys and to nomads who engage in transhumance. Rice and corn are common crops, along with fruit. This is the only part of Iran which grows olives.

The valley of the Alamut River, a tributary of the Shah Rud, is famous as the home of a fanatical variety of Shiites known as Assassins. The order was founded in 1071 and spread across Iran and Syria until it was wiped out by the Mongols in 1256. This secret society was organized into hierarchies from whom unquestioning obedience was demanded. Tales of the Crusaders and Marco Polo brought the Assassins and their leader, the Old Man of the Mountain, into European folklore.

Three roads and one railroad cross the central Elburz. These highways involve passes at 8,500 feet (in a tunnel), 8,700 feet, and 6,620 feet, so that communications may be blocked by snow. The railway from Tehran to Bandar Shah is 285 miles long, and has 104 major bridges and ninety-six tunnels of which eleven are spirals. It crosses the range in a tunnel at 6,924 feet.

The Talish Mountains are the northwestern extension of the Elburz, only slightly lower since elevations rise to 8,000 feet. They extend from the valley of the Sefid Rud to the Soviet frontier and separate the basin of the Qizil Uzun from the Caspian. The rainfall, and hence the vegetation, are

The Trans-Iranian Railway climbs the humid Elburz slopes in a series of tunnels and bridges. (Courtesy Iranian Information Center, New York.)

somewhat heavier than in the Elburz proper. There are good upland meadows for grazing, and wheat is grown in the valleys. Some of the people are classed as Tallish in language and tend to be Sunni rather than Shia in religion.

Northern Khurasan includes a series of roughly parallel ranges to the east of the Elburz, with intervening alluvial plains. The northernmost is the Kopet Dagh, separated from the Elburz by a broad saddle with elevations below 5,000 feet. The mountains lie partly in northern Khurasan but also across the border in the Turkmenian Soviet Socialist Republic. The structural trend is east-southeast, almost at right angles to that of the nearest Elburz structures, and the region continues to the Afghan border. The Kopet Dagh with its extensions has a length of 300 miles and a width of forty miles; elevations exceed 6,000 feet over most of the distance.

Parallel and farther south is a twin range, of which the chief line is the Kuh-i-Binalud; crest lines are above 8,000 feet. The Kopet Dagh and Kuh-i-Binalud are separated by the west-flowing Atrek River and the east-flowing Kashaf. Both valleys have considerable cultivation and are regarded as the best part of Khurasan. Nearby lies the Shia pilgrimage center of Meshed. Elevations in each range exceed 10,000 feet opposite Meshed, and their melting snow gradually

This combination of snow-capped mountains and cultivated basins near Hamadan is typical of many Iranian landscapes. (Courtesy Raymond Wilson.)

supplies streams for summer irrigation.

Other and lower ranges with approximately east-west trends extend to latitude 36° N. and enclose broad alluvial plains, generally too dry for unirrigated agriculture but more humid than the actual deserts farther south. The size and distribution of villages reflect the availability of water from the mountains. One town of interest is Nishapur, the birthplace of Omar Khayyam. The poet Firdausi was born at Tus near Meshed.

The mountains of northern Khurasan bear a slight similarity to the Elburz Mountains, but since deserts rather than the Caspian Sea lie to the north, they lack humid north slopes. Winter snow and summer meadows characterize the higher elevations in each area. Fruit and nut trees surround prosperous villages, but most lower landscapes are bare. Broad alluvial fans border the Khurasan mountains, with many qanats for irrigation.

The Zagros Highlands

Western and southern Iran is enclosed by a great arc of folded and faulted mountains. Next to Iraq and the Persian Gulf are the 1,000-mile long Zagros, while for 400 miles eastward along the Arabian Sea lie the Makran Mountains. Widths range from 100 to 200 miles; many elevations exceed 10,000 feet. The Makran is more or less of a unit, but the Zagros may conveniently be divided into the High Zagros on the east and the Zagros Foothills to the west.

While the Zagros form less of a climatic barrier than the Elburz, they also mark the border of the arid plateau and bar any outward drainage to the sea. Only one railway and half a dozen roads cross the chain in its 1,400-mile length. No highway parallels the coast.

From north to south, parts of eight Iranian provinces are involved: Kurdistan, Kermanshah, Laristan, Isfahan, Khuzistan, Fars, and the southern parts of Kerman and Baluchistan.

The High Zagros consist of numerous linear ridges. Some are elongated anticlinal domes, commonly forty miles long by four miles wide, with streams which flow parallel to the structure in open valleys and then cross it in gorges. Many of these streams rise on the eastern or inner side of the Zagros and thus have an antecedent course across the mountains, in some places with intrenched meanders. The fact that several rivers have cut canyons across the structural ridges, even though softer rock and lower ground are available a few miles away, suggests that their patterns are inherited from old peneplain surfaces.

Ten west-flowing streams and two interior basins account for the drainage of the High Zagros. The rivers of the Zagros with their drainage areas, are listed in the accompanying table, reading from north to south.

ZAGROS RIVER BASINS

Diyala River	1,600	square	miles
Karkeh River	16,300	"	"
Diz River	6,800	"	"
Karun River	12,300	"	"
Marun River	2,550	"	"
Zuhra River	3,750	"	"
Shahpur River	3,500	"	"
Mand River	20,000	"	"
Khamir River	3,600	"	"
Shur River	15,600	"	"
Neyriz Basin	11,300	"	"
Shiraz Basin	1,600	"	"
High Zagros Total	98,900	"	"

The first four rivers form part of the Shatt-al-Arab drainage; the others flow directly to the Gulf. Although the Mand River has the largest catchment basin, it collects little water since the rainfall is low and there is insufficient snow to feed its tributaries in spring and summer. Like many other rivers in the Zagros, the Mand follows so many linear structures that its course is about 380 miles long whereas the direct distance from source to mouth is only 120 miles. Broad valleys at elevations of 4,000 to 6,000 feet provide pasture and patches of cultivation.

The rocks of the Zagros are predominantly limestones which are thick, massive, and resistant. The sandstones are generally weak, but conglomerates form bold crags. Granites and a few interbedded lavas are present in the north. In age, formations range from Cambrian through most of the Paleozoic and Mesozoic periods into the Miocene. Most of these sediments were laid down in the ancient Tethys Sea which persisted irregularly until the end of the Middle Cretaceous. Coincident with the withdrawal of marine conditions, thick beds of continental sediments accumulated, including conglomerates and evaporites such as salt and gypsum.

Folding and faulting occurred at three times, in each case with pressures directed from interior Iran. In the northeast, deformation started in the late Jurassic Period; in the southeast, the date was Upper Cretaceous. Both areas, along with the west, were again compressed in the Eocene Period, continuing into the Pliocene. The most intense alterations and the highest elevations are along the eastern or inner side of the Zagros where Jurassic beds have been squeezed three times, in comparison with more open folding toward Mesopotamia and the Persian Gulf.

The dry foothills of the Zagros near Lali provide a meager livelihood for a few pastoralists. Stone houses blend into the natural landscape. (Courtesy Iranian Oil Participants.)

A west to east cross-section across the Zagros shows broad open folds in the western foothills, dating from the Miocene, commonly formed by limestone anticlines. Occasionally the synclines are somewhat pinched, so that the valleys are narrower than the "whale back" ridges. The high central range is marked by close folding and great overthrust faults, of Upper Cretaceous age, which altered the Miocene structures. Still farther east these two periods of deformation are superimposed on the original Jurassic folding, with increased complexity in structure.

A unique feature of the southernmost Zagros is the presence of over 100 salt domes, roughly cylindrical columns of pinkish Cambrian salt which have punched up through the surrounding sediments. Some salt plugs rise 3,000 and 4,000 feet above their surroundings, and in places are bordered by talus tongues of salt, gypsum, and rock debris which resemble glaciers. Hormuz Island also contains a number of salt domes, 300 to 700 feet high, encrusted with vari-colored minerals. Red iron-oxide associated with the salt has been mined for centuries. Unlike comparable domes along the Gulf of Mexico, none of the Iranian plugs appear to have developed oil-bearing conditions.

Along the Persian Gulf, as far south as

Bushire, there is a narrow coastal plain with conditions resembling those in Mesopotamia. Along the Gulf of Oman, that is to the east of Bandar Abbas and the Strait of Hormuz, the coastal plain varies in width from one to twenty-five miles. The population is limited to a few palm oases or scattered fishing villages.

Both flanks of the High Zagros tend to be barren, somewhat resembling the southern side of the Elburz. Snow covers the mountains above 4,000 feet in the south and at heights of 3,000 and above in the north. When this melts, upland meadows result. Almost no forest remains, although trees would cover wide areas if goats and charcoal makers could be kept out. The Zagros Foothills generally have only a low herbaceous vegetation, with a few scattered areas of scrub oak. Acorns supply food for the local inhabitants.

The Makran has a width of about seventy miles and is a wilderness of dissected hills and east-west ridges. Elevations in the interior reach 6,000 feet and gradually decrease toward the Gulf of Oman. River terraces are widespread and may be correlated with raised beaches along the coast.

The northern Zagros are more humid than the south, with as much as forty inches of precipitation on exposed slopes in comparison with less than half that in the south. The Makran are even drier and carry snow only in December and January.

The Zagros and Makran are the home of many nomadic tribes who move up and down the slopes from summer to winter pastures with their sheep, goats, horses, and cattle. This migratory life is known as transhumance. Their number is unknown, and many nomads in fact are partly sedentary, but the government of Iran estimates the total for the entire country at one-fifth the population, or roughly 5 million people. The majority of the tribes live in the Zagros Highlands. From north to southeast these are the Kurds, Lurs, Bakhtiari, Kuh Galu, Mamasani, Qashqai, Arabs, Khamseh, and Baluchi. Scores of subgroups are involved, and in places the clan may be more important than the tribe.

The distance of the seasonal migration varies. Kurdish tribes in the north commonly travel fifty miles. In the central Zagros many groups of Bakhtiari move seventy to eighty miles from the foothills to the highlands, often crossing high ranges en route, while farther south the Qashqai migrate as much as 200 and 300 miles. These movements may require two months in each direction. A rough count of animals accompanying such movements amounts to fifty head per person. One Qashqai, when asked how many people were involved, replied that his clan numbered 40,000 people in twenty groups; another and perhaps more accurate reply was, "Like the stars in the heavens, only God knows."

Efforts have been made in recent decades to settle the nomads as farmers, but with only partial success. In many cases, nomadic groups have long assigned some of their members to cultivate limited areas, but there is probably not enough agricultural land to replace the income from grazing.

Inner Persian Basins

Less than 20 per cent of Iran has any possibility of drainage to the ocean. Other areas contribute to the Caspian Sea; some center on the Urmia or Seistan basins. About half of the country lies in the Inner Persian Basins. Here evaporation exceeds the contribution from local rainfall or runoff from the encircling mountains.

Climatic conditions in Inner Persia are harsh. Rain does fall but nowhere amounts to more than a few inches, and it only falls in winter. Summer temperatures are very high, probably among the highest on earth, but winters are bitterly cold due to the elevation. Settlements are confined to the

The railroad from the Persian Gulf to Tehran winds across a barren landscape, treeless and almost uninhabited. (U. S. Air Force.)

few agricultural areas where mountain-fed streams supply an oasis; pastoralism is almost out of the question.

Local highlands divide the region into scores of separate basins. Toward the center of these drainage areas is a terminal lake which may remain dry for eleven months, or as many years, at a time. Such playas usually have slopes which are so gentle in grade, that a little inflow may create a lake a mile in area but only a few inches deep. When the water evaporates, a saline flat or *kavir* appears, creating a waste of crusted salt or a mud flat which may be either rockhard or a slimy morass, depending on recent rainfall. The surface of the kavir is generally broken into polygonal sheets of salt about half an inch thick and with upturned edges. These layers rest on dark slime which usually hardens in summer so that the kavir may be crossed by caravans. Here and there beneath the salt are channels of ooze which never dry.

The word *dasht* applies to the flat gravel plain which may border the kavir. The term *rig* is used for areas of sand dunes, several of which lie near the shores of intermittent lakes. Broad alluvial fans border the surrounding mountains and give the basin a cross-section similar to arid profiles in the American Basin and Range country.

Six major basins are recognized. In the northwest, extending from Tehran to Qum, is the Masileh Basin with a cultivated margin supplied by streams from the Elburz. To the east is the Great Kavir, while further south is Southern Lut, and beyond it the Jaz Murian Basin, each of them arid and nearly lifeless. The two remaining basins occupy linear areas next to the Zagros and are bordered by high mountains which yield some runoff. These are the Isfahan-Sirjan and the Ardistan-Yezd basins.

The Masileh Basin is the most humid of the depressions and contains several semipermanent lakes which total a thousand square miles. Surrounding Tehran and in the Veramin Plain are large areas of prosperous irrigation, with water supplied by mountain streams or from qanats.

The Great Kavir lies south of the railway and road from Tehran to Meshed. This is the largest of the Inner Persian Basins. The subregion covers about 50,000 square miles. The central kavir is virtually impossible to cross, because of either the mud or sharply crusted salt. Elevations approximate 3,000 feet.

Southern Lut is surrounded by mountains 10,000 feet high, but the air over interior Iran is so dry that little rain is extracted. The lowest area has an elevation of some 800 feet and is probably the driest and hottest part of Swasia. Both kavir flats and rig dune areas are widely developed.

The Jaz Murian Basin adjoins the Makran Mountains and is sometimes grouped with them, but it is an inland drainage area similar to those just described. The area measures 26,560 square miles, and the central elevation approximates 1,000 feet. Water is scanty everywhere.

The two remaining basins, those of Isfahan and Yezd, are somewhat different. Each area is about thirty miles wide and 300 miles long, with elevations of some 3,000 feet in the first and 5,000 feet in the second. The former has high mountains on both sides and is well watered; the latter is drier. Each contains several linear kavirs, in most cases with encroachment by the surrounding alluvial fans. The Isfahan Basin is fed by the Zayandeh Rud, already described in Chapter 5, which drains into the Gavkhaneh marsh or kavir. A succession of depressions continues southeast to Sirjan. The Yezd Basin begins near Kashan and extends past Nain and Yezd to Kerman. These mountain-girt basins just to the east of the Elburz somewhat resemble the nearby Niyriz and Shiraz basins within the mountains. Snow-fed streams supply a number of oases, as around Isfahan and Shiraz; while Yezd and Kerman depend on qanat water.

Eastern Persian Highlands

Eastern Iran has two geographic divisions; a succession of mountains, trending north and south, and a series of lowlands along the Afghan border. The latter are more developed in Afghanistan and are considered in the next chapter.

No single name applies to all of the eastern mountains. The area extends from the Soviet frontier some 800 miles south and southeast to the Pakistan border, roughly along longitudes 160° E. and 162° E.

In the Birjand area to the north, numerous elevations reach to a height of 7,000 and 9,000 feet, with villages and grazing grounds above 4,000 feet. Scrub and camel thorn grow on the lower slopes, with scattered trees above. Crops include wheat, barley, opium, melons, grapes, fruits, and vegetables.

Near Nasratabad in the center, rugged chains of mountains up to 7,000 feet enclose a central tableland. Conditions are inhospitable, and there is only a sparse nomadic population. To its east lies the desolate Seistan Basin at the terminus of the Helmand River, and south of it is the frontier railroad town of Zahidan next to Pakistan.

Most Iranian homes are built of mud or stone. This hillside village is near Masjid-i-Sulaiman. (Courtesy Iranian Oil Participants.)

To the south of the point where Iran, Afghanistan, and Pakistan join is a great volcanic area, dominated by the partly active cones of the Taftan group which reach 13,034 feet. These elevations are high enough to induce considerable precipitation so that valleys are well watered. Since the mountains are surrounded everywhere by the most arid of deserts, they form a highland oasis. Numerous relict peoples have found a refuge for their ancient cultures. Along the Gajjari River to the southwest there is a meteorite crater, formed in 1870, which measures 100 by 70 feet, with a depth of thirty-five feet.

The southernmost subdivision of the Eastern Persian Highlands is known as Sarhad. This is a region of parallel ridges and open valleys extending from northwest to southeast. Elevations reach 9,000 feet. Most of the people are Baluchi nomads. Cultivation generally depends on water from qanats.

IRANIAN CITIES

THE CITIES OF IRAN have many things in common. All have grown dramatically in recent decades, notably the capital at Tehran and the oil center of Abadan. Most cities lie on alluvial fans within sight of high mountains and receive their water supply from melting snow, except those near the Persian Gulf. Since these mountains are geologically young and are still growing, many towns have repeatedly experienced severe earthquakes. With the exception of those near the Caspian coast, each city lies in an oasis which abruptly gives way to the desert. Water is a problem almost everywhere.

Most cities have had a long history; several have served as the capital. Invasions have led to the ruin and destruction of many cities so that few great buildings remain from antiquity. Most of the invaders were Afghans, Mongols, Turkmen, or others. The names of Genghis Khan and Tamerlane fit into many urban histories. Even within the twentieth century, Russian, British, or American troops have occupied several centers.

While every city of importance has regular air service, there are many which have no rail connections. Abadan and Ahwaz are the only two cities on navigable rivers. Only a few large cities are connected with paved highways.

Most urban centers have served as local market towns, and their industries reflect the agricultural or pastoral products of the immediate countryside. In the absence of cheap transport, each serves a local market. Cotton and wool textiles, leather goods, or grain milling are found in many cities. Persian carpets are world renowned, and dozens of centers are noted for special patterns.

In one section of each town it is customary to find a covered bazaar, teeming with craftsmen whose methods have scarcely changed for a century; invariably a modern area is nearby, with wide streets and shops which carry an assortment of international merchandise.

The current growth of cities has brought major social changes, for urban population is growing much more rapidly than that of the country as a whole. Due to the influx of rural people and nomads, many cities have doubled their population within two decades. By 1958, there were 278 chartered cities. The population of the ten cities with 100,000 and over exceeds 3 million. Eight other cities are known to have over 50,000 people, so that Iran's urban population is approximately 4 million, or 20 per cent of the national total.

Abadan

Abadan dates only from 1909 when it became the site of the great oil refinery. The city lies on an island, with the Shatt-al-Arab to the west and a distributary of the Karun to the east. Abadan is surrounded by date groves and has an oppressively hot and humid summer climate. Access to the port is limited by sand bars in the Shatt-al-Arab, so that supertankers cannot enter the river. The port handles only oil, but a few miles to the north is the commercial seaport and rail terminal of Khorramshahr. Another rail terminal on the Gulf is at Bandar Shah, and a second oil loading port is at Bandar Mashur. The new offshore terminal at Kharg Island has water deep enough for the largest supertankers.

Ahwaz

Ahwaz lies on the left bank of the Karun River, seventy miles from its junction with the Shatt-al-Arab. Low rapids on the Karun at this point interrupt navigation and make Ahwaz the head of continuous navigation; the city is thus the only inland port in Iran. Ahwaz has long been a bridge city, for Alexander the Great crossed the Karum here on a bridge of boats; today there are both a highway and a railroad bridge, each over 3,000 feet long. The city dominates the plains of Khuzistan, and many of the people are Arab rather than Persian. Although Ahwaz lies some distance from the oil fields, it serves as a local supply center, and its growth has been related to oil production. It is also the

Abadan is Iran's great port for the shipment of refined petroleum. This is a view from the Shatt-al-Arab. (Courtesy Iranian Oil Participants.)

focal point for large scale agricultural developments.

Hamadan and Kermanshah

Hamadan and Kermanshah have much in common. Both lie high in the Zagros Mountains, and both have a rich history. Because of their position, each city is somewhat more humid than many Iranian towns. Both cities lie along the main highway from Baghdad to Tehran, and each is surrounded by a fertile agricultural area. Hamadan is one of the oldest cities in Persia. Under the name of Ecbatana, it was one of the capitals of the Medes in the sixth century B.C. No major ruins remain, but the city does claim the tombs of Esther and Mordecai. Near Kermanshah is Behistun, the great cliff where Darius carved his inscription in three languages.

Isfahan

Few cities in Southwest Asia have the charm of Isfahan; it is a "must" for every traveler since here is the best of Persian architecture. Like so many cities, Isfahan has had a long history of pillage by Afghans, Mongols, and others. The city became the capital about 1063, but it owes its grandeur to Shah Abbas who ruled from 1587 to 1629. A European visitor shortly afterwards reported that the population numbered 600,000, thus rivaling that of London; the walls

IRANIAN CITIES

	Population [1]	*Elevation*	*Airport*	*Railroad*	*Rainfall*
Abadan	226,103	7	x		10″
Ahwaz	119,828	200	x	x	4″
Hamadan	100,029	6,487			14″
Isfahan	254,876	5,817	x		4″
Kermanshah	125,181	4,860			13″
Meshed	242,165	3,104	x	x	9″
Resht	109,493	−50	x		56″
Shiraz	169,088	5,639	x		13″
Tabriz	290,195	4,423	x	x	13″
Tehran	1,513,164	4,002	x	x	9″

[1] *United Nations Demographic Yearbook*, 1957.

measured 24 miles and within them were 162 mosques, 48 theological colleges, 1,802 caravanserais, and 273 public baths. The magnificence of this fabulous city gave rise to the phrase *Isfahan nisf-i-jahan:* "Isfahan is half the world."

Isfahan reached its peak when it was the capital of the Safawid dynasty in the seventeenth century. Here Persian art found its full flowering, with magnificent carpets made with silk and gold threads, miniature paintings, and ceramic and metal work. When Thomas Herbert saw Isfahan in 1628 he wrote, "Gardens here for grandeur and fragour are such as no city in Asia," and twenty years later a French traveler wrote that it was "one of the finest and largest towns I have ever seen."

The city of Hamadan lies on an alluvial fan at the base of snow-crowned mountains; most fields are irrigated. (U. S. Air Force.)

The city is located in a lovely oasis created by the Zayandeh Rud shortly after it leaves the mountains. It lies at 5,800 feet, one of the highest elevations among the major towns of Iran, and enjoys a delightful climate. (See pages 123–127.)

The center of ancient Isfahan was the great square or Maidan, 560 by 174 yards in dimensions. On two sides are tile-domed mosques, on another is the entrance to the covered bazaars, still the most colorful in Swasia. The fourth side contains the Ali Qapu pavilion or lofty gate. Here the Emperor watched polo on the Maidan, the stone goal posts of which still stand. Behind the Ali Qapu is the Hall of Forty Columns where royal emissaries were received.

The main street is the mile long Chehar Bagh, Isfahan's Champs Elysees, which leads to one of five bridges across the river. The name of the street means "four gardens" in reference to the lines of irrigation

The bazaar at Isfahan includes miles of covered lanes, illuminated by openings in the arched roof. (Courtesy Iranian Oil Participants.)

canals and trees. Along this street is the most handsome of the theological colleges, the Madressa, built in 1708–14. The dome, minarets, and walls are covered with exquisite tile patterns, chiefly in turquoise blue, but with yellow and black arabesques.

Across the river, in the suburb Julfa, is a colony of Armenian Christians who transferred here in 1604 from the Russian border city of the same name.

Meshed

Meshed and Qum are the two Iranian cities most sacred to Moslem Shiites. The former is the burial place for the Imam Reza, eighth in line following Mohammed, and also for Harun al Rashid. The latter city holds the tomb of Fatima, sister of Reza. Both shrines have magnificent gold-covered domes, and rank next to Najaf and Kerbela in Iraq as pilgrimage centers. An inscription in the shrine at Meshed praises its beauty by saying "In order to appreciate its full height and glory, the Heavens use the Sun and Moon as binoculars." As with most pilgrimage towns, each city is well supplied with mosques, bazaars, craftsmen, caravanserais, and baths.

Meshed dominates the northeast. The city is on a tributary of the Hari Rud, which leads to Afghanistan and to Soviet Middle Asia. The former lies 100 miles to the east, while the Soviet border is half that distance to the north. Only negligible trade moves to either country; but invasions have frequently come from both directions, and Persian influence has equally penetrated east and north. The railroad from Tehran was opened in 1957. The rainfall amounts to nine inches, falling on twenty-three days per year. January temperatures average near freezing and may drop below zero Fahrenheit during four months. Summers are mild, although temperatures occasionally exceed 100° F. The city is surrounded by orchards and vineyards and is famous for its apricots and cherries. Nearby is one of the world's major sources of turquoise.

Resht

Resht is unique among Iranian cities for its rainy climate and because it is below sea level. Many houses are of timber construction, something which is quite impossible in the desert. The city lies on the delta of the Sefid Rud, some fifteen miles inland. Local industries reflect the climate, with rice, silk, tea, and jute mills predominant. The city owes some of its growth to the development of trade with the Soviet Union. There was a brief period of Russian occupation in the eighteenth century under Peter the Great. Thirty miles away is the Caspian seaport of Pahlevi.

Shiraz

Shiraz had a glorious past when it was the capital of the country. Still earlier, nearby Persepolis was the center of Persian power. A commentary on the city's past is found in the expression, "When Shiraz was Shiraz, Cairo was one of its suburbs." The city's claim to fame rests equally on its two great poets, Saadi, 1184–1291, and Hafiz, 1325–1388, who praised its beautiful gardens and excellent wine. Remaining as souvenirs of its past, Shiraz has some of the finest covered bazaars in all Iran. Along with old streets, the present city has broad avenues and modern buildings. Thanks to the generosity of one of its overseas citizens, Shiraz was the first city in Iran to have a modern municipal water system, and its hospital is one of the finest anywhere.

The oasis of Shiraz occupies a valley six miles wide by twenty miles long, surrounded by barren hills. Conditions of climate and agriculture somewhat resemble those of Isfahan except that Shiraz is lower in elevation and farther south.

A few miles from Shiraz is the ancient capital at Persepolis, center for the international empires of Cyrus, Darius, and Xerxes. The palace was destroyed by Alexander in 330 B.C., but the ruins are still magnificent. The great hall had a hundred columns sixty feet in height.

Tabriz

Tabriz is the metropolis of northwestern Iran and owes much of its history and present role to its proximity to Turkey and the Soviet Union. The former lies 100 miles to the west, while the latter is sixty miles to the north. Invasions in wartime and commerce during peace have brought a mixture of cultures. Many of the inhabitants are Azerbaijani and Armenians; others are Turkish. This diversity is reflected in language. Turkish is widely used in speech, Persian is the common written language, while Arabic is used for prayers. There was a time following the fall of Baghdad, when Tabriz was the greatest center for trade between the East and West and a major point for commerce from China.

Many of the fine buildings of Tabriz are gone or are in ruins, though they are still magnificent in decay. In reply to the suggestion that Isfahan was once "half the world," local patriots reply that this might have been true had there been no Tabriz.

A glimpse of Tabriz early in the fourteenth century is provided by the Arab traveler, Ibn Batuta, who journeyed there from Baghdad:

> We reached the town after ten days' travelling, and encamped outside it in a place called Ash-Shem. Here there is a fine hospice, where travellers are supplied with food, consisting of bread,

The ruins of the ancient capital at Persepolis, near Shiraz, convey only a suggestion of the grandeur of ancient Persia. (Courtesy Iranian Oil Participants.)

meat, rice cooked in butter, and sweetmeats. The next morning I entered the town and we came to a great bazaar, called the Ghazan bazaar, one of the finest bazaars I have seen the world over. Every trade is grouped separately in it. I passed through the jewellers' bazaar, and my eyes were dazzled by the varieties of precious stones that I beheld. They were displayed by beautiful slaves wearing rich garments with a waist-sash of silk, who stood in front of the merchants exhibiting the jewels to the wives of the Turks, while the women were buying them in large quantities and trying to outdo one another.

The city lies on an alluvial plain which slopes to Lake Urmia from the volcanic peak of Sahand, 12,138 feet high. Hot springs above the city give rise to its name. In the year 1404, when the population numbered 200,000, one visitor reported that Tabriz had the finest baths in the world. Tabriz often has experienced severe earthquakes, reflecting its volcanic and tectonic position. In the earthquake of 1721, 80,000 people perished.

Tabriz also holds the distinction of being the coldest city in Iran, a logical result of its high latitude and altitude. Temperatures have dropped to -18° F., and the monthly averages for January and February are below freezing.

The broad gauge railroad from Julfa on the Soviet frontier was completed in 1916, and the standard gauge line to Tehran was opened in 1958. The city has long served as a gateway for European trade brought overland from Erzurum in Turkey, 409 miles to the west, or from the Black Sea port of Trabzon, 206 miles farther on. A new rail link across the Turkish border will be of commercial importance.

Tehran

The capital city of Tehran, at an elevation of 4,000 feet, lies on a broad alluvial fan which sweeps south from the Elburz Mountains. The older part of the city lies downslope, the modern center is farther up, and the best residential section lies in the Shimran suburb at the base of the mountains, a thousand feet higher than the central business district. As is the case in Salt Lake City near the Wasatch, one may look up many streets and see snow-covered mountains. The volcanic cone of Demavend is often visible, fifty-six miles to the northeast. Irrigation ditches known as *jubes* flow down many streets, providing water for gardens inside courtyard walls. Dozens of qanats terminate in the city. They were once the chief source of domestic water.

The climate reflects Tehran's interior position and elevation. Rain falls on about twenty-seven days, occurring irregularly from November to April, with a total of nine inches. Summer temperatures occasionally exceed 105°F. and may drop to zero or below in winter. January and July monthly averages are 36°F. and 86°F. respectively. The rainfall is too low for unirrigated agriculture, but the combination of thousands of qanats and mountain streams which flow across the piedmont fans have turned large areas into productive gardens. Immediately across the outermost irrigation canal, the desert begins.

The capital was moved to Tehran in 1788 by the founder of the Qajar Dynasty. The Gulestan Palace is famous for its jeweled Peacock Throne, valued at $30 million, which was brought from India where it had been made for Shah Jahan, builder of the Taj Mahal. The city is now the political, cultural, and commercial center of the nation. Its population numbered 300,000 in 1939, but grew fivefold in the next two decades. Tehran so dominates the urban life of Iran that its population equals the combined population of all other cities of over 100,000.

The railroad from the Persian Gulf to Tehran was opened in 1938, and the city now has rail connections in four directions. By rail, the Persian Gulf is 575 miles to the south and the Caspian Sea is 287 miles to the north. Meshed is 575 miles east, while Tabriz is 461 miles to the northwest. Thirty miles to the south is the city of Veramin, on the fertile plain of the same name. About the same distance to the west is industrial Karaj, where a dam and reservoir provide hydroelectricity and water for Tehran. At least one-quarter of Iran's industries, chiefly chemicals and textiles, are concentrated around Tehran.

PROBLEMS AND PROSPECTS

Iran is in a hurry to become modernized, and thanks to the royalties from oil, this is now possible. It is well to recognize, however, that material progress cannot safely outrun social advancement. Centuries of inertia and entrenched interests such as the landlord system cannot be altered overnight.

Many of the problems of modern Iran resemble those of ancient Persia, including the wise use of water, national coherence in the face of physical disunity, difficult communications across rugged mountains and barren deserts, wide economic and cultural differences between rich and poor, the presence of diverse ethnic groups, and political pressures from the outside. Current interest in Communism finds a parallel in the sixteenth-century teachings of Mazdok.

Tehran lies at the base of the Elburz, snow crowned for much of the year. The building at the left is a modern department store. (G. B. C.)

To these problems are added the opportunities and responsibilities associated with oil revenues, the ideological contests between constitutional monarchy and democracy, Iran's position as a contest zone between the Soviet Union and the United States, and the tempo of twentieth-century changes.

In Iran, perhaps more than elsewhere, the four landscape colors presented in the opening chapter of this book provide a key to geographic understanding. Brown deserts, white snow-covered mountains, green oases, and black oil: these are the elements with which the planner must deal. The cash value of oil royalties is dramatic, but the basic importance of melting snow ranks first. Without melted snow from the mountains, there would be few cultivated fields and few people. Iran's long-range future rests on the wise management of water. Oil and mineral resources are transitory, whereas agriculture is permanent, or may be if properly managed.

The original Seven Year Development Law was passed in 1948 and provided that 60 per cent of all oil royalties were to be turned over to a semi-independent authority known as the Plan Organization. The law for the Second Seven Year Program, 1956, stated the objectives as " . . . increased production, developing exports . . . , agriculture and industries, discovering and exploiting mines and natural resources, improving and completing means of communication, improving public health . . . , raising educational standards . . . and living conditions." Expenditures of over a billion dollars were envisioned under the Second Plan. The Plan Organization operates under four divisions. Their titles and the amounts expended between 1955 and 1958 are shown in the accompanying table.

IRANIAN PLAN ORGANIZATION [1]

A. Agriculture and Engineering	
Irrigation and dam construction	$ 39,764,000
Agricultural credits	6,148,000
Khuzistan development program	5,498,000
Qanats and deep wells	4,779,000
Total	$ 77,704,000
B. Communications and Transportation	
Railways	$ 47,223,000
Road construction	36,608,000
Airports	7,000,000
Tele-communications	6,548,000
Total	$110,726,000
C. Mines and Industries	
Textiles	$ 14,026,000
Cement	12,718,000
Industrial Credit Bank	9,547,000
Sugar	6,789,000
Total	$ 46,022,000
D. Social Development	
Municipal improvements	$ 12,933,000
Public health	11,588,000
Education	10,818,000
Total	$ 41,404,000

[1] Expenditure September 25, 1955 to March 20, 1958. *The Plan Organization of Iran.*

Agriculture is the prime activity in Iran, for it involves 70 per cent of the population. Since the rainfall in most of the country is far below crop requirements, it is most fortunate that Iran has a carry-over of winter moisture in the form of snow. Without its mountains, 95 per cent of Iran would be a desert and there would be almost no source of water for irrigation.

Four irrigation projects, relatively small, were completed during the First Seven Year Plan. One is on the Bampur River west of Iranshah in the Jaz Murian Basin, where a dam provides water for 1,500 hectares. Two low dams on the lower Helmand divert water for 20,000 hectares in Seistan. A dam near Golpayegan, north of Isfahan, has added 2,000 hectares to the irrigated area. The fourth project is the Dasht-i-Moghan network of canals in Azerbaijan, which irrigate 18,500 hectares.

The Second Plan called for three major river projects, already referred to in the section on Resources, with each involving large-scale electrical and irrigation works. The Sefid Rud Dam stores 1,688 million cubic meters of water and irrigates 300,000 acres in the western Caspian plain. The Karaj Dam supplies domestic water for Tehran, thirty-five miles to the east. The Diz River Dam provides for irrigation, flood control, and electricity in the Khuzistan Plain along the Persian Gulf; the reservoir stores sufficient water to irrigate 360,000 acres. Surveys for numerous other dam sites have been initiated, looking toward the irrigation of 450,000 acres.

The most comprehensive agricultural project of the 1960's is the Khuzistan program on the alluvial fans and coastal plains at the head of the Persian Gulf. The Karun and numerous smaller rivers flow out of the Zagros Mountains, and ruins of ancient irrigation works suggest that this was once a major granary. Plans call for a local authority analogous to the Tennessee Valley Authority; in fact, some of the same engineers who developed the T.V.A. are involved.

Communications have long been an Iranian bottleneck and have perpetuated the cultural diversity and economic isolation of the country. During World War II, the newly built Trans-Iranian Railway enabled 5 million tons of supplies to reach the Soviet Union. The two terminals of the east-west line from Meshed to Tabriz were finished

Transportation is one of Iran's major problems. Bus services connect all cities, but roads are poor. This scene is in Tehran. (Courtesy Near East Foundation.)

respectively in 1957 and 1958. Work was started decades ago on a railway to Yezd and Kerman, and on to the Pakistan railhead at Zahidan, but has never been completed.

At the beginning of the Second Plan, only 2,045 out of 21,162 kilometers of the road system were hard-surfaced. Progress has been slow, in part due to topographic barriers. Good roads are a major need.

Iran has international airports at Tehran and Abadan, as well as eight local facilities, all enlarged with Plan funds.

Port facilities have been increased at both Khorramshahr on the Shatt-al-Arab and at nearby Bandar Shahpur at the head of the Gulf. These are the only ocean-rail terminals and the only ports of importance for overseas shipping other than oil.

Industrial developments are all of recent date, especially since 1930. Textiles lead in value, and expansion under the Second Plan was expected to make the country self-sufficient, with a capacity of some 250 million square yards of cotton textiles. One of the largest plants is at Shahi near the Caspian, others are near Tehran.

Sugar has long been produced from beets, but cane mills are included in the Khuzistan program.

Cement is in wide demand, with new or enlarged mills in several centers. Aside from petroleum refining, other aspects of chemical industries are in their infancy.

Geological surveys were included in the program of the Second Plan, and numerous mines are being enlarged. Plans for a steel center point to Azna, 100 kilometers south of Arak and thus roughly midway between Tehran and the Gulf. Iran's mineral assets appear modest, but adequate.

Social development programs call for a major advance in civic welfare, public health, and education. Municipal assistance has been provided for water supplies, street pavement, and electrification. Public health projects have involved disease control, hospital construction, and the training of public health technicians. During the first two and one-half years of the Second Plan, 400 schools were built under the program, and the new campus for the University of Tehran was completed.

While this fourth group of expenditures is the smallest, it is supplemented by tax-derived revenues and is clearly fundamental to all progress. Explosive ideas are sweeping Iran, as elsewhere, raising many problems such as farm tenancy, the control of water rights, and urban development. Some of these can be resolved only after a wise understanding of geographic relations.

REFERENCES

General References

Blanchard, Raoul: "L'Iran," in GEOGRAPHIE UNIVERSELLE, VIII, ASIE OCCIDENTALE. Paris: Armand Colin (1929), 128–170.

Bobek, Hans: "Die Naturlichen Walder and Geholzfluren Irans," *Bonner Geog. Abhandlungen,* VIII (1951).

Brenn, Harry A.: DEVELOPMENT OF RESOURCES: KEY TO IRAN'S FUTURE. Washington: Dept. of State (1959).

Farman, Hafez F.: IRAN: A SELECTED AND ANNOTATED BIBLIOGRAPHY. Washington: Library of Congress (1951).

Clapp, Frederick G.: "Recent Investigations in Iran," *Geog. Rev.,* XXV (1935), 337–339.

Curzon, George: PERSIA AND THE PERSIAN QUESTION. 2 vols., London: (1892).

Edwards, K. C.: "Routes to Russia through Iran," *Geog. Jour.,* XCIX (1942), 44–46.

Elwell-Sutton, L. P.: MODERN IRAN. London: Routledge (1941).

Elwell-Sutton, L. P.: A GUIDE TO IRANIAN AREA STUDY. Ann Arbor: Edwards (1952).

Field, Henry: "Contributions to the Anthropology of Iran," 2 vols., *Field Mus. of Nat. Hist, Anthrop. Ser.,* XXIX (1939), 1–507, 511–706.

Frye, Richard N.: IRAN. London: Allen & Unwin (1954).

* Ghirshman, R.: IRAN FROM THE EARLIEST TIMES TO THE ISLAMIC CONQUEST. London: (1954).

Greeley, John N.: "Iran in Wartime," *Nat. Geog. Mag.,* LXXXIV (1943), 129–156.

* Haas, William S.: IRAN. New York: Columbia Univ. Press (1946).

Kernan, Henry S.: "A Policy of Conservation for the Caspian Forests of Iran," *Middle East Jour.,* VII (1953), 228–234.

Kernan, Henry S.: "Forest Management in Iran," *Middle East Jour.,* XI (1957), 199–202.

Lambton, Ann K. S.: "Persia," *Jour. Royal Central Asian Soc.,* XXXI (1944), 8–22.

Mason, F. C.: IRAN. London: H.M. Stationery Office (1957).

Roberts, N. S.: IRAN: ECONOMIC AND COMMERCIAL CONDITIONS. London: Board of Trade (1948).

Sykes, Percy: A HISTORY OF PERSIA, 2 vol. London: Macmillan (1950).

U. S. Board on Geographic Names: IRAN. Washington: Dept. of Interior (1956).

Warne, William E.: MISSION FOR PEACE: POINT 4 IN IRAN. Indianapolis: Bobbs Merrill (1956).

* Wilbur, Donald N.: IRAN. Princeton: Princeton Univ. Press (1955).

Wilber, Donald N.: IRAN: OASIS OF STABILITY IN THE MIDDLE EAST? New York: Foreign Policy Assoc. (1959).

Wilson, Arnold T.: A BIBLIOGRAPHY OF PERSIA. Oxford: Clarendon Press (1930).

Wilson, Arnold T.: PERSIA. London: Ernest Benn Ltd. (1932).

Travel and Description

Bell, Gertrude: PERSIAN PICTURES. London: Ernest Benn (1928).

Blunt, Wilfred: A PERSIAN SPRING. London: Barrie (1957).

Case, Paul Edward: "I Become a Bakhtiari," *Nat. Geog. Mag.*, XLI (1947), 325–358.

Clapp, F. G.: "Tehran and the Elburz," *Geog. Rev.*, XX (1930), 69–85.

Cooper, Merian C., and Schoedsack, Ernest B.: GRASS. New York: Putnams (1925).

* Costa, A., and Lockhart, L.: PERSIA. London: Thames & Hudson (1957).

Cowan, J. M.: "Persia and its Desert-Gardens," *Scot. Geog. Mag.*, XLVIII (1932), 193–196.

Cronin, Vincent: THE LAST MIGRATION. London: Hart-Davis (1957).

Douglas, William O.: STRANGE LANDS AND FRIENDLY PEOPLE. New York: Harper (1951).

* Douglas, William O.: WEST OF THE INDUS. New York: Doubleday (1958).

Douglas, William O.: "West from the Khyber Pass," *Nat. Geog. Mag.*, CXIV (1958), 1–44.

Gabriele, Alfons: "The Southern Lut and Iranian Baluchistan," *Geog. Jour.*, XVII (1938), 193–210.

Garrod, Oliver: "The Nomadic Tribes of Persia To-day," *Jour. Royal Central Asian Soc.*, XXXIII (1946), 32–46.

Garrod, Oliver: "The Qashqai Tribe of Fars," *Jour. Royal Central Asian Soc.*, XXXIII (1946), 293–306.

Hackin, J.: "In Persia and Afghanistan with the Citroen Trans-Asiatic Expedition," *Geog. Jour.*, LXXXIII (1934), 353–363.

Harrison, J. V.: "The Bakhtiari Country, South-Western Persia," *Geog. Jour.*, LXXX (1932), 193–210.

Harrison, J. V.: "Kuhgalu: South-West Iran," *Geog. Jour.*, LXXXVIII (1936), 20–36.

Harrison, J. V.: "The Jaz Murian Depression, Persian Baluchistan," *Geog. Jour.*, CI (1943), 206–225.

Harrison, J. V.: "South-West Persia: A Survey of Pish-i-Kuh in Luristan," *Geog. Jour.*, CVIII (1946), 55–70.

Huntington, Ellsworth: "The Basins of Eastern Persia and Seistan," in Pumpelly, R., EXPLORATIONS IN TURKESTAN. Washington: Carnegie Inst. (1905) 219–317.

Ivanov, W.: "Notes on the Ethnology of Khurasan," *Geog. Jour.*, LXVII (1926) 143–158.

Ivanov, W.: "Alamut," *Geog. Jour.*, LXXVII (1931), 38–45.

Jacob, A.: "Waziristan," *Jour. Royal Central Asian Soc.*, XIV (1927) 238–257.

Lamb, Harold: "Mountain Tribes of Iran and Iraq," *Nat. Geog. Mag.*, LXXXIX (1946), 385–408.

Lockhart, L.: FAMOUS CITIES OF IRAN. London (1939).

Lockhart, L.: "Khuzistan Past and Present," *Asiatic Rev.*, XLIV (1948), 410–416.

Lockhart, L.: "Isfahan," *Jour. Royal Central Asian Soc.*, XXXVII (1950), 248–261.

Long, George W.: "Journey into Troubled Iran," *Nat. Geog. Mag.*, C (1951), 425–464.

McMahon, Henry: "Recent Survey and Exploration in Seistan," *Geog. Jour.*, XXVIII (1906), 333–352.

Mustoe, J. E. H.: "Contrasts in the Elburz," *Geog. Mag.*, XXX (1957), 273–282.

Noel, J. B. L.: "A Reconnaissance in the Caspian Provinces of Persia," *Geog. Jour.*, LVII (1921), 401–418.

Norden, Hermann: UNDER PERSIAN SKIES. London: Witherby (1928).

Payne, Robert: THE SPLENDOR OF PERSIA. New York: Knopf (1957).

Poidebard, R. P.: "The Junction of the Highways in Persia," *Jour. Royal Central Asian Soc.*, III (1924), 206–228.

Powell, Edward A.: BY CAMEL AND CAR TO THE PEACOCK THRONE. London: J. Long (1923).

Prickett, Margot Peel: "Persepolis and the Tombs of the Kings," *Geog. Mag.*, XV (1942), 80–87.

Ravensdale, Mary Irene Curzon: "Old and New in Persia," *Nat. Geog. Mag.*, LXXVI (1939), 325–355.

Rickmers, W. R.: "Lazistan and Ajaristan," *Geog. Jour.*, LXXXIV (1934), 465–480.

Schmidt, Erich F.: FLIGHTS OVER ANCIENT CITIES OF IRAN. Chicago: Univ. of Chicago (1940).

Shor, Jean, and Shor, Franc: "We Dwelt in Kashgai Tents . . . With Nomad Shepherds of Iran," *Nat. Geog. Mag.*, CI (1952), 805–832.

Skrine, C. P.: "The Highland of Persian Baluchistan," *Geog. Jour.*, LXXVIII (1931), 321–340.

* Smith, Anthony: BLIND WHITE FISH IN PERSIA. New York: Dutton (1953). [Qanats]

Stark, Freya: "The Bronzes of Luristan," *Geog. Jour.*, LXXX (1932), 498–505.

Stark, Freya: THE VALLEYS OF THE ASSASSINS AND OTHER PERSIAN TRAVELS. London: Murray (1934).

Stark, Freya: "The Valley of the Assassins to the Caspian Sea," *Scot. Geog. Mag.*, LIII (1937), 156–166.

Stein, Aurel: "Archaeological Reconnaissance in Southern Persia," *Geog. Jour.*, LXXXIII (1934), 119–134.

Sykes, Edward: "Life and Travel in Persia," *Scot. Geog. Mag.*, XX (1904), 403–415.

Sykes, Edward: "Isfahan," *Jour. Royal Central Asian Soc.*, XXXIII (1946), 307–317.

Sykes, Christopher: "Persian Gardens," *Geog. Mag.*, XXX (1957), 326–329.

"Trebizond and the Persian Transit Trade," *Jour. Royal Central Asian Soc.*, XXXI (1944), 289–301.

Ullens de Schooten, M. T.: "Among the Kashkai: A Tribal Migration in Persia," *Geog. Mag.*, XXVII (1954), 68–78.

Ullens de Schooten, M. T.: LORDS OF THE MOUNTAIN, SOUTHERN PERSIA AND THE KASHKAI TRIBE. London: Chatto and Windus (1956).

Wilson, Arnold T.: "The Bakhtiaris," *Jour. Royal Central Asian Soc.*, XIII (1926), 205–225.

Wilson, Arnold T.: EARLY SPANISH AND PORTUGESE TRAVELERS IN PERSIA. London: (1927).

Agriculture

Beckett, P. H. T.: "Agriculture in Central Persia," *Tropical Agriculture*, XXXIV (1957), 9–28.

Beckett, P. H. T.: "The Soils of Kerman, South Persia," *Jour. of Soil Science*, IX (1958), 20–32.

Hadary, Gideon: "The Agrarian Reform Problem in Iran," *Middle East Jour.*, V (1951), 181–196.

Lambton, Ann K. S.: LANDLORD AND PEASANT IN PERSIA. London: Oxford Univ. Press (1953).

Tannous, A. I.: "Agricultural Production and Flood Consumption in Iran," *Foreign Agriculture,* VIII (1944) 27–42.

Climate and Irrigation

Beckett, P. H. T.: "Waters of Persia," *Geog. Mag.,* XXIV (1951) 230–240.

Clapp, G. R.: "Iran: a TVA for the Khuzestan Region," *Middle East Jour.,* XI (1957), 1–11.

Fisher, B.: "Irrigation Systems of Persia," *Geog. Rev.,* XVIII (1928), 302–306.

Fitt, R. L.: "Irrigation Development in Central Persia," *Jour. Royal Central Asian Soc.,* XL (1953), 124–133.

* Ganji, M. H.: "The Climates of Iran," *Bull. Soc. Geog. d'Egypte,* XXVIII (1955), 195–299.

Neumann, Heinrich: "Die Physisch-Geographischen Grundlagen der Kunstlichen Bewasserung des Iran und Irak," *Deutsches Institut fur Landerkunde Wissenschaftliche Veroffentlichungen,* XII (1953), 4–46.

Peterson, A. Delbert: BIBLIOGRAPHY ON THE CLIMATE OF IRAN. Washington: U. S. Weather Bureau (1957).

Scharlau, Kurt: "Zum Problem der Pluvialzeiten in Nordost-Iran," *Zeitschrift Geomorphol,* II (1958), 258–277.

Geology (See Chapter 8, Oil)

* Bobek, Hans: "Features and Formation of the Great Kavir and Masileh," Tehran: Arid Zone Research Center, Pub. 2 (1959).

Clapp, F. G.: "Geology of Eastern Iran," *Bull. Geol. Soc. of Amer.,* LI (1940), 1–102.

* Elwell-Sutton, L. P.: PERSIAN OIL. London: Lawrence and Wishart (1955).

Harrison, J. V.: "The Gypsum Deposits of South-Western Persia," *Econ. Geol.,* XIX (1924), 259–274.

Harrison, J. V.: "The Geology of Some Salt-Plugs in Laristan (Southern Persia)," *Quart. Jour. Geol. Soc.,* LXXXVI (1930), 463–522.

Lees, G. M.: "Reservoir Rocks of Persian Oil Fields," *Bull. Amer. Assoc. Petrol. Geols.,* XVII (1933), 229–240.

Lees, G. M.: THE GEOLOGY OF THE OILFIELD BELT OF IRAN AND IRAQ. London: Oxford Univ. Press (1938).

CHAPTER 17

Afghanistan

Four Roads
The Afghan Landscape
Time and People
Seven Regions
Livelihood and the Future
References

FOUR ROADS

THE LAND of the Afghans is one of the largest land-locked nations in Asia. It lies near the heart of the continent, and has been an historic transit way as well as a buffer between larger states.

Unfortunately, none of Afghanistan's neighbors are dependably friendly, but since these neighboring countries are rivals, Afghanistan can probably count on at least one avenue to the outside world. The boundary next to Pakistan measures 1,200 miles, that along the Soviet Union extends 1,000 miles, and the Iranian frontier is 500 miles long. In the far northeast, Afghanistan has a common border with China for fifty miles.

Two roads lead into Afghanistan from Pakistan on the east, two cross from Soviet territory to the north, and one leads from Iran on the west. All of these gateways are linked by a circular road which surrounds the central mountains and joins the four main cities of Kabul, Mazar-i-Sharif, Herat, and Kandahar. These cities are the key points in Afghan life, centers of distinct geographic regions and points of departure and destination for travelers.

As an introduction to the Afghan landscape, it may be helpful to follow these four connecting routes. Travel is difficult since the roads are notoriously bad. Major improvements are slowly changing conditions, so that the following paragraphs will omit reference to impassable mud roads, deep dust, poor bridges or their absence, and the lack of repair facilities.

From the Khyber to Mazar-i-Sharif

The historic eastern gateway to Afghanistan is by way of the Khyber Pass, which for the past forty centuries has witnessed tides of invaders pouring through toward the plains of India. Some of the conquerors who have swept through this mountainous region were Alexander, Mahmoud of

(Opposite) This scene includes many of the components of Afghan landscapes: rugged mountains, fertile valleys, and karakul sheep. (Courtesy James M. Cudney.)

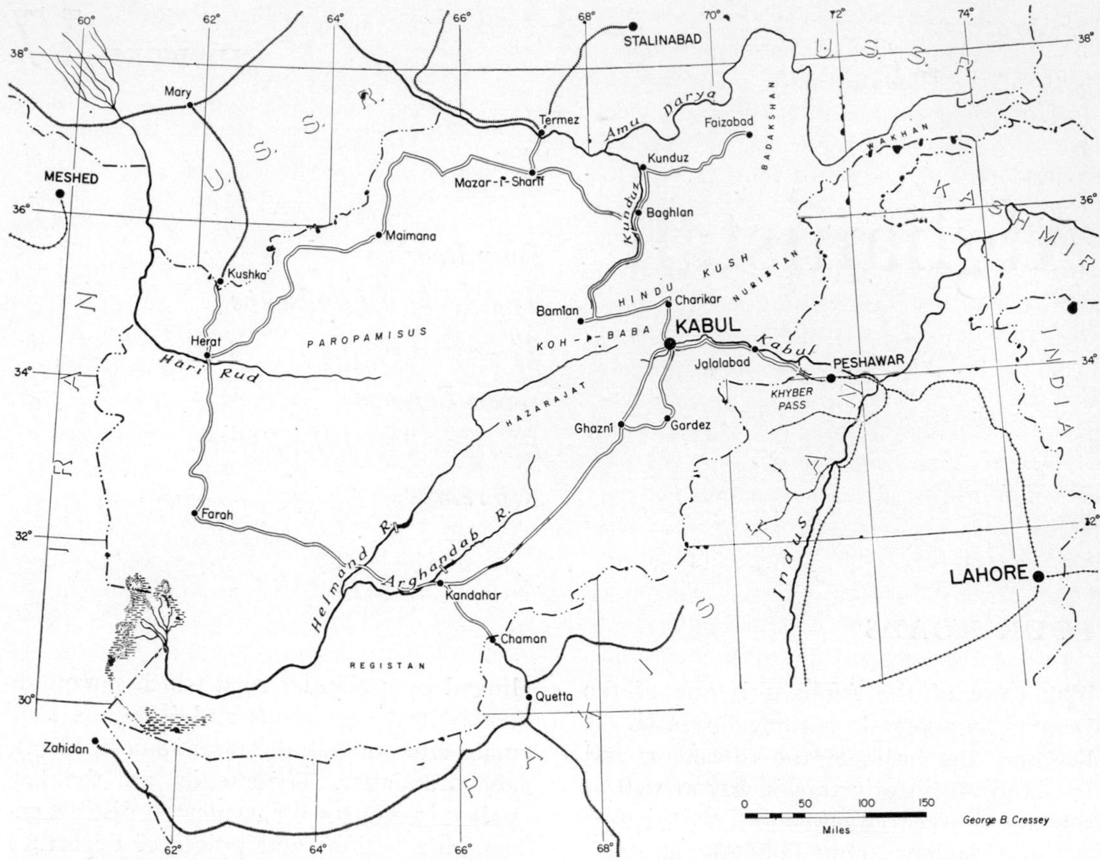

Afghanistan lies astride the Hindu Kush system, with the two sides linked by a circular road. The country has two gateways to Pakistan on the east and two avenues northward to the Soviet Union.

Ghazni, Genghis Khan, Tamerlane, Baber, and, coming in from the reverse direction, the British. Local tribesmen still make trouble, so that the pass is open only during daylight hours, except with special permission and with military escort.

AFGHANISTAN DATA

Area	251,000 square miles
	650,000 square kilometers
Arable area	90,150 square kilometers
Population	13,000,000

Travelers from the east usually start their journey from Peshawar in Pakistan, the beginning of the route which leads deep into Central Asia. Peshawar lies in a broad basin near the Kabul River, but there are impassable gorges upstream so that the road winds up and over the Khyber Pass. The pass begins fourteen miles west of the city, and the summit is seventeen miles farther on.

Many travelers find the Khyber disappointing, for although the hills are barren and rocky, the elevation is only 3,500 feet; it is its history and the many fortified points which lend glamour to the Khyber Pass. Ex-

NOTE: For additional material, see Chapter 5, The Helmand River, page 136. For hospitality and assistance, I am indebted to Mr. J. Christy Wilson, Jr., Mr. Harold Amos, and Mr. Aloys A. Michel.

tending through the pass is a modern two-lane highway, several caravan trails, and a railroad which extends only to the border.

Afghanistan begins just across the pass. Here most men carry a rifle, all but nomadic women are veiled, and one finds no trace of the veneer of Westernization left by British rule in India. Long processions of nomads with their camels and sheep crowd the road each spring and fall, contesting for space with trucks grossly overloaded with modern merchandise. The old is more impressive than the new; friendship and hospitality are given in return for a smile.

The rainfall to the east of the pass is no more than fifteen inches. falling mostly during the summer monsoon, whereas to the west, the amount drops to eight inches, occurring largely in winter. Here is the easternmost extent of Mediterranean climate.

West of the pass for forty miles, the landscape is dry and lifeless—a furnace of dust in summer and a dry steppe in winter. Then the road enters the oasis of Jalalabad, set in a fertile plain along the Kabul River, where irrigation water has transformed the steppe into a verdant garden. The contrast between the surrounding brown landscape and the green fields was strikingly described by one traveler as the passage from Hell to Paradise. In place of desolation, there are fruits and flowers. Since Jalalabad is lower in elevation than most Afghan cities, it has groves of dates, oranges, and pomegranates, and even grows some sugar cane.

The road west to Kabul is a continuation of the same contrast between dry landscapes and irrigated fields. Farmsteads are commonly surrounded by high adobe walls with a high corner tower which holds a living room for the men. Tall poplars and fine mulberry and locust trees grow where planted, but only traces of the once extensive natural forests remain.

As the traveler continues westward along the road, the countryside becomes more rocky and one sights occasional glimpses of distant snow peaks. A succession of barren passes carries the highway to 7,500 feet elevation. Farther on, it enters the gorge of the Kabul River where major engineering operations have opened a modern road to the capital.

The wise traveler will allow a long day for the 187 miles from Peshawar to Kabul,

CITIES OF AFGHANISTAN

City	*United Nations Demographic Yearbook*	*Statesman's Yearbook*	*Local Estimate*
Kabul	154,134	206,208	200,000
Kandahar	—	77,186	75,000
Herat	—	75,632	
Mazar-i-Sharif			50,000

Afghan boys like to dress up, even though the bullets are only wooden. (Courtesy James Cudney.)

for any misfortune or bad weather may lengthen the trip to two days.

Kabul is the metropolis of Afghanistan, surprisingly cosmopolitan with its wide, Russian-paved streets, ultramodern German street lighting, and block after block of three- and four-story modern buildings. Souvenirs of the seventeenth-century bazaars remain, but much of historic Kabul has been destroyed by successive invaders, notably during the wars with Britain in 1842 and 1880. Remnants of the old city wall and the Bela Hissar fort contrast with the modern airfield. In one section of the old town, merchants display piles of carpets or bales of karakul ready for export; nearby the shops are filled with cotton cloth from Japan or canned food from Britain.

Kabul became the capital under Baber in 1505, but an important settlement has existed here or nearby for a long time, since it commands the passes to both India and Russia. Darius was here or at nearby Charikar in 516 B.C., later came Alexander the Great. Like all cities of Swasia, Kabul is in the midst of dramatic metamorphosis. The ethnic diversity of Kabul is a miniature of the country as a whole. Fewer than half the people speak Pushtu or Pathan, terms for proper Afghan. Others are Tajiks, Hazaras, and representatives of the twenty different people who make up Afghanistan. Many people speak Persian. The university, founded in 1946, has over a thousand students divided among eight faculties.

This Afghan girl is dressed for a fair in Kabul and holds a miniature water jar. (Courtesy James Cudney.)

Snow-covered mountains surround the broad Kabul basin, those to the west and north being higher than anything in the continental United States. The city lies at 5,955 feet. Irrigation canals and qanats provide water for fields of wheat and barley and for the many orchards. So much water is withdrawn from the Kabul River that in the fall it shrinks to a small stream.

Only four automobile roads lead out of the Kabul basin; one extends east to Peshawar, two others go south to Kandahar, and the fourth leads north over the Hindu Kush to Soviet Middle Asia. More than a dozen historic trails cross the mountains, but only one pass lies below 10,000 feet. The most direct route is the 12,000-foot Salang Pass, but snow closes the trail for several months. A modern highway and tunnel are under construction in order to facilitate travel.

In 1933 the first automobile road across the Hindu Kush was completed. It extends north of Kabul through rolling country for thirty-eight miles and then turns west up the Ghorband Valley to wind over the 9,800-foot Shibar Pass. In places, the road follows a precarious ledge blasted out of the cliffs, while far below a stream rushes down the narrow valley. The driver must be careful, for around the next hairpin curve, the road may be solidly blocked by herds of sheep or trains of camels. Stone castles overlook tiny

Kabul is both old and new; these modern buildings line one of the main streets of the capital. (G. B. C.)

flood-plain fields of wheat, barley, and rice.

Beyond the pass, the road leaves the watershed of the Kabul River and descends into a north-flowing tributary of the Amu Darya which cuts across the main range of the Hindu Kush in an antecedent canyon so deep and narrow that the great snow peaks on either side cannot be seen. Three hundred and ninety miles to the north of Kabul is the city of Mazar-i-Sharif, and forty miles farther on is the Soviet frontier with the border city of Termez. From the Khyber Pass to the Amu Darya, it is 617 miles, which can be traveled in three days of hard driving.

Mazar-i-Sharif is a city of some 50,000 people and the chief political and commercial center of northern Afghanistan. The city is noteworthy for its large mosque, erected in 1481, which replaced an earlier shrine built in 1136. This is said to contain the tomb of Ali, the son-in-law of Mohammed, who is more commonly thought to be buried at Najaf in Iraq. Mazar-i-Sharif is the major port of entry for Soviet merchandise, including gasoline. Some of these goods are brought from the rail terminal at Termez in the Soviet Union, while others arrive up the Amu Darya by boat. Camel caravans and big trucks pass through Mazar-i-Sharif daily on their way to Kabul. Other towns nearby include Baghlan with its beet sugar mill and Kunduz and Pul-i-Khumri, each with cotton textile plants.

In the midst of the Hindu Kush, some eighteen miles off the main road, is the secluded Bamian Valley. Here is a veritable Shangri-La, a lovely, well-watered oasis sur-

The Bamian valley is a "Shangri La" oasis in the midst of the barren Hindu Kush. The valley walls are cut by hundreds of monastery caves and by a 175 foot statue of Buddha. (G. B. C.)

rounded by lofty snow-covered mountains. The attraction of Bamian, however, is not in its productivity but in its monuments to Buddhism. During the period of Buddhism's spread from India to China in the seventh century, Bamian became a great monastery attracting over a thousand monks. For five centuries, they decorated cave temples with Graeco-Buddhist art. Two enormous statues of Buddha, carved in the sandstone cliffs, still remain, along with innumerable cave temples decorated in fresco. When visited by the Chinese pilgrim Hsuan-tsang in 630 A.D., the main 170-foot statue was said to have been covered with gold.

Both slopes of the Hindu Kush are dry, perhaps a little drier on the north since any rain which falls must have come far overland from the North Atlantic. Even on the south side, there is little possibility of receiving moisture from the Indian Ocean. Irrigation is almost essential everywhere in Afghanistan. On the south slopes of the Hindu Kush, nomads live in black goat hair-cloth tents and many migrate during winter to the Indus Valley; to the north are the round yurts of Central Asia, covered with felt.

Whereas the import and export traffic east of Kabul involves trade with Pakistan and overseas, that north of Kabul is with the Soviet Union. Trucks are gradually replacing the camel, although the latter are still able to compete with trucks in the transport of bulk commodities such as salt and wheat.

Great red cliffs rise above the Kunduz River at Doab in the northern Hindu Kush. The group of flags mark a Moslem cemetery. (Courtesy James A. Cudney.)

In place of trade in European textiles, there is gasoline and cement from the U.S.S.R.

Mazar-i-Sharif to Herat

The first of our four journeys has brought us northward to the plains of northern Afghanistan; the second will lead westward to Herat across what is sometimes known as Afghan Turkistan. This route, seldom traveled by foreigners, leads along monotonous plains and foothills between the Hindu Kush, here more properly known as the Paropamisus, and the Soviet border along the Amu Darya, locally known by its ancient name of the Oxus. The aridity is indicated by the fact that in many areas the water table lies as much as 200 feet below the surface.

The area is so dry that most of the north-flowing streams fail to reach the river. Even the Murghab and the Hari Rud in the northwest lose themselves in the desert. As these streams wither and deposit their sediment, the wind from the north picks up the fine silt and carries it southward and uphill, where it is trapped by the scanty vegetation and builds up deposits of loess. Erosion then carries it northward again and downhill to complete the cycle.

Along these foothills, linking one oasis to another, is one of the great highways of antiquity. Caravans of silk and porcelain from China to Europe, adventurers like Marco Polo and Alexander, and Mongol invaders from interior Asia bound for Iran or Mesopotamia—all passed along this route. This is the ancient Bactria, and here are the ruins of Balkh, "Mother of Cities." On these plains we find the cultures of Greece, Persia, India, China, and the Tatars. Christians, Zoroastrians, Buddhists, and Moslems have each left their impress.

All of Afghanistan has delicious fruit, but nowhere are the grapes and melons sweeter than in the north. Although poleward from Kabul, the climate is warmer since elevations are below 2,000 feet. The sun shines brightly through the dry air and fruit seems sweet in proportion to the aridity. Many Afghan grapes are dried to form raisins, generally in special raisin barns. Marco Polo praised the fruit, writing that the area is

> plentifully supplied with every kind of provision, and is particularly celebrated for producing the best melons in the world . . . They preserve them by paring them round into strips and drying them in the sun. When dry they are sweeter than honey and are carried off for sale over the country.

One should not travel casually from Mazar-i-Sharif to Herat. The road is deep in loess dust and in places branches aimlessly without indication as to the proper course. Five miles an hour is a good average speed in some sections. Much of the plain is a dry, empty steppe, but where streams descend from the mountains, there are oases, large and small. Dust blows continuously. Cotton and grain are grown, but the most profitable product is karakul lambskin.

Eighty-eight miles west of Mazar is the provincial capital of Maimana, center of a small agricultural area with some dry farming and many sheep. Round yurts and black tents dot the hillsides. Farther on, the road steadily climbs to the western spurs of the Paropamisus range which it crosses through the Zermast Pass at 7,774 feet. Although the elevation is lower than that over the Hindu Kush, there are occasional patches of juniper trees and broad alpine meadows. Then the road drops swiftly to the basin of Herat, at an elevation of 3,000 feet, 217 miles from Mazar-i-Sharif.

The city of Herat lies in the productive Hari Rud Valley, where cultivated land extends for a hundred miles, with a width of up to fifteen miles. The history of the city reveals that this is one of the commanding sites of antiquity, on the watershed between two worlds. The beginnings are unknown, but Herat was a Persian settlement about 500 B.C., and later the site of one of the many cities named after Alexander the Great. When the Mongols destroyed the city and massacred its people in both 1232 and again in 1398, the population was estimated at over a million. In the fifteenth century Herat was again a great center of literature and art, particularly known for the Herat School of Miniature Painting. In addition, there were a number of noble buildings, only traces of which remain. During this period, Herat was essentially Persian, but Afghans arrived in the eighteenth century and have controlled it since that time. Herat's great architectural show pieces are the Gauhar Shah Mosque with its brilliant green-tiled dome and the remaining minarets of the 700-year old Mosalla shrine, mosque, and university.

Two roads lead across flat, desolate country to the nearby Soviet and Iranian borders, each about seventy miles distant. Herat handles a substantial share of Russian imports including gasoline for all southern Afghanistan, but there is very little commerce with Iran. The nearest railways are at the Soviet frontier and at Meshed about a hundred miles inside Iran.

When one examines the map of inner Asia as a whole, it is clear that two main east-west routes of trade and conquest cross Afghanistan, one on either side of the central mountains. Both pass through Herat. The shorter but more difficult road is that

The great Mosque at Mazar-i-Sharif in northern Afghanistan is representative of Moslem shrines in the larger centers. (Courtesy James A. Cudney.)

east from Herat over the Hindu Kush and the Khyber Pass to Peshawar. The longer but more level and desolate highway follows the southern fringe of the mountains to Kandahar and on to Quetta and the Bolan Pass. On each road, Kabul or Kandahar serve as way stations along the route from Russia or Iran to India. Other trails are available for caravans or for rugged jeeps, but these two avenues are the only regular automobile routes. Small wonder that the British made Peshawar and Quetta their main military bases during their days in India and that Herat has been a contested city throughout history. Our route from the Khyber Pass has covered the north. Let us now turn east along the southern side of the mountains.

Herat to Kandahar

The road southeast from Herat to Kandahar climbs south over a pass, 6,000 feet in elevation, near the end of the Paropamisus Range, to Farah and then curves along the foothills eastward. Three days are usually necessary for the 401-mile trip, but there are so many unbridged streams to cross that the bus has been known to require nine days. The prudent motorist will carry extra gasoline and water and preferably extra leaves for the springs of his car.

East of Farah, the road lies between the mountains and the desert. To the north, the

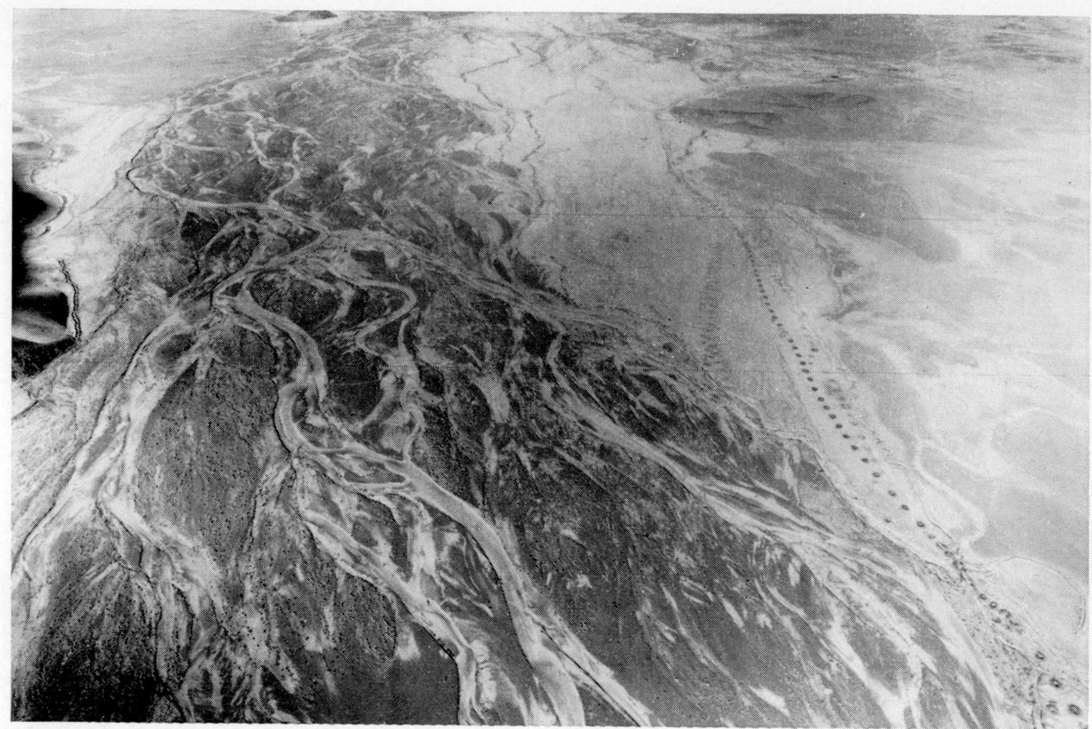

The braided bed of the Arghandab River reflects the overloaded character of streams which pour out of the central mountains. A line of qanat or karez shafts parallels the river. (Courtesy Morrison-Knudsen-Afghanistan.)

country rises from completely barren foothills to distant ranges only slightly more moist. To the south is the broad desert plain of the Helmand River and its terminal marsh and lakes in the Seistan Basin, so arid that few nomads find any pasture. Where snow-fed mountain streams emerge onto the plain, there are small agricultural areas, in many places on alluvial fans next to the hills; these oases die out downslope as the streams lose their water by diversion and seepage. Most of these oases are able to support only a few hundred people, and each is isolated from the others.

Toward Kandahar, the road crosses the Helmand River and, farther on, its main tributary, the Arghandab. Here is the most dramatic irrigation area in Afghanistan, for both rivers have been dammed and modern canals have transformed several thousand acres of wasteland into prosperous farms. The Helmand River is described in Chapter 5, and the agricultural developments are considered later in this chapter.

Kandahar shares the stormy history of Herat and Kabul, a tribute to its attractiveness and location. Somewhere near modern Kandahar, Alexander constructed another Alexandria. In the eleventh century, Kandahar was captured by Mahmud of Ghazni. In the thirteenth century, it was destroyed by Genghis Khan, later on rebuilt and again destroyed by Tamerlane in the fourteenth century. In the sixteenth century, the city was captured by Baber. The Afghans recaptured it in the same century, but lost it to Shah Abbas of Persia in the seventeenth century. The Afghans again took possession in

The road from Kandahar to Chamun on the Pakistan border was one of the country's first modern highways. Rocky mountains alternate with alluvial plains. (Courtesy Morrison-Knudsen-Afghanistan.)

the eighteenth century, and this led to the formation of modern Afghanistan. Even during the nineteenth century, there were two periods when Kandahar was seized by British armies.

Just as the road from Kabul to Peshawar is the chief gateway from the east, so the road from Kandahar to Quetta and on to Karachi is the principal avenue for the south. Both routes meet railways at the Pakistan border; the first uses the Khyber Pass and the second route crosses the mountains via the Bolan Pass. Karachi is the main seaport for Afghanistan so that any improvement in access would be of material advantage. From Kandahar, a good highway extends southeast to the border railhead at Chaman, sixty miles away. Proposals have been made for a parallel railway which might be continued to Kabul.

Afghanistan's access to the sea depends on favorable relations with Pakistan.

Kandahar to Kabul

The fourth and last leg of our journey completes the circuit, covering 220 miles from Kandahar to Kabul. This is one of the most important areas of the country both in history and in current economics. The first half of the road follows the dry, rocky valley of the Tarnak River and then climbs over high passes to the Kabul Basin. Ghazni is midway to Kabul and was once the fortress capital of medieval empires which accumulated immense wealth derived from trade with India. At one time, this commerce amounted to 5 million dollars worth of indigo a year. There are numerous settlements and considerable agriculture en route, almost all irrigated, with some surplus of fruit for export to Pakistan and India.

THE AFGHAN LANDSCAPE

Relief and Structure

Afghanistan somewhat resembles the roof of a house, with the irregular crest of the Hindu Kush as the ridge line and the main parts of the country on the opposite slopes. The simile is imperfect, for the Hindu Kush, higher in the east than in the west, has numerous offshoots so that the slopes of the roof are cut by gables. Nevertheless, it is true that the towering central mountain range sharply divides Afghanistan into two parts. Not until 1933 was there an automobile road across the mountains.

One might expect a considerable change in natural vegetation with altitude, for the lowlands are hot while the peaks average tens of degrees cooler; however, both areas are dry. Although deserts lie on either side of the highland core, pastoral steppe continues to the snow line. Only scattered forests are found, generally in areas relatively inaccessible to the lumberman or to one gathering fuel. In the more humid highlands, summer meadows develop stands of grass after winter snows have melted, and tiny fields high in the mountains take advantage of snow-fed streams.

The Hindu Kush system is one of the great chains which radiate from the Pamirs. Beginning near the frontier with China, the mountains extend westward for 700 miles to the valley of the Hari Rud near the Iranian border. The term Hindu Kush is sometimes limited to the first half of this distance; then the Hindu Kush proper gives way to the Paropamisus. Parallel to the latter and south of the Hari Rud, lies the Koh-i-Baba, or "Father of Mountains," Range, where the highest peak reaches 16,872 feet. Another range, parallel to the Paropamisus but farther north, is the Band-i-Turkestan. Elevations of the Hindu Kush system within Afghanistan exceed 24,000 feet in the east, and even in the west there are many peaks above 12,000 feet.

The earliest European reference to the mountains is by Aristotle, about 330 B.C., who used the term Parnasos, possibly an Indian name. Following the travels of Alexander the Great, the term was altered to Paropamisus. This term once applied to the range as a whole, but today it is restricted to the western half. During this period, the Hindu Kush was also known as the Caucasus; the city which Alexander founded north of Kabul was called "Alexandria under the Caucasus."

The term Hindu Kush first appears in the writings of Ibn Batuta who crossed them about 1334. He describes the word as meaning "Hindu killer" due to the legend that "so many of the slaves, male and female, brought from India die on the passage through this mountain owing to the severe cold and quantity of snow." The name may also be a corruption of Hindu Kuh, or Hindu Mountain.

The axial trend of the four linear ranges is roughly east to west, diverging westward and dividing Afghanistan into two parts. The northern lowlands are considerably smaller than those to the south.

The geology of Afghanistan is imperfectly known, but it includes a series of altered Mesozoic and Cenozoic formations along with crystalline rocks. The rugged topography reflects the recency of the folding.

Many streams cross high ridges in deep antecedent canyons. Rathjens has mapped four dozen of these deep gorges, while Griesbach has written of them as follows: [1]

> Some are exceedingly narrow like the Yakhdara . . . southeast of Maimana, scarcely wide enough to admit an unladen mule being driven through with considerable difficulty. Many of these defiles surpass in picturesque grandeur any-

[1] C. L. Griesbach: "Field Notes from Afghanistan," *Records of the Geological Survey of India,* XIX (1886), 230.

Snow-covered mountains and barren valleys dominate the landscape of the Hindu Kush range in Badakhshan. This is the valley of the Kokcha River. (Courtesy Ernest F. Fox.)

thing I have seen elsewhere, as for instance the course of the Astarab below Faughan where the river is in a narrow gorge often not more than thirty yards wide and enclosed by vertical walls of limestone some 1,500 feet in sheer height above the stream bed. Most of the rivers flow from south to north and hence form transverse valleys through the ranges of Turkestan. They have eroded gorges where they cross anticlinals and formed wider valleys with side streams when on a syncline.

Among the other mountain systems which radiate from the Pamirs are the southwest trending ranges near the boundary between Afghanistan and Pakistan. These include the Safed Koh or "White Mountains," with peaks to 15,619 feet; the Sulaiman Mountains farther south, reaching 11,532 feet in the "Throne of Soloman"; and the Kirthar ranges which swing across Baluchistan. Just as Hindu Kush structures continue westward across northern Iran and Turkey, so the Sulaiman are part of a long mountain arc which extends through the Zagros and Taurus.

More than two-thirds of Afghanistan is mountainous. Within the main highland area are a dozen linear basins, commonly down-faulted and floored with late Tertiary sediments; elsewhere, level land in the mountains is restricted to flood plain ribbons or high level peneplain remnants. The only large areas of rolling plain lie near the Amu Darya in the north, the Helmand in the south, and smaller basins around Herat and Kabul.

Several regional names are in use. In the

extreme east are the province of Badakhshan and the Wakhan Corridor, which separate the Soviet Union from Pakistan. South of Badakhshan lies the region of Nuristan, partly in the Eastern Province. The central mountain area, spreading across the provinces of Kabul and Herat, is known as Hazarajat, the land of the Hazara Mongols. To the north of the mountains, in the provinces of Maimana, Mazar-i-Sharif, and Kataghan are the plains of Bactria which drain toward the Amu Darya. Westernmost Afghanistan is dominated by the drainage basin of the Hari Rud which merges with the Persian region of Khurasan. In the south lies the Helmand Valley, which terminates in the Seistan or Chakhansur Basin. Along the left bank of the Helmand is the sand-filled Registan Desert, while on the right bank is the Dasht-i-Margo or "desert of death."

Climate

The climate of Afghanistan varies with elevation and exposure, ranging from alpine and subarctic in the high northeast to absolute desert along the Amu Darya and the Helmand River. The north is generally colder and drier than the south. The seasons bring continental extremes of temperature. In Kabul, at an elevation of 5,955 feet, the thermometer may register 50° F. at sunrise and rise to 100° F. by noon. Extreme winter temperatures in Kabul have ranged from a maximum of 58° F. to a low of —6° F. in January, and Kabul has a summer range of 101° F. and 51° F. in July. Even during summer, the nights are cool. Farther south, in Ghazni at 7,280 feet, winter temperatures drop to as low as —10° or —15° F., and snow may lie on the ground for three months. At Kandahar, farther southward and at 3,462 feet, January extremes fluctuate between 70° F. and 14° F., while July has a range from 108° F. down to 53° F.

Afghanistan experiences the extreme eastward penetration of Mediterranean-type climate, with its winter precipitation maximum and summer drought. The rainy season extends from October to April, but the average annual precipitation is only thirteen inches in Kabul, seven inches in Kandahar, and as little as two or three inches in the lowlands. Kabul occasionally receives as much as two inches in twenty-four hours.

With such low rainfall and relatively high temperatures, it is not surprising that the humidity is low. Kabul has an 8 A.M. yearly average of 65 per cent, and at 4 P.M. the humidity drops to 36 per cent. Afternoon figures in the summer and fall drop below 24 per cent. Kandahar figures are similar. In comparison with an annual precipitation of seven inches, measured evaporation from an open pan shows a yearly total of seventy-four inches.

Although winter precipitation predominates, the south occasionally receives rain from the Indian monsoon. Thus Kandahar, which normally has a completely dry summer, experienced sharp rains for three weeks in July 1956, with a total of 1.6 inches. Such untypical conditions distort the monthly averages.

Winds tend to be from the north and northwest throughout the year, especially in western Afghanistan where they sweep out of inner Asia through the gap between the end of the Paropamisus and the Elburz mountain systems. From June to September hot gales, accompanied by dust, may reach a velocity of 100 miles an hour, especially in Seistan where they are known as "the wind of 120 days."

Weather observations are unavailable from the mountains, but all higher elevations receive considerable snow cover. It is doubtful whether many mountains have an annual precipitation of more than twenty inches. Some of this stored moisture remains until fall. After the snow melts, streams generally become almost dry. Only light snow occurs in the lowland agricultural areas.

Rivers

Four main river systems take their rise in the Hindu Kush highlands. Each starts in a radial direction, but only one has sufficient water to flow to the sea. First in length and volume is the Helmand in the south and its tributaries, such as the Arghandab and Tarnak. While the Arghandab rises in snow-covered mountains and has some flow throughout the year, the source of the Tarnak is at a lower elevation, and it becomes dry by early summer. (See page 136.)

Second in size within Afghanistan is the Amu Darya, the ancient Oxus. The river

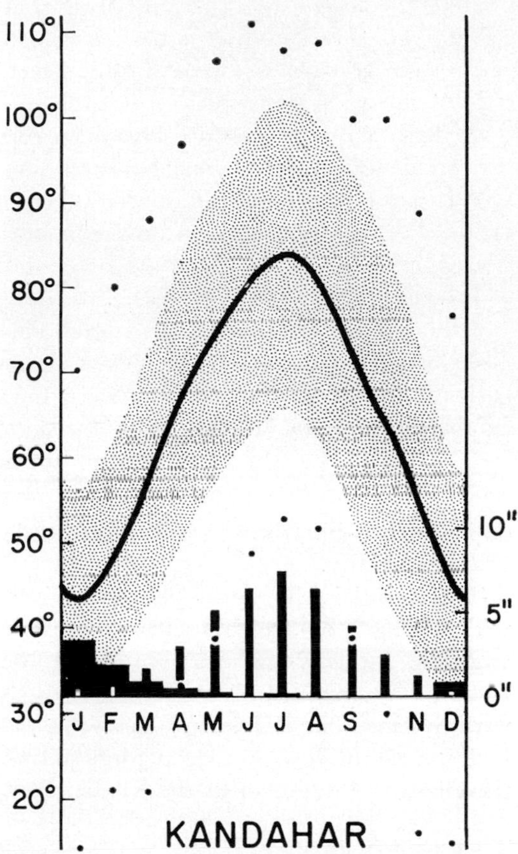

Kandahar's climate is representative of southern Afghanistan. Elevation 3,462 feet, annual precipitation 7.0 inches.

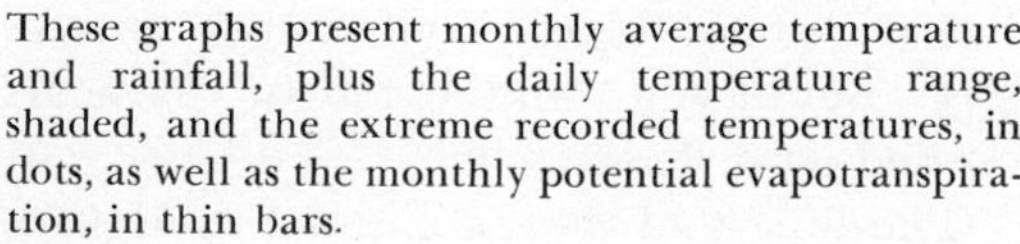

These graphs present monthly average temperature and rainfall, plus the daily temperature range, shaded, and the extreme recorded temperatures, in dots, as well as the monthly potential evapotranspiration, in thin bars.

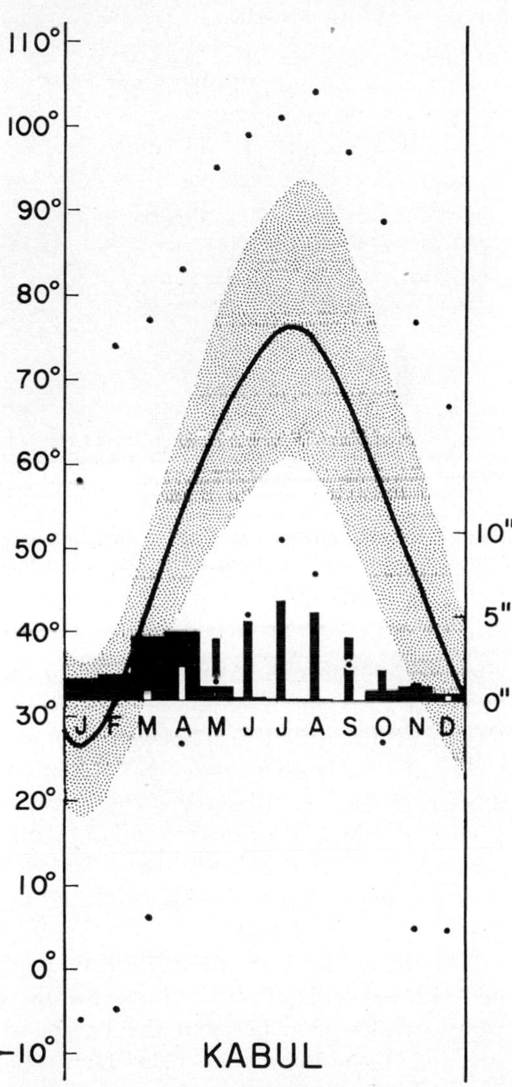

The Kabul basin enjoys a subtropical high altitude climate. Elevation 5,995 feet, annual precipitation 13.3 inches.

Cultivated areas line most perennial rivers, their seasonal extent determined by the availability of water from canals, qanats, or near-surface ground water. This view is near Kandahar. (Courtesy Morrison-Knudsen-Afghanistan.)

rises at 13,400 feet in Lake Victoria near the Wakhan Corridor and flows across Soviet territory into the Aral Sea. For 680 miles, the river forms the Afghanistan–U.S.S.R. border. The main Afghan tributary is the Kunduz, a part of which rises near Bamian. Other north-flowing streams, such as the Sangalok and Murgab, wither before reaching the Amu.

The third river is the 650-mile Hari Rud, or Arius River. Half of the course follows a westward direction between the Paropamisus and Koh-i-Baba, but near Herat the river turns northward and forms the Afghanistan–Iranian border. Extensive areas are irrigated near Herat, forming a rich oasis which is in striking contrast to the enveloping aridity.

The Kabul is the country's fourth river, with a length of 300 miles to its junction with the Indus. Near the capital are the Kabul, Charakhar, and Logar basins, each with considerable agriculture. Below Jalalabad, the Kabul flows in a deep gorge so that travelers must detour over the Khyber Pass.

TIME AND PEOPLE

THE VARIED HISTORY of Afghanistan is not so much due to the assets of the country itself, as to the lands which lie on either side. Here are crossroads which have linked China with Rome and Central Asia with India. Across Afghanistan, Greek culture met Buddhism, and Mongol invaders clashed with Persia.

The long and diverse history of Afghanistan is typical of inner Asia. Although little of the country is arable, and although travel is far from easy, the region has experienced repeated tides of invasion. Seldom has Afghanistan been an independent state with anything similar to its current boundaries. The current variety in ethnic and linguistic features is a by-product of these migrations. Nowhere is there any group resembling a pure race, no group makes up half the population, nor is there even a national language.

The character of the original inhabitants is unknown, but it is probable that the early Scythians and Dravidians were not the first occupants. Next came Indo-Aryans in the second and first millennia B.C. Ptolemy applied the name "Aryana" to what is now western Iran and Afghanistan, and the name is still in wide local use, as for instance in the "Aryana Airlines."

The country was conquered by Persia under Cyrus about 540 B.C., and later on, during the time of Darius, Afghanistan was one of the important parts of the Achaemenian Empire. There were then seven satrapies or provinces in the area: Bactria, Herat, Kabul, Seistan, Kandahar, Merv, and Hindu Kush.

In 330 B.C., the area was conquered by Alexander the Great who used it as a base of operations against Turkestan and India during the next few years. Greek influence continued on and off for two centuries and left its record in the style of Buddhist art.

Iranian and Turanian invasions came next, followed by influences from Inner Asia. In the seventh century A.D., the Chinese traveler Hsuan Tsang passed through Afghanistan on his way to India. Later on, sixteen kingdoms on both sides of the Hindu Kush paid tribute to Peking for a hundred years.

Islam arrived in the seventh century, and still has a monolithic hold today. Thus, all civil judges must be Mullahs, and the present Constitution provides that Islam is the official religion and law of the land.

The native Ghaznevid Dynasty arose in the tenth century and, with help from the Caliph at Baghdad, directed seventeen invasions into India. This was a Sunni regime, in opposition to the Shias of Iran. Under Mahmud of Ghazni (997–1030), Afghan rule extended from Kurdistan to Kashmir and from the Amu Darya to the Ganges; at this time, 400 poets were said to have lived at the capital.

Mongol invasions followed, including those under Ghengis Khan, his grandson Hulugu, and Tamerlane. These invasions were interrupted by periods of Tajik and local rule. During the thirteenth and fourteenth centuries, successive hordes of nomadic Mongols, Turks, and Uzbeks poured out of inner Asia, some of them bound for the plains of India.

A century after Tamerlane, one of his descendants known as Baber ruled from 1505 to 1530. Baber occupied much of Afghanistan, and in 1526 moved east to capture Delhi where he established the Mogul Dynasty. During the Mogul period, the eastern areas of Afghanistan, such as Kabul and Kandahar, were usually tied to India, while Herat and Seistan on the west tended to gravitate to Iran. Balkh and Badakhshan in the north were at times semi-independent. Both the north and west were frequently invaded by Uzbeks and by Persians. The cities of Herat and Kandahar thus changed hands many times with considerable destruction of the cities in the shift of rulers. The greatest of the Mogul emperors was Shah Jahan who ruled from 1627 to 1666 and built the Taj Mahal in Agra. As the Mogul Dynasty weakened, the Safawid Dynasty in Iran took advantage of the opportunity and absorbed western and southern Afghanistan.

Through all of these external waves of conquest, local tribes offered strong resistance and in many places were never fully

Many nomads or *kuche* have no fixed dwelling but spend their lives in tents, moving with their flocks in search of pasture. (Courtesy James A. Cudney.)

conquered. During that era, and continuing to the present, their pacification required large-scale bribery, and the loyalty of local chieftains changed frequently. The tribal character of earlier times persists today, for the lower house of Parliament is largely made up of tribal chiefs and the heads of important families. In the eighteenth century, one of the tribal leaders became Ahmad Shah and took the title of Pearl of Pearls or Durr-i-Durran, from which his tribe came to be known as the Durrani. The Durrani Dynasty was the first purely Afghan rule. The Durranis lasted from 1747 to 1835 and were replaced by the Barakzais in 1835 when Dost Mahmud became Amir.

No consideration of Afghan history can be complete without reference to the steady expansion of Russian territory during the eighteenth and nineteenth centuries. It was to check this advance from the north, with its potential threat to India, that Britain became interested in Afghanistan. Complicated events brought on a succession of wars with Britain. The First Afghan war occurred from 1838 to 1842, the Second Afghan War from 1879 to 1880, while the Third Afghan War ended in 1919. Russia, in turn, was alarmed over British expansion in India with the threat to its southern frontier.

Several hundred thousand nomads migrate each spring and fall between the high mountain pastures of central Afghanistan and the plains of the Indus. (Courtesy James A. Cudney.)

The present Soviet republics of the Turkmens, Kirghiz, Tajiks, Uzbeks, and Kazaks were all once independent areas. Tashkent was captured in 1865, and Bukhara fell the same year. Samarkand was occupied in 1868, and by the following year Russian influence reached the present Afghan border. The current relations of the two countries thus proceed under the memories of past Russian objectives.

The present boundary between Afghanistan and Pakistan follows the Durand Line, a compromise established by Britain and Afghanistan in 1893, whereby each party agreed not to "exercise influence" beyond this limit. Unfortunately, the line was illogical since it did not conform to ethnography, geography, or history; it merely delimited the extent of British control. Certainly the tribes whose territory it cut have never agreed to it. Out of the confused border problems which followed has arisen the agitation, especially since World War II, for a new state to be known variously as Pushtunistan or Pakhtunistan which would be carved out of western Pakistan, either independent or, if possible, as part of Afghanistan. Some enthusiasts would extend the limits to the Indus.

Such a development would recognize the fact that the people are the same as those in

Afghanistan and that the country once extended this far and beyond. The practical realities of the proposal are very complex and obviously do not lend themselves to close relations between the two neighbors. Between 5 and 6 million Pushtuns live in "Pushtunistan," probably more than live across the border in Afghanistan.

Fraser-Tytler, once British Minister to Afghanistan and author of a volume on its history, writes as follows: [1]

> Afghanistan is the core and the remnant of a once mighty Empire; it is the glacis of a great mountain range, an outpost designed by nature to guard the approaches to India, and decreed by man to survive in this capacity. Unfortunately the Pathan races, which make up the ruling portion of the Afghan nation, have spilled over their mountain boundaries and spread down into the plains, so that in large areas of Pakistan dwell a people whose affinities are with Kabul, so far as they are with anybody, and not with Karachi. As it stands at present behind the artificial boundary of the Durand Line, Afghanistan is ethnographically, economically, and geographically an incomplete state.

While the details of its history are imperfectly known to most Afghans, popular legends lend an air of past glory, evoking memories of their country when it was part of a vast empire. Archaeological research is still in its infancy, but the crossroads position of Afghanistan suggests that rich discoveries are still to be made.

Many racial groups live in present-day Afghanistan with diverse languages and sometimes antagonistic interpretations of Islam. In the absence of census data or anthropological studies, only the broad outlines are known. Five groups of people number each at least half a million; in all there are over two dozen ethnic variations.

The so-called true Afghan speaks Pushtu which is linked to the Iranian group of languages. They are thus called Pushtuns or Pathans and make up some two-fifths of the total population. Some legends trace their ancestry back to Biblical genealogy, but this is meaningless since even the Mongol nomads in nearby Iran claim Noah as one of their ancestors. More probably, the Afghans are one of the many groups which moved out of Central Asia about the time of Christ, but they are not known until the sixth century, when they lived in the Sulaiman mountains along the present Pakistan border. For the most part, they now live south of the Hindu Kush. Some are city dwellers, some farmers, and some nomads. Among the nomads are tribes whose areas are so unproductive that brigandage has been a necessary source of income, as with the Afridi who live near the Khyber Pass.

Persian is the second language, spoken by at least one-third of the population. Most of these people are ethnic Tajiks whose ancestors once occupied much of the country. The Tajiks are merchants and artisans as well as farmers and as such are found in all areas. Thus, Persian is the principal language of the cities.

Along with the Tajiks who live in the plains, a few tens of thousand Tajiks live in the high mountains of Badakhshan. One writer describes their life as follows: [1]

> They were the poorest people we had ever seen . . . . The men wore goatskins across their shoulders, and the women were clad in filthy rags. The children wore nothing at all. The men, who wore no shoes in summer, waded barefoot through the icy streams and could travel all day over the rugged, rocky terrain at a pace equal to that of a horse. The women aged very rapidly. At thirty they were toothless old crones, and they rarely lived beyond forty.

Another Persian speaking group are the Hazaras of the central highlands; hence the term Hazarajat for the mountains between Kabul and Herat. They are Mongol in

[1] W. K. Fraser-Tytler, *Afghanistan*. London: Oxford Univ. Press (1950), 300. Quoted by permission.

[1] Quoted in Donald N. Wilber: *Afghanistan*. Human Relations Area Files, 45–46.

THE PEOPLE OF AFGHANISTAN [1]

Ethnic group	*Approximate population*	*Language and group*	*Religion*
AFGHANS or PUSHTUNS	4/5,000,000	Pushtu (Iranian)	Sunni Moslem
Ghilzai (Southeast Afghanistan)			
Durrani (Southwest Afghanistan)			
TAJIKS		Persian (Iranian)	
Mountain Tajiks (Wakhan Corridor)	–		Shia Moslem
Plains Tajiks (cities and towns)	2,500,000		
HAZARA MONGOLS (Central Mountains)	500,000	Archaic Persian (Iranian)	Shia Moslem
Western Hazara			Sunni Moslem
TURKO-MONGOLS (Northern Afghanistan)			
Turkmens	200,000	Turkmen (Turkic)	Sunni Moslem
Uzbeks	800,000	Uzbek (Turkic)	Sunni Moslem
Kirghiz	30,000	Kirghiz (Turkic)	Moslem
Qizil Bash (Kabul)	60/200,000	Persian	Shia Moslem
NURISTANI or KAFFIRS (Northeast Mountains)	60,000	Dardic (Sanskrit)	–
CHAHAR AIMAK (Western Afghanistan)	500,000		Shia Moslem
BALUCHI	20,000	Baluchi (Iranian)	–
BRAHUI	–	Dravidian	
HINDUS	–	Lahnda	Hindu
JEWS	–	Hebrew	Hebrew
ARABS	–	Arab	Moslem
KURDS	–	Kurdish	Moslem

[1] Some of these data are based on Donald N. Wilber: *Afghanistan*, New Haven: Human Relations Area Files (1956).

origin and probably settled between the thirteenth and fifteenth century, probably related to the conquests of Genghis Khan.

Well over a million Turk and Turko-Mongol people live on the northern slopes of the Hindu Kush, the "other side" from the Pushtuns. These include Uzbeks, Turkmen, Kirghiz, Kazaks, and Kara Kalpaks, all relatives of groups found across the frontier in the Soviet Union. As Czarist Russia advanced into Middle Asia during the eighteenth and nineteenth century and as Communism appeared in the twentieth, various ethnic groups were displaced and boundaries appeared where none had been earlier.

To weld these diverse people with their ancient record of conflict into a modern nation is no easy task, and it is made the more difficult since Afghanistan is split in two by great mountains and because the country lacks an economic core. None of these groups are found exclusively in Afghanistan, and many have their main cultural center elsewhere. Even the Pushtuns may have their cultural center in Pakistan.

Population figures are only estimates, for no detailed census has been taken. The government reported a 1951 total of 12 million people, roughly divided as follows: urban, 1 million; villagers, 3 million; nomads, 2 million; farmers, 6 million.

Provisional estimates place the total gross national product for 1954 at 12 million Afghanis. Depending on the rate of exchange employed, this means a per capita income of $25 to $60.

Since Afghanistan covers 264,000 square miles, roughly the area of Texas, it apparently has a population density of forty-five per square mile as compared with twenty-two for America's "largest state without a glacier," or Iran's thirty people per square mile. This seems high and raises a question as to whether Afghanistan actually has 12 million people or 8 million as some estimates indicate. The larger figure may represent an inflated estimate of the Pushtu population for political reasons.

SEVEN REGIONS

SEVEN GEOGRAPHIC regions may be identified, none of them with precise limits. Since Baluchistan has many similarities with Afghanistan, a few paragraphs have been included.

Badakshan

Badakshan is the name of a province and also the general term for northeastern Afghanistan, dominated by the main range of the Hindu Kush. The region includes the area known as Nuristan; in other cases the term Badakhshan is limited to the district north of the Hindu Kush, while Nuristan is applied to the south slopes. The region as considered here includes all of the highlands north and northeast of Kabul as far as the Pamirs.

Some idea of the rugged landscape may be inferred from the following description by Ernest F. Fox, telling of his experience in crossing one of the lower ranges south of Faizabad at the end of October: [1]

> Shortly after we started again, the gradient steepened rapidly, and, shortly, we came to the foot of a tremendous talus fan bordered by high mountains on either side. Up this the faint shadow of the trail switchbacked sharply and repeatedly to a vanishing point in a little notch high in the snowy, serrate crest of the range. Climbing became increasingly difficult as we advanced; the depth of the snow—wet, soggy snow—increased; the loose slabs of rock beneath the snow slid down under us . . . Fifty yards, in many places only fifty feet, was as far as we could climb without a halt . . . .
>
> By my aneroids, our elevation in the pass was 15,050 feet above the sea—5,000 feet *above* the village of Anjuman, several thousand *below* the peaks on either side of us. To the southward, and far beyond the valley of the Anjuman, the great masses of the mighty Hindu Kush, with its mighty peaks and horns and cols, filled all the southern sky and dwarfed the range on which we stood, while northward, dropping abruptly from the pass through the deep, gray shadows of the only valley open to us, there stretched a rough wilderness of barren rock and frozen snowdrifts: a scene more desolate than the Greenland icecap; . . . more rugged than the trails across the central Andes; a scene, a place, in which no one would choose to linger long.

Summit elevations in Badakhshan increase from 15,000 feet in the west to more than 24,000 feet in the east. Large areas of rugged country are snow-covered for much of the year. From these majestic peaks, torrential streams lead north to the Amu Darya and south to the Kabul River. Sheer cliffs form a massive wall through boulder-choked ravines. Stream courses alternate between impassable gorges and open valleys where softer rocks have enabled erosion to widen the floor to a few tens of yards; occasionally terrace gravels veneer the lower slopes.

Small wonder that isolation has been the major cultural note. The residents of re-

[1] Ernest F. Fox: *Travels in Afghanistan.* New York: Macmillan (1943), 87. Quoted by permission.

mote mountain valleys once knew little of what lay beyond the ridge. At present, there is a surprising amount of local mobility. Every village has its radio, so that news travels fast. There are almost no roads, and the trails are usually mere tracks which run along a ledge above a rushing stream, in places too narrow for a horse burdened with goods. Elsewhere, they skirt the base of great talus slopes or climb over high spurs. Where there is no alternative, the trail is supported by poles wedged into the sheer rock walls. Most streams must be forded, but there are a few bridges, commonly a flimsy set of poplar poles, supported by a cantilever projection from either side, which bend alarmingly beneath the weight of a horse.

Climatic conditions are known only by inference. During clear nights, bitter cold develops, while at noon, sunburn conditions appear. It is surprising to find such snowy mountains so far from sources of moisture. Above 12,000 feet, winter comes early and remains long, but the seasons along the slopes change rapidly. Much of the mountain area has little or no soil cover, so that vegetation is sparse. Oak, mulberry, and poplar trees grow in the lower valleys. In the southeast, there are said to be "magnificent forests of deodar, pine and larch," but this is true only in the more inaccessible areas.

The distribution of population reflects man's ability to combine soil and water to produce food. Aside from the few trade centers, villages are a function of the local irrigated land. Most settlements depend on a few acres of flood plain or terraced hillsides. Barley is the common crop, along with rice, apples, and other fruits. Opium was once a significant cash crop.

In the north, many of the people are Tajiks. Elsewhere, they were formerly known as Kaffirs, because they were once infidels; since their conversion to Islam in 1896, however, they have been termed Nuristani, namely, "those who have seen the light." The Nuristani number some 60,000, and although their origin is uncertain, they may be among the oldest tribes in Afghanistan.

Northeastern Afghanistan contains many peaks over 20,000 feet in height. This is a view of the upper Kokcha valley. (Courtesy Ernest F. Fox.)

Badakhshan has no mines of importance, but small amounts of placer gold, lead, lapis lazuli, and rubies have been produced for centuries. Lapis lazuli has been mined in the Jurm valley since antiquity, and some of it has been found as far away as Crete.

The output of all these items probably represents the low cost of labor rather than any abundance of reserves.

The chief city is the provincial capital of Faizabad, in the north, which may be reached by an automobile road. A secondary road leads into the Wakhan Corridor, the long projection of Afghanistan along the upper Amu Darya created to isolate Russia from contact with British India.

A century ago, prior to Russian advances into Middle Asia, Badakhshan included the lowland areas to the north of the Amu Darya. As described by Josiah Harlan,[1] the first American to appear in this part of the world, the province was "one of the most famous countries in the Empire of Samarkand. It is celebrated in Persian poetry for its fertile soil, amenity of climate, fine and luscious fruits, its beautiful gardens, and valuable ruby mines."

Hazarajat

Hazarajat, or the land of the Hazaras, takes in the central mountain area between Kabul and Herat. Although less rugged than Badakhshan, many peaks exceed 15,000 feet. Two roughly parallel mountain ranges dominate the area, the Paropamisus in the north and the Koh-i-Baba farther south. Both are part of the Hindu Kush system. Farther north lie the Band-i-Turkestan, with peaks above 10,000 feet.

These mountains form the divide between the south-flowing Helmand and other rivers tributary to the Seistan Basin and the north-flowing streams which aim toward the Amu Darya and its terminal basin in the Aral Sea.

Climatic statistics are lacking, but snow covers the mountains in November and persists in patches into the following September.

Serving as a scanty cover of vegetation are coarse grass, thistle, hogweed, rhubarb, and cushion plants; trees are uncommon except for planted poplars and willow around the settlements. Fuel and forage are sought diligently and the result is a denuding of the hillsides so that scrub and brush are almost absent. Dried dung is a common fuel.

Wilfred Thesiger, whose travels have also made him an authority on southern Arabia and the marshlands of Iraq, gives us an interesting glimpse of the landscape: [2]

> I had supposed that the Hazarajat was a desperately poor country and my first view from the slopes of Kuh-i-Baba confirmed this impression. I looked out across a succession of deep valleys and over bare, stony, rolling hillsides, parched and tawny coloured. In the valley below me I could see a few patches of cultivation, green and especially noticeable in this empty landscape. But I soon realized that this impression of barrenness and desperate poverty, although a very natural impression, was a totally false one, due to the configuration of the ground. There are many springs on the mountain, especially on its southern slopes, and streams in all the valleys. As I wandered through the country, I discovered that almost every fold and wrinkle in the ground to which water could be conducted was cultivated. Walking up the valleys it often seemed that the cultivation would peter out round the next corner, and yet it would go on, sometimes widening out and sometimes narrowing until eventually we came to the high valleys where all cultivation ceased. Even the hillsides above the villages were sown with rain-grown wheat (*lalni*). All ploughing was done with oxen, and it was surprising on what steep hillsides they had been used.
>
> In some of these mountain valleys the houses are strung out along the hillsides above a narrow ribbon of cultivation, farm house succeeding to farm house throughout the day's march; in others they are grouped in small villages, one village perhaps separated from the next by miles of stony track. Here a dozen adjoining houses clung to the mountain side, there twenty or thirty houses were collected round a spring or on a convenient piece of level ground. Nowhere did I see any towns or even large villages.

Two different people inhabit these mountains, the more or less sedentary Hazaras and the migratory Pushtun tribesmen known as *Kuchi,* meaning "the marchers." The Hazaras are Mongols, some of whom were settled here in the thirteenth century by the conquests of Ghengis Khan as guardians of the frontier. In place of the Mongol language, they now speak a modified dialect

[1] Josiah Harlan: *Central Asia.* Edited by Frank Ross. London: Luzac (1939), 42.

[2] Wilfred Thesiger: "The Hazaras of Central Afghanistan," *Geog. Jour.* CXXI (1955), 314.

This view of the Bamian Valley is taken from the head of the Great Buddha shown on page 551. The high Koh-i-Baba range appears in the distance. (G. B. C.)

of Persian. The Hazaras may number half a million people. Some live in villages where two or three dozen mud and stone houses cluster about a spring; elsewhere scattered homes adjoin ribbons of hillside cultivation. Flat earthen roofs, supported by poplar logs, are commonly used for drying fuel or feed. Watchtowers guard the approaches to some settlements. Wheat, barley, peas, and beans are the common crops, with apples, apricots, walnuts, and almonds in the favored valleys. Sheep, goats, and a few cattle supplement the diet and are the basis for the two exports of the area: the clarified butter known as *ghi* and the cloth called *barak* used for clothing and blankets. Most of the Hazaras live at altitudes between 8,000 and 12,000 feet. Below these elevations it is commonly too dry; above them it is too cold.

The second ethnic group in the region are the nomadic Pushtuns or Pathans known as Kuchi. Large numbers of these people graze their flocks on the mountain slopes during the short summer and then migrate two or three hundred miles to the Indus lowlands in Pakistan for winter pasture.

Almost no roads penetrate the area, so that travel is on foot or horseback; cultural change is slow. Most of the Hazaras are Shia Moslems, in contrast to the dominance of the Sunni sect elsewhere in Afghanistan.

Bactria

The plains of Bactria are rich in history, for the steppe lands and oases on the north-

The main street of Kunduz, in northern Afghanistan, is a reminder of the untouched character of many smaller towns in Bactria. (G.B.C., Courtesy *Saturday Review* Travel Contest.)

ern slopes of the Hindu Kush system and along the valley of the Amu Darya have been avenues of travel since very early times. Persian control alternated with Mongol conquests. After Alexander the Great, Greek rule continued for two centuries, but our knowledge of the details is largely limited to the sequence of rulers as recorded on their coins. Arab, Indian, and Chinese cultures have also left their mark. When fully deciphered, the history of Bactria will reveal the age-long contest between the nomad and the city dweller, between the desert and the sown field.

Among the most ancient of the cities was Balkh, once known as the garden spot of Asia and the center of a civilization which rivaled Babylon and Nineveh, but today a collection of shapeless mounds and rubble. The walls of the city measured seven miles in circumference, but only the beginnings of archaeological work have been undertaken within them. The city is reputed to have been the home of Zoroaster, founder of the religion which bears his name.

Several oasis cities in modern Bactria are each dependent on local sources of water. The largest is the political and trade center of Mazar-i-Sharif in the center. To the west is Maimana, and in the east are three towns along the Kunduz River. Reading downstream, these are Pul-i-Khumri, Baghlan, and Kunduz.

Most of Bactria is a sun-drenched dusty plain, not unlike Arizona. Rainfall is generally under ten inches. Most of the area is a desert, or no better than a dry steppe. A veneer of loess, blown southward from the flood plains and deserts of Soviet Middle Asia, blankets the alluvial lowland and piles up against the foothills.

Irrigated fields raise excellent crops of wheat, barley, corn, and rice, along with sugar beets, cotton, exceptionally sweet melons, grapes, and deciduous fruits. Under favorable conditions, some dry farming is possible. Between the oases is a dry steppe where the major product, and Afghanistan's leading export, are karakul skins. All in all, Bactria is the leading agricultural region of the country. When reservoirs are constructed in the mountains, cultivated land can be considerably expanded.

The nomads of northern Afghanistan include various racial groups also found north of the border, such as Turkmens, Uzbeks, and Tajiks. Their affinity with inner Asia is shown in the use of the round felt yurt common in Mongolia, in place of the black cloth tent typical of Arabia. The two-humped Bactrian camels of Mongolian origin begin to replace the one-humped dromedary variety. It is interesting to note that one of the principal Soviet studies on Afghan agriculture reads: "In regard to language and religion, northern Afghanistan forms one whole with the adjacent central Asian republics of the U.S.S.R."

Isolation is significant, for only two avenues lead to the rest of Afghanistan, one south to Kabul and the other the little-used road west to Herat. Contacts with the Soviet Union are limited to regulated trade across the Amu Darya, the volume and character of which fluctuates with the political climate.

Afghan Khurasan

Afghan Khurasan is a continuation of the similar geographic region in Iran described on page 522. The northern half lies in the broad valley of the Hari Rud, to which the high Paropamisus provides melting snow and a year-round flow. The south drains into three enclosed basins along the Iranian border, each of them with a central salt lake, marsh, or kavir, depending on the season, and surrounded by alluvial aprons on which grows scanty camel brush.

Since the various small streams rise below the snow line, they dry up in the summer. Large areas of rolling desert plain, at elevations of 3,000 to 4,000 feet, are interrupted here and there by low mountains. Although farther south than Bactria with its parallel in Arizona, the greater elevation in Khurasan gives it a dry landscape comparable to Wyoming.

In the drier areas, one may travel for mile after mile without seeing a trace of human habitation. Sheep and camels provide a meager livelihood for the few nomads, who live in black tents rather than white yurts.

In contrast to this parched, brown land, the 200,000 acres of cultivation around Herat stand out as a green island. Cropland extends for 100 miles east and west of the city, with a width of eight to fifteen miles.

Bright costumes and huge turbans are typical of many people in Kunduz. (G. B. C.)

Wheat and cotton are important crops, some of them raised without irrigation. A wide variety of crops are grown although the actual list may not reach the reported total of 100 varieties. As the Hari Rud is incised from twenty to fifty feet below its flood plain, there are many places where it is not feasible to divert water for irrigation.

Herat is the only city in Khurasan. The stupendous earthworks of the old city wall, with its 150 towers, suggest its former importance; there was seldom a war or revolution in Central Asia which did not affect Herat.

During the nineteenth century, Britain several times became interested in Khurasan as a defense against Russian advance toward India and at one time even proposed its return to Persia, to which it had frequently belonged.

The Helmand Valley

Between the ranges of the Hindu Kush and those of the Makran system near the Arabian Sea are a series of desert basins. In climate and landscape they are not unlike the Mohave Desert and adjoining parts of Arizona. The southern half of the area lies within Baluchistan and need not be discussed here other than to point out its similarities.

Most of southern Afghanistan is empty, so dry and lifeless that only a few nomads can find pasture for their sheep and camels. A series of local desert names are employed, but the area is part of the greater Iranian waste which extends from the Zagros to the Sulaiman Mountains. On the right bank of the lower Helmand is a broad alluvial plain known as the Dash-i-Margo, or desert of death. On the left bank is the Registan, a sand-choked reddish area which continues to the Pakistan frontier. Such areas merely hold the map together.

Only those streams which originate in mountains that experience heavy snowfall, notably the Helmand and its tributary the Arghandab, continue to flow throughout the year. Other Helmand tributaries, for example the Tarnak, are completely dry in summer as are also independent streams such as the Kash and Farah.

The Helmand River occupies a position in southern Afghanistan somewhat comparable to the Amu Darya in the north. Both river systems rise in high snow-covered mountains, irrigate extensive oases, and end in salt lakes outside Afghanistan; both areas have also had a stormy history. Many of the hydrographic details for the Helmand have been considered in Chapter 5, and the main road across the region is briefly described in the travel section earlier in this chapter.

Parts of the Helmand Valley have been cultivated for 2,000 years. A modern irrigation project was started by the Japanese in 1937, but was interrupted by World War II. Between 1946 and 1959, the government of Afghanistan employed the American engineering firm of Morrison-Knudson to undertake a large-scale program, financed in part by loans from the Export-Import Bank of Washington.

The Helmand Valley Authority, or H.V.A., is the country's major effort at overall planning. Although the engineering operations represented American enterprise, this is now an Afghan operation. Two high dams, one on the Helmand and the other on its main tributary, the Arghandab, store up spring floods for later diversion through several hundred miles of modern canals. Provision is also made for hydroelectricity.

Prior to World War II, about 194,000 acres were irrigated in the central Helmand basin, largely by hand-dug canals which diverted water from the rivers only at high water stages. By the mid 1950's the area had increased to 300,000 acres, while by the early 1960's, the agricultural land to be supplied by modern canals with a regulated supply from the river, exceeded 500,000 acres. This

High mountains, often snow covered, and broad valleys, irrigated in part, make up much of the Afghan landscape. (Courtesy Morrison-Knudsen-Afghanistan.)

last figure includes both old farm lands, which were given a more dependable supply, and new areas reclaimed from the desert. Optimistic estimates place the ultimate irrigable land at 1 million acres, capable of supporting 800,000 people. Some of the new farmland has been used to settle nomads.

Rainfall records at Kandahar give an average for each rainy season of 7.4 inches, while the measured evaporation from a water surface averages seventy-two inches. Experience has shown that Helmand valley crops require the addition of from 5.2 to 6.4 acre feet (sixty-two to seventy-six inches) of irrigation water to supplement the local rainfall. If all of the million acres planned for development were to receive this much water, assuming that the bulk of the run-off could be conserved and applied at the proper time and without waste, the normal discharge of the two rivers would barely be adequate. In dry seasons, some areas will be in short supply; unfortunately, such dry seasons are also those of extra warmth and high evaporation when more than normal amounts of water are called for.

The large amounts of salt in the soil of the middle Helmand Basin present a problem. At least one-third of the land which it is proposed to irrigate has too much salt, some of it with 3 to 5 per cent in the upper six inches of topsoil. This can usually be leached out if enough water is applied and deep drainage ditches are available. Some of the newly reclaimed land is nearly flat and quickly becomes waterlogged unless deep drainage is introduced. Even in the once saline areas, good crops of wheat may be obtained from soil that has been thoroughly washed.

The Helmand Valley Authority represents one of the best-integrated development programs in Southwest Asia. It has had the benefit of sound engineering, extensive hydrographic and soil surveys, and good management. The main operations start with the dams on the Helmand and Arghandab rivers; these supply several hundred miles of main canals. A dozen settlement areas are involved, each with model villages and supervised agricultural practices. The average farm allotment ranges from seven and one-half to fifteen acres per family, according to the quality of the land. Modern roads link these settlements with the headquarters of the Authority at the new town of Lashkar Gah, near the junction of the Helmand and the Arghandab.

The Authority is primarily concerned with irrigation and land development. Flood control and the production of electricity at the dams are secondary objectives. Although the middle Helmand valley is certainly not by nature a forestland, several hundred million seedlings have been set out with some success, especially along canals.

One of the wisest actions of the Authority has been the recognition of the salt hazard. As a result, a network of deep drainage ditches was dug prior to introducing irrigation water. In some cases, the soil required thorough leaching before it could be cultivated; elsewhere, the problem was to keep the water table, raised by irrigation, at least four or five feet below the surface in order to avoid capillary lift. Here, as in all irrigated lands, the net movement of soil moisture must be downward, thus carrying away any concentration of soil salts in solution.

Desert reclamation is expensive. The total cost of irrigation and land development along the Helmand reached $97 million by 1960. This represented a capital investment of $225 per acre for all cultivated land, both old and new, and it is doubtful whether the new settlers can afford to repay such costs. In one project area, Nad-i-Ali, the costs amounted to $457 per acre; in the lowest cost district, the North Arghandab area, the investment was $96 per acre.

Still other irrigation schemes are proposed; in total, however, these will cover no more than 2 or 3 per cent of the Helmand lowland. This is desert country, and most of it will so remain.

The possibilities of irrigation in the Helmand area are shown on the opposite page, with a currently planned total which amounts to 539,823 acres, or nearly 850 square miles.

To these figures may be added a potential of 163,000 acres in Seistan, 250,000 hypothetical acres along the Kash Rud, and 200,000 possible acres in the Dasht-i-Bakwa.

Settlements outside the area of the Helmand Valley Authority are restricted to areas with natural supplies of fresh water and suitable soil. These oases are commonly found on alluvial slopes at the base of the mountains where streams leave their rock-floored valleys, but before their flow is dissipated through seepage and evaporation. Where such streams flow part way across the desert, or where ground water can be brought to the surface by qanats, here known as karez, fingers of cropland project tentatively into the desert. Most of these oases are linked by the road from Farah to Kandahar, described on page 553.

Kandahar is the leading city of the region, now in the midst of rapid transformation. It is a major entrepot for foreign trade, exporting fruits and nuts, wool and hides, and cotton; in return, it receives a wide array of manufactured goods from the outside world. Nearby is a new international airport, designed to accomodate jet planes flying between Europe and eastern Asia.

Seistan

The terminal basin of Seistan lies partly within Iran but is generally known to the Afghans as the Chakhansur Basin, from the name of a town on their side of the border. Only the Helmand regularly persists across the desert to reach Seistan, but seasonal streams enter the depression from all directions.

The lakes and marshes of Seistan, known as *hamuns,* fluctuate widely in size. At a maximum they total 7,006 square miles, of which 4,159 lie in Afghanistan while 2,847 are in Iran. Maps differ widely in their representation of the area, doubtless reflecting the year of survey. Water bodies 100 miles long may shrink to a series of shallow disconnected ponds bordered by a wide reed marsh. In one year, the lakes almost completely disappeared; in contrast, old terrace levels lie 400 feet above the present lakes. The origin and persistence of the basin represents an unsolved problem, especially since the Helmand brings large amounts of silt and yet is currently dissecting its delta.

Seistan is a region of sharp climatic contrasts. Spring and fall are unknown, because in a matter of hours, the frigid temperatures of winter disappear as the summer season unfolds. Temperatures are known to exceed 120°F. and may approach the world's record of 133°F.; while during winter, the temperature has been known to approach zero, Fahrenheit. Rainfall is no more than two or three inches, while evaporation is reported at ten feet. Surprisingly, the water in the hamuns is fresh. This area is famous for its "wind of 120 days" in summer. Strong winds also occur in winter; during one March, winds were recorded at an average of eighty-eight miles per hour for a sixteen-hour period, reaching a maximum of 120 miles per hour. Wind scour, with resulting deflation, may account for the maintenance of the basin.

HELMAND BASIN IRRIGATION[1]

Area	*Irrigated Acreage* Formerly	1956	Plan
Arghandab Valley	85,000	110,000	184,060
Upper Helmand Valley	59,000	138,345	247,288
Lower Helmand Valley	50,000	67,500	108,475
Total	194,000	315,845	539,823

[1] Tudor Engineering Co: *Report on Development of Helmand Valley.* Washington, (1956), 18.

Seistan has had a remarkable history, but the extensive ruins are only in part deciphered. Prior to the tenth century, the Helmand delta was a prosperous region with large cities surrounded by extensive areas of irrigation; then came a succession of invaders from whose devastation the area has never recovered.

The present population, on both sides of the international border, may number 250,000. Some of these people dwell in the marshes where they live in reed houses and use reed rafts under conditions which resemble those of southern Iraq. Many villages are on mounds in order to escape the seasonal floods.

At present, the region is unattractive and inhospitable but its soil is fertile, and if water could be properly regulated, a large agricultural expansion might occur. However, so flat is the country and so uncertain the inflow of water, that the engineering problems are difficult. On paper, this might be another Mesopotamia. Rice is the chief crop.

Around and within the Seistan marshes are several oases, often nearly isolated during the high water period when all roads are submerged. An elaborate network of canals provides water for crops of wheat, barley, and cotton. The people take advantage of the strong winds to operate windmills, with horizontal vanes, to grind grain. Seistan is the meeting point for several types of vegetation; here are found date palms, cypress, and eucalyptus.

Life in Seistan has discomforts apart from heat, wind, and flood waters. Sir Henry McMahon describes [1]

> . . . the outburst of insects which come to life the day after winter ends. Midges, mosquitoes, and every kind and sort of flying, creeping, crawling beast imaginable, large and small, fill the air, and cover the ground as evening sets in. To sit near a light is impossible, and so one has to eat one's dinner, insects and all, in semidarkness, and to find one's way to bed in the dark.

Eastern Afghanistan

Eastern Afghanistan is the most important region of the country. Parts of four mountainous provinces are included: Kabul, Ghazni, Eastern, and Southern. Here also is the largest city, Kabul, and a number of smaller but important centers such as Jalalabad, Charikar, Ghazni, and Gardez, each with a few tens of thousands of people.

The economic significance of the region lies in the presence of fertile basins, commonly measuring about 100 square miles, surrounding each of the above cities. As spring rains are seldom adequate for dependable rain-fed crops, safe cultivation requires irrigation. On two flights over this area in September, no more than a trace of cultivated land was to be seen outside the above basins, probably less than 0.1 per cent. Even the level land is only partly productive. Ribbons of cultivation follow some flood plains. Elsewhere canals divert water from the apex of the various alluvial fans while, farther downslope, lines of karez capitalize on the ground water, each watering a few tens of acres. Thousands of these tunnels or "horizontal wells" are present in Afghanistan, especially in the east. On some broad slopes, low check dams detain some of the runoff so that the ground may be moistened sufficiently for cultivation.

An ambitious valley development program, initiated in 1960, looks to a seventy-foot dam on the Kabul River which will irrigate 120 square miles near Jalalabad. Both this dam and a 344-foot dam near Sarobi will supply hydroelectric power.

Where water is available, the basins form garden spots, in striking contrast to the treeless and nearly soil-free mountains which surround them. Wheat, barley, rice, alfalfa, and cotton are grown, along with a variety of fruit trees such as apricots, cherries, quince, pears, pomgeranates, and mulberry. Grapes and melons are exceptionally sweet. No wine is produced since this is proscribed by Islam, but grapes are dried in specially ventilated raisin buildings.

Crops in Eastern Afghanistan have a distinct vertical zonation, especially on south-facing slopes, as shown in the table on page 578. In addition, there is a marked localization due to moisture and to custom.

Much of old Kabul has been destroyed during its many wars, but parts remain. As is true almost everywhere, the old and the new stand side by side in sharp contrast. To the tribesman from Hazarajat, Kabul must seem as modern as New York City appears to a backwoodsman on his first visit from the Kentucky hills. Regular air services lead to each of the three surrounding countries, as well as to India and Lebanon, so that Kabul is increasingly in touch with the outside world.

Baluchistan

Although this volume is limited on the east by the political borders of Afghanistan, the geographical and cultural character of Swasia continues into Western Pakistan. If

[1] Henry McMahon: "Recent Survey and Exploration in Seistan," *Geog. Jour.*, XXVII (1906), 334.

Cultivated fields lie outside the ancient walls of Balk, watered by tributaries of the Oxus. (Courtesy James A. Cudney.)

it is proper to include a chapter on Egypt, it may also be appropriate to add notes on Pakistan, or at least to its province of Baluchistan.

Baluchistan borders Afghanistan on the south and is comparable in geography and history since it has a Mediterranean climatic regime, a combination of snow-crowned mountains and desolate deserts, and a history with roots in the north and west. The province covers 134,002 square miles, or one-third of Pakistan as a whole. At the time of the 1951 census, the province had a population of 1,174,036, as compared with 834,703 in 1911.

The province may be divided into three regions: the high Sulaiman, Kirthar, and other ranges of the east with numerous peaks above 10,000 feet; the arid Makran Mountains of the south; and the Registan and other deserts of the northwest and center. Climate varies with altitude. Lowlands have a long and intensely hot summer with a moderate winter. Above 3,000 feet, winter months bring freezing temperatures and snow, but summers are warm. Sharp contrasts from one area to another characterize all of Baluchistan. Rainfall thus varies from three inches in the plains to fifteen inches on mountain slopes.

Agricultural land may be divided into three categories: lands which depend on rain or snow; areas watered by flood inundation; and fields which are supplied by irrigation from karez, wells, or perennial

VERTICAL CROP LIMITS [1]

Barley	11,200 feet
Spring wheat	10,900 feet
Apricots	9,600 feet
Winter wheat	9,250 feet
Apples	8,250 feet
Melons	7,900 feet
Rice	7,000 feet
Cotton	6,950 feet
Figs	3,500 feet
Sugar cane	3,400 feet
Date palms	2,800 feet
Bamboo	2,200 feet

[1] N. I. Vavilov and D. D. Buckinich: *Agricultural Afghanistan*. Leningrad, 1929 (in Russian with long English summary). Heights converted from meters.

streams. Only in a few favored areas does the extent of cultivated land reach 10 per cent; more commonly, agriculture covers 3 per cent or less. *Rabi* harvests are those gathered in the spring, chiefly wheat, while *karif* crops such as millet and maize mature in the fall.

LIVELIHOOD AND THE FUTURE

Agriculture supplies three-quarters of Afghanistan's national income.[1] The country normally feeds itself although, after poor harvests, imports are necessary. According to government figures for 1953–54, 85 per cent of the people were engaged in agriculture. The total cultivated area is estimated at somewhat over 7 million acres, or less than 1 per cent of the total area. Other figures of cropland are considerably larger. If the population is indeed 12 million, 7 million acres of cultivated land scarcely seem adequate for the food supply even if supplemented by grazing. Roughly a million acres are irrigated, two-thirds of it in the north.

About half the cropland is devoted to wheat, but yields are low, amounting to 2 million metric tons per year. Raw cotton averaged 20,000 tons before World War II, but it has since been increased some 50 per cent through the introduction of better methods. Modern cotton textile mills operate at Gulbahar, Pul-i-Khumri, and Jebal-us-Siraj. Woolen fabrics are woven in Kabul and Kandahar. Silk is produced near Kabul, Baghlan, and Herat. Sugar beets represent an expanding product, thanks to new mills in the north.

The livestock population includes 12 to 14 million sheep, 6 to 8 million goats, nearly 3 million cattle, half a million camels, and 42 million chickens. The number of karakul sheep has varied considerably since as many as one-third of the flocks may die during severe winters. The export of karakul fluctuates between 1 and 3 million skins a year. These variations, plus changing fashion abroad, make Afghanistan's dependence on karakul skins for one-third of its export income somewhat precarious.

Fruit and nuts account for another third of the export trade. Fresh fruits along with raisins and dried apricots are shipped to Pakistan and India.

Early industrialization was handicapped by inadequate electric power, expensive transport, and a shortage of skilled personnel. Considerable amounts of hydroelectricity are now available from the Helmand Valley dams, the Sarobie plant near Kabul, and elsewhere. The rapid growth of educational facilities in the capital is meeting the need for engineers, but improvement is slow.

Afghan mining is in its infancy. Estimates of future production as a base for industry can only be tentative; in general, the prospects appear poor.

Coal of good quality is produced in the important mines at Darra-i-Suf southeast of Mazar-i-Sharif, where reserves are estimated at 50 million tons. Inferior coal,

[1] United Nations Economic Commission for Asia and the Far East, Bangkok: *Economic Survey*. (1955), 57.

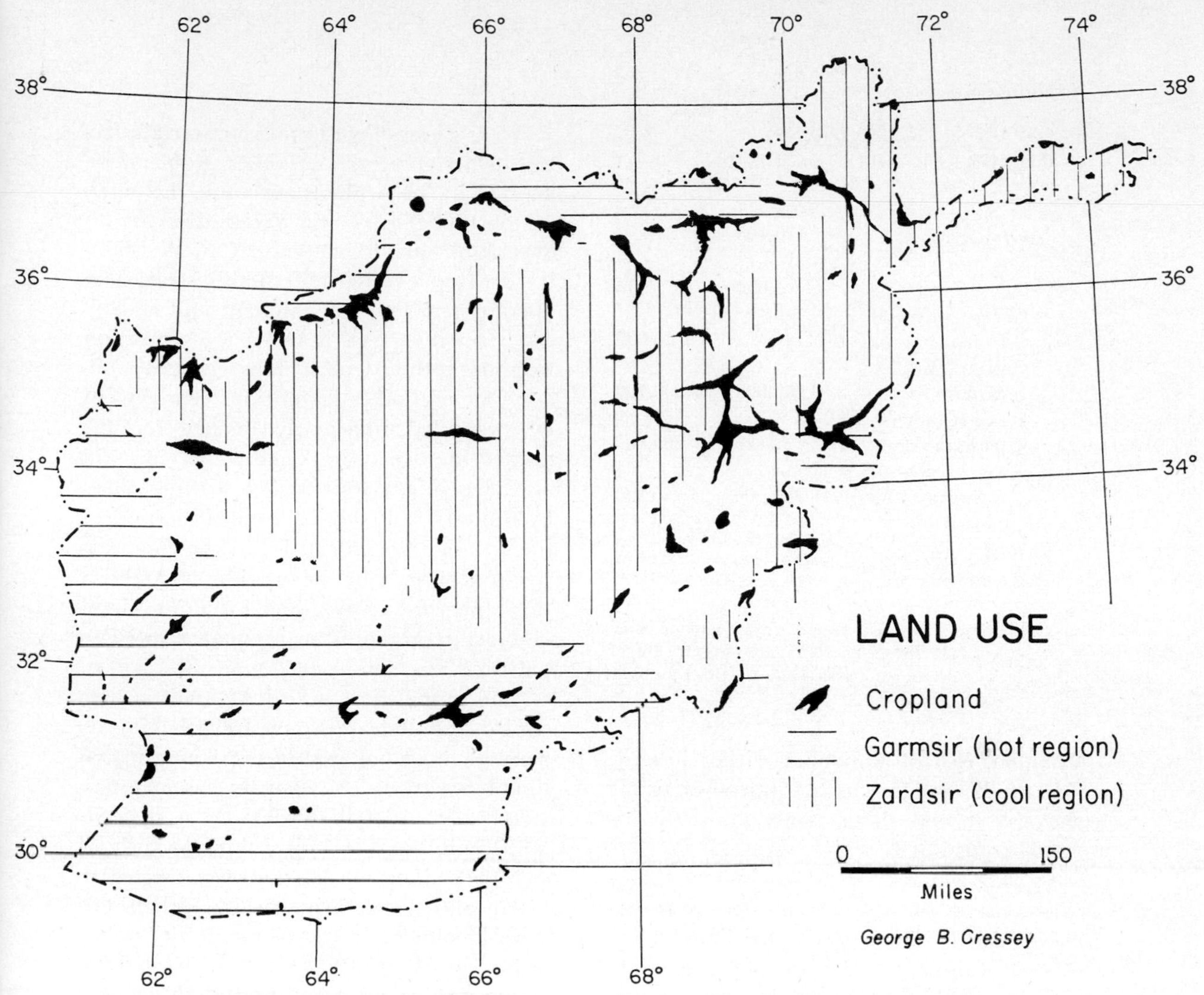

Only 1 per cent of Afghanistan is cultivated. Garmsir regions are hot with mild winters; Zardsir areas experience at least two months with snow. (Data from Wenschow: *Atlas for Secondary Schools in Afghanistan,* and Vavilov and Bukinich.)

which needs briquetting, is obtained at Ishpushta and at Karkar near Pul-i-Khumri. All coal deposits are of Jurassic age, and none are known south of the Hindu Kush.

Other minerals are present, but either poor quality or expensive transport have limited production to nominal amounts. These include chromium, beryllium, talc, lead, and zinc. Salt is obtained from desert lakes. Cement is manufactured at Jebel-us-Seraj and Pul-i-Khumri, and oil is thought to occur in a number of locations both north and south of the Hindu Kush, but the reserves are still unknown.

A succession of development programs include plans for major improvements in many aspects of agriculture and industry; such as irrigation, better kinds of seed, model farms, community development, education, roads and airports, hydroelectricity, textiles, and fruit processing.

Afghanistan's access to the outside world would be materially improved if she were to secure transit rights across Pakistan with a free-port zone at Karachi. Proposals also look forward to extending the railhead at

AFGHAN MINERAL AND INDUSTRIAL PRODUCTION [1]

	1950/51	*1955/56*
Coal (tons)	10,100	21,100
Salt (tons)	—	22,600
Sugar (tons)	4,600	4,900
Cotton, ginned (tons)	—	20,000
Cotton fabrics (square meters)	9,100,000	17,500,000
Woolen fabrics (square meters)	—	205,000
Electricity (kilowatt hours)	8,300,000	24,300,000
Wheat (tons)	—	2,100,000
Barley (tons)	—	730,000
Rice (tons)	—	250,000

[1] United Nations: *Economic Survey of Asia and the Far East.* (1956), 61. Also U.S. Dept. of Commerce "Basic Data on the Economy of Afghanistan."

Chaman, east of Kandahar, either just inside the border for customs purposes, or all the way to Kabul. Certainly improved internal transport is a major need.

So long as imperial Britain was in India, Afghanistan formed a contested zone between the British and the Russians. Thus Abdal Rahman, ruler during the nineteenth century, could write in his autobiography, "This poor goat, Afghanistan, is a victim at which a lion on one side and a terrible bear from the other side are staring and ready to swallow at the first opportunity afforded to them."

With the establishment of India and Pakistan, Britain has ceased to be interested in Afghanistan since it is no longer a strategic frontier of its empire. The Kremlin still looks southward, but until recently it made light of Afghanistan as a corrupt feudal state and only developed a good neighbor policy during the 1950's. Afghanistan's willingness to accept American assistance may represent a desire to find a new counterinfluence against the Soviet Union.

While geography can measure certain factors of the environment, other problems remain. Can the Afghans overcome the barriers of topography and racial diversity to develop national coherence? Can the country develop enough able administrators to operate a modern government and a modern economy? Can it make the transition from the former feudal monarchy to a modern state without a revolution? Can exports be expanded sufficiently to pay for the needed imports? Can Afghanistan maintain an independent position in a world divided by contesting ideologies? One suggestion of the economic problem lies in the comparative cost of an hour's plane ride; in America this represents a day's wage for an unskilled laborer, in Afghanistan it equals a month's pay for a teacher.

American policy toward Afghanistan recognizes the desirability of strengthening its domestic economy and of preserving its national integrity. The country has many assets, but in order to develop them, it needs both capital and technical skill. As with all countries along borders between the totalitarian and democratic worlds, Afghanistan is an ideological contest zone. Soviet policy following World War II was directed toward winning good will and establishing a reputation as a helpful neighbor. Behind these objectives, and beyond the Khyber, the U.S.S.R. looks toward India.

Cultural relations are a two-way street. As Justice Douglas has written in words which form a fitting close to this volume:

> We of the west have all the rudiments of civilization, all the dividends of a mounting standard of living. But the Afghans—one thousand years behind us in many respects—have a warmth of human relations that is often missing all the way from New York City to San Francisco.[1]

[1] William O. Douglas: *Beyond the High Himalaya.* Garden City: Doubleday (1952), 265. Quoted by permission.

REFERENCES

General References

Ali, Mohammed. AFGHANISTAN: THE MOHAMMEDZAI PERIOD. Kabul: The Author (1959).

Cervin, Vladimir: "Problems in the Integration of the Afghan Nation," *Middle East Jour.,* VI (1952), 400–416.

Elphinstone, Mountstuart: AN ACCOUNT OF THE KINGDOM OF CAUBAL AND ITS DEPENDENCIES. London: Longman (1815).

Franck, Peter G.: "Problems of Economic Development in Afghanistan," *Middle East Jour.,* III (1949), 293–314, 421–440.

Franck, Peter G.: "Afghanistan," in Teaf, Howard: HANDS ACROSS FRONTIERS. Ithaca: Cornell (1955).

Franck, Peter G.: "Economic Progress in an Encircled Land," *Middle East Jour.,* X (1956), 43–59.

Fraser-Tytler, W. Kerr: "Afghanistan," *Scot. Geog. Mag.,* LIX (1943), 1–6.

* Fraser-Tytler, W. Kerr: AFGHANISTAN: A STUDY OF POLITICAL DEVELOPMENT IN CENTRAL ASIA. London: Oxford Univ. Press (1950).

* Humlum, J.: LA GEOGRAPHIE DE L'AFGHANISTAN. Copenhagen: Gyldenal (1959) [Outstanding monograph with bibliography]

Linchevsky, I. A., and Prozorovsky A.V.: "The Basic Principles of the Distribution of the Vegetation of Afghanistan," *Kew Bulletin,* No. 2 (1949) 179–214.

* Michel, Aloys Arthur: THE KABUL, KUNDUZ, AND HELMAND VALLEYS. Washington: National Academy of Sciences (Office of Naval Research) (1959).

Peter (Prince of Greece): "Post War Development in Afghanistan," *Jour. Royal Central Asian Soc.,* XXXIV (1947), 275–286.

Schurman, H. F.: THE MONGOLS OF AFGHANISTAN. (1960).

Stenz, Edward: THE CLIMATE OF AFGHANISTAN, ITS ARIDITY, DRYNESS AND DIVISION. New York: Polish Institute of Arts and Sciences in America (1946).

Sykes, Christopher: A HISTORY OF AFGHANISTAN. New York: Macmillan (1940).

Trinkler, Emil: "Afghanistan," *Petermanns Mitt., Erganzungsheft* No. 196 (1928).

Trinkler, Emil: THROUGH THE HEART OF AFGHANISTAN. London: Faber & Gwyer (1928).

* Vavilov, N., et Bukinich, D. D.: AGRICULTURAL AFGHANISTAN. Leningrad: The Pan-Soviet Institute of Applied Botany (1929).

von Niedermayer, Oskar: "Persien und Afganistan" in KLUTE HANDBUCH DER GEOGRAPHISCHEN WISSENSCHAFT, VI, VORDER UND SUDASIEN. Potsdam: Akademische Verlagsgesellschaft Athenaion (1937), 63–125.

Wenschow, Karl: ATLAS FOR SECONDARY SCHOOLS IN AFGHANISTAN. Munich: Geographical Institute (1955).

Wilber, Donald N.: "Afghanistan, Independent and Encircled," *Foreign Affairs,* XXXI (1953), 486–494.

Wilber, Donald W.: AFGHANISTAN. New Haven: Human Relations Area Files (1956).

Travel and Description

Bacon, Elizabeth E.: "The Inquiry into the History of the Hazara Mongols of Afghanistan," *Southwestern Jour. of Anthrop.,* VII (1951), 230–247.

Barger, Evert: "Exploration of Ancient Sites in Northern Afghanistan," *Geog. Jour.,* XCIII (1939), 377–398.

Barger, Evert: "Some Problems of Central Asian Exploration," *Geog. Jour.,* CIII (1944), 1–18.

Afghanistan

Cresson, Rebecca Shannon: "American Family in Afghanistan," *Nat. Geog. Mag.,* CIV (1953), 417–432.

DeBaer, August: "August in Badakhshan," *Geog. Mag.,* XXIX (1956), 77–86.

Douglas, William O.: WEST OF THE INDUS. New York: Doubleday (1958).

Douglas, William O.: "West from the Khyber Pass," *Nat. Geog. Mag.,* CXIV (1958), 1–44.

Fox, Ernest F.: TRAVELS IN AFGHANISTAN. 1937–1938, New York: Macmillan (1943).

Hay, W. R.: "Band-i-Amir," *Geog. Jour.,* LXXXVII (1936), 348–350.

Howland, Felix: "Crossing the Hindu Kush," *Geog. Rev.,* XXX (1940), 272–278.

* Keffel, Joseph: AFGHANISTAN. London: Thames and Hudson (1959). [Handsome photographs]

Rathjens, Carl: "Afghanistan, Ein Land Junger Wirtschaftsentwicklung," *Geog. Rundschau,* IX (1957), 463–472.

Shor, Jean, and Shor, Franc: "We Took the Highroad in Afghanistan," *Nat. Geog. Mag.,* XCVIII (1950), 673–706.

Snow, Peter: "Last Pagans of the Hindu Kush," *Natural History,* XLVIII (1959), 520–528.

Thesiger, Wilfred: "The Hazaras of Central Afghanistan," *Geog. Jour.,* CXXI (1955), 312–319.

Thesiger, Wilfred: "The Hazarajat of Afghanistan," *Geog. Mag.,* XXIX (1956), 87–95.

Thesiger, Wilfred: "A Journey in Nuristan," *Geog. Jour.,* CXXIII (1957), 457–464.

Williams, Maynard Owen: "Afghanistan Makes Haste Slowly," *Nat. Geog. Mag.,* LXIV (1933), 731–769.

Williams, Maynard Owen: "Back to Afghanistan," *Nat. Geog. Mag.,* XC (1946), 517–544.

Glossary

(A) ARABIC (P) PERSIAN (T) TURKISH

Aba (A), woolen cloak
Abat (T), cultivated, inhabited
Ada (T), island, isle
Agal, Igal (A), head cord for kaffiyeh
Agha (T), a title, chief or mister
Agul (A), camel thorn bush
Ain, Ayn (A), spring, well
Akhbar (A), greater
Akhdar (A), green
Ala (T), very high
Amir (A), prince, leader
Arbob (P), landowner
Arish (A), grass hut or shelter
Asir (A), isolated

Bab (A), gate, strait
Badia (A), untilled waste
Bahr (A), sea, lake
Bait (A), house
Bait Allah (A), house of God, Mecca
Balkan (T), chain of mountains
Bani, Ben (A), sons of . . . , plural of ibn
Barasti (A), hut of wood and matting
Batin, Batu (A), shallow valley
Bedouin (A), nomad
Beg (T), tribal chief
Bekaa (A), fertile plain
Beled (A), village
Bin (A), son of . . . , variant of ibn
Bir (A), dug well
Birket, Birkah (A), pool, reservoir
Bisht (A), cloak, (*see* aba)
Bum (A), sailing ship
Buyuk (T), great, big

Cadi (A), an ecclesiastical judge
Cal (T), escarpment, scarp, cliff
Caliph (A), Khalifa, authoritative religious ruler, "one who comes after"
Caravanserai (P), caravan inn
Col (T), desert

Dag (T), mountain
Daglari (T), range, mountains
Dahanah (A), hard pebbly desert with dunes
Daimi (P), rain-fed cultivation
Dar (A), house
Darb (A), road
Dasht (P), flat gravel or silt desert
Deir (A), monastery
Derbent (T), defile, pass
Dervish (P), member of Sufi brotherhood
Dhow (Swahili), Arab sailing boat
Dhura (A), millet
Dibdibah (A), desert surface with scrub jungle
Dikaka (A), sand hummocks around clumps of vegetation
Diwan (A), a court, guest house
Dogu (T), sunrise, east, levant
Durbar (P), royal council

Effendi (T), Turkish title of respect, a foreigner
El (A), the
Erg (A), sandy waste

Faqir (A), a poor man
Fellah, Fellahin (A), cultivator, peasant

Galabiya (A), Egyptian tunic
Gaud (P), depression
Gebel (A), mountain, (*see* jebel)
Gezira (A), island, (*see* jezira)
Ghab (A), forest
Ghazzu (A), a raid
Ghor (A), low ground, swamp
Gol (T), lake
Gufa (A), round boat, waterproofed with bitumen

Hadhar (A), town dwellers, sedentary people
Hajj (A), pilgrimage to Mecca
Hakim (A), ruler, official judge
Halwa (A), sweet
Hamad (A), dry barren region
Hamun (P), reed filled marsh, lake
Harem, Haram (A), reserved place, forbidden
Harra (A), rough lava surface
Hegira, Hejira (A), Mohammed's flight from Mecca, 622 A.D.
Hejaz (A), boundary
Hilal al Akhdar (A), fertile crescent
Hisar (T), castle, fort
Hor (A), depression, marsh

Ibn (A), son of
Ikhwan (A), Moslem brotherhood
Iklim (T), climate, zone, country
Ilkhani (P), Bakhtiari chief
Imam (A), "one who leads in prayer"
Inshalla (A), "if God wills"
Irmak (T), river
Irq (pl. Uruq) (A), long sand ridge
Islam (A), "resignation to the will of God"

(A) ARABIC (P) PERSIAN (T) TURKISH

Jangal (P), forest, as near Caspian Sea
Jauf (A), large plain, a depression
Jebel, Jabal (A), mountain, hill
Jezira, Gezira (A), island, as between two rivers
Jihad (A), holy war
Jinn (A), evil spirit
Juss (A), gypsum, cement

Kala (A), fort, (*see* qalah)
Kara (T), black
Karez (P), tunnel for irrigation, qanat
Kasr, Qasr (A), castle, fort
Katkhoda (P), landowner's resident agent
Kavir (P), salt flat
Kebab (T), roasted meat
Kebir (A), great
Khafs (A), rocky hollow, usually with water
Khamsin (A), "fifty day" summer wind from south
Khan, an inn, tribal chief
Kharif (A), autumn
Khirbet (A), ruin
Khuwiyah (A), servants, armed escort
Kir (T), uncultivated land
Koh (P), mountain
Kuh (T), mountain
Kum (T), sand

Leben (A), milk, usually sour
Liman (T), harbour, port, bay
Liwa (A), province

Maaden (T), mine
Madrasah (A), school, college
Mafraq (A), road junction
Maidan (P), open place, a plain
Majlis (A), reception room, tribal council
Mar (A), saint
Marhaba (T), a greeting
Masjid (A), a place of prayer, mosque
Memleha (T), temporary salt pan
Mera (T), pasture ground
Millet (T), administrative system for religious minorities
Mina (A), harbor
Mir (A), prince, descendant of Mohammed
Miri (T), state-owned land on long lease
Mulk (A), private land fully owned
Mullah (P), Muslim cleric

Nafud (A), large area with sand dunes
Nahr (A), river
Nejd, Najd (A), plateau or elevated ground
Nili (A), autumn season

Ova (T), plain, basin

Pasha (T), title of high rank
Pinar (T), spring, fountain
Pushtin (P), sheepskin coat

Qadhi (A), a judge, (*see* cadi)
Qalah, Kala (A), a fort
Qanat (A), irrigation tunnel, karez
Qarn (A), projecting hill
Qasr (A), fort, castle, palace, (*see* kasr)
Qibla (A), toward Mecca
Quran (A), Koran, the Moslem scripture

Ramadan (A), ninth lunar month, for fasting
Ramazan (T), month of fasting
Ramlah (A), sand area
Ras (A), promontory, cape
Raudha (A), wide depression with good grazing
Riyal (A), Maria Theresa dollar
Riz (P), area of sand dunes
Rud (P), river

Sabkhah (A), clay flat with saline crust
Sahara (A), wide waterless desert
Sahil (A), plain
Sahil (T), shore, coast, bank
Saif (A), summer
Saif (A), sword
Salam aleikum (A), "peace be on you"
Sambuk (A), pearling boat, dhow
Sanjak (T), Turkish province
Sardsir (P), summer pasture
Sayid (A), descendant of Mohammed through Fatima
Shadoof (A), device for lifting water with hinged pole
Shafi (A), one of four schools of Sunni law
Shamal (A), dry north wind
Sharia (A), traditional Moslem law
Shargi, sharqi (A), east wind
Shatt (A), river
Sheikh (A), tribal head, old man
Shia (A), Moslem sect which "follows Ali"
Shitwi, shita (A), winter
Shuqqan (A), linear depression between dunes
Simoon (P), "poison wind," hot and southerly
Sinir (T), boundary
Sirocco, hot, dry south wind
Su (T), river, water
Suhaili (A), south wind
Sunna (A), Moslem customs and traditions
Sunni (A), Orthodox Moslems who acknowledge the first four Caliphs

Suq (A), bazaar, market

Tapu (T), state-owned land with guaranteed tenure

Tawayih (A), forfeited or twice-used water

Tel (A), artificial mound, usually an ancient town

Tepe (T), peak

Tuz (A), salt

Ulma (A), man learned in religion

Uruq (A), long sand ridges, plural of irq

Vilayet (T), Turkish province

Wadi (pl. Widyan) (A), dry stream bed

Waqf (A), land held in religious trust

Yar (T), precipice, abyss, cliff, hill

Yoghurt, milk thickened by fermentation

Yurt (T), native land, habitation, home

Zam Zam (A), holy well in Mecca

Zibarr (A), rolling sand surface

Ziggurat, terraced pyramid

Zor (A), escarpment, also jungle, thicket

Index

Pages in *italics* refer to illustrations

Abadan, 211, *214*, 232, *513*, 518, 530, *531*
Abbasside Caliphate, 56–58, 375–378
Aden, 22, 27, *190*, 230, 327, *328*, *337*, 338
Afghanistan, 17, 27, 65, 66, *77*, 136–139, *188*, 232, 234–235, 238, 545–580
Agri, Mountain, *80*
Agriculture, 3, 157–173
  Afghanistan, 552, 578
  Arabia, 309, 312–318
  Egypt, 358–362
  Iran, 509–512
  Iraq, 390–396
  Israel, 479–487
  Jordan, 462–463
  Syria, 435–438
  Turkey, 267–272
Ahwaz, 514, 530
Airways, *24*, 227–228
Alanya, *261*
Aleppo, 420, 422, 425, 443–445
Alexander the Great, 55, 62–63, 253, 391, 426
Alexandretta (*See* Iskenderon)
Alexandria, 362, *364*
Aluminum, 280
Amanus Range, 74, 412
American interests, 242–245, 455, 580
American University of Beirut, *222*, 242, 454, *455*
Amiran, D. H. K., 487
Amman, 421, 457, *460*
Amorites, 47, 424, 438
Amu Darya, 551–559
Analogies with United States, 6, 17, 94–95, 416, 454, 482, 503, 572
Anatolia, 61, 74, 260, 266, 283–284
Anglo-Persian Oil Company (*See* British Petroleum Company)
Ankara, 252–253, 259, *260*, *270*, 282, *287*
Antalya, *254*
Anti-Lebanon Mountains, 74, 414–415, 452
Antimony, 187, 276, 279
Aqaba, 230, 240, 416, 457, 495
Arab empires, 56–59
Arab League, 241, 350
Arab nationalism, 233, 241, 348–354
Arab states compared, 351–354
Arabia (*See also* Saudi Arabia), 292–340
Arabia Deserta, 304
Arabia Felix, 304, 305, 328
Arabia Petra, 304
Arabian American Oil Company, 196, 197, 200, 218
Arable land, 157–160
Arabs, *10*, *35*, 46–48, 350
Araks River, 515
Ararat, Mountain, 80, 515
Arghandab River, 554, 559
Armenians, 266, 286, 438, 515
Aryan, 118, 561
Asbestos, 189–190, 276
Asir, 331
Assassins, 521
Assyria, 51–53, 371, 375, 386
Aswan Dam, 356

Baalbek, 450–451
Babylon, 50–53, 371–375, 386
Bactria, 552, 569–571
Badakshan, *557*, 558, 566–568
Baghdad, 16, 21, 64, *120*, *141*, 375–376, *381*, 382, 387, 397–400, 401
Bahrein, 198, 200, 218–219, *244*, *321*, 334
Bakhtiari, 39, 503, 526
Balfour Declaration, 234, 474
Balkh, 552, 570, *577*
Baluchistan, 576–577
Bamian, 549–550, 569
Bananas, *168*
Barada River, 442
Barley, 164, 269, 394, 511
Basra, 21, *239*, *379*, 400–401, *403*
Bedouin (*See also* Nomads), 37–38, 296, *300*, 306, 308, *317*, 318–321, 378, 380, 438–440
Beirut, *13*, 14–15, *222*, 227, 231, 416–417, 419, *449*, 454–455, *456*
Bekaa, *95*, 414, 452, *453*
Biblical references,
  II Chronicles VIII:4, 429
  Daniel III:8–30, 194
  Deuteronomy VIII:7–9, 485
  Deuteronomy XXXIV:1, 416
  Genesis XVII:8, 474
  Genesis XXXVII:25, 302
  I Kings XVIII:17–40, 415
  Mathew VII:25, 120
  Numbers XXXI:22, 177
  Numbers XXXIII:50–55, 473
  Psalms CXXII:3, 426
Bitumen, *194*, *195*, 373
Boracite, 189–190
Boron, 276, 280

Bosporus, *225,* 226, 236, 247–250, *285,* 286–287
Brestead, James H., 42–43
British interests, 334–338, 381, 424, 553, 562–563, 580
British Petroleum Co., 195, 197, 200, 210, 211–212, 215
Bromine, 463–464
Brown, White, Green, and Black, 3–10, 256, 305, 329, 537, 547
Bryce, James, 265
Burami, 336
Burgan, 215–216
Bursa, *258*
Butzer, Karl W., 96–97
Buyuk Menderes River, 134–136
Byblos, 425–426
Byzantium, 61, 250, 254

Cairo, *348, 352,* 359, *360,* 362, *363, 367*
Camels, 171–172, *296,* 306, 319, 320–321, 571
Canaanites, 424, 474
Carmel, Mount, 415
Caspian area, 107, 116, 518–520
Cedars of Lebanon, *5, 408, 418,* 422–423, 451
Cement, *178,* 280
Christianity, 47, 312, 339, 427–428
Chromium, 184, 187, 276, 278–279, 514
Churchill, Winston, 354–355
Cities, 38–40
  Afghanistan, 547–548
  Arabia, 321–327
  Egypt, 362
  Iran, 529–536
  Iraq, 397–401
  Israel, 489–491
  Jordan, 426–428, 457–458
  Lebanon, 425–426, 453–455
  Syria, 428–431, 441–445
Citrus crops, 166, *229,* 485
Climate, 16, 23, 93–116
  Afghanistan, 558, 567
  Arabia, 310–311, 324–325
  Iran, 521, 526
  Israel, 482–483
  Levant, 416–424
  Turkey, 263–264
Climatic changes, 95–97, 423–424, 482
Climatic regions, 111–116
Climatic tables, 113–116
Coal, *180,* 181–182, 274, 276, 512, 578
Coast line, 224–225, 261, 411
Coffee, 170, 320, 331
Coon, Carleton, 49–50
Copper, *183,* 187, 276, 280, *493,* 494
Cornwall, J. H. M., 263
Cotton, 169, 359, *361,* 396, 436, *487,* 511
Cragg, Kenneth, 479
Crops (*See also* Agriculture), 162–171
Crossroads, 14, 23–26, 223–228, 247, 410, 560
Crusades, *233,* 241, 250, 426, 427
Ctesiphon, *378*
Culture areas, 10–13, 46–50

Damascus, 16, 416–417, 419, 432, 433, 441–443, 445
Dams, 275, 277, 354–357, 382, 514, 538
Darb Zubaida, 295–297
Dardanelles *(See* Bosporus)
Dasht, 527
Dates, 166–168, *311,* 312, 314, 370, 394–396, 511
Davis, Richard S., 129
Dead Sea, *82,* 130, 132–134, 463–465, 493–494
Decapolis, 458–459
Demavend, Mount, 81, 520, 536
Desert, 4–5, 16–17, 22, 83–91, 296, 306–307, 416, 526–528, 572, 575
Development programs, 288, 381–382, 537–540
Dhahran, 217, 324–325
Dhufar, 198, 300–304, 337–338
Dikaka, 86, *297*
Diyarbekir, 265
Diz River, *181,* 507, 514
Donkey lift wells, 314
Douglas, William O., 580
Dry farming, 160, 268
Durand Line, 563
Dust storms, 84, 101–102, 386

Earthquakes, 81–83, 256, 261
Economic Problems, 157–158, 195–196, 200–201, 228–232
  Arabia, 325–327
  Iran, 536–540
  Iraq, 381–382
  Israel, 491–493
  Lebanon, 453–455
  Syria, 445–446
  Turkey, 285–288
Egypt, 221, 348–368
Elath (Eilat), 226, 230, 492, *495*
Elburz Mountains, 74, 520–522
Emery, 189–190, 276, 280
Erzurum, 82, 83, 284
Esdraelon, Plain of, 415, 480
Etesian winds, 100
Euphrates River, 140–149, 371, 373, 382, *384–385,* 433, 435
Evapotranspiration, 107–111, 311, 421

Fedden, Robin, 442, 443
Fertile Crescent, 20, 42–43, 285, 422
Fish, 173, 272

Fisher, W. B., 71, 96
Flax, 170
Floods, *120,* 146, 357–358, 373, 381–382, *385,* 387, 397–398
Foreign Trade, 228–232
Afghanistan, 550, 578
Israel, 485, 496
Syria, 445
Turkey, 288
Forests (*See also* Natural Vegetation), *94,* 174–175, 259, 272, 422–423, 451, 519, 521
Fox, Ernest F., 566
Fraser-Tytler, W. K., 564
French interests, 26, 232, 241, 286, 424

Galilee (*See also* Tiberias), 480
Gas, 194, *196,* 209
Gaza, 478
Geographic Regions,
Afghanistan, 566–578
Iran, 515–529
Iraq, 383–388
Turkey, 283–285
Geography, 7, 11, 34, 41, 78, 245
Geology, 69–76, 201–203, 256–257, 273–274, 283–288, 411–416, 515, 521–526, 556–557
Geostrategy (*See also* Political Geography), 23–26, 223–232, 235–245
Ghab, 413, 434, 435
Gharraf Canal, 146, 372
Ghawar, 217
Ghor, 132, 416
Ghuta, *169,* 434, 437, 442, *446*
Goats (*See also* Sheep), 172
Gold, 177, 185, 280, 445
Grapes, 168, 552, 571
Greater Syria, 238, 425, 456, 473
Griesbach, C. L., 556

Hadhramaut, 302, 315–318, 338
Haifa, *229,* 230, 415, 457, 490–491, 492
Hail, 297–298
Hamadan, 531, *532*
Hamites, 349–350
Hari River, 560
Harun-al-Rashid, 57, 295, 375, 397
Hasa, 60, 306, 312
Hatay, 286, 411, 447
Hazarajat, 564–565, 568–569
Hebrews, 47, 424, 426, 473–479
Hejaz, 75, 298, 303, 328
Helmand River, 136–139, 554, 559, 572–575
Hemp, *169,* 170
Herat, 552–553, 571
Herodotus, 194, 360, 362, 390–391
High Dam, 357
Hindu Kush Mountains, 17, 74, 80, 548–550, *551,* 556–557, 566–568
History, 41–45
Afghanistan, 560–564
Arabia, 324, 332
Iran, 501–503
Iraq, 371–381
Israel, 473–479
Levant, 424–431
Turkey, 253–256
Hit, 194, *195*
Hitti, Philip R., 375, 376, 449
Hittites, 59–60, 253
Hofuf, 313–315
Hormuz, 183, 226, 514, 525
Hoskins, Halford, 366–367
Huleh, Lake, *481,* 493
Hunt, Richard P., 326–327
Hydroelectricity, 182, 275, 277, 354, 357, 512–514
Hydrography, 107–111, 119–124

Ibn Batuta, 65–66, 556
Igneous activity, 79–81, 256, 260, 265–266, 273, 303, 529
Incense, 66, 300–304
Indo-Europeans, 46–48, 424
Industry,
Afghanistan, 578–579
Iran, 514, 539–540
Israel, 485, 494–496
Lebanon, 454
Syria, 445
Turkey, 181, 272, 277–278, 280–281, 288
Ingrams, Harold, 316
Iran (*See also* Persia), 28, 123–127, *150, 158, 181,* 197, *201,* 209–212, 230, 232, 234, 237–238, 501–540
Iran versus Turkey, 20, 266, 503, 515, 519
Iranian Consortium, 212
Iraq (*See also* Mesopotomia), 28, *70, 120,* 140–149, 167, *195, 196,* 197, 212–215, 229, 230, 240, 351–354, 371–404
Iraq Petroleum Co., 195, 197, 212–213
Iron, 177, 183, 185–186, 276, 279, 362, 445, 494, 514
Irrigation, 20, *158, 162, 163*
Afghanistan, 572–575
Arabia, 312–314
Egypt, 360
Iran, 504–509
Iraq, 376, 390
Israel, 483–484
Syria, *437*
Yemen, 330
Isfahan, *109, 123,* 124–126, 518, 528, 531–533

Iskenderon, 231, 239, 286, 411, 445, 447
Islam, 47, 293, 354, 428, 502, 561
Israel (*See also* Jordan, Palestine), 28, *94, 96,* 220, 229, 234, 240–241, 475–496
Istanbul, *59,* 61, 231, 246–252, 283
Izmir, *109, 242,* 257, *270,* 284

Jaffa, *229,* 481, *482*
Jalalabad, 547, 576
Jarmo, 391–392
Jazira, 386, 438
Jebel Ansariya, 413
Jebel Druze, 416
Jebel Zawiyeh, 74, 413
Jerash, 459
Jericho, 43
Jerusalem, 240, 421, 422, 426–428, *458,* 491
Jews, 47, 424, 426, 473–479
Jidda, 231, 299, *320,* 322–323
Jordan (*See also* Israel, Palestine), 28, 130–134, 230, 240, 455–465
Jordan River, *118,* 130–134, 415–416, 461, *462,* 463, *464*
Judea, 94, 415, 456, 460, 481

Kabul, 17, 547–548, *549,* 558, 559, 560, 576
Kandahar, 77, 554–555, 558, 559, *560,* 573, 574
Karabuk, *185,* 277, 278
Karaj, 514
Karakul, 571
Karez (*See* Qanats)
Karun River (*See also* Shatt-al-Arab), *139,* 140, 142, 147, 149, 538
Kavir, 527–528
Keban Dam, 275
Kerbela, 379
Kerman, 64–65, 507–508, 528
Kermanshah, 516, 531
Kharj, 101, 311, 312–313, *333*
Khobar, *325*
Khurasan, 522, 571–572
Khuzistan, *509,* 524, 538
Khyber Pass, 545–546
King-Crane Commission, 243, 447, 475–476
Kirkuk, 20, 194, *196,* 213–214, 401
Kizil Irmak, 134, 261–262
Krac des Chevaliers, 413, *414*
Kunduz, 560, 570, *571*
Kurd Dagh, 74, 413
Kurds, 36, 48–50, 236–237, 282, 379, 518, 526
Kut, *144,* 146, 149
Kuwait, 21–22, *25,* 197, 200, 215–216, 325–327, 334–336

Land Forms (*See also* Geographic Regions), 76–79
Land of the Six Seas, 23, 223–227
La Roque, 304
Latakia, 412, 438, 445
Lava flows, 79–80, 260, 265–266, 303, 529
Lead and Zinc, 186, 276, 280
Lebanon, *5,* 15, 28, *71, 95, 167, 178, 207,* 231, *233,* 239–240, *411, 412, 413, 417,* 447–455
Lebanon Mountains, 74, 414, 452
Levant, 409–411, 424–425
Lewis, Bernard, 254–255
Lignite, 182, 275
Litani River, 74, 414, 452–453
Livestock, 171–174
Locusts, 396
Loess, 84, 551, 571
Ludwig, Emil, 357–358
Lynch, W. F., 131

Magnesite, 276
Makran, 74, 526, 577
Manganese, 187, 189–190, 276, 362
Marco Polo, 63–65, 552
Marib, 302, 305
Marmara, Sea of, *173,* 247, 257
Marsh (*See* Swamps)
Masjid-i-Sulaiman, 210
Masqat (Muscat), 29, 241, 332, 337
Mazar-i-Sharif, 549, 553
McMahon, Henry, 576
McMahon-Hussein Agreement, 233, 474
Mecca, 293, 299–300
Medina, *292,* 299
Mediterranean climate, 93–97, 416–424, 558
Meerschaum, 276, 280
Menderes R. (*See* Buyuk Menderes)
Mercury, 187, 276, 280
Mersin, 209, 231, 284
Meshed, 151, 514, 517, 522, 533–534
Mesopotamia (*See also* Iraq), 20, 50–54, 143, 371, 386
Middle East, 7–10, 25
Millet, 164, 305, 330
Mineral resources, 177–191
  Afghanistan, 578–579
  Egypt, 362
  Iran, 512–515
  Israel, 493–494
  Jordan, 463–465
  Turkey, 272–281
Minority peoples, 46–50, 236–237
  Afghanistan, 548, 561–562, 564–565, 571
  Iran, 502, 515
  Iraq, 379
  Levant, 431–432, 448, 459
  Turkey, 282

Miri land, 162, 393, 463
Mitchell, Raul C., 387
Moab, 416
Mocha, 170, 304, 331
Mohair, 272, 274
Mohammed, 56, *292,* 299, 428
Mongols, 60, 378, 561
Morris, James, 332
Mosul, 286, 392, 400–401
Mukalla, 315, 338, *339*
Mulk land, 161, 393
Muscat (*See* Masqat)

Nafud, 297
Nahrwan Canal, 376–377
Najaf, 295, 549
Natural vegetation, (*See also* Forests), 174–175
  Afghanistan, 556, 568
  Arabia, 296, 308
  Iran, 519, 521, 526
  Iraq, 393–394
  Levant, 422–423, 439, 460–461
  Turkey, 258–259
Near East, 7–10
Negeb (Negev), *96,* 473, *476, 477,* 481, 483
Nejd, 298, 323
Neutral Zones, 216, 336
Nile River, 354–361
Nimrud, *32*
Nineveh, 401
Nomads (*See also* Bedouin), 37–38, 236, 272, 526, *562, 563,* 568
North Anatolian Mountains (*See* Pontus)
Nuristan, 566

Oases, *166,* 310, 312, 328, 357–359, 441–442, *446,* 532, 534, 551, 570–572, 575
Oil (*See also* Pipelines, Refineries), *7,* 20, *21,* 193–221, 275
  Arabia, 324
  Egypt, 362
  Iran, 512
  Iraq, 382
  Israel, 494
  Neutral Zone, 336
  Syria, 445
  Turkey, 275
Olives, 165–166, 269, *486*
Olympus, Mount, *106, 259*
Oman (*See also* Masqat), 29, 337
Ommiad Caliphate, 56–58, 442–443
Opium, 170, 511
Oppenheim, L., 122
Oranges (*See also* Citrus), *229*
Orontes River, 74, 413, *433,* 434
Ottoman Empire, 59–62, 232, 378–381
Oxus (*See* Amu Darya)

Palestine (*See also* Israel, Jordan), 233–234, 415, 455, 473–496
Palgrave, William G., 297
Palmyra, *2,* 428–431
Pamirs, 74, 556–557, 566
Paropamisus Range, 552, 556
Pearls, 325, 334
Persepolis, *53,* 55, 534, *535*
Persia (*See* Iran)
Persian culture (*See also* Iran), 10, *11,* 46, 502, 564
Persian empires, 54-56, 501
Persian Gulf,
  Oil, 202–203, 205, 145, 208, 217, 219, 220
  Shoreline changes, 386–387
Persian water wheel, *163*
Petra, 303–304
Philby, H. St. J., 320
Philistines, 424
Phoenicians, 424
Phosphate, 189–190, 362, 464, 494
Pipelines, *192, 199,* 206–208, *213,* 215, 275, 306, 494
Pliny, 302, 358
Political Geography, 23–29, 223-232, 235-245
  Afghanistan, 562–564, 580
  Arabia, 332–340
  Iran, 536
  Israel, 473–479
  Lebanon, 454–455
  Turkey, 285–288
Pontus Mountains, 19, 74, 257, 259, 262, *263,* 265, 284
Population, 33–41
  Afghanistan, 566
  Arabia, 317–318, 332
  Egypt, 361
  Israel, 478–479, 487–491
  Turkey, 281–283
Portugese interests, 334, 338
Potash, 189–190, 463–464
Pushtuns, 235, 564
Pushtunistan, 563–564
Pyramids, *351*

Qanats, 148–154, 505–508, 574, 576
Qashqai, *502,* 526
Qat, 331
Qatar, 198, 200, 218–219, 336
Qatif, 21, *156,* 306, *307*
Qizil Uzun Valley, 517–518
Qum, 211, *500, 515*

Races of Swasia, 46–50
Railways, 227
  Arabia, 299, 323, *333*
  Iran, 521, *522, 527,* 535, 538–539
  Iraq, 382, 403
  Turkey, 287
Rainfall (*See also* city graphs), 104–107, 113–115, 308, 392, 418–420, 423–424, 521
Raman Dag, *220,* 221, 275
Rawlinson, George, 194
Red Sea, 94, 98, 107, 223–224, 322, 331
Refineries, *199,* 208–209, *211, 214, 531*
Refugees (*See also* Minority peoples), 236, 240, *431*
Resht, 534
Rice, 165, 394, 511
River problems, 13, 119–123, 354–361, 377, 381–382, 397–399, 433–435, 452, 462–463, 538, 559–560, 572–576
Riyadh, 22, *126,* 127–129, 313, *321, 322,* 323–324
Roads, 227
  Afghanistan, 545-555
  Arabia, 293–309
  Iran, 538–539
  Iraq, 402–404
  Lebanon, 453–454
  Turkey, 287–288
Rostovtzeff, M. I., 429–430
Rub al Khali, 83, 85–91, 218, *298*
Russian interests, 26, 212, 234, 236, 242, 286, 449, 503, 562–563, 565, 580

Sabkha, 307
Sakarya River, 258
Saline soil, 20, 143–145, 313, 360, 373, *374,* 377, 389–390, 573–574
Salt, 143–145, 188, *190,* 276, 280, 327, 338, 340, *411,* 445, 527
Salt domes, 525
Samaria, 480–481
Samarra, *56,* 148, *377,* 380
Samsun, *235, 262,* 284
Sanaa, 305, 340
Sand dunes, 68, 83–91, 297, *298,* 527, 572
Sand storms (*See* Dust storms)
Saudi Arabia (*See also* Arabia), *4, 6,* 29, *85, 101, 126,* 127–129, *162, 166, 171,* 217–218, *192,* 197, 231, 241, 332–334
Sea of Galilee (*See* Tiberias, Lake)
Seifi (summer) crops, 361, 392, 510
Seistan, 137–139, 519, 554, 575–576
Semites, 46–47, 424
Seyhan River, 263
Shadoof, 99, 308, 314, 361
Shamal, 98–99 324–325
Shatt-al-Arab (*See also* Euphrates, Karun, Tigris), 140–149, 206, *214, 237*
Sheep, 172, 306, *397,* 512
Shiraz, 66, 534
Shitwi (winter) crops, 361, 392, 510
Sidon, *207, 233,* 306
Silk, 170
Sirdab, 399
Sirocco, 100, 421
Snow, 6, 106, 256, 537, 558
Soils, 158
  Iran, 508
  Iraq, 388–390
  Turkey, 267
Standard of living, 447–448
Steel mills, *176, 185,* 277, *352*
Sudan, 354–357
Suez Canal, 226–227, 354, 363–368
Sugar beets, 170, 271, *273, 512*
Sulphur, 188–190, 276, 280
Swamps, 355, 373, *385,* 393–394, *395*
Swasia, 7
Syria, 29, *169,* 198, 220, 231, 238–239, *415,* 432–447
Syrian Desert, 416, 428
Syrian Saddle, 20, 422

Tabriz, 534–536
Taiz, 320, *329,* 340
Talish Mountains, 521–522
Taurus, Mountains, 17, 74, 257, 260, 263, *264,* 265, 284
Tea, 170, *520*
Tehran, 17, *92,* 505, 517, 536, *537*
Tel Aviv, *472,* 489–490
Temperature (*See also* city graphs), 102–104, 416–417
Tenancy, 160–162, 393, 440, 463, 510
Tethys, 69–71, 524
Thesiger, Wilfred, 568
Tiberias, Lake, 131–132, 462, *475*
Tigris River, *120,* 140–149, 371, 373, 382, *384–385,* 397–398, 399
Tihama, 304–305, 311
Tobacco, 170, *242, 272,* 396, 511
Trabzon, 226, 265
Trans-Arabian Pipe Line, *192,* 206, 305–309
Transhumance, 526
Tripoli, 206, 452
Trucial States, 198, 241, 334–337
Turkey, *9,* 10, 29, *34, 80, 106, 133,* 134–136, *160, 173, 183, 184,* 198, 220–221, 231, *235,* 236, *242,* 246–288
Turkey vs. Iran, 20, 266
Turkish empires, 58–62

Turkish influence, 379, 398
Turkmen, *164*
Turquoise, 514
Tuz, Lake, 260
Tyre, 65–66, 411, 450

United Arab Republic (*See also* Egypt, Syria), 239, 340, 350, 447
Ur, 50, *51, 194,* 374, 392
Urmia Basin, 515–517, 535
Uruq, 87–88
Uskudar (*See also* Istanbul), 250, 283

Van, Lake, 266
Volcanoes, 80–81, 260, 265, 529

Wadi Araba, 416
Wadi Hanifah, 126–129, 312, 323
Wadi Tharthar, 148, 398
Wahabi, 324, 332
Wakhan Corridor, 567
Walsh, Robert, 251
Waqf land, 393
Warriner, Doreen, 157
Wells, *99, 101,* 306, 312, 314, 317, 323
Wheat, 162–163, 268, 394, 436, 511
White Paper of 1939, 474
Wind of 120 days, 99–100, 558, 575
Winds, 98–102, 324–325, 421, 558, 575

Yarkon River, *483*
Yarmuk River, 130–132, 462–463
Yemen, 29, 241, 304–305, 328–331, 338–340
Yezd, 64

Zagros Mountains, 16, 202, 210, 213, 383, 523–526
Zayandeh Rud, *123,* 124–127, 532
Zinc (*See* Lead and Zinc)
Zonguldak, *180,* 181, 274, 278
Zoroastrianism, 47, 54, 502

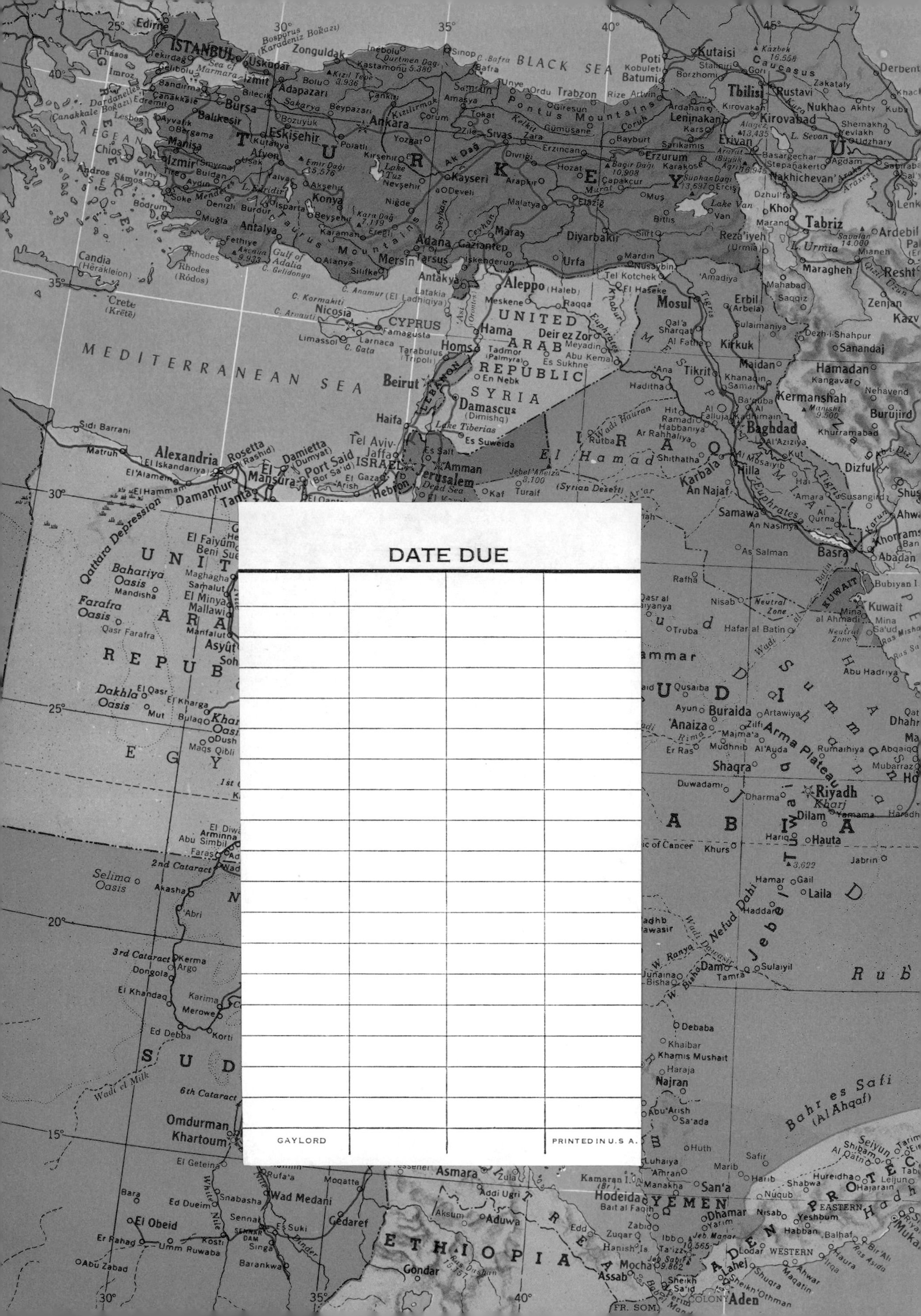
BLACK SEA
ISTANBUL
Sea of Marmara
Edirne
Üsküdar
Izmit
Zonguldak
Bursa
Balıkesir
Ankara
Eskişehir
Samsun
Trabzon
Pontus Mountains
Sivas
Kayseri
Konya
Izmir
AEGEAN SEA
Chios
Antalya
Taurus Mountains
Adana
Mersin
Tarsus
Gaziantep
Malatya
Diyarbakir
Urfa
Erzurum
Lake Van
TURKEY
Kutaisi
Batumi
Tbilisi
Caucasus
Kirovabad
Erivan
L. Sevan
Leninakan
Nakhichevan'
Tabriz
Ardebil
Resht
L. Urmia
Reza'iyeh
Mosul
Erbil
Kirkuk
Aleppo (Haleb)
Hama
Homs
UNITED ARAB REPUBLIC
SYRIA
Deir ez Zor
Euphrates
Tigris
Damascus (Dimishq)
Beirut
LEBANON
CYPRUS
Nicosia
Famagusta
Crete (Krētē)
Candia (Herákleion)
Rhodes
MEDITERRANEAN SEA
Haifa
Tel Aviv-Jaffa
ISRAEL
Jerusalem
Amman
Hebron
Dead Sea
Lake Tiberias
Alexandria
Rosetta (Rashid)
Damietta (Dumyat)
Port Said
El Mansura
Damanhur
Tanta
Qattara Depression
Bahariya Oasis
Farafra Oasis
Dakhla Oasis
UNITED ARAB REPUBLIC
EGYPT
Asyût
Selima Oasis
2nd Cataract
3rd Cataract
Dongola
Karima
Merowe
6th Cataract
Omdurman
Khartoum
Wadi el Milk
SUDAN
El Obeid
Wad Medani
Gedaref
Kosti
Asmara
ERITREA
ETHIOPIA
Gondar
Assab
Aden
YEMEN
San'a
Hodeida
Dhamar
Mocha
ADEN PROTECTORATE
Baghdad
Karbala
An Najaf
Hilla
IRAQ
El Hamad
(Syrian Desert)
Basra
Abadan
Khorramshahr
KUWAIT
Kuwait
Hamadan
Kermanshah
Sanandaj
Dizful
SAUDI ARABIA
Buraida
'Anaiza
Riyadh
Arma Plateau
Jebel Tuwaiq
Shaqra
Nefud Dahi
Najran
Rub' al Khali
Bahr es Safi (Al Ahqaf)
30°
35°
40°
45°
25°
20°
15°